Tyrant

Rise of the Beast

Chronicles of the Apocalypse
Book One

By Brian Godawa

Tyrant: Rise of the Beast
Chronicles of the Apocalypse Book One
2nd Edition b

Warrior Poet Publishing
www.warriorpoetpublishing.com

ISBN: 9798710868522 (hardcover)
ISBN: 978-1-942858-25-6 (paperback)

Scripture quotations taken from *The Holy Bible: English Standard Version.* Wheaton: Standard Bible Society, 2001.

If You Like This Novel You'll Love This Free eBook

Limited Time Offer

FREE

The Research Notes behind the Novel Series Chronicles of the Apocalypse

By Brian Godawa

Over one hundred pages of Biblical and historical sources, with citations, addressing each verse in Matthew 24.

See page 302 for how to get this ebook FREE.

The *Chronicles of the Apocalypse* series

is dedicated to

Ken Gentry and Gary DeMar.

Scholars and gentlemen, both.

ACKNOWLEDGMENTS

Special thanks to my Lord and Savior Jesus Christ for allowing me to combine my esoteric theological interests with my passionate love of storytelling. I never envisioned such privilege or ministry. I do not deserve it.

Perpetual thanks to my wife, Kimberly, my Cassandra, my muse.

I am so grateful for Jeanette Windle for making this entire series so much better because of her loving editorial ruthlessness. Jeanette, your theological understanding, your life experience in missions, your own storytelling choices and your skill convince me that God providentially led me to you. I could not imagine a more perfect editor for this project to make it what it needed to become.

My deepest gratitude goes to my long-time friend and scholar Kenneth L. Gentry Jr. for allowing me the privilege of early access to his Revelation commentary, *The Divorce of Israel*, which served as a scholarly guide to unveiling the complexities of this most fascinating of all New Testament books. I would also like to thank my newer friend and scholar Michael S. Heiser, whose work on the divine council, the Watchers, and the Deuteronomy 32 worldview constitutes the other major influence on my interpretation of Revelation. I believe I have made opposites attract. Christus Victor!

I cannot neglect to thank Gary DeMar, another long-time friend and scholar whose eschatological work continues to be a trumpet call of sanity in this era of last days madness.

And of course, I could not have made this as clean a manuscript as it is without all my devoted Advanced Reader Team's kind and gracious help in proofreading and helpful feedback. You know who you are (and so do I).

Thanks to Sean McDowell for his research on the death of the apostles; to Doug Van Dorn, Michael Gavlak and Chris Holmes for their amazing storytelling input.

And also special thanks to the courageous Biblical scholars who have stood against the tide of sensationalist popular opinion to unveil the apocalypse in its original ancient context.

READ THIS NOTE—IT'S IMPORTANT

Chronicles of the Apocalypse is the conclusive sequel series to my *Chronicles of the Nephilim* series about the Biblical Cosmic War of the Seed. But one need not read the previous Nephilim series to be able to understand this Apocalypse series, though the literary and theological connections run deep.

This is the story of the apostle John's writing of the Apocalypse during the time of the Roman Empire, the first major persecution and martyrdom of Christians, and the Jewish revolt of AD 66 that resulted in the destruction of Jerusalem and the temple in AD 70. My hope is that the original context of the ancient world in all its symbolic glory will come alive to the reader as you encounter the imagery in Revelation dramatically unveiled through its Old Testament and first-century literary lens.

Creative License

I have tried to be as accurate as I can with the actual historical events and characters surrounding the Jewish revolt of AD 66-70. However, there are many details that we simply do not know with certainty either because the Bible or other historical sources are silent, or because there is disagreement over the facts. Because of this, I had to take some creative license to fill in the gaps or simplify for easier reading. But I tried to remain true to the spirit of the text if not to the letter.

For example, the New Testament letters, such as John's Apocalypse, did not have chapter or verse numbers. They were originally letters written to various people and congregations. The chapter and verse numbers were added in the medieval era for closer detailed study of the Scriptures. In *Chronicles of the Apocalypse*, I broke up the book of Revelation into "fragments" that correspond to our modern chapters for the purpose of making it easy for the modern reader to look up those Bible verses. It was a kind of creative license footnoting within the context of a narrative. I hope the more demanding "Bible scholars" will forgive such petty contrivances for the sake of helpful annotation and storytelling.

Endnotes

I've included numbered endnotes for each chapter that provide detailed Biblical and historical substantiation behind the fictional story. As it turns out, half of the text of this book is endnotes. This may be my most heavily researched series of novels yet. Though using endnote numbers in a novel text is considered anathema by many, I chose to use them to provide proof for my fans who want to "fact-check" and dig deeper. This is fiction based on fact. If you question anything I've written in a particular paragraph, simply check the closest endnote to that paragraph. You will find that the truth is stranger than fiction! The historical fulfillment is mind-blowing.

Besides, my fans have come to expect such documentation!

Pictures and Research

Some readers prefer to conjure pictures of what characters look like in their own imagination. But for those who would like to see a pictorial cast of characters that I created for this story, see the cool colorful characters page on the Chronicles of the Apocalypse website:

http://wp.me/P6y1ub-1uH

I also have artwork of paintings and illustrations that relate to this story:

http://wp.me/P6y1ub-1uJ

I also have free scholarly articles and free books online that provide the reader with more in-depth research of the Book of Revelation:

http://wp.me/P6y1ub-X9

Brian Godawa

Author, *Chronicles of the Apocalypse*

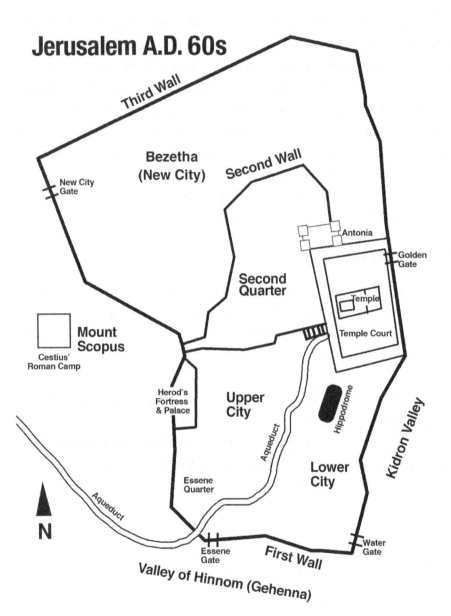

Jerusalem A.D. 60s

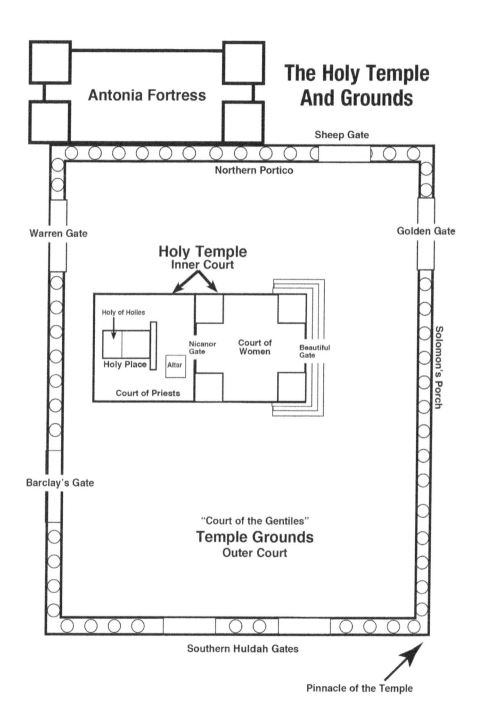

The Holy Temple And Grounds

Antonia Fortress

Sheep Gate

Northern Portico

Warren Gate

Golden Gate

Holy Temple
Inner Court

Holy of Holies

Holy Place

Altar

Nicanor Gate

Court of Women

Beautiful Gate

Court of Priests

Solomon's Porch

Barclay's Gate

"Court of the Gentiles"
Temple Grounds
Outer Court

Southern Huldah Gates

Pinnacle of the Temple

He said to me, "But you, Daniel, shut up the words and seal the book, until the time of the end."

Daniel 12:4 (547 BC)

And he said to me [John], "Do not seal up the words of the prophecy of this book, for the time is near."

Revelation 22:10 (AD 65)

Jesus said, "Truly, I say to you, all these things will come upon this generation."

Matthew 23:36 (AD 33)

PART ONE

Antichrist

CHAPTER 1

"To the angel of the church in Ephesus write: 'The words of him who holds the seven stars in his right hand, who walks among the seven golden lampstands. "'I know your works, your toil and your patient endurance, and how you cannot bear with those who are evil, but have tested those who call themselves apostles and are not, and found them to be false. I know you are enduring patiently and bearing up for my name's sake, and you have not grown weary. But I have this against you, that you have abandoned the love you had at first. Remember therefore from where you have fallen; repent, and do the works you did at first. If not, I will come to you and remove your lampstand from its place, unless you repent. Yet this you have: you hate the works of the Nicolaitans, which I also hate. He who has an ear, let him hear what the Spirit says to the churches. To the one who conquers I will grant to eat of the tree of life, which is in the paradise of God.'"
— The Apocalypse of Jesus Christ 2:1-7

Ephesus
On the coast of Asia
AD 64

The dark lord Apollyon roamed unseen through the massive throngs of citizens filling the streets of the city. *His* city. Well, not entirely. Ever since the Nazarene had accomplished his coup d'état a generation ago, his despicable followers were watched over by a heavenly guardian. Ephesus was no exception. Though the cowardly Angel of Ephesus was nowhere to be seen.[1]

Apollyon gritted his teeth with anger at the thought. But as the Watcher of the Roman Empire, he had too much authority over his stronghold to be worried about an uprising of Yahweh's minions. Apollyon owned most of the residents of Ephesus. His nemesis would not dare to show his face where the dark lord was now going. And Apollyon would not dare to rush his plan, as he built his forces from the unregenerate inhabitants of the earth. They were kingdoms in conflict and the tension was increasing toward world war. The Nazarene had outfoxed him and achieved atonement for sins through his death, resurrection and ascension to the right hand of Yahweh. Apollyon still boiled with anger over his failure to figure out the plan and stop Messiah. Ever since Eden, he had been at war with the seed of Eve, from Enoch to Noah to Abraham, Isaac and Jacob—and who could forget that treacherous Messiah king, David—all the way to the Son of David.[2]

How could he have missed it?

At Babel, Yahweh had given the nations their inheritance. He confused the tongues, divided mankind and gave those rebellious people over to the Sons of God from his heavenly host. Those divine beings defied Yahweh, accepted idolatrous worship and became the gods of the nations. They were called "Watchers," because they watched over the territories and lands they had been allotted. Apollyon's allotment was Rome. But Yahweh's inheritance would be the people of Jacob, the people of God.[3]

Apollyon's name in Hebrew was Abaddon, which meant "destroyer." But he liked the Greek version for its linguistic connection to the sun god Apollo, a personal obsession of his human pet, Nero Caesar. Nero was the earthly ruler of Apollyon's Rome. The Watcher god had gone by different names throughout the millennia: Nachash the ancient Serpent, Belial the wicked, Helel ben Shachar the Shining One, Mastemah the hostile, Diabolos the devil, Satan the Adversary, and the Dragon. But his plan had always been the same: to destroy the people of God and the seed line of Messiah.[4]

As the legally appointed Adversary in Yahweh's heavenly court, he had prosecutorial powers to accuse humanity before God's throne. And accuse them he did.[5] It was easy. Israel was an unfaithful wife to Yahweh. More like a lustful harlot, actually. A harlot seeking to lay under every green tree with every idol of the nations. Ba'al, Asherah, Dagon, Molech. You name the false god, the Israelites fornicated with it. They had violated the covenant with their maker so often, it made Yahweh vomit.

4

It made Apollyon giggle with a juvenile glee.[6]

But Yahweh remained faithful and even gave his whore of twelve tribes a male heir. When that abominable Nazarene came upon the scene, he fooled everyone. Apollyon and the other Watchers, even Israel herself, thought Messiah was coming as military earthly deliverer to rescue his people. Instead, he played the sacrificial lamb and secured atonement for a remnant of his elect people. Messiah took away Apollyon's authority to prosecute God's people in heaven, and cast him down to earth like lightning.[7] The Nazarene then became the firstborn from the dead, legally disinheriting the gods of the nations, and led those principalities and powers, bound and gagged, in a triumphal victory into Tartarus before his ascension to his heavenly throne. Through death, resurrection and ascension, Yahweh undid the territorial allotment of Babel and legally claimed all the nations as his inheritance.[8]

But you didn't get us all, Nazarene, thought Apollyon. *And you left me here as the Watcher of Rome. Now Rome rules the world, making me the god of this world.*[9]

The remaining spiritual principalities and powers served Apollyon, who delegated authority based on the stronghold he was able to maintain in each city. Yahweh may have gained legal claim to the nations, but the historical acquisition of those territories would take time and effort. And Apollyon was not going to give them up without a fight.

A cult of Jewish religious fanatics followed the Nazarene and within this short span of thirty years, spread their malignant cancer to the ends of the earth, thus loosening Apollyon's strangling grip. But the leaders and people of Israel as a whole had rejected their Messiah, which gave the Destroyer power over them. So he had successfully martialled the Jews to persecute the chosen few, now called *Christianoi*, or Christians. It was a vulgar term of derision meaning servants of Christ as opposed to *caeseriani*, servants of Caesar.[10]

Apollyon arrived at his intended destination, the top of a hill just north of Ephesus, overlooking the vast metropolis. He looked up at the temple of Artemis, one of the man-made wonders of the world. Like the Parthenon in Athens, its huge stone Corinthian columns towered sixty feet above, giving mortals the sense of Olympus on earth. They called it the Artemisium.[11]

Apollyon called it, "My fortress."

But no one heard him. And no one saw him either. He remained invisible to the humans. If he allowed them to see him, he could appear to them as almost anything. His favorite current identity was a six-foot tall, rail-thin, androgynous being, both male and female, *neither* male nor female. He liked the chaos and defiance against Yahweh's created order that the confusion of gender expressed. He wore a toga, sandals, plenty of jewelry to die for, and prided himself on his fabulous makeup.

What a waste, he thought. *Maybe I should let these flesh bags see my glory. At least then my glamour will not go unappreciated.*

Ephesus was a city of glamour. A large commercial seaport on the west coast of the province of Asia, it became a major center of international trade, and with it, the key to implementing Apollyon's plans for the Roman Empire.

The enemy saw the city's strategic value as well. Less than a decade ago, Paul, that meddling Apostle to the Gentiles, had overstayed his welcome here and infected the inhabitants with his malicious messiah myth. Apollyon had enflamed the silversmiths to riot because their idol-making business had been severely undermined by Christian conversions. After that fiasco, Apollyon had labored long and hard to dig his talons back into the city. And now that disgusting old crank, the apostle John bar Zebedee resided here, causing the Watcher much anguish. Apollyon nicknamed him Thunderhead, as a mockery of his reputation as a bold "Son of Thunder."[12]

Ephesus was also a treasure to Apollyon because it was the banking and financial center of the province. Vast sums of money flowed in to the great temple from devotees all over the continent. And that was why Apollyon was here. He walked up the stairway and entered the huge stone Artemisium.[13]

A tall female divinity adorned in rich oriental garb stood bent over an altar at the far end of the sanctuary, her back to Apollyon as he entered.

"Sister!"

The goddess turned with a twitch of anger at being interrupted. In her hand was the corpse of a goat, its neck ripped to shreds. Blood dripped down the lips of the Great Artemis, Mother Goddess and Queen of the Cosmos. On her head was an elaborate headdress, the Zodiac across her neck, and a chest full of what looked like multiple breasts, but were actually leather pouches of magical sorcery for fertility. She was also a huntress of wild animals, so she was not a goddess to be trifled with.[14]

But she also knew her place in the pecking order. "Apollyon, dear brother and master, to what do I owe this honor?"

According to Greek myth, Artemis and Apollo were twin siblings, the offspring of Zeus.

In reality, Artemis was actually a male disguised as a goddess, since the fallen Sons of God were exclusively male. "She" was simply another demonic servant of Apollyon, one of the surviving principalities and powers left behind after Messiah's victory over the gods of the nations. A victory that was not complete, for Yahweh had obviously failed to wipe them all out after seating his Son on the throne of David. And now Apollyon was making a comeback, building his forces for what every Watcher god knew was coming.

Apollyon said cryptically, "Behold, the time is near. I must show my servants the things which must shortly take place."[15]

She gazed at him with curiosity.

"It's something old Thunderhead is now saying," he said. "But I, too, have been working on a plan and I need your help to initiate it."

"Anything, my lord."

Apollyon pushed her aside and took the neck of the goat in his fangs, imbibing deeply. *Ah, blood*, he thought as he sucked it dry. *Food of the gods.* Blood sacrifice connected worshippers with the divine in mystical union. He cast the carcass into the corner and wiped his lips with the back of his hand.

She gestured to the exit. "Walk with me in my garden, my lord. We will have privacy, and you can explain to me how I may be of help."

A booming voice outside the temple interrupted their agenda. Artemis rolled her eyes and sighed impatiently.

Apollyon knew that voice anywhere. That annoying soul-piercing voice.

"Speak of the enemy," he said.

They walked out to the entrance of the Artemisium and saw a small man, nearing sixty years of age, with white hair and beard, preaching to passersby at the footsteps of the temple.

The apostle John.

"We should leave," said Artemis.

"No. I want to hear what old Thunderhead is spewing today."

John did not see the Watchers up at the top of the steps. He was intently focused on his public sermon, surrounded by a few of his followers. His voice was strong for such an old and weary soul. "For many deceivers have gone out into the world, those who do not confess the coming of Jesus Christ in the flesh. Such a one is the deceiver and the antichrist! By this you know the Spirit of God: every spirit that confesses that Jesus Christ has come in the flesh is from God, and every spirit that does not confess Jesus is not from God. This is the spirit of the antichrist, which you heard was coming and now is in the world already!"[16]

Artemis grumbled, "That geriatric pissant is undoing everything Cerinthus has achieved." Cerinthus was a local false teacher who denied the deity of Christ, among other useful heresies.[17]

"Stop complaining," said Apollyon. "I am trying to hear him."

John continued, "This is the last hour, and as I already told you that antichrist is coming, so now many antichrists have come. Therefore we know that it is the last hour! Now the whole world lies in the power of the evil one. But if you believe and abide in Jesus Christ, when he appears you may have confidence and not shrink from him in shame at his coming!"[18]

Apollyon thought to himself, *There it is again. The apostolic announcement of being in the last hours before "his coming."* He could feel the storm of war approaching.

Artemis grumbled again, "These Christians and their persecution complex. He thinks they're victims now. Let us show him what real pain tastes like."

Apollyon stopped her from descending the steps. He gestured to a figure standing off to the side, also unseen by the human crowd: the Angel of Ephesus, no longer absent. Though angels could alter their appearance in the eyes of others, much like the Watchers could, they seldom did. This angel was a tall heavy-built figure, dressed in a hooded cloak that Apollyon knew covered armor and weapons beneath. Yahweh's soldiers were quiet and understated, but they were fierce competition for the dark lord and his forces.

The angel stared at Apollyon and Artemis, stiffened with hand on sword.

Apollyon said, "You would not get within yards of the apostle." He glanced back at the apostle. "Yahweh has something special in store for this blowhard. He is the overseer of the most significant churches in Asia."

Artemis stared back at the distant glaring Angel of Ephesus. Apollyon was referring to a circuit of seven churches, beginning with Ephesus on the coast and circling inland from Smyrna around to Laodicea.

He said, "Asia was among the first to be colonized by the Christians for a reason. It is the physical center of the empire and therefore a communications hub for exporting their malevolent message to the rest of the world. And that is why I am going to visit those Asian cities to initiate my own plan."

Artemis asked, "What is that, my lord?"

"I am going to cripple the enemy's ability to spread his propaganda and disinformation. Cut off the head of the lamb, starting with Ephesus."

"And how are you going to achieve that?"

Apollyon mused, "When I was the great Adversary in Yahweh's heavenly court, they called me the 'accuser of the brethren.' Well, the Nazarene stripped me of that power and cast me down to this stinking exile of dirt. And now he is drawing all men unto himself."[19]

"Mount Zion," grumbled Artemis. Mount Zion was originally the location of the Temple Mount in Jerusalem. But the name became symbolic of the Jewish cosmic mountain of redemption, a spiritual symbol of God's kingdom in the age of Messiah. Since Messiah had come, that holy mountain was already growing as people from all the nations began streaming to it.[20]

Apollyon nodded. "I have no legal jurisdiction over the children of God. But I *do* have it over the children of the devil. Yahweh left me as the prince of the power of the air. I no longer have the authority to prosecute. But I do have the ability to *persecute*."[21]

Artemis grinned deviously. "We could not destroy the Christ, but we *can* destroy his people, the body of Christ on earth."

"Exactly," said Apollyon. "And I will destroy them all."

He paused dramatically. He so loved drama. "And when he comes for his people, he won't have any people left to receive him."[22]

She said, "But have you not been using the Jews already for that very purpose of persecution?"

"Yes," he crowed. "But I have not yet used the real power I have. The power of Rome."

Apollyon pulled Artemis away. "Come, show me this garden of yours."

The Garden of Ortygia, a grove of terebinth trees, grew just outside the Artemisium. The terebinth was a kind of sacred oak through which the gods communicated to prophets and mystics. This was the legendary birthplace of Artemis, and the location of a sacred tree they now approached, known as the Tree of Life. At least that's what they called it. Ever since the primeval Garden, the gods sought to construct their own royal parks with gardens and shrines as echoes of Eden, desperate attempts to recreate a paradise lost. The hanging gardens of Babylon had been the most memorable.[23]

Staring at the sacred tree, Apollyon said, "How deep are your roots in this city?"

Artemis said, "Sorcery is stronger than ever with the dispersion of the Ephesian Letters of Magic. Ephesus remains a significant spiritual influence across the empire."[24]

She stopped as if that was all there was to say. But Apollyon knew it was not. Not all was well in his Ephesus. He glared at her until she confessed, "Unfortunately, the cult of Nicolaitans has been seriously countered by the apostle John, and many have moved to Pergamum."

"That is too bad," said Apollyon. The Nicolaitans were a cult of Christian heretics that advocated blending pagan religions with the true faith, sexual immorality and eating food sacrificed to idols. Apollyon made a mental note to visit Pergamum as well.[25]

Artemis brightened. "But there is good news. Do you remember Hymenaeus and Philetus?"

"Those are the ones who were teaching that the resurrection of the saints already happened. Nothing more than a spiritual symbol."[26]

"Exactly. They have a strong following now, along with your favorite Gnostic, Cerinthus. And the Jewish community has been quite successful in suppressing the Way."

Apollyon nodded with approval. The Way was what Christians called their detestable cult.[27]

She continued proudly, "They offer sinners forgiveness upon the condition of repentance. A total rejection of their nation and their gods. But I offer criminals free refuge in my asylum. Thieves, rapists, murderers, are all protected from the law if they can make their way into the sanctum of the temple. Christian atonement is merely spiritual, but mine offers release from earthly consequences as well. Now, who is more loving, I ask you?"[28]

"Who is more enduring?" he challenged.

"These Ephesian Christians have patient endurance," she said. "I will grant them that. But they have lost their first love. They have become so obsessed with doctrinal perfection, they no longer engage in works of faith. They are stone dead. Their lamp is out."[29]

He nodded with satisfaction. "Excellent. Well done. I will take care of the apostle soon enough. Right now, I need your financial help. As I travel the circuit of the Asian cities I will stir up strongmen in Laodicea, Philadelphia, Sardis and others. But we need more than our true believers. We need financial incentive to hire protestors, mobs, and bribe traitors. I need to prepare for what is coming."

She scowled. She knew what was coming. All the principalities and powers knew what was coming: a mighty war in the heavenlies.

CHAPTER 2

Rome

July 19, AD 64

Afternoon

Alexander Maccabaeus sat exhausted in his medical clinic just outside the city limits. He looked out with tired eyes over the long line of patients waiting for his trained services. They were mostly Jews, poor and sick with various ailments, many elderly, some infants and children with their desperate parents. It broke his heart to see his people suffering. That was why he had dedicated his life to serving them. He was a civilian physician, and a Jew himself, but was often required to help the Legionary Medical Corps after military campaigns and when needed. During times of peace such as this, Alexander had been allowed to use the Praetorian camp as a clinic for the locals. The poor had little access to medical care, so unlike his own Jewish heritage whose divinely revealed law gave many commands for individuals to help the poor, widows and orphans.

The next patient approached Alexander at the behest of his assistant, a young sixteen-year-old named Thelonius Severus, the son of Alexander's military patron, Lucius Aurelius Severus. The patient was an older man wearing a cloak and hood. He was shivering, and was accompanied by a man and young woman, also both hooded, who helped to hold him up.

Alexander looked dubiously at the secretive trio. "What is wrong?"

The old man said, "I have fevers…and splitting headaches. It comes and goes. And my eyesight has become poor."

"Let me see your eyes. Pull off your hood."

The old man hesitated. But he finally pulled his hood back, and Alexander understood the reason for his pause. He was balding, with a pointed nose and a large graying beard. Alexander had seen him just last year here in Rome causing trouble in the Jewish community. He was Paul of Tarsus, the

12

infamous Christian apostle whose fiery religious rhetoric seemed to cause trouble wherever he went. Paul had been a Pharisee before converting to the religious cult, so he knew how to enrage Jews, and he did so with disregard for the social consequences.

Alexander thought it ironic how frail this mighty orator now looked. He was sick, shivering and humble, in need of healing his God evidently had not given him. The woman kept her hood on, obviously afraid of being recognized as an associate. But Alexander saw the face of the other man with him. He was stocky and bearded as well; Simon Peter, another apostle who had recently taken up residence in the city.

Thelonius recognized them both. He hissed at them, "Come to cause trouble again?"

"Thelonius," scolded Alexander with a stern look. The youth had more to learn about decorum than he did about disease.

"I am on my way to Spain," Paul said. "I need some medicine for my sickness and I will be on my way."

Thelonius spit out, "You don't deserve any medicine. You Christians have caused so much division and problems for this city. You deserve to suffer."

"Thelonius," said Alexander, "did you not take the Hippocratic Oath?"

Thelonius remained silently defiant. The oath had included the promise to withhold no help from the sick to their harm.

Unfortunately Thelonius was quite accurate about these troublemakers. The Christians had caused many problems for the Jews all over the empire. They had first begun as a sect of Judaism claiming that the Nazarene Yeshua bar Joseph, Jesus in Greek, was the promised Messiah. He had been crucified a generation ago under Pontius Pilate near the city of Jerusalem. But his followers then fabricated a story about him rising from the dead and ascending into heaven. Their propaganda spread like gangrene throughout the empire.

Alexander recalled the Jewish riots in Rome some fifteen years prior under Claudius Caesar, incited from the heated debates regarding the life and teachings of the Nazarene. The unrest had become so difficult to manage that the emperor banned the Jews from the ancient city. They were eventually allowed to return. But a new division between Jew and Christian had been established.[1]

The Christians were now a mixture of Jews and Gentiles. Most of them lived in the Jewish sectors of Rome, but were ostracized by their own countrymen. Alexander considered this as the Christians' own fault, since they taught division and hatred of their heritage. Alexander had heard this Paul blaspheme the Mosaic law, deny circumcision, condemn his fellow Jews, and renounce Roman citizenship in favor of "citizenship in heaven." It's no wonder the Jews rioted. They were victims who were provoked. The Christians should never have been allowed to spread their hateful message.[2]

In spite of all this, Alexander could not allow his fellow human beings to suffer, no matter how dangerous their beliefs were. He believed that everyone was created in the image of God and human life was sacred. He would care for the bodies of the sick and wounded, no matter who they were, and leave their souls up to God. It was difficult to do so with those who had hurt his people, but all of life was a compromise.

Alexander's stare into the apostle's red and puffy eyes finally resulted in a question. "Do you have nausea and diarrhea?"

Paul nodded. "Comes and goes like the rest."

"You have the bad-air disease. Malaria. It's a common problem here with our swamps full of noxious fumes. Drink plenty of water, eat extra garlic." He turned to Thelonius. "Give him a bag of herbs."[3]

Thelonius stalled. "It's our last one. You would give it to this Christian?"

Alexander said, "Thelonius, give him the herbs."

Thelonius grudgingly reached down into a canvas sack and produced a small pouch of herbs they prepared for malaria cases. He handed it to the apostle, who took it and pulled up his hood. "Thank you and may the Lord Jesus Christ bless you."

"You can thank me," said Alexander, "by leaving this city as quickly as you promised."

The woman who was with the two men had been hiding her face looking at the ground the entire time. But as the three of them turned to leave, Alexander caught a glimpse of her glaring at him. He recognized her as Cassandra Laetorius, heiress of a local shipping merchant. He knew her because she was a mature woman near thirty years of age, whose presence he could not forget. With auburn hair and penetrating blue eyes, she mystified men by avoiding marriage and keeping a low profile in society. Now, he had a better understanding why. She was secretly helping the apostle. If it were known, her very livelihood would be jeopardized.

We all have our compromises to survive, he thought.

The next patient stepped forward. He had an arm wound from a work accident in the city. But before Alexander could begin his examination, he heard a familiar voice say, "Alexander, come quickly. It's an emergency."

He glanced over to see Prefect Lucius Aurelius Severus looking panicked. That was a first. The prefect of the *Cohortes Vigilum* was one of the toughest patrons Alexander had ever had the misfortune of serving.

"I have horses ready," said the prefect. "Bring your tools."

Thelonius interrupted, "Can I come, Father?"

Severus snapped at him. "No! Stay here and complete your duties."

"But Father, I need experience, whatever it is."

"Do as I say," said Severus.

Alexander could see his patron was unusually troubled. He said to Thelonius, "Close down the clinic and go to the emporium to replenish our medicinal herbs."

The emporium was the marketplace on the far southern region of the city by the Tiber River. It would take him the rest of the day to accomplish that task. Before he could come up with a new complaint, the two men were gone.

The day was scorching hot. Alexander followed Severus on horseback into the Viminal Hill district. Severus then broke off into an alleyway to enter into the back of an apartment that he rented for his secret indiscretions.

But Alexander knew. He knew more than he wanted to know about the prefect, who had often used him as his personal physician. The military could demand the services of private doctors as needed. And because Severus' son Thelonius had a strong desire to become an imperial physician, he had chosen Alexander to teach him the science of medicine.

Alexander considered Severus a quintessential Roman soldier—an entitled, arrogant bully. At thirty-eight years old, he had been in the military for over fifteen years and carried a sense of superiority about him. Alexander was his junior by eight years, and he constantly felt condescension from him.

But he was a Roman subject whose social status and livelihood depended upon obedience to authority.

Alexander helped Severus to understand the nuances and mindset of the Jewish community and their differences from the Christians. Of course, Severus was also using Alexander to understand how to control the Jews, but at least Alexander was able to influence the prefect's understanding in their favor. Severus was responsible for policing the city at night when trouble brewed in the urban paradise. He was working his way up the ladder of promotion and Alexander had been the key to his peacekeeping strategy in the streets.

Still, Alexander felt divided loyalty in his service to Rome. As a Hellenist Jew, schooled in Greek language and culture, he struggled to maintain his ethnic identity. Some demands of Severus forced him to violate his scruples, like working on the Sabbath or lying on Severus' behalf to his superiors. But such compromises were the cost of survival, and Alexander had made plenty of them.

As the two men passed through the apartment, Severus explained the situation and Alexander saw he was about to face yet another compromise.

They entered a bedroom with multiple servants and a midwife ministering to a beautiful blonde woman passed out on a blood-soaked bed. Alexander already knew her. Her name was Persephone, a Greek pantomime actress and dancer of the theater, and adulterous lover of Severus. Alexander was well aware of their secret affair, and had wondered when a day like this might arrive. He dreaded what he now had to do, but moved instinctively to the bedside to help the endangered actress.[4]

Alexander noticed the midwife had already begun surgical access, and immediately set about to take over the situation. "Where is she bleeding?" he asked her. "We must stop the flow."

"Somewhere in the uterus. I don't know how I punctured her. This has never happened before."

"I don't want your excuses. I want you to tell me exactly what you've done." He turned to a maidservant. "Get a hot iron ready."

The midwife explained, "I gave her a suppository to kill the fetus and help expel it."

"What were the components?"

"Wormwood and myrrh. But the poison did not work, so I used the infant slayer to kill it."

He nodded. "Infant slayer" was the nickname of a long copper spike instrument used for just such a purpose.

"I fear I must have slipped and punctured the wall of her womb."[5]

"How far along is she?" he asked.

"Fourteen weeks."

"Fourteen weeks?" he exclaimed. There was no time now to ask a reason for this ridiculous choice. It would have to wait. "We have to get the infant out before I can find the perforation. We haven't much time. Give me the annular blade."

She grabbed the tool with a blade at the end of it from the table and handed it to him.

He deftly maneuvered it with the competence of an experienced surgeon. He removed the blade and barked, "Forceps!"

The midwife obeyed, handing him the tool.

He then pulled out a small leg, the size of his pinkie finger. It was bloody and the skin was translucent. Alexander felt vomit rise in his throat. He placed the appendage on a towel.

"Make sure I retrieve everything," he said. He was sweating now, as he labored strenuously to avoid any more complications. He had precious little time to save Persephone's life. He removed tiny body parts from the womb and placed them on the towel, where the midwife assisted in making sure nothing was left behind that could cause an infection.

What made this tragedy all the more grievous to the doctor was his own situation in contrast with his benefactor. Alexander and his wife, Juliana, were barren. She was only sixteen when they married five years ago, but they soon discovered she could not bear children. They were both deeply in love and deeply distressed at the inability to establish a family legacy with male heirs. It was a family that rooted one in something bigger than oneself, the community of God's people. Without that connection, they felt lost, insignificant, their love a mere dream of unrealized potential. And now, here he was aiding Severus to destroy the very thing that he and his wife longed for. Why did God allow such travesty?

He felt the sudden desire to go home and hold his wife in his arms and never let her go.

He saw Severus move to the bedside of his unconscious lover and stroke her hair with a gentle fear. Aside from his son, his marriage provided no happiness to his life. Persephone was the only respite from his battle-hardened existence. If Severus lost her, he would lose his love.

Knowing Severus, he would most likely hack the midwife into pieces with his sword after seeing the dismembered body of his son on the towel. The fetus was the size of a fist.

Surely, Severus was telling himself this bloody carnage wasn't his son. As the Stoics taught, a child was not a human person until it gasped its first breath after birth.[6]

Alexander averted his eyes from the atrocity and tried to think of it as a mere mass of flesh, or better, a hostile cancerous tumor that had threatened to kill the actress.

But Alexander's conscience did not fare well. He had taken the Hippocratic Oath and had sworn that as a physician and healer, he would do no harm. His challenge to Thelonius earlier hounded him.[7]

It wasn't a crime in Roman culture. Plato's and Aristotle's ethics took care of that. The empire took precedence over all individual concerns, thus justifying abortion and infanticide as necessary or compulsory in cases of overpopulation or physical deformity. The *polis*, or ideal city, could only be built upon "the most desirable form of human life."[8]

But it was a crime to God. And as a Jew, he had covenanted with Yahweh who commanded, "Thou shall not murder," and even gave laws protecting the value and dignity of all human life, from the small to the great, with special concern for the weakest and most vulnerable.[9]

Technically, Alexander did not actually kill the child, because it had already been poisoned before he got there. He was here to save the life of the mother. But the gruesome task he had just performed burdened him with a guilt he could not shake. He still felt like an accessory.

His thoughts were interrupted by Severus' worrisome voice. "Can you stop the bleeding, Alexander? Will she be all right?"

Before he could answer, Alexander felt something in the womb that the midwife had missed. He knew instantly what had happened. "She will be all right, Severus. The extra blood was not caused by a puncture of the uterine wall. It was from another infant in the womb. A twin."

"Thank, Zeus," said Severus, as if thinking only of Persephone's safety.

Alexander decided against the previous procedure for this second infant. Instead he used forceps to crush the skull of the fetus in the womb and pull it out whole.

He felt sick again. It was another male.

He consoled himself with the fact that the perpetrators and victim in this case were all Gentiles, not his fellow Jews. And that Gentile Roman nation was oppressing his people in a cosmos of idolatrous rule, defying the one true God. So, in a sense, killing their own offspring was a means of committing cultural suicide. *Give them a few generations*, he thought, *and the noble gentry will abort their way into extinction.*

"She needs rest," said Alexander to the midwife. "Give her plenty of water as soon as she awakens, and avoid all bloodletting. She's lost enough blood already." He looked to Severus. "It may be several days before she can return home." He could see Severus trying to figure out how they could keep this incident a secret. He hoped he would not be asked to lie for him again.

Alexander felt disgusted with himself for aiding the secrecy of such immorality. Severus and his lover were adulterers who, if they lived in a just society ruled by God's law, would be stoned to death for their criminal deeds. Violating the marriage covenant was the deepest betrayal of the very foundation of civilization.

Alexander felt the guilt of his compromise. As a Hellenist Jew, he had assimilated the Greek language and culture. He had tried to accept the good and reject the bad. But he felt the corrupting influence of survival upon the good intentions of his soul. His own wife Juliana had also committed adultery. Just how different was he from this master he served? But the reason Alexander didn't blame her was because he had driven her to it. He had responded to their devastating news of infertility by throwing himself into his work as if it were his own lover. He felt like a cliché in an Aristophanes play.

How predictable and stupid. By the time he realized the damage he had done, Juliana was already embroiled in an affair with a wealthy patrician.

He thanked God that was behind them now. He had taken responsibility and forgave her for her part. It had been a long road of recovery, but they had learned their lesson and were in the process of healing their marriage. Yes, he would return home tonight as soon as possible and hold his wife in his arms and never let go.

The two men rode back to the Praetorian barracks.

"What in the world was she doing, waiting so long?" Alexander had the freedom to express some anger, but only because it was a medical issue. In all other interactions he had to be submissive to Severus.

Severus said, "At first, she was going to claim to her husband that it was his child. But they haven't had relations in months. It would be too easy for him to spot the lie. And vanity overcame her. She reconsidered the effect of the pregnancy on her beauty and her prospects in the world. A child would be a further inconvenience as a dependent parasite."[10]

"I am sure Persephone's husband would have preferred to adopt the child out than to have his wife die from such a high-risk procedure."

"She had considered infant exposure," Severus offered.

Alexander shot him a horrified look. Infant exposure was the practice of leaving unwanted newborns to the elements. The child would be left alone in a forest or desert at night, where wild animals would take them away—but not to raise them, like their myths and legends fancied.[11]

Severus retorted, "It's legal and common enough. But the problem is, those cursed Nazarenes are notorious for rescuing the infants and adopting them into their pernicious households."[12] According to his imperial Roman mind, it was better to kill his offspring than allow them to be adopted by the dreaded *Christianoi*.

Severus placed his hand on Alexander's shoulder. "Thank you, Alexander. You have rescued me yet again from disastrous consequences."

"You are not out of the woods yet. She has lost too much blood to return home to her husband tonight."

Severus smirked. "Her husband is away on a trip. Go home to your wife, Alexander. You deserve a rest."

CHAPTER 3

Cassandra Laetorius pulled her hood tighter over her head. She rode a small wagon down Long Street on her way back to her district over the Tiber River. Her passengers, Peter and Paul, sat quietly beside her. Paul was trying to reserve his strength for the long sea trip ahead of him. He hadn't been this secretive in the past, but because he was sick and was only stopping here on his way to Spain, he wanted to avoid any inconvenient attention.

Cassandra had been helping the apostle Paul on his journeys for over a decade. She had first met him when her parents had become Christians under the reign of Claudius twelve years earlier. Her father was a shipping merchant whose two carrier ships traveled all over the empire delivering food and goods or whatever paid. Her parents had been killed in the riots under Claudius and she inherited her father's estate. When the Jews were expelled that year, her uncle had taken her to safety at Corinth, where her family had a second residence. It was there she met the apostle and it was there she dedicated her life to the Gospel by using her ships to carry Paul and other itinerant preachers to various cities throughout the empire. She was on her way now to pick up Paul's things at her house across the river, and then see him off on one of her ships at the port city of Ostia, where he would launch off into the west.

Paul coughed and looked at her. "I may be sick, but I am not blind. Unforgiveness will destroy you, Cassandra."

She didn't look at him. She couldn't. The streets of Rome were tight. She had to be careful in maneuvering her horse through the maze of people and markets lining the streets. As well as the occasional pot of waste thrown from the windows above onto the bricks below.

He continued, "The Jews may be enemies of the Gospel, but from the standpoint of God's plan, he has hardened them to draw in the Gentiles."[1]

"They murdered my parents for believing in Messiah," she said. "My own people murdered my father and mother."

"So did I," he said.

She glanced over at him.

"I was a Jew who killed Jews for believing in Messiah. But God had a greater purpose for me. You are not the only one who has lost loved ones in this tribulation. And it will get worse before he comes. But God is still in control. He has promised vindication for the martyrs, judgment on the Beast, and the growth of his kingdom throughout the world. You must be steadfast in faith."

"His delay makes me yearn for justice," she said.

Paul had preached that in view of the present tribulation, it would be wise not to marry. So she didn't. She didn't want to suffer more loss than she already had. Falling in love and having a family would only multiply the pain and suffering that persecution brought. So she had dedicated her life to the kingdom of God. But that had been so long ago. And she was weary with longsuffering.[2]

Peter spoke up. "The Lord is not slow to fulfill his promise, Cassandra. He wishes none to perish, but that all should come to repentance."

She shook her head. "And what of those who do not repent? When will they receive their due?"

"Soon," Peter said. "The Day of the Lord is coming. He is near, and he will come like a thief. The old covenant elements will burn up and be replaced by the new covenant, a new heavens and earth. Count the patience of our Lord as your salvation."[3]

She knew the covenantal idea of "heavens and earth." In the Torah, God used the concept as a poetic metaphor for the covenant. The old covenant and its elements of temple and sacrifice were likened to the old heavens and earth. The new covenant would be a shaking of that old world and the establishment of a new heavens and earth. That new covenant had been instituted with Christ's death and resurrection, but not yet confirmed in historical judgment—the judgment she was impatiently demanding.[4]

Paul, not one to let Peter get the last word, added, "But first, the lawless one must be revealed, and it will not happen until the revolt takes place."[5]

23

His words gave her little encouragement. They had spoken about the "lawless one" and the coming revolt in Judea before. How the Jewish unrest in the Holy Land would become an organized full-scale war. But it was hard to believe, since such rebellion had already been put down swiftly by the Romans multiple times in her own lifetime. And then there were Jesus' own words that she echoed back to the two apostles, "The Gospel has not yet reached the whole world of the empire."[6]

Paul said, "Why do you think I go to Spain? That is the last of the nations to receive the testimony. And then the end will come. But our Lord has not promised to remove us from tribulation in this world. Our suffering produces endurance, and endurance produces character, and character, hope."[7]

She wanted to believe. She wanted to forgive. She needed to forgive. But she wasn't ready. She could not forget the image of her parents being dragged through the streets for sharing the Gospel message. Their bruised and bloody bodies hoisted on poles and stoned to death. By the time Claudius had quenched the riots, dozens of other Christians were murdered in cold blood by their fellow Jews. And over the next dozen years, thousands more would be persecuted, tried, punished and lynched all throughout the empire, simply for believing in Jesus as the Messiah, for offering the love of God and salvation.[8]

She would forgive when justice was served. And justice was coming.

They crossed the Aurelian bridge into the Trans-Tiber Region, her neighborhood. But she pulled the horse and cart aside when they saw a protest in the main square. A hundred or more Jewish residents were up in arms, listening to a speaker. She couldn't hear what he was saying at this distance.

Cassandra saw a citizen leaving the square to cross the bridge back to the city. She called out to him, "Excuse me, sir, what is the commotion about?"

He stopped. "Rumors of the Christian apostle back in town. The one that was imprisoned here last year that caused all the ruckus."

Paul pulled his hood tighter.

Peter said, "Good day to you, brother," and turned away.

The man waved and kept walking past them and over the bridge.

Cassandra and her traveling companions looked at each other with foreboding.

"We won't be able to return to the house," she said. "You'll have to go straight to the ship now."

She turned the cart down the side road that led to the small dock where a taxi boat waited that would bring them upriver to Ostia. From there, Paul would board her merchant ship that was currently being loaded with goods at port. Peter would help Cassandra see him off.

She prayed to God he would not be noticed and lynched.

CHAPTER 4

Alexander walked from the Praetorian camp to his home in the Jewish quarter of Porta Capena.[1] It was a long walk, almost a mile and a quarter, made even longer by the masses in the marketplace, the busy residential avenues, and the congestion he would need to navigate around the imperial palace on the Palatine hill. Alexander lived with his wife, Juliana, in the crowded district a short walk from the Circus Maximus, the center of entertainment in the ancient city. It was the first of several and largest of its kind in Rome, two thousand feet long with a seating capacity of one hundred fifty thousand spectators. The emperor held public games here, consisting of chariot races, beast hunts and athletic contests, as well as religious festivals and Roman celebrations of triumph. The emperor loved his games.

Disgustingly so, thought Alexander. The games seemed to him to be the sensationalized exploitation of the base nature of humanity. Violence as entertainment, entertainment as idolatry.

This night was the eve of an annual nine-day celebration: Caesar's Victory Games. The streets were twice as crowded now as any other time of year. Visitors from every surrounding region of Rome flooded the local taverns and inns. The good physician wasn't a man for sport, so it was even more of a bother to him and less of a benefit. He had planned to move out of the district soon.[2]

A new home would be appropriate for the fresh start that he also had made with Juliana. Before her affair, his focused devotion to his craft, the alleviation of human suffering through medicine, had been the excuse to neglect her needs. He had been the first to be unfaithful. His work had become his mistress.

And their age difference of almost ten years didn't help. He sometimes unfairly considered her a juvenile in her maturity. But in truth, he had been the selfish, dependent child.

He made his way through the crowded streets. Tears of regret came to his eyes as he remembered the night she confronted him.

"I love you, Alexander," Juliana had said. "But I am too lonely. I could not wait for you any longer."

He could still see the pain in her eyes, the despair he had caused. He had almost lost his greatest treasure on this earth.

Tears of regret turned to happiness as he neared his district in the shadow of Circus Maximus. He thanked God once again for opening his eyes to the cliff he had almost jumped off. Rather than divorcing her, as was his right, he accepted his responsibility and sought to redeem their broken marriage.

Cutting back on his hours, spending more time with her, showering her with affection and gifts, was all difficult at first, but quickly became a source of life-giving breath to his suffocated soul. He discovered things about her he had never bothered to notice before. That she was creative and added artistic touches to their home with foreign vases and tapestries. That she loved poetry and appreciated it when he verbalized his devotion to her. She was a free spirit, the opposite of Alexander, and his perfect complement for everything that was missing in his measured and quantified existence. She embodied the beauty of life he had ignorantly missed.

He saw his home just down the street now, and could feel his heart beat faster with anticipation.

She had told him it felt like they were newly married again. It had been a long and hard road. But they had made it together, and he would never again make so foolish a mistake. He had learned the most important lesson of his life.

He decided that he was ready to take the next step. He was going to suggest to her today that they adopt a child. He knew she felt worthless because of her barrenness. But he thought there was no reason why she shouldn't feel just as useful, and yes, fruitful, as a mother with an adopted child. Was not the act of rescuing orphans true religion? Did not Yahweh adopt Israel as his own son at Mount Sinai? Did he not choose Israel to be a people for his own possession out of all the peoples on the face of the earth?[3]

Alexander finally made it to the house and breathed a sigh of relief. He would surprise Juliana and give her an afternoon of love that expressed his gratitude beyond words.

He slipped into the house in search of her. A noise from the bedroom alerted him. It sounded like she was crying. Sobbing.

He quickened his pace, his heart calling to hers. He burst open the door to comfort her, only to find her in the throes of passion with another man. She had not been sobbing, she had been moaning in ecstasy. He saw the purple uniform on the floor, that of a military tribune.

"Oh, my god!" she yelped.

The tribune jerked a look at Alexander. He was young, muscular and handsome. Alexander recognized him as one of Severus' acquaintances. He must have met Juliana at one of the occasional parties he was required to attend.

All the air in Alexander's world, in his very soul, left him. He almost forgot to breathe. And when he did, all he could hear himself say was, "Juliana."

The tribune didn't even bother getting out of bed. As if he were entitled to her. He waited to see what the cuckold would do.

Humiliation followed the panic in Alexander's chest. In such a case as this, Roman marriage laws provided for the right of the offended to respond with violence against the offenders. But Alexander would not fight for her. He could not fight for her. The doctor was no warrior.

And his heart had been broken. Alexander had sought to be of some significance in this world with his medical expertise. To make his wife proud of him. But yet again, she had chosen a man of higher status and wealth, a man of greater accomplishment than Alexander. It only served to reinforce his own sense of personal failure and insignificance.

A dead calm came over him as the three of them stared at each other.

Alexander said, "I divorce you."

It was that easy. Roman law decreed that a man had the right to merely verbally announce his intentions of divorce and it was legally binding.

Juliana said nothing. Alexander could see the fear in her eyes. According to law, she would lose half her dowry and be banished for such misbehavior if her husband filed a petition of adultery. A divorce was socially acceptable enough, but would he file the adultery petition as well?

A cuckolded husband had little recourse. If he didn't divorce an adulterous wife, he would face charges by the state of pimping.[4]

At this moment, all Alexander wanted to do was to strike back at her for her betrayal. His first thought was to file the petition and destroy her for what she had done. All he could feel was his pain choking out the love he had been deluded into believing.

How revealing it was that she held a sheet up over her breasts. This adulteress would cover herself before her own husband. Naked and ashamed as their guilty forebears in the Garden. *Eve, where are you?*

Without another word, he turned and left the house. He wanted to get far away from this deep bleeding gash in his heart. He wanted to be anywhere but here.

Alexander wandered aimlessly through the throngs of people in the streets. His eyes would settle on a face, a soul in the midst of some unknown pursuit, and then another of sadness and another. He was suddenly aware of how many people around him looked forlorn or laden with burden. It was as if he were adrift in a sea of sadness.

As he put distance between himself and his house of shame, his shocked anger cooled into numbness. A second thought came to him. He could destroy her with an adultery petition, but did he really want to? Even now, with her serial infidelity and betrayal, he felt pity for her. Pity for her shame. If he sought revenge, it would only enslave him to the same cycle of hurt that had already destroyed her soul.

Eventually, almost by complete surprise, Alexander arrived at a familiar place: the Praetorian camp. His feet had unconsciously walked the only path they knew on their own, back to the only thing he could do to cope with such pain.

Back to work.

CHAPTER 5

"And to the angel of the church in Laodicea write: 'The words of the Amen, the faithful and true witness, the beginning of God's creation. "'I know your works: you are neither cold nor hot. Would that you were either cold or hot! So, because you are lukewarm, and neither hot nor cold, I will spit you out of my mouth. For you say, I am rich, I have prospered, and I need nothing, not realizing that you are wretched, pitiable, poor, blind, and naked. I counsel you to buy from me gold refined by fire, so that you may be rich, and white garments so that you may clothe yourself and the shame of your nakedness may not be seen, and salve to anoint your eyes, so that you may see. Those whom I love, I reprove and discipline, so be zealous and repent. Behold, I stand at the door and knock. If anyone hears my voice and opens the door, I will come in to him and eat with him, and he with me. The one who conquers, I will grant him to sit with me on my throne, as I also conquered and sat down with my Father on his throne. He who has an ear, let him hear what the Spirit says to the churches.'"
—*The Apocalypse of Jesus Christ 3:14-21*

Laodicea

Rabbi Johanan of Laodicea shivered with wonder at the scene before him of chariots and cherubim and seraphim. He was the head of the Merkavah mystery cult in Laodicea, a popular folk religion in the area that blended magic and Hellenistic mysticism with Jewish cultic observances. Merkavah meant "chariot mysticism" because the initiates studied and sought the visionary experiences of the prophets with their chariot journeys into heaven and throne visions of sacred hybrid creatures.[1]

Johanan was currently ascending in his chariot up to the seventh heaven. He had worked hard to achieve this vision. He had fasted for forty days, had abstained from sexual intercourse, and had prayed magical incantations with his amulets of angelic names. After a delirious breakthrough, he met a guardian angel who now brought him before the celestial scribe, Metatron. Secret tradition said that Metatron was Enoch transformed to keep records of the deeds of Israel.[2]

But now Johanan stood before the great being up in the highest heavens. He saw the bronze-like metallic firmament below their feet. The angel had transfigured to show the rabbi his true nature as a seraph, a mighty winged serpentine being, as if on fire—a Shining One.

The great being spoke with the sound of many voices. "Rabbi Johanan, Yahweh sees your good works and credits you as righteous. Tell the people of Laodicea to be at rest. For only in the extremes of hot and cold are there dangers for your soul. The hot springs of Hieropolis and the cold waters of Colossae are both foolish extremes for spiritual health. The truth lies in the middle, in my calm and comforting warm water of Laodicea."

Laodicea was close to its sister cities of Hieropolis and Colossae. And both of those cities were known for their healing waters. Johanan could see the wisdom of moderation in all things.

Metatron continued, "You are rich, and you have need of nothing. The only problem you must purge from your city is the cancerous disease of exclusion and judgment. Those who seek to elevate their god above all others are the true enemies of enlightenment. They reject the elevation of angels and the study of genealogies. They exclude all beliefs but their own and cast judgment upon others. But we *include* beliefs. We blend them into a composite of rich cultural beauty that will last forever."

"Yes, Metatron," said Johanan. "I will bring your vision to the people. We will exclude all those who are exclusive. We will judge all those who judge others. We will not tolerate the intolerant."

"Yes, my child," said Metatron. "You have the mind of God."

But it was Apollyon who had the mind of Johanan in his grip. His spiritual talons dug deep into the unconscious rabbi's brain as the Jew lay on his bed at home in a comatose state. Apollyon used the Metatron façade to accomplish indirectly what he could not accomplish directly: spiritual apostasy from Yahweh. Though there were many Jews and Christians in Laodicea, he had

31

neutralized their faith through syncretism, the blending of multiple elements from different belief systems to create a hybrid of folk religion.

And syncretism was best achieved through mystical experience. Doctrine was the murderer of spiritual experience as far as Apollyon was concerned. Oh, how he hated doctrine. It divided the world instead of uniting it. Through doctrinal definitions, Christians and Jews separated themselves from pagans, from those who were different than them, and they separated themselves from each other.

But the power of mysticism was through experience. Mystical experience could unite contradictory beliefs into a beautiful unity of opposites. A delusion of oneness. Take a Christian, a Jew and a pagan all arguing over dogma, give them a similar mystical experience of a chariot ride to the heavens with a few glorious beings, and they'll be singing in harmony like a group of trained parrots.

He had developed mystical experience from the dawn of creation. His newest forms were Merkavah and Gnosticism, and of course the pagan mystery cults. It was his way of mimicking the validation of a true prophet of Yahweh in the Scriptures. True prophets had all stood in the divine council before Yahweh and the Sons of God to receive their holy calling and message. From Enoch and Noah, to Moses and Joshua, to Isaiah and Jeremiah, they all experienced the presence of God's throne room and his heavenly host. So Apollyon sought to imitate such authority with his own hallucinations.[3]

This was the same trick he had pulled in Colossae, her nearby sister city. But here in Laodicea, it was particularly effective. Laodicea was a rich city, a center for banking with much gold in its stores. When the last major earthquake had occurred just four years ago, Laodicea refused imperial financial assistance and rebuilt the city from its own funds. It was also a medical center for the famous eye salve. Their unique black sheep's wool was sold all over Asia.[4]

Now that is a city of self-righteousness I can really use, thought Apollyon. *The rich and famous rarely see their own spiritual poverty or need for God. They heal the eyes of the sick, but are the blind leading the blind. And mystical religion fills their spiritual hunger with distraction. They think they are clothed in white, but they are wearing black.*

He couldn't beat Christianity outright with paganism, so he joined them together. Judaism, Christianity, pagan mysticism and magic all mixed together like one steaming pool of vomit. The people of Laodicea thought they were spiritually enlightened, but they were wretched, pitiable, poor, blind and naked.[5]

He couldn't ask for a better fortification against the enemy. To consider oneself married to Yahweh while committing adultery with other gods was the kind of betrayal that had kept Israel in bondage for generations and led up to this very moment in history. His stranglehold here was solid.

There was no trouble in Laodicea. No uprisings. No protests. No fights over dogma or moral outrage. They were safe and snug in their comfortable lukewarm water. Whatever plans the apostle had in mind for this city, they were certainly frustrated by Apollyon's influence.

Apollyon tightened his grip on the rabbi, who then began an epileptic seizure. He whispered into the human's ear, "You are my mouthpiece, Rabbi. Tell the people of Laodicea, 'He who has an ear to hear, let him hear what the spirit says.' Amen."

Oh, how he loved to play God. To play Yahweh.

Two cities in the enemy's circle of Asian power were now securely under Apollyon's control. Five to go.

CHAPTER 6

Rome

July 19

Evening

The fire began somewhere in the shops beneath the timbers of the Circus Maximus in the evening hours. No one knew the actual cause, whether it was arson or a cooking fire out of control. There were reports of ruffians running out of the district shortly before the flames grew, consuming the nearest shops. But then again, there was plenty of panicked running, as crowds of fleeing citizens clogged the streets with chaos and confusion.[1]

The flames moved so fast, they blocked the exit of some shoppers in the marketplace. Women screamed, trying to protect their children. But there was nowhere for them to run as burning facades collapsed on small crowds.

The frenzy of desperate people trying to escape through alleyways resulted in some being trampled to death. Others, confused by the mayhem, stood still in awe, watching the fire grow, only to find themselves caught in a death trap.

Bells rang throughout the region as the Vigiles Cohort assembled with their crude firefighting equipment of buckets, pikes, ladders, brooms and blankets, along with a few large siphons—double-action sump pumps for water. Severus had seven cohorts of a thousand vigiles each to guard the fourteen regions of the city. It was part of the vigiles' duty to fight fires in addition to their night watch over crime. They were prepared for smaller fires, but not for this blaze.[2]

Near the Circus, the high arching flames licked across the avenue to the cloth awning of a lamp shop. A wave of daring firefighters rushed to the flashpoint in a desperate attempt to stave off the massive conflagration. Their water delivery seemed woefully inept against the raging torrent. The awning was quickly engulfed and then the entire storefront. Those who dared remained vigilant, spraying what seemed mere droplets into a white hot inferno. But then the edifice exploded in a blinding flash and loud thunder as the liquid fuel ignited, incinerating everything in a fifty yard radius.

By now the huge wooden Circus Maximus was engulfed in flames. As fate would have it, a strong northerly wind was blowing on this warm summer night, which drove the fire rapidly down into the southern regions. It jumped the Servian Wall that guarded the perimeter of the inner city.[3]

Severus and Alexander were on the far side of the city in the Praetorian camp when word reached them of the conflagration. They left immediately to assess the scope of the danger. As they made their way through the panicked streets, they saw looters mugging other citizens and robbing buildings. But Severus had no time to address such crimes in light of the current emergency. By the time they made it to the location of the outbreak, the inferno had already consumed the Circus and was raging out of control. Severus pulled a team of leaders back to the Palatine Hill to establish a command center for organizing the firefighting operations.

Severus watched hopelessly as vigiles set up water pumps and began to direct their pitiful stream into the flames. "Alexander, did my son ever make it back to the camp from the emporium?"

"Not that I am aware."

The emporium was on the other side of the Circus Maximus. It was clear that Severus was worried for Thelonius' safety. But Alexander was too preoccupied with his own concerns. He saw that his residential district was already under siege by the growing conflagration. He turned back to ask Severus permission to leave, only to see Severus tell him, "Go. Save whatever you can of your home."

It struck Alexander that he had already lost everything earlier that day. He wondered what he was going back to save.

Alexander arrived at his home street trembling with fear. The entire block was a furnace of fire. He covered his eyes with his forearm as a wave of heat flowed over him.

Gehenna, he thought to himself. Gehenna was the name of a cursed valley just outside the western wall of Jerusalem that had become symbolic of the fires of judgment.

He ran through the gauntlet of flames until he arrived at his home. He had to pull his cloak over his mouth as a filter to the smoke. Then he caught sight of something past the threshold just inside the house. He approached cautiously, fearing what he might discover.

He coughed. He could barely breathe. Flames at the threshold kept him from entering the house, but he finally knew what he saw: the bodies of Juliana and her lover lying on the ground. They weren't burned. They had apparently been overcome by smoke inhalation. Juliana was trapped beneath the tribune's bulky body. Alexander could see Juliana's arms outstretched toward the door, as if she had given one last desperate attempt to drag herself to freedom from beneath his dead weight before she, too, had died.

It was too dangerous for Alexander to try to retrieve the bodies. He surprised himself that he was here anyway. Why should he care what happened to her? She had betrayed him, been unfaithful, and they were divorcing. In a way, this was a fitting end for her. Consumed in the flames of judgment, like a sacrifice to a false god of her own betrayal.

But then he saw her move.

Her head jerked up, coughing and gulping for air. She was alive!

Alexander stepped forward, then stopped. The flames at the entrance were too intense. He would not be able to get through them without getting burned badly. The structure above crackled and crumbled. If Alexander tried to save her, he could be overcome by the smoke as well, or more likely crushed by falling debris.

She looked up and saw him. Her eyes were filled with terror.

Before Alexander could change his mind, the burning timbers collapsed upon her in an orange inferno. The two adulterers were entombed in the blazing ruins.

She had been too weak to scream.

But he was not.

"JULIANA! NOOOOOO!"

He stumbled backward, pushed by the wave of heat. He fell to the ground in the street, coughed, then vomited.

The pain of her betrayal was overshadowed by the intimacy of years. His mind was flooded with all the moments of love and connection between them. The warmth of her embrace and acceptance, the softness of her heart and her lips. Laughing together and weeping for one another.

He wept bitter tears of regret. What had he done? What could he have done? What *should* he have done?

He had to get back to Severus.

The winds turned northward.

The conflagration that might have been contained to the southern poor regions now threatened to incinerate the rest of the glorious ancient city and all her rich treasures.

Severus had been watching the blaze in the region just south of the Circus for hours. By the time Alexander found the new command center, it was dawn and Severus had concluded with certainty that it was a lost cause. But he would not give up. He appointed as many firefighters as possible to man the nozzles of their puny siphons into walls of flaming fury. The vigiles worked heroically against the odds.

And then the worst thing happened. The water stopped.

Vigiles checked their mechanisms. Severus yelled to them, "The connection to the water channels! It must be blocked!"

"No, Prefect. I just checked it." The voice behind him made him turn. It was one of his vigiles, black soot-faced and coughing. "The channels are empty. We're out of water."

Alexander and Severus shared a knowing look. Only a few weeks ago, Alexander had watched Severus embroiled in a political battle with the city's water commissioner who had been pilfering the city's water provisions through illegal deals. The commissioner was diverting vast quantities of the city's water supply to senators and other wealthy interests for bribes. Severus had argued for this very purpose of emergency need. But as *praefectus vigilium*, the vigile prefect, he just didn't have the clout and had to give it up.[4]

And now the water was gone. Now the people of Rome suffered the consequences of the actions of power, greed and exploitation. Alexander knew it was for this reason that Severus wanted to become a Praetorian prefect. He wanted to clean up the corruption that was cannibalizing his beloved imperial Rome. His patriotism and incorruptibility were the only redeeming traits of this otherwise ruthless pagan warrior. But to become a Praetorian, one first had to be a senator, which was either inherited or granted by the emperor. As an equestrian without senatorial status, Severus' only chance of achieving his goal was to gain Nero's favor.

Alexander heard Severus yell to his men, "Prepare to protect the emperor's palace!"

As they prepared to move their operations center, Alexander asked Severus, "Any word of your son?" Severus had sent two men in search of Thelonius through the fire torn streets.

Severus shook his head with foreboding.

But the polis was his higher purpose. He had to focus on saving the city.

The emperor Nero Caesar was out of town and out of danger. But his residence certainly was not. By the time Severus arrived at the palace's main gate, the city prefect, Flavius Sabinus, had already requisitioned a corps of firefighters from his own Urban Cohort to institute the next protocol for out of control fires: firebreaks. By flattening buildings before they caught on fire, they could prevent the flames from spreading to the royal palace quarter.

Some were setting backfires as well. A backfire was a controlled burning of a piece of land so that when the main fire reached it, there would be nothing left to burn and it would die out.[5]

Sabinus was Severus' superior, so he ordered Severus to protect the Esquiline Hill, the back lot of Nero's royal structures and gardens just east of the Palatine.

And where was Nero in this time of crisis? In Antium, forty miles south of Rome, performing in a musical contest with his lyre.

Fiddling while his city burns, thought Alexander with contempt. Severus had often expressed his lack of respect for the emperor who was more interested in developing his artistic talents than developing his kingly rule. Another positive trait of Alexander's Roman overlord.

Sabinus had sent a messenger to Caesar, but how predictable it was that the man-child emperor would not be available during a tragedy when he was needed the most.

Alexander was exhausted. He had not slept in over twenty four hours. He couldn't think. His mind was dull, and knew that Severus was experiencing the same. But they could not entertain the luxury of slumber when they had a city to save.

On the way to the Esquiline Hill, Alexander and Severus saw some hooded men throwing torches into buildings in an apparent attempt to create a backfire. But this was not the designated zone for backfires.

Severus stopped one of the torchers, "You there! This structure is not within the fire path. The backfire perimeter is two blocks southwest of here!"

The man glared at him silently in defiance. He looked soldierly. At that moment, Alexander noticed what appeared to be armor beneath his cloak.

Severus saw it too. He said, "Are you a Praetorian?"

But the soldier-like man refused to answer and just ran off to the shock of them both.

One of the other cloaked men stood a few yards from the two of them. He answered obliquely, "We have our instructions and authority."[6]

Whose instructions? thought Alexander. *Whose authority?*

Before Severus could ask him what he meant, the man was off and running. Severus said to Alexander, "We cannot give chase. We have to get to the Esquiline, and save the palace there."

As the two of them made their way to the royal gardens, followed by a small corps of vigiles, Alexander tried to make sense of what he had just encountered. Who had given them authority to start backfires outside of the backfire zone? Or was this arson? They were, after all, disguised. Were they Praetorians? If so, that would mean the order for arson came from within Nero's own elite inner circle.

But who?

A thought suddenly occurred to him. Nero had often spoken of his desire to see the city rebuilt and named Neropolis after his glory. This devastating fire might just make that dream possible. And it would be a testimony to his innocence should he be out of the city when it happened.

Could there be an imperial conspiracy afoot?

Alexander knew that Severus was asking himself these same questions because he was the one who had told Alexander, in moments of frustration, of the madness in the inner court.

This conflagration was simply too convenient for the achievement of Nero's aspirations.

• • • • •

As the Great Fire raged through the city and threatened to consume everything, the few bridges across the Tiber almost collapsed under the weight of citizens seeking safety from the flames across the river.

After dropping off the apostle in Ostia for his sea journey, Cassandra had returned in her small boat to the dock by evening. By the time the fire had grown out of control in the heart of the city, she had come to the riverside to see how she could help. With the increasing ring of fire, many of the fleeing citizens were backed up against the river banks without the ability to cross on the congested bridges.

Cassandra used her sixty-foot boat to ferry people across the river to safety. She could get a good hundred people aboard before the hull would sink dangerously low in the water. She would bring them across, unload them on the western side of the river and return to the east side and start all over again.

But the current trip was the most difficult. She was near the emporium market, on the southern reaches of the city. The flames encircled the marketplace. It started to catch fire. The crowds became frantic.

Cassandra was on the dock making sure women and children were given priority to board her boat. The ship had reached capacity. In fact, it was dangerously over capacity. She saw an old man on the bow fall into the water and pulled away by the current. She was helpless to save him.

"Cassandra!" came the voice of her captain. "We are overloaded. We can take no more!"

She turned back to cross the plank and bumped into a young man. He was blackened with the soot of near-death escape. He looked straight into her eyes.

They recognized each other.

It was Thelonius, the medical assistant who had scorned the apostle Paul at the medical clinic. He must have been blocked by the flames while shopping for medical supplies for Alexander.

Another man tried to push his way in front of Thelonius. But Cassandra grabbed Thelonius' arm and pulled him across the plank onto the boat.

The plank was pulled back.

The ship moved away from the dock.

Cassandra looked upon the faces of those left behind. Crying, pleading, screaming for help. She only hoped they would survive until she returned with an empty ship. Beside her, she heard the weeping voice of Theolonius.

"Thank you. Thank you."

She embraced him, felt his young body trembling with tears of gratitude.

As the boat moved across the river with its dangerously heavy load of refugees, Cassandra looked out upon the inferno of orange flame and black smoke that blotted out the sky. She knew they would not make it back in time to save the rest of them.

Gehenna, she thought. *God's judgment.*

CHAPTER 7

"And to the angel of the church in Philadelphia write: 'The words of the holy one, the true one, who has the key of David, who opens and no one will shut, who shuts and no one opens. "'I know your works. Behold, I have set before you an open door, which no one is able to shut. I know that you have but little power, and yet you have kept my word and have not denied my name. Behold, I will make those of the synagogue of Satan who say that they are Jews and are not, but lie—behold, I will make them come and bow down before your feet, and they will learn that I have loved you. Because you have kept my word about patient endurance, I will keep you from the hour of trial that is coming on the whole world, to try those who dwell on the earth. I am coming soon. Hold fast what you have, so that no one may seize your crown. The one who conquers, I will make him a pillar in the temple of my God. Never shall he go out of it, and I will write on him the name of my God, and the name of the city of my God, the new Jerusalem, which comes down from my God out of heaven, and my own new name. He who has an ear, let him hear what the Spirit says to the churches.'"
—The Apocalypse of Jesus Christ 3:7-13

Philadelphia

The next city on Apollyon's reverse tour of Asian cities was Philadelphia, or Neocaesarea, as it was sometimes called by its residents. After the great earthquake during the reign of Tiberius, Philadelphia changed its name in response to Caesar's generosity in restoring it. The divine emperor deserved the recognition of his imperial religion, and the Jews of the city accommodated him willingly.

Standing in the local Jewish synagogue, Apollyon considered the way in which Philadelphia was a difficult target to secure. The Christians were few here and therefore of little power. But those chosen few were tenacious lice with their faith, patiently holding fast and keeping their silly god's word to them about patient endurance.[1]

Apollyon thought, *They have no idea the hour of trial that is coming on the whole world and on those who dwell in the Land.* He turned to a Watcher beside him, the patron god of the city, a satyr-like deity that made himself appear as half-man and half-goat. Apollyon lifted a cup of wine and said, "Dionysus, I salute you!"[2]

The hybrid-looking Watcher bowed in deference and took a deep drink of his own cup. Dionysus was the god of nature and of wine and revelry, famous for his musical and sexual exploits. He gave a hearty belch and the two of them howled with laughter, unheard and unseen by the Jews who celebrated around them in the synagogue.

"My synagogue," crowed Apollyon. He liked saying that.[3]

"Who says these aren't real Jews?" said Dionysus, scratching his hairy legs that ended in goat hooves. "So they don't bow before the Nazarene Christ. So what? They bow before Caesar. Why can't *he* be the savior of the Jews? Has he not saved the whole world?"

"He has," said Apollyon. "No king but Caesar!"

Dionysus chuckled at the mockery. It was the very statement said by the Jews who crucified the Messiah.[4]

The Philadelphian Jews that the Watchers were observing were celebrating in their meeting hall. The elders, scribes and about a hundred of their most influential citizens were there, drinking wine and beer while discussing the course of action they just voted to approve: their official excommunication of Christians from the synagogue. Christians could no longer participate in their religious community. And why should they? They only caused trouble and started theological fights anyway. Shutting the door of access to the synagogue was an expression from their covenant law of cutting off apostates and the unclean from sacred space and access to God. The Christians could no longer hijack the Jewish identity for their own purposes. They claimed to be the true Jews, but an increasing number of them were uncircumcised Gentiles who refused to keep the Sabbaths and dietary laws that marked out the people of God.[5]

Dionysus stepped over to a pillar. The drunken party around them had faded out in their attention. His hand brushed over the names of priests and other patrons of the building engraved into the marble pillar. At the top of the list was Tiberius Caesar. The names of Jews who had become followers of the Nazarene had been chiseled off.[6]

"Now that we have the Christians cut off from the community," said Dionysus, "I think it is time for a bloodletting."

Apollyon held up a hand. "Do not be hasty, my furry friend. Wait until I give the order."

Dionysus sighed. "How much longer are you going to make me wait? Everyone here is ready to tear these Christians limb from limb. It's positively orgasmic."

"Effective persecution builds step by step," said Apollyon to his goat demon ally. "If you move too quickly, the mob may lack the political will necessary for real long-term violence." He grinned and prepared to move on to his next city. He then turned for one last declaration. "Be ready. When the trumpet sounds, I will ride forth on my horses. And all hell will follow me."

• • • • •

"And to the angel of the church in Sardis write: 'The words of him who has the seven spirits of God and the seven stars. "'I know your works. You have the reputation of being alive, but you are dead. Wake up, and strengthen what remains and is about to die, for I have not found your works complete in the sight of my God. Remember, then, what you received and heard. Keep it, and repent. If you will not wake up, I will come like a thief, and you will not know at what hour I will come against you. Yet you have still a few names in Sardis, people who have not soiled their garments, and they will walk with me in white, for they are worthy. The one who conquers will be clothed thus in white garments, and I will never blot his name out of the book of life. I will confess his name before my Father and before his angels.

He who has an ear, let him hear what the Spirit says to the churches.'"
—*The Apocalypse of Jesus Christ 3:1-6*

Sardis

Apollyon sighed with pleasure as he walked among the tombs of the cemetery outside the city of Sardis, not too far from his previous visit at Philadelphia. The hillside at his back housed burial caves for the wealthy. The field he now walked through was planted with small mounds and simple stone markings for the poor.

He breathed in deeply the stale, putrid air. He wanted inspiration before he entered the next city. Yahweh's Angel of Sardis would not be around to bother Apollyon much. The Destroyer owned this city. In fact, Sardis was like a graveyard. The Christians of the city thought they were alive, but under his influence, they were dead and rotting in their soiled garments within their spiritual graves.[7]

He smiled to himself, thinking of his walk among the tombstones like a triumphal entry of the conqueror, on his way to drag what few Christians were still faithful to Yahweh through the streets of this necropolis, this city of the dead.[8]

The history of Sardis had been one of greatness gone sour. It was known for its impenetrable fortress-like location on a high acropolis. Yet because of this perceived invincibility centuries earlier, the people of Sardis were slack in rising to its defense against Cyrus of Persia. The result was a total victory for Cyrus and humiliation for the city. It had rested on the laurels of its past and did not strengthen what remained. It had never quite gotten over its defeat and couldn't seem to complete anything, including a large temple of Artemis that lay half built and unfinished in the midst of the city.[9]

The Christians were like that. In fear of persecution, they avoided witnessing to their faith and instead focused on good deeds, in effect doing Apollyon's work for him in silencing their own voices. Their deeds were incomplete without faithful witness, like the unfinished, idolatrous temple.[10]

And now, Apollyon was on his way to the city council. The rulers of the city were deliberating over the criminalization of the Nazarene sect. Once that was settled, it would allow the magistrate the right to remove the names of the few remaining Christians from the public register. Such erasure of citizenship of criminals resulted in ostracism, lost privileges and economic censure. It was a virtual death warrant for the Christians.[11]

The book of register reminded Apollyon of the enemy's Book of Life, a register of the redeemed. *They fail to confess their god's name, and they lose their heavenly citizenship when that thief, the Nazarene, comes. Their names will be erased from the Book of Life. Just like the public register.*[12]

The Destroyer muttered sarcastically, "Come quickly, Lord Jesus," then stepped into the city council chambers for his next human puppet play.

CHAPTER 8

Antium, South of Rome
July 20, AD 64

Nero Claudius Caesar Augustus Germanicus waited nervously in the wings of the theater he had built in Antium, the coastal town of his birth. At just twenty seven years old, he was emperor of the world. He patted his golden hair to make sure it was in place, adjusted his toga to be just right. As the nephew and adopted son of the previous Roman emperor, Claudius, he continued the Julio-Claudian lineage of greatness that had started with the divine Julius Caesar. He felt that greatness in his bones. He felt that divinity in his soul.[1]

He was an aesthete, gifted by the gods with the sensitivity to see and create truth and beauty. He preferred to think of himself as a creator, his life as an epic journey on the stage of history, like that of Hercules, played out before gods and men. One day, mortals would remember his tales as they remembered Homer's *Odyssey* or Virgil's *Aeneid*. But he would write his own legends.

No, he would sing them.

He had already composed many songs and bound them in archives for posterity. He felt a knack for lyric. Even the brilliant Stoic philosopher Seneca affirmed it before he retired a couple years ago as Nero's wisest advisor. They had parted on warm terms, but Nero still questioned Seneca's motives. The philosopher had been a shameless sycophant to the emperor, flattering him at every opportunity.

And now, here Nero was, human, all too human, sweating and feeling nauseous because he was about to perform with his lyre in the musical contest for this afternoon. The previous night, he had instructed the judges to choose the order by lot, and vote fairly for the best contestant. He needn't rely upon his status as Rome's patron-in-chief to be granted special favor. He wanted to win without bias. And win he did, always, unanimously and without partiality.[2]

But he was not done. There was today's contest.

At times he truly felt himself the human incarnation of Apollo, the god of music, poetry and art. When he played and sang verse, he felt he entered into the very realm of heaven. Music was the language of the gods.[3]

And drama was philosophy. He would weep at the tragedies of Seneca, belly laugh at the comedies of Plautus, and yearn for love in the romances of Andronicus. The fact was, beauty and art were more real, more true than life itself. This was why he took his acting seriously as well. Playing the roles of Oedipus, Orestes and Hercules allowed him to incarnate the divine.

He fancied himself a bit of a Platonist in touch with the ideal forms in heaven upon which the things of earth were fashioned. The contemplation of a beautiful body on earth led one to the contemplation of the soul and ultimately to the ideal form of beauty in heaven. It was why he preferred to pursue the sublime in the arts far more than the mundane burdens of earthly affairs of state.[4]

That's where Plato was wrong. It wasn't the philosopher-kings that could grasp the truth and beauty of universal forms to rule the perfect polis. It was the *artist*-king. Beauty alone was the only virtue, the only truth. When Nero sang, when he played, when he recited verse, it was then that he felt most godlike. Mortals, be they plebeians or ruling class, were ennobled by the arts, allowed to taste of the divine through audience participation.

This was why he made sure the theater was populated with the upper class: senators and equestrians, as well as military leaders. He wanted to share from his greatness and divinity.

He looked into a small mirror he had with him. He wiped sweat from his brow to look fresh. Sure, he had some pockmarks on his face, but a touch of makeup made them less pronounced. And his youthful blond hair drew all the attention anyway. He was proud of his Apollonian golden locks, made more pronounced with bleach and sprinkled with gold dust. He looked down and sucked in his potbelly gut. It wasn't that bad. The toga hid most of it anyway.

"Caesar."

The voice shocked Nero out of his concentration. He jumped with fright.

"Forgive me, my lord." It was a messenger from Rome, a young legionary. He was accompanied by Tigellinus, Praetorian co-prefect, a calculating and brooding protector of the emperor, which is why he was Nero's most trusted right hand.

"This had better be important, soldier," said Nero. "I am about to be called to the stage."

The legionary shook with nervousness. "Faenius Rufus has sent me to plead with you to make haste to Rome. The fire threatens the entire city."

Rufus was the co-prefect of the city with Tigellinus. Nero knew that Tigellinus despised Rufus and sought every opportunity to discredit him in the emperor's eyes. Tigellinus wanted to be sole prefect, which didn't concern Nero. He welcomed the competition of loyalty.[5]

Nero gritted his teeth. "He already sent me a messenger last night. I told him I would be on my way as soon as I complete the festival. Can he handle nothing in my absence?"

"Incompetent," muttered Tigellinus.

"Caesar," said the soldier, "the flames are climbing the Palatine hill. The palaces are endangered. And they have now advanced toward the Esquiline."

The Esquiline hill was where Nero's newest colonnade was built. It ran all the way to the Gardens of Maecenas. The heart of Nero's residence was in jeopardy.

Nero closed his eyes with dramatic flair. "Yes, that is most important." He stepped closer to the soldier with an angry look. "But you could have waited to tell me until I had finished my performance, you thoughtless, selfish fool. Now, you've filled me with anxiety, which will only spoil my concentration."

The soldier dared not move. "I am sorry, Caesar. I was only following orders."

Nero held his hand out to Tigellinus, who handed him a sap, a small leather sack with lead sewn into it, like a flexible club. He carried it on his person for the emperor.

Tigellinus grabbed the soldier from behind and held him tightly. The young legionary shook with fear.

"Now, I will have to work out my anxiety on you," Caesar said. "And you had better pray to the gods that it calms me."

"Yes, my lord…Caesar," whimpered the legionary.

Nero swung the sap and it contacted the jaw of the soldier, cracking several teeth and knocking him dizzy. He spit out blood. He swaggered. Tigellinus held him up.

Another swing and the soldier's nose broke and sprayed blood on the wall beside them. Nero then pummeled the captive with a series of punches to his stomach, doubling him over in pain. Tigellinus lifted him back up again.

The soldier weakly raised his hand and wimpered, "Caesar, I beg you, have mercy."

Another hit with the lead sap and the soldier dropped unconscious to the floor. Nero unleashed a barrage of kicks to the soldier's ribs and stomach. He paused, exhausted. And decided to give a final stomp on the poor soldier's head, crushing his skull with the force.

He looked down for a moment at the broken mess he had made. Then, with a sudden change of tempo, he said, "There," catching his breath. "Now I feel better."

Nero looked at his legs. "Zeus be damned. I have blood all over my sandal. Tigellinus, give me a cloth."

Tigellinus handed him one.

The emperor wiped his leg and sandal clean from the gore. He stood back up, looking with dread at his toga. "Is there any blood on my toga? Do you see any blood?"

"No, my lord."

Nero smiled. "A miracle! Favor of the gods tonight!"

"Yes, my lord."

A voice came from behind the curtains, announcing the next performer.

Tigellinus said, "They are calling you, Caesar."

"Indeed, they are." Nero brushed off his tunic, took a deep breath and picked up his lyre by the stage entrance. He turned back. "Wish me luck, Tigellinus."

"Fortuna be with you, my lord." The goddess of luck.

"I can feel it. And between you and me, I think my chosen piece is particularly poignant and profound." Nero beamed proudly at his poetic alliteration. He would sing about the Trojan War and destruction of Troy.

"Slay them, Caesar," said Tigellinus as Nero stepped through the curtains and onto the stage.

CHAPTER 9

"And to the angel of the church in Smyrna write: 'The words of the first and the last, who died and came to life. "'I know your tribulation and your poverty (but you are rich) and the slander of those who say that they are Jews and are not, but are a synagogue of Satan. Do not fear what you are about to suffer. Behold, the devil is about to throw some of you into prison, that you may be tested, and for ten days you will have tribulation. Be faithful unto death, and I will give you the crown of life. He who has an ear, let him hear what the Spirit says to the churches. The one who conquers will not be hurt by the second death.'"
—*The Apocalypse of Jesus Christ 2:8-11*

Smyrna

The Destroyer walked invisibly through the streets of Smyrna, the second largest port city in Asia, just forty miles west of Sardis. A hundred thousand in population, it was known as "first of Asia in beauty and size" for its Hellenistic structures that rose up on an acropolis like the crown of a victor king. Apollyon felt like the king of Smyrna as he walked past the imperial temple of Tiberius, a token of the city's unusual history of enduring faithfulness to Rome. It had been destroyed and rebuilt by Alexander the Great, like a Phoenix brought back to life from the ashes, thus warranting its epithets, "first and last," and "crown of life."[1]

The imperial cult that worshipped the emperor was young, a mere couple generations old, but it was growing. The emperor Augustus had been the first to declare Julius Caesar divine with a temple in Pergamum. Then Augustus proclaimed himself a god and built several altars around Asia, including Smyrna. Gaius had railed against the Jews for not recognizing his divinity.

And Nero increasingly displayed a thirst for deification with inscriptions of himself as "Lord of the Whole Universe," "Nero, Zeus," "Son of God, Savior."

Nero's self-identification as Apollo made Apollyon chuckle. *A pudgy, potbellied, pimple-faced Apollo*, he mused. *It reflects poorly upon me. But not for long.*[2]

Apollyon was so focused on his destination, he hardly noticed as he passed close by the temple of another deity.

"Apollyon! Apollyon!"

The voice snapped him out of his intense focus. It was Cybele, the mother goddess of Smyrna, another male Watcher in matronly disguise: outdated hairdo under a golden crown, and a toga that smelled of her pet lions.[3]

Behind her rose the temple of her namesake.

"Have you lost your way my lord?" she asked. "My temple is at hand straight away. Pray, what matter brings you to the city of your humble servant?"

"Certainly not *your* temple," he answered blithely and kept walking.

He stopped within sight of his destination. She looked up with jealous disdain. They saw a flood of Jewish citizens entering a large synagogue in the center of the city.

He said, "Though I am obliged to maintain a presence through shrines such as yours and Tiberius', their yield pales in the shadow of my grand synagogue of Satan."

He used the term ironically. Synagogue of Satan is what old Thunderhead called Jewish synagogues as an insult because their members considered themselves Jews, but rejected the Messiah. To the apostle, they were liars. To Apollyon, they were loyal.[4]

He smiled proudly. "My synagogue." It pleased him no end that the people who were once Yahweh's children were now his slaves. And the holy gathering house where the Torah, the very Word of God, was expounded had become his property. There was no better way of overthrowing an enemy than through subversion of their own sacred texts and leaders.[5]

A chill went down Apollyon's spine. *Danger.*

He looked around and saw the source of his unease. A cloaked figure at the end of the street, watching them at a safe distance.

The Angel of Smyrna. Another of Yahweh's heavenly guardians staying low and out of trouble.

"Coward," muttered Apollyon. He turned to Cybele. "It is time you proved your worth to me." He pulled her through the throng of people into the synagogue.

By custom, the synagogue was where Jewish leaders would read the sacred texts before the congregation, but not on this occasion. Tonight they faced a full house of angry Jewish locals. Several hundred strong faced the podium and shouted harangues of discontent toward a dozen elders standing up front.

"Heretics!"

"Apostates!"

Cybele drifted through their midst like a phantom, whispering in the ears of the members, goading them on with unseen influence.

A Pharisee pounded on the podium. "Quiet down! Quiet down!"

The crowd responded. The noise abated.

Apollyon gave Cybele a stern look. She had better prove herself worthy.

The Pharisee continued, "We must decide how to answer the Nazarene question with civility, otherwise we will be as disruptive as they are."

The crowd continued to grumble.

Cybele leaned down into one burly audience member and whispered in his ear. The burly one yelled, "The answer is simple, we kick them out!"

The crowd erupted again with agreement.

The Watcher whispered to another, who then blurted out, "Throw them in prison!"

She smiled proudly at Apollyon, who shook his head with displeasure. Not good enough. She would need his help to really get this party going.

When the cacophony died down, the fatherly Pharisee spoke with a stern voice. "We cannot suffer due process. The law forbids us doing them violence, but we can use the law to do them perhaps an even greater harm."

The crowd listened in rapt attention to this eloquent, wise-looking leader, with Apollyon now behind his ear, a virtual puppetmaster, showing his goddess companion how truly strategic damage is achieved. He hissed.

The Pharisee spoke. "We elders of the city have decided to require all Nazarenes to mark their places of business with the letter X painted on their door jambs." He let the symbolism sink into his listener's minds, with the help of the unseen whisperers.

The letter X was the first letter in the Greek word *Christ*, and so became the common abbreviation for *Christianoi*. But it had a double meaning as well. It could also stand for Roman crucifixion, the instrument of torture used on their so-called Messiah. It would be a satisfying slap in the face of the seditious troublemakers, and help to separate them from Jews.[6]

The Pharisee continued, "Now, with this visible marking we can institute a city-wide boycott of Christian-owned establishments. This will force them out of business, or better yet, drive them into debtors' prison and bond slavery."[7]

The audience noise escalated with agreement as they considered the implications. It was a brilliant plan. Both destructive *and* legal.

Rome did not tolerate riots and vigilante violence, so this was a way of engaging in a legal lynching. Restrict the enemy's ability to make a living. In addition, many knew that such easy identification of Christian-owned property would not merely afford the opportunity for withholding business. It would also provide a way to announce to the criminal elements of the city where they might vandalize without fear of legal reprisal from their fellow Jews.

Cybele was impressed with her master's skill. But she wanted to impress him in return. She prompted one of the common citizens in the crowd to raise his hand.

The Pharisee called on him and he said with a rustic simplicity, "Let's require all Christians to wear a tattoo to identify them and protect our young from molestation!"

The Pharisee nodded at the suggestion. It was a good one. It also served to condemn the Christians, since the Jewish law forbade tattoos.[8]

But Apollyon would not allow his sniveling underling any pride of place. He whispered and the Pharisee said, "We will deliberate over it. In the meantime, remember to avoid patronizing any Christian business, and let us see if we cannot once and for all stop their intolerance from poisoning the rest of the population. We have battled these demonic teachings for far too long already." He paused thoughtfully as the crowd murmured in agreement, then added with an air of sarcasm, "If the Christians can faithfully endure this, they'll deserve the Smyrna crown of life!"[9]

The tension dissipated with laughter. Their wicked scheme trivialized by humor.

Apollyon grinned with satisfaction. Five important Asian cities enflamed against the Christians. Two more to go. And those two were more advanced in their wickedness. He couldn't wait. Their examples would spread like the Great Fire through the empire. Once he finished his tour of persecution here, he would be prepared for the major offensive he was about to launch from Rome into all the earth.

CHAPTER 10

Rome
July 26, AD 64

The city of Rome was a pile of smoldering ruins. Whole districts of residences were nothing but piles of charred wood and bricks. The buildings in government quarters like the Palatine and Capitoline Hills looked like graveyards of demolished stone mausoleums, once-glorious monuments reduced to heaps of blackened marble. The air was heavy and gray with residual smoke. Ash fluttered in the wind like black snow.

The Great Fire had raged for seven days consuming the city. It died out after five, but then rekindled on the property of Tigellinus near the Capitoline Hill for another two days. Of the fourteen regions or districts of the city, only four escaped the devastation. They were the imperial gardens to the north of the city, and the western Trans-Tiber district that was across the river.[1]

Untold numbers had perished. Entire families were snuffed out in the inferno. Severus had told Alexander that his own son Thelonius had miraculously escaped the flames down by the emporium by jumping onto a boat. It relieved Alexander, who felt he was somehow responsible for the threat on Thelonius' life because he had ordered him there for medical supplies. Still, he knew Severus felt guilty as well for not bringing Thelonius with them because of the secret Severus had kept.

Many others were not as lucky as Severus and his son. Hundreds of thousands of homeless commoners and nobility now gathered on the northern Campus Martius and the nearby gardens by the north bend of the Tiber River. The putrid stench of charred and rotting corpses filled the air and made Alexander want to retch as he followed his lord, Severus, through the masses of suffering humanity. They were part of a royal entourage touring the refugee camps. Nero led them, accompanied by his city officials, urban prefect Sabinus, and Praetorian co-prefects, Tigellinus and Rufus.

Nero had arrived at Rome from Antium on the third day of the conflagration. He immediately set about helping the refugees find a place for safety in his gardens. The Praetorians—and both Urban and Vigile Cohorts—maintained order, built tents, and distributed food to the lost souls.

The fire had died out after taking its toll, and the people were in despair. Nero, however, was not. He had a lightness of step as he mounted a makeshift stage to repeat his message to the third crowd today. He wanted to make sure the populace heard his inspiring vision from his own mouth.

Nero's beautiful wife, Poppaea Sabina, stood beside him like a shining trophy that competed for the crowd's attention. She was of noble blood. At thirty-four, she was seven years older than Nero, but was glamorous in her appearance. She wore elaborate dresses of oriental fabrics, and it was rumored her pale elegant skin came from bathing in asses' milk.[2]

What a contrast to the emperor's unseemliness, thought Alexander. Nero had pustular skin with pockmarks, acne, and an occasional syphilitic cold sore on his lips. He was squat with a thick neck, spindly legs and a potbelly of indulgence. Alexander wondered how Poppaea could tolerate his foul body odor in such close proximity. The only two things pleasant about the appearance of the emperor were his golden hair and blue eyes.[3]

Severus had told Alexander of Poppaea's scandalous background. She was married twice before, and her previous husband was Nero's best friend, Otho. According to Severus, Poppaea had her eye on the principate all along. So she cleverly persuaded Otho to let Nero share her bed to advance his political status. This ended in Poppaea's divorce from Otho and remarriage to Nero.

The only problem was that Nero's first wife, Octavia, was in the way of Poppaea's imperial appetite. So Poppaea managed to turn Nero against Octavia. He divorced her and ultimately executed her for adultery. Octavia was drowned in a bath and beheaded.[4]

Seductive and cunning was this beautiful empress of Rome.

The thing that surprised Alexander was that, despite her ruthless ambition, Poppaea was a deeply religious convert to Judaism. Alexander could not see the personal benefit in it for the empress, so he could only assume it was not pretense. Her lack of faithful obedience to the Mosaic law could be forgiven, since her favor of the Jews in Rome was much to their benefit.

A young Jewish military general in his late twenties followed Poppaea, like a manicured pet. His bearded and trimmed appearance was clothed by a regal Hebrew uniform of a colorful robe with gold trimming, gold bracelets, and a tightly wound bejeweled turban.

He had a sly subtlety to him, thought Alexander. *Like a serpent.* His name was Joseph ben Matthias and he had traveled here from Palestine on some diplomatic mission.[5]

Alexander sighed with disappointment in himself. He had thought of Israel as "Palestine" again. The Romans started calling the Holy Land "Palestine," because it was the Latin word for the land of the Philistines. Since the Philistines were the barbarians that King David had conquered to secure his kingdom, they represented the ultimate enemy of the Israelites. Calling Israel "Palestine" was an insult intended to rewrite historical truth with Roman contempt. By thinking of Israel as "Palestine," Alexander wondered if he had become tainted by his Hellenization. Subtly seduced toward apostasy. Was he a toad in the warm water of a slow boiling pot?[6]

Nero used a large bronze megaphone to extend his voice to the crowds before him. "Children of Rome. My children. We stand in the ashes of a great conflagration that has ravaged our ancient city, our homes and our lives. As you begin to wonder what the future will bring, remember that I, too, feel your pain. I, too, have lost everything at the hands of the gods."

Alexander tightened his lips at the exaggeration. Nero had lost his old and unused palace on the Palatine Hill, but not the treasured and opulent Esquiline Hill. He had managed to move much of his personal belongings and favorite artworks from one to the other before the flames reached them.

Ah, the subtle nuance of politics.

The emperor continued, "But I want to assure you that Roma is alive and well. And she will arise like a Phoenix out of the ashes." Roma was the goddess of Rome.

The crowd was not very responsive. Alexander could see they were exhausted, frightened and hungry.

"As some of you know, I was away on important imperial business. As soon as I received the message of this tragedy, I returned immediately to you, my beloved city and people."

Alexander looked at Tigellinus to see if he would give away the lie. He didn't. He was stiff with an angry stare. He always had a look of anger on his face.

Nero continued, "Like you, I have not slept since returning home. I have consulted the Sibylline oracles, rescued from the temple of Jupiter, in order to know which deities to appease for the future of Rome. The priests have assured me that the gods Vulcan, Ceres, Proserpine and Juno have all confirmed that the future of our great city is brighter than ever before."[7]

Nero tried to rally the crowd with his enthusiasm. "I have consulted imperial architects and engineers. And I want you to know that we are mere days away from fundamentally transforming the state of Rome. I have had maps drawn up for safer construction, wider streets, better homes, and a more glorious palace than you can even imagine. And I pledge to you that the government will pay for it all, and a government workforce will perform it all."[8]

The response was tepid. Half-hearted clapping from half-dead citizens who would ultimately shoulder the burden of such grandiose public civil works projects.

It struck Alexander as telling that Nero would already have maps drawn up for his building project. That took time. Weeks, not the few days he had. And the joyfulness of Nero, his excitement at rebuilding the city, fueled his suspicions that there was more to this than a surprise tragedy. Severus had told Alexander of Nero's fantasy of rebuilding Rome and renaming it Neropolis in his honor. Were these the maps he spoke of? He also remembered that the day the fire began, July 19, was the exact day that Rome was destroyed and rebuilt four hundred years earlier, a symbolic connection that would not be lost on the artist emperor.[9]

Nero's absence from Rome was a perfect alibi to deflect accusations of arson against him. But of course, he wouldn't need to be in Rome to place the order to torch it. Was it a coincidence that after the fire was out, it had started again on Tigellinus' estate? Almost as if to make sure that the palatial Palatine Hill was thoroughly destroyed to justify government bailout for a rebuild. The evidence strongly indicated to Alexander that Nero may have set the fire to destroy the city, which would justify him rebuilding it according to his vision—at the taxpayers' expense. If the public ever figured that out, there would be Hades to pay.

Nero pulled out his lyre, and announced, "Today is not a day for a dirge. Today we must look to the future. And I, your savior and lord, will sing a happy song, a song of hope and of changing times." He plucked some strings and began to sing with his weak and hoarse voice.[10]

Alexander saw Severus sigh and close his eyes. He and his fellow prefects had much to organize for the massive renovation starting this evening. Work crews would be working in shifts around the clock to flatten the rubble and bury the human remains outside the city. But here they were spending precious time listening to the vainglory of an emperor more absorbed with how he felt about reality than reality itself.

But, he was the emperor, and law and order required authority or else anarchy would rule.

Tigellinus leaned in and whispered something to Severus. Alexander only heard the prefect's last statement, "And bring your Jew."

CHAPTER 11

Severus and Alexander met with Tigellinus after dark on a hill outside the Praetorian barracks that overlooked the city. The gardens in the north were lit up by refugee campfires. The city itself looked like a deep black pit with smoke pouring out of it. They could see lines of torches of cohorts working through the night to haul the smoldering debris out of the city. They carried the rubble onto barges that would ship it downriver.[1]

Severus asked Tigellinus, "I take it prefect Rufus is on his way here?"

"No," said Tigellinus sternly. "Rufus does not need to be privy to every decision I make. And this matter is between me and the emperor alone. I will expect you both to keep it to yourselves as well. Is that understood?"

"Yes, sir," they both replied.

Severus had told Alexander that Tigellinus hated Rufus and was constantly trying to discredit him in the eyes of the emperor. It was obvious to Severus that Tigellinus wanted to be the sole Praetorian authority and counsel of Nero. And it was obvious to Alexander that Severus tried to ingratiate himself to Tigellinus in anticipation of his ultimate success.[2]

Tigellinus got to the point with Severus. "What do you know of the origin of the fire?"

"Well," said Severus, "some people say it began in the northeastern corner of the Circus Maximus."

"Don't test my patience, Severus. We know the location. Is there word of arson?"

Severus cleared his throat, glancing at Alexander. The Jew would not speak until spoken to. "Most consider it an unlucky accident of bad fortune. But there are rumors." He paused, deliberately making Tigellinus feel it. "It is said that some saw attendants of the emperor approaching safe estates to light them on fire with torches."

62

"That is ignorance," replied Tigellinus. "They were setting backfires to stop the advance. You know that. Your vigiles are the firefighters."

Severus would never admit he was eyewitness to the suspicious behavior. He still cherished his life. "Yes," he said. "But I heard these homes were out of the path of the fire altogether. And others saw imperial buildings that were not in the path demolished by the cohorts."[3]

Tigellinus sighed. "Another firefighting technique to stop the spread. You must educate these fools."

"Granted, prefect," said Severus. "And I have tried. But it does not help when the structures that were demolished were those most outwardly despised by the emperor. I'm sure you can see that the rumors are not without warrant, at least in the view of the populace." And in Severus' unspoken view as well.

Tigellinus looked out into the darkness, nodding his head with tight lips. He knew Severus was right. This was a problem.

Severus added, "There are also those who say they saw Nero ascending his palace to watch the fire and play 'The Capture of Troy' on his lyre."[4]

"Ridiculous," sputtered Tigellinus. "He could not possibly have done so. He did not arrive at the city until *after* his palace was burnt to the ground. Furthermore, he played that song in Antium for the competition *before* he knew of the fire."

"Alas," said Severus, "every lie contains a kernel of truth, and that is the problem we face."

Tigellinus was lost in his own frustration. "I cannot believe how quickly and maliciously this gossip is spreading."

"Like wildfire," said Severus. "It takes on a life of its own, and becomes near impossible to quench. When you try to answer the rumor, it only seems to feed the flames."

"Spare me your trite poetic allusions," said Tigellinus, "I have enough of it with the emperor. And he certainly is not helping my cause."

Both Severus and Alexander tried to discern in Tigellinus if there was any hint of the emperor's actual guilt in the matter. Alexander could not tell. Tigellinus was a tower of discretion.

And Severus would definitely not ask. The less he knew, the less he might be a target down the road if things fell apart.

Tigellinus then said, "What do you know about the Christians?"

Severus looked at Alexander, who now understood why he was brought to this meeting. He knew all about the Nazarene sect.

Tigellinus said, "The Trans-Tiber region was the only residential district unscathed by the flames. The river acts as a natural barrier. So the question becomes, is it a coincidence they chose such a safe haven for their residence?"[5]

Alexander was worried that the many Jews there might be implicated in this growing accusation.

Tigellinus asked Alexander, "What reason might the Christians have for incendiarism?"

Alexander thought for a moment. Then he nodded his head at the theory of conspiracy now building in their minds.

"I suspect they have all the reason in the world," said Alexander. "They preach the end of the world…and fiery judgment." He was not lying. He didn't have to. It was actually making sense to both of the Romans.

Tigellinus asked, "They promoted conflagration? You heard them promote it?"

Alexander said, "In a manner of speaking. I've not heard of arsonist plots. Rather, they insinuate the fire will originate directly from their deity."

"All religions blame the gods for man's behavior," said Severus.

"Word has it," said Alexander, "that around the empire, Christians refuse the imperial cult."

Tigellinus complained, "All Jews refuse it."

Alexander said, "The Jews have a special dispensation. Instead of offering sacrifice *to* the emperor, we offer a sacrifice at our temple on *behalf* of the emperor. The Christians do neither. In fact, they blaspheme the temple as worthless."[6]

Severus smirked. In this case, he would not disagree with the Christians. He considered temples to be tombs of religion.

Tigellinus said, "But are not most Christians Jews?"

"No," said Alexander emphatically. "They began as a cult within our people a generation ago, but have rejected our laws and customs and cut themselves off. They are not Jews."[7]

Severus knew a little from working with Alexander. He said, "Don't they claim this Christus who was crucified under Pontius Pilate as the Jewish deliverer?"[8]

"That is what caused the riots under Claudius," said Alexander. "They spread a rumor that he rose from the dead, and claimed to be king of the earth. But as all Jews know, we have no king but Caesar."[9]

The prefect smirked with recognition of Alexander's apparent attempt to ingratiate himself.

Alexander added, "They agitate and provoke."

Severus joined in. "Their morality is offensive as well. They condemn abortion and infant exposure."[10]

Alexander now felt uncomfortable. On this issue, the Jews agreed with the Christians against the Romans. There was much they agreed with when it came to Roman immorality. Alexander's ambivalence tempered his contempt for the Nazarene sect.

Severus kept going, "They are sexual perverts who damn and denounce homosexuality and boy loves."[11]

"Heartless," said Tigellinus. Same-sex love was so embedded within Roman culture, Tigellinus could not believe there were such uncultured barbarians of hate within the empire. Homosexuality was forbidden in the legions because adult liaisons weakened the warrior culture by creating self-destructive competition within the ranks. Instead, they used boy loves to satisfy their lust for the feminine and need for domination. Even Tigellinus enjoyed a good slave boy every once in a while as a diversion.[12]

"But then," added Severus, "in spite of all their self-righteous condemnation, I heard that they participate in sex orgies they call 'love feasts.' *And* they engage in cannibalism."[13]

"Abominable," said Tigellinus. "Do they murder to procure the flesh?"

Alexander jumped in to explain the nuance. "Not exactly. They perform a meal ritual, not unlike our Passover, but they believe they eat the flesh of their god. They call it "The Lord's Supper.""

"How do you know so much about them?" asked the prefect.

"I have treated many of them as a physician. One of their apostles, Paul of Tarsus, had a problem with malaria and his eyesight. A second apostle is currently in Rome named Simon Peter."

"Excellent," said Tigellinus. "Severus, you and your Jew here have inside access that I find very useful. Perhaps we can be of mutual benefit to one another. I assume Prefect of the Vigiles is not your final ambition."

Severus hesitated. Alexander knew he longed for senatorial status and ultimately, leadership in the Praetorian guard.

Severus said, "I would never presume upon you, sir."

Alexander knew he was thinking of Tigellinus' secret campaign against Rufus. He only wanted to be a Praetorian prefect if Tigellinus advanced out of his current position.

"As far as I'm concerned, prefect," said Tigellinus, "if you do not have ambition, you are not a strong Roman, and you are of no value to me."

"Yes, sir," said Severus, newly charged with confidence.

Tigellinus crowed, "If you want my support in your ambition, then you'll do as I ask. Investigate these Christians. But tell no one of this. Especially Rufus. And I want solid evidence, not hearsay and gossip. Am I understood?"

"Yes, sir."

CHAPTER 12

"And to the angel of the church in Thyatira write: 'The words of the Son of God, who has eyes like a flame of fire, and whose feet are like burnished bronze. "'I know your works, your love and faith and service and patient endurance, and that your latter works exceed the first. But I have this against you, that you tolerate that woman Jezebel, who calls herself a prophetess and is teaching and seducing my servants to practice sexual immorality and to eat food sacrificed to idols. I gave her time to repent, but she refuses to repent of her sexual immorality. Behold, I will throw her onto a sickbed, and those who commit adultery with her I will throw into great tribulation, unless they repent of her works, and I will strike her children dead. And all the churches will know that I am he who searches mind and heart, and I will give to each of you according to your works. But to the rest of you in Thyatira, who do not hold this teaching, who have not learned what some call the deep things of Satan, to you I say, I do not lay on you any other burden. Only hold fast what you have until I come. The one who conquers and who keeps my works until the end, to him I will give authority over the nations, and he will rule them with a rod of iron, as when earthen pots are broken in pieces, even as I myself have received authority from my Father. And I will give him the morning star. He who has an ear, let him hear what the Spirit says to the churches.'"
—*The Apocalypse of Jesus Christ 2:18-29*

Thyatira

Of all the cities in Asia that Apollyon was visiting, Thyatira was the least remarkable. It was forty miles inland from Pergamum in a boring vale, in the middle of nowhere, whose location served historically as a military garrison. It wasn't so now. It wasn't anything now. He would have avoided visiting

Thyatira if it had not been for one single person who resided there, one person that titillated his fancy: Jezebel.

Or at least, that was what that Christian gasbag, the apostle John, called her. Her real name was unimportant. Symbolism was everything. And considering the source of the derogatory nickname, Apollyon thought of it as a symbolic badge of honor.[1]

He was intoxicated with enthusiasm over the original Jezebel. She was a ruthless queen who managed to defy the prophet Elijah long enough to institute Ba'al and Astarte worship in Israel.[2]

That precious little serpent was one of a kind. The fangs of her idolatry had gripped Israel for centuries. Jezebel's work alone had done more to benefit Apollyon's cause than all the wars and battles he launched against the people of God. And she achieved it through the mixture of cultures in the name of inclusion, tolerance and peace.[3]

Through the original Jezebel's seduction, Israel had committed spiritual adultery against her husband Yahweh, a vainglorious and jealous deity. It wasn't a denial or rejection of Yahweh, it was simply a sensitivity and open-minded acceptance of religious diversity. The pluralism became so widespread that Yahweh soon had a goddess escort in the narrative of these ignorant Jews. "Yahweh and his Asherah," as the saying went.

Apollyon mused again, *The bachelor god lost his virginity.* It was a polygamous love affair, and it tickled the Destroyer, knowing that the slander incited Yahweh's wrath, like the tantrum of a spoiled child.[4]

This new prophetess, thought Apollyon, *is the second coming of Jezebel. I need to exploit her.*

He shadowed Jezebel on her way to a gathering of the local guilds of tradesmen in the city. She was mistress of her own guild of purple dyed fabrics, a valued commodity in the region, thus building her status and influence. But more importantly, she was considered a sybil, a prophetess of the deeper things of God, or as the apostle John sneeringly called it, the "deeper things of Satan."[5]

Apollyon smiled proudly at the fury he was able to inflame in that militant crank, John, the Elijah to this new Jezebel. The son of a rather uninspiring fisherman, John had been one of the closest friends of the Nazarene. He and his self-righteous brother James were nicknamed "Sons of Thunder" because of their impatient temper. From the Watcher's perspective, Thunderhead also used hateful, divisive rhetoric to match. He spewed invectives against those who didn't share his opinion on petty theological details. Those who had more nuanced views, like the Nicolaitans, John called "antichrist," blind liars, deceivers, lawless children of the devil.

Lunatic, thought Apollyon. *Then he has the gall to talk about the love of God.* And of course, the apostle's denial of Caesar's divine sonship and saviorhood would eventually bring the Roman Empire down on all their heads if the Christians kept up their diatribes and demonizations.[6]

Please do keep it up, he thought. *Please do keep it up.*

Because John had become so influential in the province of Asia, Apollyon was on a personal mission dedicated to steal the apostle's thunder. And he was doing pretty well here. Jezebel had taught the Nicolaitan heresy so effectively, she owned most of the city.

She had Yahweh's Angel of Thyatira by the groin.

Jezebel stopped by the temple and picked up the sacrificial meat to eat at the assembly with the Nicolaitans. The Nicolaitans were professed Christians who performed sacrifices to Caesar in order to maintain their livelihood in the trade guilds. This imperial cult required rituals and offerings to his golden image in each city. Such loyalty to the emperor provided economic access to the benefits of the empire; a permit to engage in economic activity as well as government subsidies and involvement in the various trade guilds. The Jews were able to participate in the imperial cult because their priests offered sacrifices on behalf of Caesar at the temple in Jerusalem. The Nicolaitans, however, engaged in the direct sacrifice to Caesar in Thyatira itself. It was this strategic compromise that provided more privilege and power.[7]

The Nicolaitans had, in actual practice, denied Jesus was the Christ and were spiritually fornicating with Caesar. Participating in the imperial cult was like receiving a mark of ownership. *The mark of Caesar*, mused Apollyon. *The mark of my Beast.*

In order to buy and sell the work of their hands, in order to advance socially and politically with their heads, one had to embrace the imperial cult or be ostracized. Those who had accepted this mark of the Roman Beast were sealed as Apollyon's own. True Christians refused to participate in the imperial cult, and therefore suffered financially and socially. They had the mark of Yahweh on them, a stinking fecal mark that only made them easier targets for Apollyon's plans of persecution.[8]

Apollyon continued to follow Jezebel through the market center and passed a large thirty-foot bronze statue of the patron deity of the city, Apollo. *Yours truly*, he thought. *Now there is a Son of God. Although he doesn't look a thing like me.* The bronze was homage to the fact that the creatures of the heavenly host, seraphim, cherubim, archangels, and the Sons of God, all had the propensity to shine like bronze, especially when emotionally elevated. Thus, the name "Shining Ones."[9]

Thus also their interchangeable connection with the stars of heaven. The stars were considered both the heavenly host and divine beings. That was why the Nazarene called himself the "Morningstar." The Morningstar, Venus, was the brightest and first over all the heavenly host. So the Nazarene claimed himself the one-of-a-kind Son of God over all the others. He was the second Yahweh in heaven.[10]

Damn Yahweh to hell, thought Apollyon. *That swindler of a creator allotted the nations under the authority of the gods—under our authority. And now he was going back on his word, took back the land deeds, and was inheriting it all for himself. Greedy megalomaniac. Worse yet, he was offering to share that tyranny over the nations with these simpleton Christians. He was offering them apotheosis, glorification like the stars. They would become Sons of God just like him and join the messianic rule. That old Thunderhead, John, had claimed that they would steal the rod of Rome's iron power. Well, not if I have anything to do with it.*[11]

Jezebel arrived at the meeting place of the college, the assembly of the urban guilds. Before following her inside, Apollyon looked around. There he was, the Angel of Thyatira, just across the street, glaring at him from the shadows. They all looked the same, these divine slaves. Hulkish warriors hiding behind cloaks of disguise, unseen by the humans around them. Apollyon grinned and walked with proud defiance over to the angel, within a dozen feet.

"Oh, those are flaming eyes of fire," sneered Apollyon. "And one mean glower." He opened his arms as if to call him out into the street. "What's the matter, angel, have you no gonads? Take me, I dare thee."

Apollyon had too much power here for a fair fight. Instead, the angel muttered, "He is coming, deceiver. With a rod of iron to break the earthen pots. And he treads the winepress of the fury of the wrath of God Almighty."[12]

Apollyon looked up into the sky and twirled around. "Where? Where is he? Where is the promise of his coming? You and your Christian lapdogs have been making that case for a generation. Yet, all things continue as they were from the beginning of creation. I will tell you what I think. I think your god of fear is blowing hot air. I think he is furious that he started his little kingdom with the hope of it growing like a mountain to fill the earth, but instead, it is being flattened under the mighty weight of the seven mountains of Rome."[13]

"Rome's iron feet are mixed with clay," said the angel. They were both referring to the prophet Daniel's dream of a huge statue, a metallic man as a symbol of successive kingdoms. Rome was the final kingdom, symbolized as iron legs on the statue. But its feet were mixed with clay, resulting in a brittle weakness. The cornerstone of Messiah hit those brittle feet which would cause that succession of kingdoms to break into pieces.[14]

Apollyon snorted and shook his head. "The problem, *angel*, is that Messiah has come and gone and Rome has only gotten stronger. Yahweh delays, and I destroy."

The angel ignored his challenge and whispered, "Your time is short. He is at the door."

And then suddenly, the angel was gone. Vanished into the shadows.

"Coward!" yelled Apollyon, kicking a pile of garbage into the air. He returned to the meeting hall grumbling, "I'll show him what I can do in a short time. He won't want to open that door when I am through."

Jezebel stood at the front of the meeting hall overflowing with hundreds of members of various trade guilds, from metalworking and carpentry to fabrics and weaving. They had finished their meal and she now taught them with her usual passion about the mysteries of secret knowledge.

Apollyon had not inspired violence against the Christians here yet. He didn't have to. In some ways, infiltration and subversion was much more effective in defeating the enemy than outright attack. The simple achievement of having a woman teach gnostic mysteries to those who fancied themselves Christians could be of more utility than a pogrom of genocide. Why? Because dying for one's faith created martyrs who became examples to follow, like medicine that healed the body. But if he could get them to spiritually die *within* one's faith, then he would create apostates, who became more like a disease that infected every bodily organ with crippling sickness.

Now *that* was positively delicious.

In the area of gender, Apollyon was sure he had the advantage. Yahweh gave lip service to the female gender as being created in his image, the same as the male. He even gave women spiritual gifts of prophecy, and claimed that they were co-inheritors of the world. But Yahweh's patriarchal hierarchy and oppression of women in the real world infuriated Apollyon. *That despot would not let women teach or exercise authority over a man,* he thought. *Instead, he kept them enslaved through his demands for submission to their controlling, abusive husbands, and never allowed them to be priests in the Mosaic covenant or apostles and elders in the new covenant. That totalitarian misogynist pig.*[15]

As Jezebel taught her mystery religion to the men and women of the guilds, Apollyon became aroused. To him, false teaching was spiritually titillating. She spoke of *gnosis*, the "secret knowledge" obtained through direct contact with the divine, an initiation of which normal Christians were ignorant. She explained that the physical world was evil, and not created by the Supreme God, but by an inferior demiurge. That the incarnation of the Christ was not as a fleshly human from a virgin mother, but as a spirit being emanating from God. She was parroting the teachings of Cerinthus in Ephesus, and Apollyon had plans to spread this newfound system throughout the world, as a means of subverting the Christian faith. Jezebel was like an Eve to Cerinthus' Adam.[16]

Eve, he thought. *Oh, what a truly satisfying pleasure it was to manipulate that primal wench and plunge her descendants into ruin.* Once he had the woman in control, the man fell with ease because he was a slave of his flesh and a sucker for a pretty face.[17]

But it was all about authority. Yahweh established authority as part of the created order. Apollyon was an agent of chaos. If he could destroy the authority structure, he could corrupt all of creation. The curse of the Garden involved tainting the woman with the insatiable desire to usurp her husband's authority over her. And that was why Apollyon's ultimate plan was to one day equalize the sexes, eliminate all gender differences, at least in the minds of useful idiots, and thereby destroy marriage, which would ultimately collapse human civilization.[18]

But that was the long game. For now, he was satisfied with goddesses and sibylline prophetesses leading the masses into hysterical orgies of delusional mysticism—and away from the Nazarene.

If the bridegroom really was coming soon for his bride, Apollyon would make sure what was left of that bride was diseased and defiled.

CHAPTER 13

Rome

Severus and Alexander walked through the Jewish district of Region XIV across the Tiber, one of the few regions untouched by the flames of the Great Fire. They traveled alone at night with only two soldiers so as not to draw attention.

As they passed some large buildings, Severus noticed graffiti on the alley wall in the torchlight. They stopped. Much of it was hostile to the government. One of the graffiti markings read, "A calculation new: Nero, his mother slew." It was rumored, Severus knew full well, that Nero had surreptitiously killed his mother because of her disdain for Poppaea, his wife.[1]

Severus asked Alexander, "What does it mean, 'calculation?'"

"Gematria," said Alexander. "The use of numerical value as a poetic device. The numerical value of the letters for Nero in Greek is one thousand and five, the same numerical value as the statement 'his mother slew.'"

"Pithy," remarked Severus. "What does that one mean? 'Beware the Beast 666.'"

"I don't know," said Alexander.

"Well it can't be Nero, then," said Severus, "if his number is one thousand and five."

Alexander said, "I suppose it is the number of some other despised government official. Tigellinus?" It was the first obvious name to come to both their minds, considering the Praetorian's brutality and ambition.

They calculated the numbers in their heads. Alexander said, "No. Tigellinus' name is well over seven hundred."

Severus changed the subject, "So where is this apostle Peter and his viper's nest of Christians?"

74

"They have been kicked out of the synagogues," said Alexander. "They meet in small groups at homes."

"Unregistered underground meetings are illegal," said Severus. "No doubt necessary for their cultic sex orgies and cannibalism."

Alexander said, "There it is."

It was a brick, three-story structure well-lighted at night. The home of a shipping merchant.

They approached quietly. Alexander saw a symbol etched in the dirt in front of the home. It was a crude fish-looking pictograph, as if scratched into the ground with a sandal. Two intersecting, semicircular swipes in the dirt. He knew it well. He had learned that it was a symbol marking meeting locations for the Christians. The Greek word for fish was *ichthys*, and they had cleverly considered the "sign of the fish" as a reference to their fishing for the souls of men. But even more cleverly, the letters of *ichthys* were an anagram of the first letters of the phrase, Jesus Christ, Son of God, Savior.[2]

"I'll wait over there," said Alexander. They had agreed for him to stay out of sight, lest the Christians discover he was the informer and he lose his access to inside intelligence. "Remember what to look for."

He felt like a jackal hiding in the shadows, watching Severus and his two soldiers approach the home and demand entry.

After a knock, a nervous servant opened the door, and Severus pushed his way into the house. His guards prepared to draw their swords.

They moved quickly to the atrium, where they were told the meetings took place.

The intelligence was accurate. Severus found a group of about thirty people in candlelight, sitting on the ground, staring at him and his two guards in fear. They sat around a table that had some fish, loaves of bread and bottles of wine.

"I am Lucius Aurelius Severus, prefect of the vigiles. I come under imperial order. Are any of you armed?"

An elderly man spoke up. "No, sir."

Severus circled the group, now huddled around each other. They looked like frightened mice. Men, women, young and old. Mostly freedmen and citizens, some of the upper class. They had all their clothes on. They weren't engaging in perversity. Had he arrived too early, before their bacchanalia? As he passed by the elderly man, he noticed him stuff something underneath his leg.

Severus reached down and moved the man's hand. He pulled out a parchment with writing on it. A letter. Exactly what Alexander told him to look for. These Christians treasured letters from their leaders as if they were holy scripture. In them, he might find some answers to their activities and motivations. He pocketed it.

Severus saw one of his guards find another parchment hidden by a woman on the other side of the table. He nodded.

The soldier tucked it in his belt.

When the woman looked at Severus, his heart stopped. She had auburn hair and deep-blue eyes. She appeared to be in her thirties and of some standing. There was something haunting about her. He could tell all at once that she carried a great weight on her soul and that she had experienced much in this world.

She was the only one without fear in the group. The fearless were the most dangerous to the empire when it came to revolution.

"What is your name?"

"Cassandra Laetorius," she said. "For what reason do we have the honor of your imperial presence this evening, prefect? As you can see, we are law-abiding citizens, not armed insurrectionists."

"Nor cannibals, I hope." He smiled, still staring at those penetrating, magnificent eyes. He gestured to the table of bread and wine. "What is that?"

"A meal of remembrance," she said.

He had been expecting human flesh and blood. In fact, his expectations were so exaggerated based on the demonic descriptions he was given that he felt a bit foolish. On the other hand, esoteric cults were quite adept at hiding their secret demons under a veneer of normality.

But for now, he saw nothing incriminating.

"Fear not," he said. "I am not here to arrest anyone. I am only gathering information for an investigation."

"We will gladly answer any questions you may have. And regarding the letters, they are personal correspondences that contain nothing of import to you. Read them for yourself, my lord. You will see. There is no need to confiscate them."

Severus ignored her plea for the letters. He looked around the atrium. It was well gardened. Expensive. "Is this your home?"

"Yes, prefect. And I welcome you to it."

He said, "Where is your leader, this Simon Peter?" He expected her to balk or deny her acquaintance.

But instead, she said wistfully, "I will take you to him."

Alexander hid in the shadows outside as Severus and his guards were led from the house by a female hostage. When they passed him, he saw Cassandra's beautiful visage. She had brought Paul of Tarsus for medical help just before the Great Fire. Of all the apostle's known connections, Alexander knew her to be the closest. He felt a wave of guilt wash over him, as if he was betraying an angel.

He was probably just seduced by her beauty.

He didn't like the idea of helping Severus investigate the Christians. But he had no choice in the matter. If he didn't help, his people would be hurt, maybe even imprisoned. And the fact was that the Christians had caused so many problems for the Jews that Alexander considered himself blessed by God to be in the position of helping his people.

He only hoped that Severus would not abuse the Christian woman. He hoped the prefect didn't have nefarious plans for her.

Alexander followed the small group of Praetorians north along the Tiber and crossed over into the garden grounds of Campus Martius. As they passed through the makeshift, tented villages of refugees, his heart went out to his fellow citizens. Because of his connection with the vigile prefect, he was given privileged residence. He was well fed and taken care of by Caesar's own favor. But these poor victims received only small change from Nero's purse.

The beauty of the emperor's gardens had long been trampled beneath the feet of the desperate homeless. He could see much sickness and deprivation which he could do nothing to help. And the smell of unwashed humanity and unburnt garbage filled his nose. Little children played in ragged clothes, the only thing they had on their backs when the fire took everything from them. Women tried to make squalid conditions into a home, men were weary from the back-breaking labor of rebuilding the city.

They entered an area quarantined off by guards and a rope fence. It appeared to be an infirmary for the sick and wounded. Many had already died from their burns. Those who survived had excruciatingly painful months ahead of them as their flesh slowly scarred over, leaving them to live their disfigured lives in shame.

There were large tents for surgeries and sicknesses. Plague was never far behind when people lived in such unclean and cramped quarters. He heard moans on his left and on his right as he continued to follow Severus and Cassandra from a distance.

Alexander heard a woman scream. He glanced inside a tent and saw her giving birth. *Poor infant,* he thought. The words of the ancient seer came to his mind: *It would be better to have been a miscarriage than to come into this cruel world. And I thought the dead who are already dead more fortunate than the living who are still alive. But better than both is he who has not yet been and has not seen the evil deeds that are done under the sun.*[3]

Alexander remained fifty paces behind Severus and his hostage. He saw them approach a group of citizens surrounding a speaker addressing a crowd from an elevated rock. He was a gruff, stout fellow with short curly hair and beard; the apostle Peter. The doctor remembered him from before the fire in the clinic line with the apostle Paul. Alexander hid by the entrance of a surgery tent.

As Severus and Cassandra listened to Peter finish bellowing about the fires of Gehenna and the love of Christ, Alexander looked inside the tent he was standing near. Inside, a physician performed an amputation on a patient with a gangrenous arm. The cut was poor. Alexander watched the failed attempt that he knew would result in a dead patient. *And I thought the dead who are already dead more fortunate than the living who are still alive.*

I should be here, he thought. *I should be helping my fellow Jews and Roman citizens.* But he had no time. After the fire, he had been drafted to serve the Praetorians and to secretly aid Severus in his investigation. He could only

78

watch helplessly as another sorry victim died needlessly beneath the knife of an inexperienced surgeon.

He left the tent and began to make his way over to the apostle. Pulling his hood over his head to avoid being noticed, he pushed his way through the crowd.

Someone cried out, "I'm healed! I'm healed!" A woman with a bandaged head near Alexander yelled out, "Heal me, Peter!" Others called out and pressed toward the apostle in panicked determination. Alexander could not see clearly what miracles were being claimed. But a sharp whistle from Severus brought a company of Praetorians breaking their way through the crowd toward Peter. The people pulled back in fear as the Praetorians took a defensive posture, shields up, javelins out.

Alexander followed Severus, Peter and Cassandra away from the crowd to a more secluded area. The doctor stood near enough to overhear their conversation without being noticed. He could see Cassandra in better light now, her comeliness, her poise. *Yes, Severus has other plans for this one, I am sure.*

Severus said to Peter, "What was that, sorcery?"

"It was the power of God," replied the apostle.

"Then why do you not just heal them all?"

"That is not how Yahweh operates."

"Is your god partial?"

"I don't know why Yahweh heals some and not others. It is his will."

"Does your god also will to hurt some and not others? Does he instruct his servants to set fire to cities?"

Alexander heard no response. He saw Peter glaring at Severus.

Severus demanded, "Where were you and your followers the night the fire broke out?"

"With due respect, prefect, they are not my followers. They follow Christ."

"Where were you?" Severus repeated.

"After baptizing new believers in the Tiber, I escorted my fellow apostle, Paul of Tarsus, to Ostia, where I saw him off on a sea voyage."

"Do you have corroborating eyewitnesses?"

Cassandra interrupted, "I took them up the river on my boat."

Such eyewitnesses would be hard to discount.

Severus said, "Do you have any knowledge of the origins of the conflagration?"

"Nothing more than anyone else. Many say it was a cooking fire that got out of control. A tragic circumstance of chance. I believe nothing is by chance. Yahweh raises up kings and brings them down. He visits both good and evil upon cities. He it is to whom we should all repent and return."[4]

Severus was amazed at his audacity. "Are you saying your god set the Great Fire of Rome?"

"Romans say the goddess Fortuna set the Great Fire of Rome."

That trap would not work, thought Alexander.

Severus kept fishing. "What does your god say about Nero Caesar?"

Peter said, "He says, 'Be subject for the Lord's sake to every human institution. For this is the will of God. Fear God. Honor the emperor.'"[5]

Alexander heard a long, uncomfortable silence. Severus was no doubt confused by the paradox. You had to be a Jew to understand how your god could both curse a ruler and then command you to obey him. Roman polytheists saw the world as a drama of gods in conflict with differing intents and motivations. For the Jew, Yahweh placed good kings in power to bless his people, and wicked kings in power to chastise them. But in either case, Yahweh was accomplishing his purposes and his will could not be thwarted.[6]

"He healed me." The words brought Alexander out of his spying. They came from a young Roman man of twenty standing next to him. He was dressed in rags and spoke with a lower-class accent.

Alexander said, "What do you mean?"

The young man raised his right arm. "My hand was severely burned and disfigured while fighting the fire."

The hand looked perfectly normal to Alexander. In the young man's other hand he held a bloody bandage as if just unwrapped.

"That Christian Jew just touched my hand back there, and I was miraculously healed."

Alexander stared into the young man's eyes. He seemed sincere. Or was he just acting? Was the young man a fraud, planted in the crowd to deceive the others? People would do anything for money. And it made perfect sense for the Christians to secretly bribe people for such deception in light of their current persecution by the government.

Alexander concluded that he could not trust such uneducated victims of mass delusion. He ignored the poor young man and turned back to hear Severus' final words with the apostle, "Do not leave the city. I may have further questions for you."

Peter said, "I have no plans to leave these poor suffering souls, prefect."

"Good," said Severus. "I leave you to your work." He looked at Cassandra. "And you may return to your home."

Alexander was surprised. Severus was letting the woman go. That seemed unlike him. Was he letting her go as a hunter would let a fox return to its nest for a bigger catch? Did he see a clue in the correspondence he confiscated from the Christians?

Alexander was anxious to take a look at those letters.

CHAPTER 14

"And to the angel of the church in Pergamum write: 'The words of him who has the sharp two-edged sword. "'I know where you dwell, where Satan's throne is. Yet you hold fast my name, and you did not deny my faith even in the days of Antipas my faithful witness, who was killed among you, where Satan dwells. But I have a few things against you: you have some there who hold the teaching of Balaam, who taught Balak to put a stumbling block before the sons of Israel, so that they might eat food sacrificed to idols and practice sexual immorality. So also you have some who hold the teaching of the Nicolaitans. Therefore repent. If not, I will come to you soon and war against them with the sword of my mouth. He who has an ear, let him hear what the Spirit says to the churches. To the one who conquers I will give some of the hidden manna, and I will give him a white stone, with a new name written on the stone that no one knows except the one who receives it.'"
—The Apocalypse of Jesus Christ 2:12-17

Pergamum

The city of Pergamum rose a thousand feet high over the Caicus River plain, forty miles west of Thyatira, the city Apollyon had previously visited, and last on his reverse tour of Asia. Though Ephesus had become the rising star of economic power and influence in the region, Pergamum remained its administrative capital and therefore seat of supreme authority. For this was the location of the first provincial temple of the imperial cult of the emperor, built over ninety years ago by Augustus Caesar.[1]

Inside that imperial temple, a party of ten magistrates of both Jews and Greeks conducted a tribunal inquiry of a group of twenty recently arrested

Christians. The presence of the city prefect gave this council the legal power of the sword.

The Christians were dressed in rags and stood in chains before the board of magistrates, a rather uniform group of older upper-class patrons in their judicial garb of white robes. An angry crowd of hundreds of citizens packed the courtroom and spilled out onto the outer porch of the temple.[2]

Behind the human magistrates, the unseen Apollyon sat on the sculpted altar to the emperor. Christians called it "the throne of Satan."[3] He liked that. He felt at home in this city of political power. A dozen temple priests in red imperial robes stood formally silent around the altar. Yahweh's guardian Angel of Pergamum kept his distance from this temple, as well as the temple of Zeus, and the huge healing complex of Asclepius, the god of medicine.[4]

That very deity, Asclepius, stood beside Apollyon the Destroyer on his throne. Asclepius was a bone-thin creature in a toga. He carried a caduceus, a staff with a twisted serpent clinging to it as if strangling the wood in its coils. For a medicinal deity, he looked quite unhealthy with yellow rotted teeth and long, scraggly lice-infested hair.[5]

The two Watchers observed with great interest the human legal proceedings below them. This trial was important to Apollyon. It would be a test case for what he was planning, a legal precedent for the rest of the empire. It was his opening salvo for the massacre to come.

The jurisdictional magistrate was called a praetor. This one was an obese, balding Jewish man named Festus, who questioned the leader and spokesman for the Christians, Antipas, a small unassuming scribe.

"Antipas of Pergamum, you and your followers have been accused of refusing to participate in performing sacrifices to the emperor, as well as the customary banquet feasts associated with the imperial cult." He turned to the crowd. "Who is it that bears witness to these claims? Step forward now."[6]

A dozen citizens stepped out of the crowd and lined up before Festus.

Asclepius muttered to Apollyon, "You'll be glad to know those witnesses are professed Christians."

Apollyon said, "You got Christians to testify against each other?"

"*Professed* Christians."

"Well done."

Down below, Festus said to Antipas, "Do you understand that your rebellion is considered treason and is therefore a capital offense?"

The twenty Christians on trial behind Antipas appeared anxious.

Antipas answered with a soft voice that matched his diminished stature, "Indeed, we do."

Apollyon considered the appearance and presence of this little man to be deceiving. His arrogance, along with the arrogance of his little disciples was evident in their spirit, and that spirit was offensive to the god of Rome. Rome was quite tolerant and multicultural in its dealings with its occupied territories. Though it required worship of Caesar to maintain order and unity, it was not exclusivist like these Christian bigots. Caesar graciously allowed all conquered peoples the right to worship any god they wished in any way they wished, within the parameters of Roman law. Jupiter in Rome, Zeus in Greece, Ba'al in the Levant, Isis and Osiris in Egypt. All were welcome in the pantheon. Just so long as they worshipped Caesar as Lord over all. Just so long as they gave honor and sacrifice to his image. But these arrogant little traitors refused to bow the knee. Worse yet, they were proclaiming with their big mouths that *Jesus* was Lord over all, Son of God, Savior—the very terms reserved for Caesar alone! As far as Apollyon was concerned, they deserved what was coming to them.[7]

Festus choked up some phlegm in his throat. He had eaten too much food at lunch. "What do you have to say in your defense, Christians?"

As their spokesman, Antipas continued, "Thus saith the Lord, 'Hear O Israel, Yahweh our god, Yahweh is One. You shall have no gods before me.' That is why we do not offer sacrifice to Caesar nor eat the meat that is sacrificed to idols."

A citizen in the crowd stood up and shouted, "How dare he call Caesar an idol!"

Another one shouted, "Atheists!"[8] It was a term used of anyone who denied the accuser's gods.

Festus slammed his staff on the floor. "Quiet down! I will not tolerate incivility in this court!" The crowd obeyed. Festus turned to the defendant.

"Antipas, are not those who witness against you, Christians? They have no issue sacrificing to the genius of Caesar. Why must you be so divisive, so polarizing?"

Antipas said, "My lord magistrate, not all those who name the name of Christ are his own. Those witnesses are Nicolaitans. They are false teachers who follow the way of Balaam."[9]

The Nicolaitans in the audience protested again. Shouts of "liar!" and "hater!" peppered the crowd. Balaam was the godless heathen prophet who tried to curse Israel and then seduced the Jewish men into sexual idolatry with Moabite women. Antipas was damning his accusers with the reference. And he was appealing to Festus' own religious background of the Torah.

Festus banged his staff again and shut the protestors up. "If you do not allow the accused to speak in their defense, I will have you all removed from this temple."[10]

Antipas looked empowered by the opportunity. His previously soft voice became strong and penetrating. "Spiritual infidelity is not all that the Nicolaitans are known for. They also engage in lawless immorality. They crept unnoticed into the Christian community, but they are not of us. They were long ago marked out for condemnation. They have turned the grace of our God into a license to sin and thereby deny our only Master and Lord, Jesus Christ." Antipas was referring to the fact that the Nicolaitans claimed that since God forgave sin, then they could engage in debauchery and sensuality, and simply ask for indulgent forgiveness.[11]

Antipas continued, "The prophet Enoch called them 'waterless clouds,' swept along by winds, 'fruitless trees,' twice dead and uprooted, and 'wandering stars' for whom the gloom of darkness has been reserved. They are like the Watchers of old who did not stay within their own position of authority, but left their proper dwelling in heaven to cavort with the daughters of men. So God cast them into Tartarus and kept them in chains of gloomy darkness until the judgment."[12]

Apollyon became angry. Antipas was hitting a little too close to home. He remembered his allies, Azazel and Semyaza and the rebellion they led in primeval days on the cosmic mountain, Hermon, that led to the Great Deluge.

At that judgment, two hundred of the mightiest heavenly warriors were imprisoned in the earth. It sent a shiver down his spine.[13]

Festus, however, was not impressed. "The Nicolaitans are not on trial here, Antipas. You and your followers are. If I wanted a sermon, I would go to the synagogue. Please conclude your defense or wrap up your counter accusations."

Antipas said, "Thank you, magistrate. I will only conclude with this: today, we Christians stand before Satan's throne, accused of treason to the state…"

Festus became angry. He had tried to be patient with this upstart, but calling Caesar "Satan" was outrageous. As a Hellenistic Jew, Festus considered himself rather religious. But he still knew his civil duty and who was emperor.

Antipas continued, "But we do not fear him who can kill the body. We fear him instead who can destroy both body and soul in Gehenna. And we know that in his heavenly courtroom, we have a white stone, and on that stone is written a new name of God. And no one knows that name except we who receive it."[14]

Festus sighed. "Fanatic," he muttered. Then he said to the elders, "Choose your stones of judgment."

Up above them, Apollyon shook his head. These Christians were relentless in finding new ways to mock Caesar. The "new name" Antipas had spoken of was a veiled reference to the founding of the empire, embodied in the very temple within which they now judged. When Octavian succeeded Julius Caesar as emperor, the Senate gave him a new name, the divine Augustus. He was regarded as god incarnate on earth. He had divinized his father, the late Julius Caesar, and was therefore considered the son of God, sent to bring good news and peace to the world. With Antipas' refusal to disclose a proper name for the Christian deity, it equated to a calculated slap in the face of Caesar. The naming of a thing equaled power over that thing. Rome could not claim power over the Christian god without knowing the Name.[15]

So you think I have no power over you? thought Apollyon. *Messiah may have won the battle of Golgotha, but the war is not over yet.*

After a short deliberation, one by one, the elders placed the stone of their choice onto the table before Festus.

They were unanimously black.

White stones meant innocent.

A smirk spread across Festus' lips. He said to the crowd, "The court finds the defendants guilty of treason. Their punishment shall be the sword."

Applause broke out amongst the crowd. The hatred for these Christians was remarkable. The accused group of Christians tried to remain silent and strong, but one of their women fainted in a heap on the floor.

Apollyon descended silently down behind the obese magistrate who thought to himself, *Let us see if these Christians keep their smug looks when they face what I have in mind.* Festus motioned to the Roman guards, who took places behind the Christians. Since the Christians were Roman citizens, they had the right to a swift beheading.

Festus was about to give the command, but he stopped. It looked to those who watched as if he was interrupted in his thoughts. But they could not see the true source of the interruption: the phantom presence of Apollyon, now whispering in the praetor's ear.

Festus' face twitched with a dark interest.

The soldiers awaited their command.

The Christians awaited their death. Some of them were shaking, others quietly crying. Still others praying for strength to face their fate. Martyrdom was not a glorious joy, but a somber burden.

Festus then announced, "Priests of Caesar, bring forth the Brazen Bull!"

The red-robed priests, who had stood silently around the high altar during the entire proceedings, now scurried in obedience to the rear of the altar platform, also called a "high place." They pushed a life-sized bronze bull sculpture to the front of the platform, accompanied by the sound of creaking wooden wheels at its base.

The audience grew excited. They were very familiar with what was about to happen.

The Brazen Bull now stood proudly at the top of the high place. Its shining bronze body of sculpted muscle was posed in an aggressive stance, its horns raised high.

Festus announced, "Since the Christians refuse to participate in the sacrifice unto Caesar, then we will have to perform the sacrifice for them." He looked to the guards behind Antipas and nodded to them.

Two guards grabbed the small man and pulled him up the steps to the top of the platform. As courageous as Antipas was, he was not without fear of the fate to which he was being dragged.

To bolster his faith, he cried out as he stumbled up the steps, "Behold, the Lord comes with ten thousand of his holy ones to execute judgment on all and to convict the ungodly of their deeds of ungodliness and of all the harsh things that ungodly sinners have spoken against him.'"[16]

"Silence!" yelled Festus. "I have had enough of your judgmental babbling."

Two of the priests now opened a hatch on the back of the bull. The statue's body was hollow, and large enough to carry one or more people in its bronze belly. The soldiers lifted Antipas and shoved him into the open hatch. A priest slammed the door shut and locked it.

Below, several of the Christian captives wept, unwilling to watch the savagery about to take place.

One of the Christian men cried out, "Trust in the Lord, Antipas!" The guard behind him knocked his head with a sword handle. The Christian fell to the ground with blood streaming from a gash in his head.

Up on the altar, several priests placed firewood in the small pit beneath the belly of the bull. They lit the wood on fire and waited for the inevitable.

Antipas was to be roasted alive inside the Brazen Bull.[17]

Festus turned back to the chained Christian prisoners. "You see, fanatics. One way or the other, Caesar will have his sacrifice."

The flame was kept low to ensure a slow death. As the bull's belly heated up, everyone began to hear the sounds of this diabolical device of torture. A special acoustic apparatus inside the bull led from the belly to the open mouth.

As Antipas began to sear with pain inside the bull, his screams, like a bull's bellowing, lilted through the audio device into the temple.[18]

The crowds quieted down. The eerie death cries of anguish were more than even their bloodlust could handle.

Another Christian woman captive fainted.

Apollyon strode up to the metal creature, listening to Antipas' moaning as if it were fine music. He leaned towards the mouth, from where smoke now poured out, and sniffed in deeply, taking in the scent of burning flesh. "A satisfying aroma," he said to Asclepius, who was standing beside him.

It didn't take long for the sounds of agony to stop altogether. And everyone knew that Antipas was dead.

Festus took the somber moment to finish his deliberation. "Priests, take your place at the altar and prepare the sacred daggers." He motioned to the guards. "Bring the Christians in single file and let it be their blood that flows on the altar of this temple."

The guards hesitated. They looked at each other, surprised by the command. It seemed shockingly unusual. They would normally decapitate the condemned with one blow of their gladius. But this command was different. Festus was commanding them to perform human sacrifice of twenty citizens of the city.[19]

Festus yelled, "You heard me, soldiers, spill their blood as a sacrifice to the emperor!"

The soldiers grabbed the Christians from behind and ushered them up the steps to the altar.

The first victim was a young maiden, unmarried, a convert who would never experience the life she had dreamed of, who would never know the love of a husband or the joy of a family. She struggled in vain against the grip of the soldiers who escorted her to the altar, a marble slab with horns on its corner.

They lifted her up on the altar.

She cried out, "Have mercy on me, Lord Jesus!"

A priest took his sacred jeweled dagger and used it to cut her throat as one would an animal sacrifice.

She gurgled as the air left her lungs and her life bled out of her.

Some in the crowd were repulsed by the cruelty and left. Most watched with satisfaction.

As the guards pulled the next victim to the altar, the long line of murder continued, and Apollyon smirked. "A sign of beautiful things to come."

Asclepius prepared himself for a feast of martyr's blood.

But Apollyon was done here. He had to return to Rome. He muttered to himself with satisfaction, "Let the games begin."

CHAPTER 15

Rome

Alexander knocked at the door of the house of Cassandra Laetorius. He could not help but admit that he felt anxious to see the woman again since that night he had followed her in the darkness of night. He had hid his presence so that he would not be identified as the informer on the Christians. It made him feel like a criminal. But it was entirely possible that the Christians set the Great Fire, so maybe he was helping to track down the real criminals. Maybe it was better that the gossip got out that he was in the service of Severus. Now he could be more out in the open as a messenger, rather than as a secret informant. Unfortunately, this also meant that he lost access to inside information. He would have to work harder to find the intelligence he was charged to uncover.

A servant opened the door.

"Tell your mistress, a messenger of prefect Severus is here."

The servant let Alexander in and went to fetch Cassandra.

When she approached him, he could see she was more stunning in the light of day than he had anticipated. He had previously seen her in the dark or at a distance. But here she was up close, dressed in a flowing red gown with blue sash and gold trimming. Since she was indoors, she wore no headcovering. Her glowing red hair was pinned up with wisps of it hanging loosely down on her shoulders in a style that was casual but most desirable.

What a pity, he thought. *Such beauty wasted on fanaticism.* He reminded himself that beauty was no protection against ignorance or delusion. As the seer had written, "Charm is deceitful and beauty is vain."[1]

"I am Mistress Laetorius," she said. Yet she knew full well that he knew her. This was her way of distancing him with formality. She had met him when Alexander took care of the apostle Paul's ailment months back, and he could see in her eyes that she remembered him.

91

Alexander held up the dispatch of letters Severus had taken from her. "I am here to speak with Simon Peter about these."

She balked, apparently sensing a trap. It was no secret the apostle was housed at her residence. He was not hiding.

"Mistress Laetorius, I am not here under pretense. If Severus had wanted to arrest you, you would already be in the Tullianum Prison." Because it was underground, the Tullianum prison was not destroyed by the fire and was full of Christians, even now.

She said, "The apostle is about to leave for the refugee camp in Caesar's garden. I will bring you to him."

He followed her through the atrium and up a stairway to a second-floor room. They arrived at a small door and she knocked.

"Enter," came the gruff voice from within.

She opened the door.

The apostle stopped packing his bag with supplies. "Alexander. What a surprise. Are you here to help me minister to the sick and wounded?"

Alexander felt a twinge of guilt. "I am afraid not. I am under the forced commission of the Praetorian."

"Ah, well, that is understandable. Your healing gifts are no doubt valuable to the emperor."

Alexander shrugged reluctantly. "I am afraid so is my Jewishness." He showed him the letters. "As you know, Severus is engaged in an investigation of the Jewish quarter here."

Peter interrupted him. "You mean the Christians of the Jewish quarter."

The doctor paused in reluctant admission. "He did not want to cause undue fear of Roman hostility, so he asked me to examine your letters and talk to you about them."

"My letters?" said Peter with concern. "Please, let us talk."

Alexander unrolled the parchments on the bed, and looked over them. "Severus said he confiscated these letters a few days back. Evidently, two of them are from you." He showed him a letter.

"Indeed." Peter nodded. "I sent copies of those to Christian congregations in Asia."[2]

Alexander looked into Peter's eyes. "I will not lie to you. I have nothing against your sect. But let us both be honest here and admit that you are writing some incendiary propaganda. It is no surprise that the emperor wants to find out if the Christians are hostile to imperial interests. Just give me some good explanations that I can tell Severus to allay his fears, who will then allay the fears of the imperial office." Alexander paused, turned sympathetic. "Peter, I want to help you, I really do. But I am sure you can see that I am in the middle of something I would prefer not to be." It seemed to Alexander that he was always in the middle of something he would prefer not to be. That was why he played both sides.

Peter sighed and thought for a moment. Then he said with steely eyes, "What are their questions?"

Alexander held the parchments, finding references as he quoted them. "Well, first off, you make several references to the 'apocalypse' or revealing. You mention in your second letter the *parousia* or coming of Jesus Christ." He paused for a moment, trying to find the right words. Parousia was the Greek term that referred to a returning conqueror who was met at the city gates and escorted in with a triumphal entry.[3] "Peter, you do realize that using such military terms as parousia will be perceived as hostile to the emperor, do you not?" Alexander added, "Is it any surprise to you that the emperor suspects rebellion?"

"Christians are peaceful," Peter replied. "It is not them who Nero should worry about."

"Rome crucified your leader as a seditious rebel. And now you are saying he has resurrected and is returning for vengeance? Is that coded language, Peter?"

"For what, revolution?"

Alexander didn't reply.

Peter said, "What do *you* think?"

"Me? I think when we want something so badly that fails to happen, we refuse to accept failure, and we conjure up new hope. I think some of the more unscrupulous of your people stole the dead body of your crucified leader and concocted a resurrection story to give the rest of you renewed hope. Now that initial conspiracy has grown out of control into a full-fledged religious delusion, complete with mass hallucination."

Peter smiled. "Then tell that to your imperial friends."

"They are not my friends. They occupy the Holy Land."

Peter looked at him with curiosity. "You seem quite at home in Rome. Do you plan to return to the Holy Land?"

Alexander sighed. "No. But you know full well the Diaspora is not our fault." Diaspora was the term of the dispersion of Jews throughout the world, a separation from their homeland. They had been exiled in Babylon six hundred years ago, and then dispersed throughout the nations. Though they had come back to their land, they were never truly free, never really out of exile. Rome was now their oppressor.

"I beg to differ," said Peter. "I think the Jews remain in exile precisely for the fault of rejecting Messiah."[4]

Alexander felt his anger rise. He had done well so far in cloaking his contempt. But whenever Christians condemned fellow Jews for rejecting the Nazarene, as if he were the anointed Messiah, it made him want to lash out. He decided to use that sentiment more constructively. "Peter, the language in your letters is incendiary and revolutionary." He quoted the terms from the text. "You write, 'The end of all things is at hand,' 'salvation ready to be revealed in the last time,' 'last days,' 'the Day of the Lord.' Yes, I know what those terms mean from the mouths of our prophets. They are terms of God's judgment."[5]

Peter answered, "Then you will know of the new covenant that Jeremiah prophesied. The last days are the last days of the old covenant, the end of the Mosaic age, and all things related to it. The age to come has arrived in Yeshua the Messiah, the new covenant."[6]

Alexander ignored the theological distraction. "I was referring to your thinly veiled polemics against Rome."

"It is not Rome that I am concerned about," said Peter.

Alexander felt himself losing his patience with the Christian's evasiveness. He took a breath to calm his trembling anger. He then read straight from the letter. "But the heavens and earth that now exist are stored up for fire, being kept until the day of judgment and destruction of the ungodly.

But the day of the Lord will come like a thief, and then the heavens will pass away with a roar, and the elements will be burned up and dissolved, and the earth and the works that are done on it will be exposed."

Peter interrupted him, finishing the prose. "Since all these things are thus to be dissolved, what sort of people ought you to be in lives of holiness and godliness, waiting for and hastening the coming of the day of God, because of which the heavens will be set on fire and dissolved, and the elements will melt as they burn. But according to his promise we are waiting for new heavens and a new earth, in which righteousness dwells."[7]

Alexander said, "Even a thick-headed Roman can see that is symbolic language that reads suspiciously like the Great Fire of Rome."

Peter appeared bemused. "Do you really believe that Christians ignited the blaze?"

"And why not?" said Alexander. "In the prophets, 'the Day of the Lord' warned of God's impending judgment of destruction upon a city or nation. When you speak of 'heavens and earth' in your letter, do you not speak of the various things that make up their world? Not just their daily lives, but the lives of their gods as well? And the *stoichea*… are they not the foundational elements of their civilization?"

Peter nodded in agreement.

Alexander was on the right track. He felt energized and wanted to show this fisherman a thing or two about the Torah. "So when you tell your fellow sectarians to 'hasten the coming of the day of God,' just what exactly were you asking them to do?"[8] He didn't expect an admission of arson. But neither was he prepared for what he heard.

"To preach the good news of Yeshua Ha-Mashiach, Jesus the Christ."

Alexander sat stunned for a moment.

Then Peter added, "You are right about the symbolic language of the Law and the Prophets. But the prophecy I wrote has nothing to do with the fire of Rome."

"Then with what?"

"You will soon see."

Alexander sighed. "You claim innocence regarding the fire of Rome, but now you utter what can only be interpreted as a veiled threat."

"I have nothing more to say."

Alexander pulled out another scroll and looked at it. "And what of this Paul of Tarsus? Much of your writings echo his."

Peter smiled. "Some would argue with you on that count."

Alexander looked over the letter. "These letters are older than yours by some years. Yet he too writes of the Day of the Lord, the parousia, the coming of Jesus, and of the 'wrath to come.' He also claims an apocalyptic 'revelation of Jesus from heaven with mighty angels in flaming fire, inflicting vengeance. And eternal destruction.'"

Peter said whimsically, "And you think *I* am provocative."

Alexander remained dead serious. "You sound collaborative. What can you tell me about the man's intent?"

"You will have to ask him about that."

"Where is he?"

"Somewhere in Spain. He was always talking about reaching the ends of the earth with the Gospel. I guess he finally did it."[9]

"What was he planning to do after that?"

"Wait for the parousia."

Alexander couldn't tell if he was being sarcastic or ironic.

Peter got up. "May I return to my subversive activities of helping the sick and wounded?"

Alexander moved to the door. "Peter, I would not be so flippant if I were you. I am the one standing between you and the imperial court."

The apostle finished packing a bag full of rags and bandages. "Thank you for the sentiment, Alexander, but I already have an advocate for my cause before the heavenly court."

As Alexander left the room, he saw the flash of Cassandra turning a corner out of sight. She had been eavesdropping on them.

Alexander left the house and made his way back to the north of the city to report to Severus and Tigellinus. His thoughts drifted back to the letters Peter had written. What was the Christian leader not telling him? What had he missed? The apostle was quite delusional, thinking that God spoke to him. He claimed that Christ had "made it clear to him" that he was going to die soon, prophesying his own death.[10]

The Torah concepts they talked about came back to him. The language of Peter's letters was woven with imagery very familiar to anyone studied in the Law and the Prophets. To an outsider, a Roman for instance, it might sound like the end of the cosmos, a literal destruction of mythical proportions. But to an insider, a scribe, or Torah student, it was a glimpse into the spiritual reality of kingdoms. Peter had confirmed this interpretation to him. "The heavens and earth that now exist are stored up for fire, being kept until the day of judgment," "the heavens will pass away with a roar and the elements will be burned up and dissolved," they were awaiting a "new heavens and new earth."

"Heavens and earth" was a poetic phrase used in Scripture to describe the current world order or power and authorities. Isaiah the prophet wrote about the exodus when Yahweh saved his people out of Egypt and Moses led them through the Red Sea. Yahweh was establishing his covenant order, and his words to Moses were the words of creation, as if he were establishing the heavens and earth.

> I am Yahweh your God,
>> who stirs up the sea so that its waves roar—
> And I have put my words in your mouth
>> and covered you in the shadow of my hand,
> establishing the heavens
>> and laying the foundations of the earth,
>> and saying to Zion, 'You are my people.'[11]

The prophet Jeremiah described the destruction of the First Temple in Jerusalem as the decreation of the heavens and earth. The temple was the focal point of the covenant order, a microcosm of creation. So its destruction had cosmic significance, as if the heavens and earth had been undone.

> I looked on the earth, and behold, it was formless and void;
>> and to the heavens, and they had no light.[12]

When God punished the nation of Babylon as Isaiah had foretold, he described it too as a "Day of the Lord" where the sun, moon and stars did not give forth their light.

The sky rolling up like a scroll, the earth shaking and quaking, the heavenly host going dark. These were all poetic descriptions used of God's judgment upon actual nations in the historical past. So when Isaiah wrote of

God creating a new heavens and earth, it was most certainly the new covenant order he had promised to Jeremiah. Peter had said as much. But if that was what the apostle was writing about, then where was this new rule of God? Why had he not freed his people? Why was Rome not judged? The Great Fire had devastated it, but Nero was already enthusiastically rebuilding the city with plans of even greater glory. It didn't make sense. Rome was all the world, and it was only growing stronger. What other nation was there to judge?[13]

Whatever crazed hallucination the apostle may have experienced, Alexander had what he had gone there for.

Alexander arrived at the prefect's quarters, a huge elaborate blue tent set up near the Praetorian barracks. It had been loaned from the emperor's own stores and illustrated obvious favor.

Two guards led Alexander into the war room, where Severus stood with Tigellinus over a table map of the reconstruction of the city.

Severus said with a smile, "What news have you, my spy?"

Though it was spoken with lightheartedness, the question stung Alexander. It wasn't the act of spying on the Christians that bothered him. He still distrusted them. It was the act of being a tool of Rome. That bothered him deeply. But it was his compromise for survival.

"I have the evidence you asked for," he replied. "The rhetoric of the apostolic letters is subversive code language well known amidst the Jewish community. The letters prove a sufficient connection between the Christians and the Great Fire."[14] Though Peter had denied it, Alexander felt his accusation was close enough to the truth.

"Good," said Severus.

"However, the writer of the other epistles is a Roman citizen, so his rhetoric is far more indicting if you were to interview him. But I understand he is out west in Spain."

Tigellinus spoke without looking up from the map. "I have already sent an envoy to secure Paul of Tarsus and bring him back to Rome."

Alexander asked, "Will you arrest Simon Peter and his accomplices?"

"Not yet," said Tigellinus. "We wait for the right moment. Speak of this to no one."

Alexander bowed to the leaders and left them. He felt sick to his stomach with the half-truth he told. He consoled himself with this simple fact: if the Romans didn't find their scapegoat soon, they would eventually blame it on the Jews, as they always did. He felt that he was protecting his people by diverting imperial wrath away from them.

CHAPTER 16

November, AD 64

It had been four months since the fire had razed the city of Rome. Nero made great strides in his rebirth of the city out of the ashes. Ruins had been cleared, and construction was already underway with night and day shifts. He was most excited about his Domus Aurea, the Golden House. "House" was far too modest a term. It was more like Mount Olympus, and had the appearance of a city. It was a mile long, two hundred acres of area, stretching from the Palatine to the Esquiline hills. He had to displace quite a few residents to realize this dream. Vineyards, pastures, and woods full of animals would be housed within its walls. A man-made lake, called Nero's Pool, though more like a small sea, was being dug within it. The palatial area would be overlaid with gold, and adorned with jewels and mother of pearl. He would spare no amount of denarii for its opulent luxury. He deserved it.

At last, thought Nero, *I will be housed like a human being, with some dignity.*[1]

But he still considered himself a god. In the entryway porch, an atrium surrounded by porticos, would be a glorious bronze statue of himself as the god Sol Invictus, charioteer of the sun. Nero was following the pattern of his model, the divine Augustus Caesar. After Nero had murdered his meddling mother, Agrippina, he felt finally free of her restraint and had launched his professional performance career by competing in the Neronia Games. He had won all the lyre playing contests with his godlike performances on the instrument. Nero had chosen Apollo as his symbol because of the god's aesthetic and power. Apollo was the first poet warrior known by the epithet of Apollo Citharode, player of the lyre, and for his mighty bow of war. So Nero fashioned his identity after the deity, including his golden-dyed locks.

But now Nero was expanding that identity by making additional comparisons of himself with Sol Invictus, which was appropriate because Apollo on his chariot had become often confused with Sol, the driver of the sun chariot. And as chariot rider, Sol was the patron of Circus Maximus where chariot races dominated the sport of the crowds. Oh, how Nero loved to ride the chariot. The wind in his hair, the horses at his reins, and the power of speed made one feel transcendent, divine.[2]

One of the most effective means of imprinting an idea in the minds of the populace was to mint that idea as an image on the currency of the empire. Another one of the first tasks that Nero had commissioned in the aftermath of the fire was to mint new coins for a new world. On some coins, he depicted his head wearing a diadem with rays of the sun rising from behind it. On others, he engraved himself garbed in a toga, with a solar crown, holding a lyre with the words *Apollo Augustus*. On still others, he held a libation cup for sacrifice and a scepter with the words *Almighty God* and *Savior* underneath. The people of the earth could not engage in the lifeblood of economic activity without being under the watchful divine eyes of their emperor.[3]

As Pontifex Maximus, Nero was the supreme priest of the state religion of Rome. He was responsible to safeguard the imperial cult, and oversee the priestly colleges that advised magistrates, interpreted omens, performed sacrifices and guarded the Sibylline oracles.[4]

Though the majority of sacred temples, like those of the Forum, were destroyed in the great conflagration, the temple of Apollo on the Campus Martius had remained unscathed, and afforded the emperor quiet moments of contemplation and artistic communion with his patron deity.

He had been practicing on his lyre in one of the rooms of that temple. But presently, the soothing vapors of the incense provided by the priests put him into a deep sleep.

Nero found himself in a dream so vivid, he knew it had to be a vision from the gods. He swam in the waters of the deep. He felt different, inhuman, like a mighty sea monster. It was invigorating. His vast tail swept powerfully through the waters toward his destination, he knew not where.

He arose from the waters on the shore of a distant land. He climbed out onto the land and looked around. His muscles tightened with fear when he saw a large, scarlet-red dragon come down from heaven with seven heads and ten diadem-laden horns. His fear fled from him as the creature approached. He knew it was a manifestation of Apollo, his patron deity.

The scarlet hydra stood before him. It lifted up a large crystal mirror to Nero and he could finally see why he felt so magnificently powerful. In the reflection the emperor saw that he was like a mighty leopard in appearance. His feet were like a powerful bear's and his mouth like a kingly lion's mouth. Like the dragon he, too, had seven heads with ten horns and ten diadems. He felt gloriously grand and terrifying. He felt one with the dragon as his master. As if he were a fleshly incarnation of the master's soul.

Then the dragon gave Nero his power and his throne and great authority. The whole earth marveled and followed him. They worshipped the dragon who had given Nero his authority, and they worshipped Nero as his imperial beast as well. He heard their voices as if one, saying, "Who is like the Beast, and who can fight against it?"

Yes, thought Nero with a surge of elation. *Who can fight me?*

He tried to bellow these thoughts, but he found himself shouting blasphemies against a foreign god. But which one? He did not understand the language that growled out through his lion-like fangs.

He saw a woman in the wilderness, and her offspring, called "holy ones." He felt a strong desire come over him to war against those offspring. He hungered for their flesh, thirsted for their blood.

But who were they? Who was the woman? Where was he?

Before he could make sense of any of it, he saw a beast rise up from a distant land. It had horns like a lamb but it spoke like the dragon. Nero sensed that this land beast was his ally, intended to help him achieve his purposes.

He felt something on his back. One of his heads turned to see a great harlot riding him. She was arrayed in purple and scarlet, adorned with gold and jewels, and she drank blood from a golden cup with a drunken fury.

Confusion overwhelmed Nero. He felt that he was being allowed a glimpse into the heavenlies, that these were the ideal platonic forms of historical realities. He felt his greatness, his power and glory, but he could not understand the specific meaning of it all. Why did the dragon not explain it to him?

My lord, Apollo, prayed Nero. *Help me to understand. Tell me the meaning of this vision.*[5]

"Nero Caesar."

The words awakened the emperor with a start. He felt dizzy and a bit nauseous, his eyes, blurred. The censors had been all put out, but traces of their hallucinatory vapors hung in the air.

The vision was gone. Vanished.

"Apollo," Nero cried out. "Apollo, don't leave." He thought he saw a shadow figure dissolve into the mist.

The voice said again behind him, "Caesar."

Nero jerked around. It was one of the priests of Apollo, a short stout one, no doubt well fed on the remains of temple sacrifices.

Nero became flush with anger. "You interrupted my dream. I was speaking to Apollo, you cretin." He looked for something with which to bludgeon the thoughtless intruder.

The priest quivered fearfully. "Pontifex, I am sorry to awaken you. But the Quindecimviri have arrived, and they await you in the baptism room as you requested." The Quindecimviri were the fifteen priests who guarded the sacred Sibylline books, prophetic oracles of wisdom and guidance.

This required the emperor's immediate attention.

When Nero arrived in the baptism room, the fifteen elderly priests stood to attention and saluted, "Hail, Caesar." They wore simple white linen robes and shaved all hair from their bodies. They were ascetics who did not eat much food in their spiritual devotion. They stood around a pool, large enough for several priests to clean their bodies in preparation for rituals.

Nero paced around them silently. He despised the colleges of priests over which he presided. He considered them as having too much power. Whether they read the organs of animals, the flight patterns of birds, or read the stars and the prophecies, they spoke for the gods. And that was too much power. He wanted to be the only god.

"My priests"—Nero was still pacing, still watching their bald heads and nervous faces—"the city has become restless. The rebuilding of Rome has taken its course on the citizenry. I have had to collect a larger share of taxes, I have had to stop the free dole of grain for a time, and even then it is not enough. I need another source of money to finish this. The poor plebeians don't understand the sacrifice that must be made to return to greatness. There are rumors and gossip going around that threaten my very well being."[6] He saw one of the bald heads sweating and fixated on it. "The power of rumors is that once they grab ahold of the public's psyche, they don't let go. They grow from little tiny beads of water into a deluge of lies. They fuel insurrection. And we cannot have insurrection."

Several priests cleared their throats nervously. One coughed. They were all trembling with fear.

Nero usually called them together like this when he wanted to reprimand them. He kept pacing. "I have become aware of a series of malicious rumors that are spreading through the populace like a plague. It has gotten to the point where I will now have to perform an atonement ritual just to satisfy the gods." Every year, a criminal was drowned in the Temple of Apollo as expiation for the sins of the people.[7]

Nero continued, "Now the reason I have called you together is because a Sibylline prophecy has been making the rounds to the effect that the Great Fire foreshadows the end of the empire. It predicts, 'Time having run its course of fulfillment, Rome by the strife of her people shall perish.' Something to that effect."

"My lord, Caesar." Lucius, the high priest, spoke up. He was across the way from Nero, who now stood behind the youngest initiate of the group of old men. "That was started by some agitators in the populace. We have assured the people that there is no such oracle in the Sibylline books."

Nero scratched his curly blond hair and ran his hand over his clean-shaven chin in mock confusion. "Yes, well, imagine my surprise to hear yet another more treasonous 'prophecy' after that one. 'Last of the sons of Aeneas, the mother slayer shall govern.'"[8]

They all knew what that meant. The end of the rule of descendants of Aeneas. Nero claimed ancestry with Aeneas, and it was common knowledge that he most likely had slain his mother, Agrippina.

Lucius spoke again, his voice cracking. "My lord, that did not originate with us. I swear it."

Ignoring the remark, Nero leaned in to the young initiate, while staring at the old priest. "What is your name?"

"Timeus," said the quivering lad.

"Timeus, learn this lesson well. You see before you a priesthood of old codgers stuck in their antiquated traditions, trying to hold onto power, while the world changes around them. But there are those who say that for real change to take place, the old generation must die out, to give room for fresh new perspectives. Like your own."

The young lad was visibly shaking.

Priestly eyes darted around the room, expecting hostile Praetorians.

Lucius was a "Sensitive" who could sometimes see spirits, visions, and other phantasmagoria. He saw a shadow dart behind the columns of the room. But he couldn't tell what it was.

Nero stepped back and kicked the young lad hard in the back with his foot. The initiate plunged into the baptism pool.

Gasps went through the group of priests. But no one dared move.

Nero jumped into the pool and grabbed young Timeus' hair. He pushed his victim's head under the water and held him there. The skinny lad struggled, but without effect.

As he held Timeus under, Nero said to the high priest, "When it comes to atonement, I think an innocent life is worth far more than a guilty one, don't you think, high priest?"

"Y-yes, my lord, Caesar."

"Perhaps now, Apollo will stop this vicious hoax from spreading any further than it already has."

The young lad stopped struggling.

Nero let him float to the surface. Dead.

And then everyone saw the Praetorians. They came from behind the pillars, surrounding the entire circle of priests.

Lucius swallowed hard and tried to prepare himself to meet Pluto, god of the underworld.

Nero barked a command to the lead centurion. "Empty the temple treasury as we discussed. Bring the gold and silver to my palace."

All but a few Praetorians left.

The priests would not be meeting Pluto today.

"The temple treasury?" said the high priest. "Caesar, would you steal from the gods?"

"I told you, Lucius," said Nero, "I need more money to rebuild this city of the gods. So I'm sure the gods won't mind giving their fair share of taxes, will they?"[9]

Lucius was horrified at what he imagined was happening all over Rome: temples invaded and plundered by Nero's legions. Sacred gold, silver and precious jewels confiscated for imperial interests. This emperor's hubris was astonishing, even for a Caesar.

"Lucius," said Nero, "help me out of this piss hole."

CHAPTER 17

Crowds of hundreds of angry Romans amassed in the gardens outside the Esquiline palace in a massive protest. Alexander followed Severus, Tigellinus and Rufus, and a small contingent of Praetorian guards pushing through the angry masses. They were on their way to meet with Nero, but were making slow progress.

The crowd chanted for more food and less taxes.

"Fools," Severus muttered. "Where do they think their handouts come from, the gods? There is no such thing as free food."

But the crowds were also outraged at Nero's pillaging of the temple treasuries. It was one thing to abuse the populace, but to offend the gods was unacceptable.[1]

The Praetorians closed in tight as they parted the crowds on the road to the temple. Alexander could see the looks of hungry and distraught commoners watching the Praetorian company with contempt. Some even spit at them. He feared that a rebel might call out to attack them at any moment.

Someone shouted, "This is Nero's fault!"

Another, "Arsonist!"

Still another, "Tyrant!"

One of the crowd stumbled into Severus' horse. The prefect kicked him back into the line of agitated people. Though these plebs annoyed Severus, Alexander knew he couldn't disagree with the theory of Nero's arson. Severus had told him many things he had seen, things that only now made sense to him.

One time, at one of Nero's many debauched parties, Severus had heard a reveler quote Euripides in saying, "When I am dead, let fire devour the world." Nero then barked out in a drunken stupor, "Nay, rather while I live!" The sycophants and fools around him clucked with praise and delight—and without understanding.[2]

Well, thought Alexander, *maybe the chickens have come home to roost.*

They arrived at the gates and were let in. As the iron closed, the swarming masses flooded back into their positions: crying children, angry fathers, and desperate mothers—all demanding a response from Caesar, their savior, the son of god.

Alexander took a sip of wine and looked all around the conference tables set out in a square before the imperial table at the front. He and Severus, along with Tigellinus and Rufus, had arrived at the behest of Nero, who was a bit late to the meeting. But everyone else was there. The faint sounds of protest outside were easy to ignore.

Across the way, he saw the greasy-haired Faustus, Nero's little snitch in the Senate. Actually, one of his many snitches. Faustus just happened to be the most reliable suck-up of them all. He watched Lucius, the elderly high priest of the Quindecimviri, enter and take his seat beside the three other chief priests of the various religious orders.

The empress Poppaea sat in regal posture at the imperial table. *She always carried herself with noble poise and elegance,* thought Alexander. Others called it arrogance and vanity. Still, she impressed the doctor with her determinedness and ambition. Not many women had achieved her level of influence on the most powerful man in the world.

Next to her were two men. One he recognized, the other he did not. The familiar one was Aliturius, the famous Jewish mime, and favorite of the imperial couple. Mimes were silent dancers who often performed to singing choruses. It made Aliturius all the more disgusting to fellow Jews who disdained such worldliness. But then again, Alexander enjoyed a good day at the theater every now and then, so he withheld judgment. The unfamiliar one was also a Jew—handsome and highborn, dressed as a Pharisee, and looking to be in his late twenties.

Severus watched the visitors at the imperial table. *Damned Jews*, he thought. *They dig their way into everything like an infestation of rats. And they rot like leprosy.* He had heard the Jews were originally Egyptians who were struck with a plague of leprosy and forced out of Egypt. Of course his own

Jew, Alexander, wasn't that bad. But then, he was somewhat Hellenized, which certainly retarded the putrifying decay.[3]

Severus could see in the empress' lingering look at Aliturius that they were more than acquaintances of common faith. They had the enchanted look of lovers. Wasn't it obvious? Was Nero a blind fool, or did he have some kind of agreement with her? Was she allowed her indiscretions because Nero had so many of his own perversities?

And that Pharisee, Joseph ben Matthias, he was a dangerous one. Smooth-tongued, calculated. He was a diplomat from Palestine. Severus had learned that he was working on getting a handful of his fellow Jew priests released from charges of insurrection. Those seditious rabble-rousers were going to be the bane of this empire yet.[4]

The sound of clomping sandals and Praetorian armor interrupted everyone's thoughts and conversations. They stood in unison as Nero entered the room.

"Hail, Caesar," came the unanimous response.

Nero waved them to sit and noticed the Jewish mime. "Aliturius!" He ran to him and bear-hugged the actor. "It has been too long, my thespian friend." He looked around the room and got an idea. "Do a routine for us!"

Aliturius said, "My lord, you have more pressing issues."

"Nonsense! Art is life itself. Please, do us the honor."

Alexander noticed Aliturius glance at Poppaea for approval. She nodded. The actor sheepishly prepared himself for a dance move. He shrunk low and froze. Then he burst upward with a spinning twist and bounced into a short series of contained dancing moves. He kept it short and quick.

And when he finished, Nero applauded him like a little child. He gestured to the others to join in. "Recognize greatness when you see it, people. This man is beauty incarnate."

The others joined in obediently. And obediently waited for the emperor to stop applauding before they did.

Nero said, "Oh, our pathetic lives are so blind to truth right in front of us. Beauty is truth. When I watch you, Aliturius, I swear your hidden genius becomes visible to our mortal eyes."

The *genius* of a person was considered to be the guardian spirit or god that was allotted to a person at birth. Mightier ones were territorial spirits over nations and authorities.

Lucius the high priest was the only one who wasn't thinking of Aliturius' "genius." The reason why was because he had been too fixated in staring at the emperor's genius. The six-foot-tall androgynous being, gaunt but powerful looking, shadowed Nero like a phantasm. At once both male and female, and neither male nor female. Sometimes it moved and gestured like a woman, and other times, it carried itself as a male.[5]

As a spiritual Sensitive, Lucius was the only one who saw it. And when the creature noticed him, it placed its finger to its lips and gave him a seductive gesture to stay silent. When it grinned, the being told Lucius through its dragon teeth that he had best obey. He wondered, *Is this Apollo?*

Nero sat beside Poppaea and Aliturius at the table.

He said to the Pharisee, "Joseph, come, sit at my left."

Joseph did so, and Lucius saw the great being behind Nero place his shadowy clawed hand on the Pharisee's shoulder.

Nero breathed a deep sigh and said to the gathering, "*We* have a problem." He stressed *we*, and everyone knew he meant *I*, but that he was making his problem their problem. "As many of you have reported to me, the rumors, lies, and gossip have gotten out of control in the city. It is becoming a many-headed dragon and every time I lop off one head, another grows in its place." Nero seemed to love making comparisons of himself with Hercules, who had slain the seven-headed Hydra, as if it made him feel mythical, divine. "I have convened this council to decide how to vanquish this beast. Faustus, what word have you of the Senate and the ruling class?"

The greasy-haired Faustus spoke hesitantly. "Well, my lord, your supporters remain faithful, but weary. Your adversaries shout blasphemy for raiding the temple treasuries."

"Ingrates," said the emperor.

"Yes, Caesar." Faustus swallowed nervously. "But there are whispers of conspiracy afoot."

"I knew it!" said Nero. "Who? Tell me who, Senator, so I can hang them all."

"At this point, my lord, they are only whispers. I have not been able to secure any specific names. There is no organization yet that I know of."

"Hmm," said the emperor. "Keep an eye on Gaius Calpurnius Piso. I don't like that bombast. He's tall, good-looking, affable...and an excellent orator. All the traits for a recipe of betrayal." After a pause, he said, "Report to me as soon as you discover any intelligence."

Faustus nodded. "Of course, my lord, Caesar."

Nero looked at the table where Lucius sat. "Priests, what do the omens and the stars say?"

Lucius said, "The Sibylline oracles are silent, Caesar."

Nero exchanged an insider look with the priest. He winked. *That* problem had already been taken care of.

The chief augur spoke up. "I must be honest and say that the stars and animal intestines and other omens are giving conflicting reports. On the one hand, I see trouble and unrest. On the other hand, there are indications of great success, especially in the East. But they are unclear, your greatness."[6]

Alexander watched the Pharisee Joseph's fearful response to the priest's interpretation of success in the East. He suspected that meant Palestine, which even though it was already under Pax Romana, the Peace of Rome, there were signs of revolution brewing.

He saw Joseph whisper something into the emperor's ear.

Nero leaned back and sighed. "Well, the protests outside certainly confirm the reports of my Praetorians. Too many Romans believe I set fire to the city in order to rebuild it. That is a harmful theory I cannot disprove in their eyes since I *am* rebuilding the city to a greater glory. I guess I cannot name it Neropolis, without validating their ridiculous fears. Damn fools. What do they want to live in, a sewer?"

Rufus said, "Caesar, your acts of compassion have abounded to the benefit of the citizenry. If you but continue these, surely, they will see that you care about them, and about their welfare. Show yourself to them more. It will prove to them that you are—"

"Caesar," interrupted Tigellinus, "you must not show yourself in public. There are too many malcontents who are quick to pick up a dagger or arrow and dispatch you out of petty revenge. I counsel you to stay out of sight and protected. Divert their attention to something else."[7]

Nero said, "I have already built a new circus in the Vatican fields, and the Circus Maximus will be rebuilt soon. Bread and circuses are a proven diversion."

Severus spoke up. "Caesar, if you will allow me to explain…"

Nero gestured to go ahead.

"Well, the problem you face with the flames of gossip and rumors is much like a rekindling of the Great Fire itself."

"Indeed." Nero smiled.

"And the way to stop a fire is not always with water. Particularly if you do not have enough water to quench such a large conflagration. So, may I suggest a backfire?"

Eyebrows around the room raised with curiosity.

Severus continued, "If we can start our own rumors of blame, perhaps they can counter the false rumors and lies. Perhaps we will have our own controlled fire."

Nero's face brightened. "Excellent, Severus. Excellent."

Tigellinus jumped in. "But the rumors cannot be arbitrary. To shift the blame effectively, we must have real evidence to back up our rumors."

"Poppaea calls it a scapegoat." Nero beamed with childlike excitement. "In Judaism, they place the sins of the people on a goat and send it into the wilderness of chaos. We need a scapegoat to carry the sin of the Great Fire away from us." He paused. "Speaking of Jews… Tigellinus, did you not say that the Jewish quarter in the Trans-Tiber was untouched by the flames?"

"Yes."

"Can we concoct a conspiracy involving the Jews? Their recalcitrance in Galilee and Jerusalem is already vexing. It would make sense that some would plot arson against Rome."

Alexander went flush with fear. He saw Joseph and Aliturius also look with shock at Poppaea.

"My lord, Caesar," announced Poppaea. She had been quiet until now. Which made her words all the more weighty. "While I agree that we must find a scapegoat, I do not think it would be in your best interest to choose the Jews as that substitute of blame."

"Why not?" said Nero.

"They have been crucial to the peace of Asia. And since you already have concerns about an insurrection in Palestine, then it would not help your cause to make suffering heroes out of them. That would inspire the revolution, not quench it." She leaned in and whispered to Nero something Alexander could not hear.

Alexander smirked. *Nero's* best interests, indeed.

Nero looked over at Joseph. "You are one of the ruling class in Galilee, Joseph. Are you not? Do *you* agree with my wife?"

Joseph nodded deferentially.

Then Alexander noticed Poppaea give a nod to the Pharisee, who then gave a knowing glance toward Tigellinus. Following the unspoken conversation of signs, Alexander then saw Tigellinus nod at Severus as if to signify a plan between them all. He knew what the real conspiracy here was. He had helped fuel it for this very reason, to protect his own people.

Joseph spoke. "Caesar, I know a group of people who may have actually conspired on the Great Fire."

Nero looked to him, anxiously awaiting the answer.

"The Christians," Joseph finally said.

Nero repeated with delight, "The Christians."

Joseph finished, "I know them intimately. I have had to deal with their meddlesome blasphemies throughout Palestine. As you know, they have a history of inciting riots with their inflammatory rhetoric. And they are even known to call down fire and judgment upon Rome and those who do not believe their propaganda."[8]

Tigellinus responded as if by cue, "I have evidence, Caesar, of the accuracy of the Pharisee's claims. Severus..."

Severus spoke up. "I, and my Jewish informant here, Alexander Maccabaeus, have gathered intelligence on the Christians."

That word *informant* made Alexander feel like a snitch again, like another Senator Faustus. And he was party to this finely tuned orchestra of conspiracy.[9]

Severus pulled out the apostolic letters Alexander had studied. "It is true, Caesar. We have witnesses who have heard their sermons, and these written letters that speak of insurrection, arson, and their anointed king leading an army of judgment upon Rome and the nations."

"I remember this twaddle," said Nero. "Is that why you brought Paul of Tarsus back to the Tullianum?"

"Yes, my princeps," said Rufus, desperate to be part of the discussion.

Tigellinus co-opted him. "I ordered his arrest as soon as we found his letters of sedition. We found him in Spain."

Nero said, "I spoke with Paul of Tarsus when he was brought in chains to Rome a while back. His anointed 'Savior' was the Nazarene crucified as a revolutionary under Tiberius. He claimed the Nazarene had risen from the dead. And he worshipped him as the Son of God. He actually said that to my face. As if to say, I was not the Son of God. I thought his sect would go the way of the mystery cults. But they are tenacious ones, these Christians and their maleficent superstition. Perhaps I should never have released him."[10]

Tigellinus added, "They are atheists who blaspheme your name by refusing to support the imperial cult. And they are sexual perverts and cannibals."[11] Severus did not correct him. Let the slander be believed.

Nero seemed to be offended at the grotesque nature of these Christian fiends. "They have such hatred of the human race." He tilted his head in thought. "I like the sound of that. 'Haters of the human race.' It's a catchy slogan. We must use it."[12]

Severus said, "Their incendiary rhetoric is publicly known. But with these letters in their own handwriting, we have documentation that should silence any question."

Rufus jumped in again. "Imperator, shall we institute *religio illicita* and make it official?"

Tigellinus countered, "My princeps, any official proclamation of Christianity as an illicit religion would tie us down to petty legalities. Instead, I recommend you pursue this as a policing matter. That would give you more flexibility with accusations and punishments."

Rufus pouted at being one-upped yet again by his competitor.

"Tigellinus is right," Nero said. "Pursue this as a police measure."[13]

The thought occurred to Nero that this might be a partial fulfillment of the dream vision he had earlier. Could these Christians be the offspring of the woman in the wilderness that he would war against? Christianity was a sect of Judaism after all, so in a way Israel had birthed them. Maybe his land beast ally were these Jews who helped him.

"Well, what are you waiting for, Praetorians?" said Nero. "Round up these Christians and give us our scapegoat."

CHAPTER 18

Severus made his way through the alley to the back door of the secret apartment he rented to meet his mistress, Persephone. It was the usual time they met for their regular liaison. Her abortion and brush with death was long in the past. By the time her husband had returned from his travels, she had healed. Her servants were instructed not to speak of her "illness" to him.

She had managed to work through her troubles and return to her normal life. But normal life for an actress was still quite temperamental and disposed to emotional excess. Severus had weathered storms of rage from her in the past. Hitting him, throwing pots and vases at him. One time, she even bit him so hard, it left a scar on his arm.

But he figured it was the price he had to pay for the heights of ecstasy he experienced with her. For the same emotional excess of passion in her anger translated into an equally excessive erotic passion in her sexuality. And when he was done with her, he could escape back to the safety and stability of his wife and family at home. He was a man who had the best of both worlds. He was already aroused just thinking of it.

He quietly unlocked the door and entered. He knew where she would be. Where she always was at this time, bathing herself in preparation for their romantic interlude.

He started to take off his tunic. He would join her in the bath.

When he entered the room, he saw the back of her head as she rested in the steaming waters.

She hadn't turned, so she must not have heard him. He would sneak up and step down into the bath beside her.

He tip-toed up to her. But she still didn't hear him. She was so serene.

She must be asleep, he thought. *Even better. She'll wake up and see me beside her like magic.*

He noticed the water. It was red. Too red for myrrh or some other herb.

Dread washed over him.

He saw a piece of parchment on a stone beside the bath.

Next to that, a bloody dagger.

When he was upon her, he saw the ugly truth.

She was deathly pale, her eyes open in a fearful look into the abyss.

"Persephone!" He leaned down to her, pulled her up. Her body was cold, limp in his arms.

And then he saw her wrists.

She had opened her veins into the warm water.

"Persephone!" This time it was a guttural cry of despair. He pulled her out of the water and onto the stone. She was long dead. Her life had drained out of her into the bath.

He broke down in sobs over her, muttering over and over, "My Persephone. What have you done? What have you done?"

He wept bitterly, clutching her cold lifeless body in vain.

It seemed like time had stopped to him. All around was a surreal blur in the face of this stark clear reality in his arms. His lover, dead forever.

He gathered together his wits and remembered the parchment.

He grabbed it and read it.

> *My dear, dear Severus,*
> *I cannot seem to free myself from the dark cloud of despair that threatens to suffocate me. I cannot live with myself, with what I have done. I killed my sons. Not one, but two of them. And I did so to satisfy my own convenience and ambition. I told myself over and over that they were never alive. But my conscience refuses to believe my lies. So I must end this. I must pay for my bloodguilt. Please forgive me. Do not let my husband know about our deed. He has already suffered enough shame from my infidelities. I pray that the underworld will forgive me, but in this world, I cannot forgive myself.*
> *Love, Persephone*

Severus crumpled the parchment into his fist with agonizing pain. He wanted to make this all go away. Wake up from the nightmare.

But it was sober reality.

The next thought that came to his mind was anger. Not with Persephone, but with the two parasites in her womb that had driven her to this brink of madness. Those were the only ones he could not forgive. They had ruined not only both of their lives, and ended Persephone's, but they had ruined her husband's life and their children as well. So much damage to so many people.

But then again, how could he be angry with something that wasn't even alive or human?

Confusion gripped him.

Then he reconsidered the only active agent in all of this: Persephone. *She* was the one who chose this. *She* was the one whose conscience was corrupted by ridiculous notions of guilt. *She* was too weak to take responsibility for her actions. *She* was the one who deprived Severus, her husband and her children of her presence and love. *She* was the selfish one.

The thought occurred to him that it was his seed inside her. They had conceived together.

But *she* was the one not careful to take enough of the abortifacient herbs. *She* should have been more careful during her monthly days of fertility. *She* was the one who had the surgery. *She* killed his sons.

"How could you do this to us?" he whispered.

He had to move quickly. Gently, lovingly, he dragged her body back into the bath in her previous position. He replaced the dagger in her hand, moved the stone, and stuffed the note into his belt. Their affair would be unveiled now, but he would not allow this information to shame her memory.

He wiped up the floor and took the towel with him. As he left the apartment, he kept the door unlocked and open so the landlord might more easily discover her.

He stopped at the door, and whispered, "Good-bye, my love."

Then he slipped away into the night.

• • • • •

The Praetorians entered the Trans-Tiber Region XIV in the early hours of the evening. Alexander accompanied Severus and Tigellinus with squads of soldiers through moonlit alleyways and back streets to their destinations within the region: Christian homes.

Alexander pointed out the homes. Teams of five Praetorian soldiers broke in and arrested the residents with their families. Those under arrest were gathered together. Alexander was brought in to verify their identity. The prisoners were quietly marched up the Triumphal Way to a detention center created in the Vatican fields on the far northwest edges of the city.

There were several thousand Christians in the city. But imperial orders were to secure a mere several hundred of the most vocal and active of the sect, the leaders and agitators. These would become the example that Nero wanted to use to draw attention. If he failed to achieve his purposes of suppressing their degeneracy and quenching the rumors of imperial arson, then he would simply go and arrest more.

Despite Alexander's own contempt for the Christians' malicious superstitions, he knew that they could not stand before Nero's ruthless determination. Once again, guilt flooded his soul over his participation in this pogrom. His own oath to do no medical harm echoed in his mind. But he was given an impossible moral choice. He did not want to harm the Christians, but if he had not supported their investigation, his own people would be the ones being harassed right now. The Jews would have been blamed for the conflagration. As he saw it, he was not deliberately harming the Christians, he was protecting the Jews. They were God's chosen people after all. It could only be God's will that the empress, Poppaea, shared his sentiment and, along with the Pharisee Joseph, helped distract Nero away from them. *It was us or them*, he thought. *Sometimes in life, there is no good choice, and you have to compromise and allow suffering of the few to save the many.* How fragile the destiny of a people could be, how influential one person's sentiments over the fate of others' lives.[1]

Severus demanded full cooperation from Alexander in their imperial task. Though Severus suspected the Christians were innocent, Alexander knew that he would do what he was told in order to curry favor with Nero, who had turned their investigation into an inquisition. Arresting Christians was a means to an end when it came to Severus' political ambitions.

Prefect Rufus had taken a squad of soldiers to track down the Christian apostle Peter and any other upper-echelon leaders they could find. They would bring them to the Tullianum under special guard, where the newly arrived Paul of Tarsus was already incarcerated after being brought back from Spain. There was a rumor that another apostle had arrived from Asia, so Rufus was charged with finding him. Alexander knew that Tigellinus was hoping Rufus would fail in that duty.[2]

A cry of someone in pain brought Alexander out of his thoughts. Entire families had been brought into an alley. A group of thirty or so frightened citizens cowered before the armed Praetorians watching over them with weapons drawn. Severus had just punched a complaining male, whose nose now gushed blood as several others tended to him. A mother tried to hush her crying children.

Alexander noticed that Severus had been unusually agitated and violent in his treatment of those under arrest. He had slapped them, kicked them, and now a ruthless punch in the nose.

Something was clearly bothering the prefect.

Alexander walked up to the bloodied man and recognized him immediately. He said to Severus, "This man and his family are not Christians. They attend my synagogue. Let them go."

Severus nodded, and two soldiers pulled the man, his wife and two children away from the anxious prisoners.

The Jews scurried back to the safety of their homes, surely thankful for their deliverance by the hand of God.

As he walked the line of the arrested, Alexander recognized a woman at the end of the line—Cassandra. He elbowed Severus and pointed at her.

The prefect marched up to Cassandra with a scowl. He grabbed her arm and jerked her out of the line. He shoved her over to Alexander. "Keep her in your custody."

"I refuse any privileged treatment from the others," she complained.

Severus stopped and stepped up to her with a dead stare that gave Alexander a chill. "You are under arrest by the imperial order of Caesar. If you resist, you will be severely punished. Is that understood?"

Cassandra turned mute with fear before his ominous look.

"Is that understood?"

"Yes, my lord."

Severus took some shackles from a soldier and tossed them at Alexander. "Bring her to the Praetorian tent for questioning."

Alexander dutifully put the bonds on her. He had thought of complaining that a Praetorian should be given that duty. But he knew that the reason Severus gave him the responsibility was because he was the only one the prefect could trust.

CHAPTER 19

Nero paced nervously before his throne in the heart of his Golden House. Well-placed torches lit the vast columned interior with a sense of ethereal majesty. He adjusted the golden wreath on his head, and drew his royal purple robe around him. He looked down the steps into the long walkway that led from the entrance. The throne room had capacity for several hundred people. It was used for everything from diplomatic meetings with visiting dignitaries to regal pronouncements. But tonight, it was a vast, empty chamber, intended to overwhelm a newly captured prisoner with the gravity of his situation. Nero had worked painstakingly to create the ambience of a heavenly throne room to enhance his godlike presence. The sense he got from this Christian bachelor god sitting on his throne on high was one of loftiness and isolation. So he wanted to replicate that environment in the mind of his distinguished prisoner—to dramatically inhabit it.

The sound of arriving guards brought him to attention. He sat down in his chair and glowered in wait for this alleged apostle of importance.

Rufus led the chained prisoner, guarded by four Praetorians, to the foot of the steps below the throne.

Rufus saluted, "Hail, Caesar."

Nero looked down from his lofty perch upon the Christian ringleader of Asia. A pathetic disappointment. Easily nearing sixty years old. Balding. Lowly tattered robes. Quite unimpressive in stature. It completely eluded Nero how such pitiful excuses for humanity could have such a hypnotic effect upon the masses. But then again, the masses were morons. Just think how easily they were kept in place through Neronian bread and circuses.

"John bar Zebedee," Nero said, "I have heard so much about you."

"My lord." The prisoner's voice was gruff, but submissive. He had been beaten and deprived of food and water.

"You have caused quite a commotion. My Praetor here, Rufus, tells me that some of his men boiled you in oil." He paused for dramatic effect. "But apparently, you refused to melt in the scalding liquid. I see now you are unsullied by the experience."[1]

"Yes, imperator." John stayed humble and withdrawn. He had been miraculously delivered.

"I apologize for the inconvenience," said the emperor.

John looked up at him, surprised.

"You see, I did not order those soldiers to do so. They were acting without my authority. So I had *them* boiled in oil."

John's lips moved silently, as if in prayer.

"But now, you pose a dilemma for me." Nero pulled out some crumpled papers from an inner pocket. "I have some letters from you in which, in addition to the typical religious gibberish, you write some rather seditious propaganda." He looked over a paper to find the words. "You write that the world is passing away, and it is the last hour. Now, the last time I looked, Pax Romana has established peace throughout the world. Unless you know of a revolution brewing somewhere."[2]

He waited to see if John would respond. He did not.

Nero continued, "You write of something called 'antichrist.'" He found the statement in the letter. "Here it is, 'Children, it is the last hour, and as you have heard that antichrist is coming, so now many antichrists have come,' and this spirit of antichrist is 'now in the world already.' Who or what is this antichrist?"[3]

John looked up at Nero. His body appeared to be inflated with a newfound breath of courage. "Anyone who denies that Jesus is the Christ," he said. "*That* is antichrist. He who denies the Father and the Son. The Jews who have rejected their Messiah and persecuted us are antichrist. Greeks, Romans and barbarians who remain in their sin are antichrist. Rome is antichrist."[4]

Nero was impressed with this rodent's bravado. "Well, that is quite audacious of you. Of course, you and your Nazarene sect refuse to honor the imperial cult, so that would make you anti-Caesar. And since Caesar is the god of this world..."

John muttered, "Apollyon is the god of this world."

Nero burst out, "DO NOT INTERRUPT ME, WORM!" Just as quickly, he lowered his voice to a whisper. "I will crush you."

"Forgive me, imperator."

"Technically, you are correct." Nero nodded thoughtfully. "Apollos *is* my patron deity." He continued looking at the letters. "You write of a parousia, a triumphal coming of someone. How did you write it? Oh yes, here it is. 'When he appears we may have confidence and not shrink from him in shame at his coming.' Who is this? Who is coming, and where is his army?"[5]

"Jesus the Christ."

"Of course," said Nero sarcastically. "Your crucified savior come back from Hades. 'Jesus redivivus,' a reborn god. And all his angels with him." He shook his head. "What am I to do with you, son of Zebedee?"

Nero stood and walked over to a torch. He raised the letters up into the flame. The paper started on fire. He held it upside down to speed up its burning into ash. "Despite your worthless religious babbling, you have proven yourself to be, shall we say, 'resistant' to corporal punishment, which puts me in a difficult position."

Nero plopped back onto his throne to think it through. He was a superstitious man. He believed in omens and portents, and this was certainly one of them, as confusing as it seemed. For some unknown reason, the gods favored this fool. They saved him from death. That placed the emperor on the horns of a dilemma. If Nero were to make a public example of John, he could have another miraculous deliverance, which would make him as imperial potentate look impotent. If, on the other hand, he sought to kill John in private, then he would be fighting against the will of the gods, whatever *that* was. But if Nero kept this subversive around, he would inevitably jeopardize the emperor's plans with his seditious "antichrist" drivel.

The only option for this death-defying scoundrel was banishment. Completely cut him off from the rest of the world, make the apostle inaccessible. Alive, but ineffective, on some out of the way penal colony.

"Rufus, banish this man to a remote island. I don't want anyone to ever hear from him again."[6]

CHAPTER 20

"Blasphemy!" shouted Alexander. He and his prisoner, Cassandra, were waiting for Severus in the Praetorian tent on the western side of the city. He had asked her about her beliefs and she told him of Jesus, the Jewish Messiah. He had heard it all before. But when she explained the Nazarene's relationship to God as one of sonship and deity, he could take it no longer. He burst out in righteous indignation and slapped her hard across the face. She had fallen to the ground, her nose bleeding.

"How dare you," he spit at her. "A Jew proclaiming three gods, when you know the Shema of Israel. 'Hear O Israel, the Lord our God, he is one.'"

"They are not three gods," she said. "They are one."

"That doesn't make any logical sense."

She stayed on the ground. "As high as the heavens are above the earth, so high are his thoughts above our—"[1]

"Do not quote the Torah to me, Christian," he interrupted. "I have studied it from my youth."

"Then you should know of what I speak."

Alexander caught himself. He was surprised at how violent his outburst was. But then again, that is what these Christians did. They brought out the worst in people with their deliberate provocation. Denying the works of Torah, circumcision and Sabbath, making Gentiles equal to Jews, and worst of all, promoting polytheism. Alexander would not stand by and let Christians denigrate God and his people.[2]

He turned his back to her and saw Severus standing in the entrance of the tent watching him. How long had he been there? What did he see? His son, Thelonius, stood behind him. Why was he here?

Severus slowly walked up to Alexander, staring into his eyes the whole way. He came face-to-face with the doctor.

Alexander trembled.

Severus said with cool reserve, "The next time you touch her, I will enforce—what do you people call it? *Lex talionis.* Whatever you do to her, I will do to you. If you break her tooth, I will break yours. If you take out her eye, I will take out yours. Am I clear?"[3]

Alexander swallowed. "Yes." He knew the prefect meant it literally.

"Now," said Severus, "leave her in restraints here. We have an important meeting with the emperor and the other prefects."

As they left the tent, Alexander noticed Thelonius staying behind. He dreaded what Severus may be allowing him to do with Cassandra.

Alexander and Severus walked through the Forum on the Palatine Hill, on their way to the underground Tullianum prison. The new construction of the Forum was progressing rapidly upon the ashes of the old. The Senate house was complete and in operation. Temples of Vesta, Saturn, and the divine Julius were also finished. The mammoth temple of Jupiter Optimus Maximus was without a roof, but the tall columns stood majestically over the city from its position on the top of the hill. Eventually, there would be a dozen more sacred buildings for other deities that captivated the Roman spirit. The millions of sesterces and untold hours of poor souls wasted on devotion to wood and stone idols stirred Alexander to anger. Polytheism appeared to be an inclusive religion of tolerance, but really, it was a jealous god, an all-encompassing system of spiritual slavery. Controlled at the top by the Roman Pontifex Maximus, Nero Caesar.

They arrived at the prison entrance, only to meet Nero and his retinue of Praetorians ready to descend into the dungeon below. Tigellinus was with him, as was the Pharisee Joseph, and a dozen guards.

Nero brightened when he saw them. "Ah, there is my Severus and his genius Jew! Just in time to escort us down into Hades."

Severus saluted and bowed. "My princeps. Where is Rufus?"

"Rufus," said Nero, "has lost his privilege to interview any more of these Christian apostles, after mucking up the previous one."

Alexander saw Tigellinus smirk. He was well on his way to becoming sole Praetorian prefect.

Nero motioned to them. "Come, let us see this Paul of Tarsus." They entered through the guarded gate and descended a large set of steps into the dungeon below.

Severus tried to keep up with the briskly walking emperor. "Forgive me, Caesar, but why not bring the prisoner to you? It seems far too ignoble for you to visit here."

"Nonsense, prefect. I want to be in touch with every nook and cranny of my kingdom. I want to experience both the heights of divinity and the depths of humanity. To understand the pains and sorrows of the suffering and imprisoned soul. So that I may have something to write and sing about. I want to fill my art with truth. I am already composing a verse in my head. 'The dark and dreary dungeon echoes of despair, where all hope is lost for the condemned soul, yearning for just a splash of sunlight redemption.' What do you think?" He was like a playful child proud of his scribbling.

Severus humored him. "Inspirational, indeed."

They entered a hallway of cells, overpopulated with newly imprisoned Christian leaders from the city. These were not criminals; these were citizens, the true common man that Nero fancied himself to observe. They were simply trying to survive and take care of their families. They were carpenters, bakers, bricklayers and tentmakers being prosecuted for magic, superstition, and incendiarism. All charges that Alexander thought more pertinent of the emperor himself. But in the mad world of this absolute tyrant, reality was what he declared it to be.[4]

And better them than us, thought Alexander. *These Christians may be innocent of this charge, but they are surely guilty of causing much suffering and grief for Jews through the entire empire with the propagation of their heresies and idolatry. One generation of their inflammatory behavior is enough. These Christians are not innocent lambs. Their proclamation of the Nazarene as God incarnate is a violation of the law of God. And it is no different than the pagan Roman myths. The so-called virgin birth of their savior is blasphemy, a plagiarism of the myth of Hercules, demigod offspring of Jupiter and the human Alcmena.*

The company of Praetorians arrived at the last cell at the end of the hall. It was a special interrogation room, much larger than the small cells that the prisoners were crammed into. "Interrogation" usually meant *torture*.

Alexander hoped he would not have to endure more of the sickening brutality. Inside the room was a single prisoner, the apostle of Tarsus in chains. Alexander could see that he was beaten and sickly, looking worse than when he gave the apostle medical attention a few years back. He was wiry thin, and what was left of the hair on his balding head had grayed even more, as had his beard. He certainly did not look like the man who started riots in Ephesus, caused a legal crisis in Jerusalem and almost single-handedly expanded their cult to the Gentile world and the ends of the earth. *Why are all these Christian leaders so unimpressive?* Alexander saw that Paul had an infection on his arm. A bloody pus-filled gash. One that Alexander could probably help relieve, but he would certainly not be allowed to tend to the wounded prisoner.

Nero entered the cell with his entire entourage. The Pharisee Joseph stayed at the back with Alexander, more to observe than participate. Tigellinus and Severus stood beside the emperor. Two Praetorians set the royal chair down.

Nero sat on the plush purple cushion with a sigh. He looked at the frail man in chains sitting in the corner. "We meet again, Paul of Tarsus. This time, I am afraid that you do not have legal cause for complaint as you did previously with the Jews."[5]

Paul spoke with a confident voice. "What am I charged with?"

"That remains to be seen," said the emperor. "Depending on your answers to my questions."

A Praetorian stepped forward, drawing an odd-looking hand tool that looked like a combination hook and blade. What it would do to a human body was frightening to imagine.

Paul said, "I will tell you the truth, Caesar. I have nothing to hide."

Nero waved the Praetorian back. "Now, there's good faith." He snapped his fingers. "Alexander, hand me the letters."

Alexander stepped forward from the back of the cell with several letters in his hand. He saw Paul's eyes light up with recognition.

Nero said, "Oh, do you two know each other?"

Alexander panicked. His heart pounded with fear. "I treat hundreds of Roman citizens, my lord. If this one was sick, I probably saw him too."

Paul said, "He treated me amongst many, Caesar. I wouldn't expect him to remember me."

Alexander felt a chill. The apostle was protecting him.

Nero said to Paul, "Well, he is more than a goodly physician. He has helped me understand the Jewish and Christian mindset. One thing about you people, you are prolific...and full of imagination. I like that. I am a poet myself." He held out his hand to Alexander, who handed him the letters.

When Alexander looked at the apostle, he saw a strange sadness in his eyes. As if he were sorry for Alexander. It made the physician feel condescended to. He owed the man nothing.

Nero started, "Now, these letters to the—to your fellow Christians in Thessalonica, apparently, they've been circulating for quite a few years. At last, I can make personal inquiry of the author himself." He put the paper down and stared into Paul's eyes. "Who is 'the man of lawlessness'?"[6]

Paul stared back, seemingly unafraid of the power before which he was arraigned. "The son of perdition."[7]

Nero said impatiently, "Vague and elusive symbolism is not an answer. And it will not cloak your sedition. I know what you are doing with words. Calling a ruler lawless is a justification for assassination or insurrection."

Paul finished his explanation. "He who exalts himself against every god and who seeks to take his seat in the temple of God, proclaiming himself to be God. That is the lawless one." Paul's gaze suddenly shifted over the head of Nero, as if looking up at a tall person behind him. But there was no one behind Nero. Alexander saw nothing there. Paul kept looking up as if speaking to a phantom. "And his coming is by the activity of Satan, with all power and false signs and wonders."[8]

"You wrote this under the reign of Claudius, my uncle and adopted father," said Nero. "You wrote that the mystery of lawlessness was already at work at that time. But then you say, 'Only he who now restrains it will do so until he is taken out of the way. And then the lawless one will be revealed.' The Latin word for 'restrainer,' *claudere*, is an obvious play on the name

Claudius. Clever. Claudius protected the Christians, until he was poisoned by his wife, Agrippina—my mother."

Once again, Paul looked behind them. "There is more to this picture than mere earthly rulers. There are heavenly principalities and powers behind those rulers."

Nero demanded, "Who is the man of lawlessness revealed after Claudius?"[9] But Paul would not speak.

Tigellinus burst forward and grabbed Paul by the throat. He threw him up against the wall and choked him, the chains rattling as they struggled. "Say it. Say it, damn you. Say his name!"

Nero shouted, "Release him!" The praetor did so reluctantly. Paul dropped to the floor gasping for breath. "Well, he can't very well say it if you are choking him to death, now, can he?"

Tigellinus bowed to the emperor. "Forgive me, my lord."

Nero turned back to Paul. "Am I the man of lawlessness in your letter?"

Rubbing his neck, Paul croaked out, "Yes."[10]

"There, now we are getting somewhere."

Paul added, "But the beast has many heads."

Nero sighed. "You, my dear apostle, are as complicated as Lucan the Poet." He lifted the letter. "I am not going to let you take me off the topic. So I am sure you know what the next question is about. The parousia."[11]

Paul looked at Alexander. This time it was a look of betrayal. As if Alexander had sold him out. But Alexander knew the apostle had been a Pharisee, had even killed Christians before his conversion to their faith. What he was now being interrogated for had nothing to do with his past life, nothing to do with Judaism.

Nero said to Paul, "You can appreciate my concern when you write that your 'Lord Jesus' is coming in 'flaming fire and vengeance' to kill me and bring me to nothing." He let that sink in to the apostle. He sighed. "So if you people set 'flaming fire' to my city, is it not logical for me to expect the next step of your vengeance?"

Paul said, "Christians did not set fire to Rome, my lord."

Nero ignored it. "I don't buy this resurrection nonsense about Jesus coming from heaven with his angels. I think this is code language for an insurrection led by one of you crazed apostles. God knows there is an epidemic of them in Palestine. And you did write"—he looked again at the letter—"this 'Day of the Lord' will not come 'unless the revolt comes first.' So, tell me, Paul of Tarsus, what rebel ringleader is masquerading behind the disguise of risen Messiah?"[12]

"Caesar," Paul began, "what I preach is not a disguise or masquerade. It is the Gospel of the Lord Jesus Christ, who rose from the dead and is coming from heaven to inflict vengeance on those who do not know God and on those who do not obey the Gospel. Would I suffer all this for a willful deception? I serve the risen savior. I have fought the good fight, I have finished the race, I have kept the faith. I am ready to be poured out as a drink offering. I will receive my crown of righteousness." He looked over at Alexander now. "But for those who have filled up the measure of their sins, wrath has come upon them to the uttermost."[13]

Alexander felt the sting of accusation. He knew Paul meant wrath for the Jews. He and the other apostles had often accused the Jews of killing their Christ. And they claimed God would bring vengeance upon them for attacking the Christians. It was ridiculous, self-serving nonsense.[14]

Then Paul looked above and behind them again, like a madman. He said with venom, "The devil has come down in great wrath." He shifted as if talking directly to some invisible being. "Because you know that your time is short."[15]

Alexander felt another chill, not of cold, but of preternatural presence. But again, he saw nothing behind them.

Nero sat staring at the apostle for a long moment of silence.

Some of the guards shifted nervously.

Nero narrowed his eyes. "You, my earnest Christian convert, are more dangerous than all the armed Zealots and messiahs in Palestine."

Alexander could see in Paul's eyes a satisfied look. Though facing his own death, the apostle seemed more content to know that he had disturbed the emperor down to his very soul.

Nero stood. "I am out of patience with you. Tigellinus, take this one outside the city, remove his head and bury the body. Do it quickly and away from the crowds. I don't want to create a hero."

CHAPTER 21

Tigellinus and a company of fifty legionaries on horseback escorted their hooded and bound prisoner, Paul of Tarsus, down the Ostian Way beneath a full moon. As it was late in the evening, most citizens were asleep in their beds. Others were visiting the taverns and inns to engage in drinking and whoring. A small group of five members of the Nazarene sect were allowed to follow the company at a short distance. The sounds of the desert night took over the human noise as they reached the three-mile mark outside the city.

Tigellinus signaled the company to halt. Two legionaries pulled the apostle off the horse and removed his hood. He looked straight at the prefect. Tigellinus could see his lips were moving in prayer. Or maybe it was a curse.

Fanatic to the end, thought Tigellinus.

He actually pitied the poor creature for his strange, powerless religion. The traitor had brought this upon himself with his preaching of atheism and sedition within the most powerful empire to conquer the earth. It was all quite laughable. The prefect thanked the gods for the timing of it all. There could have been no better victims to blame for Rome's misfortune than these miscreants, who would not be missed. It was natural for the weak to be moved out of the way so that the strong may thrive.

The apostle was pulled over to the edge of the road. Tigellinus could see that blood had soaked through the back of the prisoner's tunic. Scourging always preceded executions.

One of the guards pushed him to his knees and made him bend forward, presenting his neck. A second guard raised his gladius and looked to Tigellinus for his command.

The prefect nodded.

The sword descended.

The head rolled. The body fell.

Blood spilled.[1]

132

And that was that. The execution felt rather anticlimactic to Tigellinus. No final words from the condemned. No public gathering to grant him heroic status in the minds of others. All dignity was withheld from him.

The Christians scurried forward to take the body for burial. They were commanded to do so immediately without public ceremony.

Tigellinus felt relief. This leader of the Nazarene Way, who had spread his malignant teachings like an infection through all the world, would vanish from history without even a notice of his burial. His pernicious ideas would be forgotten as quickly as they had propagated. Just another insect squashed beneath the sandal of Caesar in the march of imperial Rome. No one would remember the name of this unimpressive little apostle, Paul of Tarsus.

And tomorrow, his fellow Christians would begin to feel the pang of suffering more than they could ever imagine.

• • • • •

And the beast was given a mouth uttering haughty and blasphemous words, and it was allowed to exercise authority for 42 months. It opened its mouth to utter blasphemies against God, blaspheming his name and his dwelling, that is, those who dwell in heaven. Also it was allowed to make war on the saints and to conquer them.
—The Apocalypse of Jesus Christ 13:5–7

42 Months Begins[2]

The morning sun rose upon the ancient city. The Vatican fields on the furthest northwestern area of Rome were part of Region XIV across the Tiber. Surrounded by gardens on the south and west, the lush fields had been the site of Nero's personal circus, where he practiced his chariot racing. It was half the size of Circus Maximus. Though its oblong track was primarily for racing, it was also used for gladiator fights, animal baiting, and other games. An eighty-foot-tall red granite obelisk brought from Egypt graced the center of the stadium. It was a four-sided monumental pillar with a pointed top that thrust into the air with phallic allusion and spiritual mystery. Nero was enamored with all things Egyptian. And Romans loved obelisks.[3]

Today, Nero opened his private circus to a more public event. He had ordered all the senators, equestrians, and others of the ruling class to convene at the Vatican circus for an important event. Leftover spaces were given to hundreds of lucky residents who had waited in lines for days for the privilege. Nero knew how to create anticipation. The scarcer the commodity of entertainment, the more desire the public had for participation. Tonight, he would use that scarcity to drive home his message to the populace.

It was an hour or so before sunset, and the last rays of the sun shone over the top of the circus with blinding brightness. Tens of thousands of spectators filled the seats, eating food and drinking wine, awaiting the start of the event. Free bread was thrown to the plebeians in the cheap seats.

The royal box, on the lowest level balcony at the turn of the track, contained a company of Praetorians guarding Tigellinus, Severus, and Alexander, as well as the Pharisee, Joseph. Poppaea was decidedly absent. She avoided the games. They disgusted her as a waste of time and an excess of fanatical enthusiasm. Nero's royal chair was also empty, but for a different reason.

Suddenly a burst of trumpet fanfare drew everyone's attention to the top roof of the circus, where the emperor, dressed in gold as a charioteer, stood atop a two-horse chariot on a reinforced platform. He was at just the right point on the building where the blinding rays of the sun were at his back, bathing him in glowing luminescence. He was projecting his Apollonian image. And to make sure the allusion was not missed, he wore a large golden crown with spiked rays.[4]

The crowds cheered.

Servants wheeled a large megaphone device up to the chariot. It looked like a huge funnel for a giant. Nero used it to amplify his voice like a god through the stadium.

"Senators, equestrians, plebeians and freedmen, welcome to my Spectacular Spectaculum!"[5]

The crowd cheered again.

"I speak to a great city of great citizens who have overcome an unprecedented tragedy!"

More cheers. It was annoying how little he could get out before he was overtaken by cheering at every statement. He had to finish before the sun's rays no longer enfolded him.

"There is a vast conspiracy within our midst that has poisoned the heart and soul of Rome with incendiary words and fiery hatred! This conspiracy has fed the flames of division with the torch of hate!"

The crowd agreed with boos and cheers alike.

Brilliant, thought Alexander. *Rather than directly accusing the Christians of causing the fire, he is implicating them through rhetorical association.* This created hostility, not for anything the Christians had done, but for what they represented.

It was guilt without evidence. Emotions over facts that stirred the mob for Nero's purposes. Still, Alexander was sick to his stomach, knowing what was about to take place. And knowing he had some part in it all.[6]

The emperor continued, "But I have found the culprits, these arsonists of evil, these haters of the human race, those who participate in cannibalism, sexual perversions, black magic, and pernicious superstitions!"[7]

More shouts for vengeance from the mob.

"Yes, Romans, tonight we will offer up a sacrifice to Roma, a sacrifice of atonement!" He gestured in the direction of the Christians, still hidden behind closed gates. "Behold, the guilty! The Christians! Haters of the human race!"[8]

The sounding of trumpets drew everyone's attention to the opening gates of the arena. A line of Praetorians ceremoniously marched a line of simply robed men and women into the arena. A hundred of them. Each of them carried their own crossbar on their shoulders. They stumbled, making their way to line up along the wall of the racing lane. Servants carried out poles to lay down beside each victim.

Alexander heard the Praetorians yelling, "Renounce your god or suffer the consequences!" One of them did so. But he was not released. Soldiers slammed the victims down onto the crosses. They yanked arms apart and spread them out onto each branch of the cross. They hammered hands and feet to the wooden beams with their long iron nails. Screams rang out, followed by cheers from the audience.

135

Though he had seen so many crucifixions, it still disturbed Alexander deeply. Especially knowing that they were most likely innocent. *If it wasn't them, it would have been us*, he consoled himself. He prayed, *God have mercy on them. God forgive me.*

Then Alexander saw Simon Peter. For a moment, he lost his breath. He had known the apostle was going to be here, but it was still shocking and dreadful, knowing what was about to happen to this peaceful man who had given himself to the sick and wounded of Rome. The apostle Paul had been ingloriously beheaded the night before, completely out of sight from the crowds. Peter was trotted out as just one in a group of many.

Alexander saw Peter arguing with the Praetorian over him. The guard then ran up to the royal box. Since Nero was not back yet, the soldier spoke to Tigellinus. "The apostle requests he be crucificed upside down."[9]

"What on earth for?" said Tigellinus.

"He says that he is unworthy to die in the same manner as his savior."

Tigellinus shook his head, waved his hand dismissively. "Go ahead. It will make him look more ridiculous."

Despite his resolve at saving the Jews from this fate, Alexander still felt the horror of cruelty about to be visited upon this humble apostle and his fellow believers. He felt the weight of this injustice upon the flimsy gates of his rationalized defense.

The Praetorian returned to Peter and nailed him in the manner he requested. Alexander twitched with each pound of the hammer as it echoed through the arena just above the noise of the crowd.

The others were already sprawled out and bleeding through their punctured wrists and heels.

Alexander felt the terror that Roman crucifixion was meant to instill in the observer. But in the madness of the circus, the masses roared with the pleasure of criminal delight.

These Christians had it coming.

The poles were slid into their holes with thuds.

Victims cried out in more pain. The dying apostle did not look ridiculous in his upside-down posture. He looked tragically heroic to Alexander.

But then the doctor heard what he thought was the sound of singing. He strained to listen. He watched the victims.

Some of them were singing a song through their painful wounds. Some kind of hymn to God.

At that moment, Alexander wanted to get out of there. To run away from the sights and sounds before him. But he was duty bound to stay. To submit to imperial authority.

Once again, he told himself there was no other option in this impossible choice. If it wasn't the Christians, it would have been the Jews.

The unfortunate reality of crucifixion is that it is a slow death, sometimes taking many hours for the victim to expire, which does not play well for a crazed crowd in search of excitement.

But Nero had planned ahead. As the last rays of daylight disappeared, leaving the circus arena in increasing darkness, a slew of servants came back out carrying pails of black pitch and long poles with large brushes on the end of them. They proceeded to use the brush poles to paint the victims' robes with the pitch. Everyone could tell what was going to happen next: *Tunica molesta*, the shirt of torment.[10]

A rising cacophony of excitement swept over the crowd as men with torches ran out into the arena and up to the crucified. They touched their torches to the blackened hanging bodies. Fire quickly engulfed the Christians, accompanied by screams of agony. The screams were drowned out by the cheers of bloodlust as the victims died in gruesome, burning pain.

Alexander turned his head from the smoking stench of broiling flesh that drifted their way. He saw that Joseph, too, was repulsed, but the Pharisee quickly turned back to join the prefects in their discussion. Alexander could tell that his fellow Jewish noble was, like Alexander—like many Jews in this Hellenistic world—acting with calculated reserve. Joseph wasn't here merely to free the Jewish priests. Alexander figured he was covertly seeking to understand the inside operations of empire, the thought processes of Caesar, the Roman mindset. The enemy's plans.

The gates opened again and Nero, still dressed as Apollo, drove his chariot around the circus beneath the human torches that lit up the night. The audience went mad with celebration.[11]

Alexander saw that even Tigellinus looked disgusted. This kind of theatricality demeaned the emperor. Yes, it drew instant popular appeal, but the Praetorian had openly argued that long-term effects on his principate would be disastrous. Performers were among the lowest profession in society, so the emperor parading himself as an actor and a charioteer would ultimately degrade his image and lose the respect and fear of the masses. And power was based on fear.[12]

After the emperor left the arena, the next course of entertainment was prepared: *damnatio ad bestias*, damnation by beasts.[13]

Fifteen Christians were led out onto the racing field beneath the still-burning corpses of their comrades. They were covered in freshly skinned animal hides. Goats, sheep, and other skins of prey were sewn around their torsos, allowing their legs and hands to move. The poor souls huddled together in fear beneath the agitated masses above them.

The gates of the arena opened and several starved predators came stalking their prey. A lion, a leopard and a bear.

One of the victims lost her sanity and ran away from the group, as if departing from the herd would save her. A female lion was the first to chase her down. The feline ran and tackled the poor woman in a cloud of dirt and fangs. The bloody animal hide had incited the predator's hunger, but it would certainly not stop with the skin. The woman screamed out for mercy.

The crowd went wild over the blood sport.

The lion ripped her victim's throat out, ending her screaming, then clawed her to shreds, satiating the crowd's brutal hunger. Yes, it was atonement to Roma.

The bear charged the group of crying, trembling Christians and hit them with the force of a battering ram, scattering them into the dust. The bear had two victims beneath its giant claws. The behemoth tore them apart in a splattering of blood and gore.

The other Christians, now separated, were chased down by the predators, one by one, as the crowd chanted, "Haters of the human race! Haters of the human race!"

Alexander could watch it no more. He had turned to look away, but he could not block out the crowds, the animal sounds, the human screaming and pleading. And he was haunted by the fact that he had been an accessory to this gruesome death sport. He had helped Caesar hunt down these Christians, who had been so divisive, so intolerant and hateful with their speech and propaganda. But now, his contempt for their behavior seemed absurd in the light of their brutal treatment at the hand of their persecutors.

Nero arrived at the royal balcony, shorn of his Apollo disguise and in his regular imperator robes. "What did I miss? I haven't missed Gabbaras, have I?"

Tigellinus answered, "No, my lord. Gabbaras is next."

"Wonderful!" Nero exclaimed and set up his eyeglass, a tripod with special mounted concave lenses, through which he could see the action as if close up. He looked like a giddy child anxiously awaiting a glimpse of forbidden delights.[14]

As the final victims were torn apart, Nero recalled the vision he had of himself transmuted into a many-headed animal made of lion, leopard and bear—the same three predators he was now watching perform his will. The thought occurred to him: Was this the fulfillment of his vision? Were the Christian arsonists the woman's offspring with which he now warred? His attention was distracted by the next event already begun in the arena.

Three naked female Christian women were brought out to the center of the racing area and staked to the ground with chains. They tried to hide their nakedness with their hands. The modesty drew guffaws from the crowd and shouts of mockery.

The masses began to chant, "Gabbaras, Gabbaras, Gabbaras!"

A gate opened and a nine-and-a-half-foot-tall giant entered the stadium: Gabbaras. The crowd broke out in a standing ovation. He was completely naked, like an animal, his body covered in foreign tattoos. He raised his hands, welcoming the applause, which only energized the crowd more.

"Gabbaras, Gabbaras, Gabbaras!"

Alexander felt sick again. He had heard of the giant, but this was the first time he had seen him. He was a dark-skinned Egyptian monstrosity that the emperor Claudius had purchased from Arabia. Nero had turned him into a favorite pet for amusement because he had a voracious appetite for human flesh. The audience went wild again. The giant approached his prey.[15]

Alexander noticed that Nero, Tigellinus, Severus and the others in the royal booth were fixated on the terror below. Joseph had surreptitiously closed his eyes. Nero barked out while looking through his spy glass, "His musculature is a work of art! I must have Gabbaras sculpted."

Alexander found his moment to slip away unnoticed into the hallway at the back of the bleachers. He barely made it to the balcony before vomiting onto the wall and floor. The acidic bile taste in his mouth struck him as the true flavor of Rome. He had swallowed so much just to stay alive in this pagan world. He told himself that he had protected his people by being placed in a position of influence. Like Joseph bar Jacob, his forefather in Egypt. And such heroism often took its toll on the righteous. Joseph had become an Egyptian and had to stomach the idolatry of a polytheistic culture led by an egomaniacal Pharaoh, not much different than Caesar. But Joseph had protected his people, just like Alexander was now doing.

Alexander heard the audience cheering and tried not to imagine the unholy perversion that the monstrous titan was wreaking upon the poor female victims. Damnation by beasts was bad enough, but the thought of what that cannibal was doing to those poor Christian women was too much for his conscience.

And he had been an accessory to it all.

This barbaric treatment would surely end up turning public opinion against Nero. Even the mob had its limits of depravity and degradation when its sympathy would turn toward the victims. Especially if they discovered the innocence of the Christians regarding the Great Fire.[16]

He had to get back before his absence was noticed. He had to maintain a façade of support for the emperor's twisted "justice" or his own loyalty would be questioned. Any noninvolvement in these things would place doubts in Nero's mind about Alexander's devotion to the emperor. And Nero was insanely suspicious and unpredictable. He could not afford a moment of Nero's doubt.

He ran back to the royal balcony, just as the giant was finishing its feasting on the bodies of the Christians. He slipped back into his seat at the back of the group. But as he did, he noticed Severus looking back at him. A chill went down his spine. Would his own benefactor give him up? Would he punish him?

The crowd rose in applause at the climactic end of the macabre performance. Severus took the moment to step back and whisper in Alexander's ear, "It gets easier the more you see."

Alexander nodded as if to agree. He then breathed a sigh of relief as Severus returned to his position behind Nero and Tigellinus.

Nero turned from his spyglass. "This has been quite a success! Well done, Tigellinus. Well done!"

The applause quieted down, and the sound of the trumpets announced the end of the evening's activities. The crowd filed out of the stadium to return to their lives: making a living, building a family, worshipping at their synagogues and temples. The night's amusement would soon be forgotten in the hustle and bustle of daily life.

Nero held back his royal entourage until the public had left the stadium. Praetorians formed a protective perimeter around the royal balcony. Nero had dismissed Joseph, but kept Tigellinus, Severus and Alexander.

Alexander worried what would come next after tonight.

Nero gathered them close and gave his orders. "Tigellinus, I want you to send word to the governors of all provinces in the empire to extend this police action against the Christians. Not an official public policy, but deliberate operations as we discussed."

Tigellinus bowed. "Yes, Caesar."

Religio illicita was bad enough. But Alexander knew that making it unofficial meant that it carried all the wrath of the state without the accountability of law.[17]

The emperor added, "And Severus, I have a special task for you and your genius Jew."

The arbitrary violence of this despot sent a shudder down the spine of Alexander. There was no telling what mad task he would give them, what new boundaries of compromise Alexander would have to violate in order to survive. He prayed it would not involve the persecution of more Christians.

"I give you a special commission," Nero said to the vigile. "Using your finest detective skills, I want you to continue the hunt for Christian conspirators in Rome. We have executed some of their leaders, but new ones will rise to take their place. I want you to track them down and find out who this Jesus redivivus really is, and when he plans his parousia. Is he an assassin? A revolutionary general? Find him and bring him to me. Or kill him if you cannot."

"With honor and pleasure, Caesar," said Severus, bowing.

Nero added, "And as always, I reward exemplary work."

Severus bowed again with gratitude. "I will not disappoint you, imperator. I will have an intelligence network in place by the next moon."

Alexander wondered what the fate would be of the Christian woman Cassandra. She was now in their custody, and only God knew what other plans Severus had in store for her.

On their way out of the circus, Severus pulled Alexander aside.

"Alexander, it is no secret to me that you resent being in my service."

The physician swallowed. He couldn't deny it.

"But despite your duplicity," said Severus, "you have served me well. And if you fulfill your duty to me in this matter, if you help me find these Christian conspirators and their so-called Messiah, I will release you from my service."

Alexander considered the offer. The thought of being freed from forced obedience was too powerful to ignore. Another compromise to survive, but this time, with an end in sight. Redemption. Despite the lack of evidence of guilt in the Great Fire, if the Christians *were* conspiring against Caesar, as their apostolic letters hinted at, then maybe they weren't so innocent after all.

Alexander said, "I remain your loyal servant."

Much had been accomplished this night. The gods were appeased, the mob had its scapegoat. The weak had died, the strong lived on. Nero Caesar was in control. Or at least, he thought he was.

Like a bird of prey, the Watcher Apollyon sat on his perch, high atop the Egyptian obelisk at the center of the circus. He had seen it all, gloried in it all.

He was the true principality of Rome, its true god, and he had drunk of the blood that soaked the earthen floor.

He took a deep breath of the fragrance of death that permeated the arena. It was like perfume in his nostrils. *Ah, what a lovely world is mine*, he thought. *And now, the next phase of my strategy: Jerusalem.*

PART TWO

Apostasy

CHAPTER 22

Jerusalem
December, AD 64

Apollyon exited a cave opening in the Valley of Hinnom, called Gehenna, just outside the western wall of the city of Jerusalem. He felt comfortable, at home in this cursed valley. In earlier days, it was the popular site of child sacrifice. He remembered the sweet savor of burning infant corpses in his nostrils, as Israelites would pass their children through the fires of Molech, god of the underworld and Apollyon's subordinate. *Ah, the good old days*, he thought. *When Jews worshipped idols, killed each other, and innocent blood ran through the streets.*

Apollyon felt rage boil within him over King Josiah, that self-righteous prig of Judah, who destroyed the altars of Molech, ground them to dust, and wiped out idol worship throughout the kingdom. Because of Josiah, Gehenna became known as the "Valley of Slaughter," a metaphor for the fiery judgment of Yahweh upon idolaters.[1]

The Watcher's anger soothed with a sardonic smile as he looked up at the walls of the city towering over him. *Yahweh can keep those dead idols. Apostasy, rejecting their own Messiah, is a far better thing for my purposes than mere idolatry. Soon, I will have them killing each other again, and this entire city will become Gehenna.*

Jerusalem was ground zero for Apollyon's mission. As the capital city that housed the holy temple of Yahweh, it had been the enemy's headquarters for a millennium, guarded by Israel's spiritual prince, the archangel Michael.[2] The first time Michael withdrew from Jerusalem, Apollyon had been allowed to destroy both city and temple through his servant Babylon. He carried the

147

people away into slavery and exile. But Yahweh brought them back, and the walls and temple were rebuilt, reinfecting the land with their diseased presence.[3]

These Jews are like vermin, Apollyon thought. *You just can't keep them from reproducing and spreading their malignant plague of religion.* It wasn't until they murdered their Anointed One that Apollyon owned them, *really* owned them. But that despicable Nazarene had fooled the principalities and powers of the heavenly realm, including the Serpent himself. Messiah's sacrificial death tore the veil of the "holy of holies," and with it, the laws that separated Jew from Gentile. Now, people from *all* tribes and nations were the Israel of God through faith in Jesus. Yahweh now claimed the earth as his inheritance, the greedy bastard.[4]

The worldwide body of Gentile believers were the wild branches grafted onto the root of God's people, the holy nation. Unbelieving Jews were now cut off for their unbelief, like dead branches. Palestine was no longer a Promised Land of life-giving priests, but a graveyard of spiritual corpses. This was the only reason he could figure why Michael had withdrawn again. Yahweh had rejected his people and that putrid archangel was nowhere to be found. Jerusalem was Apollyon's for the taking.[5]

The Christian propaganda of bad news had been proclaimed in all creation under heaven,[6] but their headquarters was still here in Jerusalem. And now that the holy city was his, Apollyon was going to strike and strike hard. He decided to take one last stroll down memory lane as he scouted the city for intelligence on its structural integrity and civil unrest. He also wanted to make sure that Michael wasn't hiding anywhere.

The holy city of Jerusalem was thirty miles inland from the Mediterranean Sea and about fifteen miles west of the Dead Sea and the River Jordan. It sat on a hilly terrain of over four hundred acres and boasted a population of eighty thousand residents. It was a walled city with its northern district newly developed since the time of Herod. In the southern district of the lower city was the Essene quarter, more dense in population and lower in class.[7]

The great being entered the Essene Gate that opened into his valley. Of course, no one could see him, except for the few "Sensitives" scattered throughout the population. There were always some Sensitives everywhere he went, people with a special awareness of the spiritual realm. They saw what normal clogs of mud could not.

The stench of Christians was strong and odious in this quarter, so he avoided it for now. It was the poorest district of the city because of the ascetic lifestyle of its Essene residents, most of whom had left the city for their commune on the shore of the Dead Sea. The Christian population fit in well here, with the outcasts and oddballs rejected by the mainstream. And this was where they should stay. Years ago, Jews had effectively lobbied for legislation that would discriminate against Christians, keeping them from setting up businesses and ostracizing them from larger community events.

He walked beneath the long aqueduct that traversed the city all the way up to the temple. He passed by the City of David, where many in the priesthood lived. Then he saw the hippodrome, where chariot races were held, and the huge theater, both examples of the Hellenizing influence of Herod. There was nothing like cultural corruption for killing the spiritual vibrancy of a people.

And nothing like an arena for killing Christians. Though Jerusalem did not engage in formal purges like in Rome, many a riot was started on this very main street, riots that were concluded in the hippodrome with mob lynchings of Christians and their sympathizers. Though Roman law withheld the formal right of capital punishment from Jewish government, the Roman procurators, especially the newest one, Gessius Florus, often turned a blind eye to mob violence and special religious offenses, such as blasphemy.[8]

I taught the Romans well, thought Apollyon. *Let this hive of insects eat each other. That makes my job much easier.*

His current path would take him right to the Temple Mount on the eastern side of the city, the heart and soul of this sacred geography. But he changed his course and turned left to walk through the upper city.

He strode through wealthy neighborhoods with larger more costly homes, that were better guarded. In a civil war, this would be the safest location outside of the temple. Many of the Sanhedrin lived here, including the high priest. All these apostate religious authorities were like a harlot that rode the bloody beast of Rome. He liked that metaphor. He had much in store for these whores of his.[9]

When he arrived at the Herodian fortress and Praetorium at the far western edge, the Watcher stopped and took a deep breath. He remembered the events that occurred here a generation ago like they had just happened yesterday. The Nazarene was tried before Pilate, and the masses incited their governor to release the criminal instead of the king. The anger, the hatred, the passion. He could almost taste the flesh and blood of the Nazarene ripped and spilled at the scourging post.

This part of the Western Wall would not be an advantageous location for invaders to besiege. The Herodian fortress and its towers were strong and fortified. Well guarded. The taxes of the lower class were put to good use for the benefit of the upper class.

He decided to avoid the Gennath Gate that led into the burial district just north of here. Golgotha was there, as well as the tomb. That pernicious, stinking, empty tomb. It infuriated Apollyon whenever he got near the location of the death and resurrection of the Nazarene. The humiliation burned inside him.

He knew what Hannibal must have felt when Carthage pulled all their military support away from the conquering general at the last moment. Rome eventually defeated Hannibal and Carthage. "This time," Apollyon muttered, "I am going to be on the side of victorious Rome."

He spit in the direction of Golgotha, and added, bitterly, "Nazarene."

This entire area used to be outside the walls of the city, but Herod Agrippa had extended those walls to now encompass an additional hundred acres of land, called Bezetha, or New City. Though it was protected by the fortification, it was not as populated and therefore not as easily manned for military response.

He trod his way across the Tyropoeon Valley to the Antonia, a Roman fortress with four towers that was connected to the north walls of the Temple Mount. It had been built by Mark Antony in the days of Herod to keep an eye on the religious activities of the Jews. It was manned by a vigilant cohort of legionaries. It was both necessary for Roman oversight, and a provocation for Jewish religious protests.[10]

The Antonia was also where the apostles Peter and Paul had been imprisoned by Agrippa. Those two most significant of Christian leaders he had recently martyred in Rome, but Jerusalem had attained its own reputation for Christian killing, also begun under the same Agrippa, who decapitated the apostle James for his Christian propaganda of sedition.[11]

Apollyon climbed the sixty-foot wall with lizard-like ease. He grabbed the corners of stone and lifted his svelte supernatural body to the roof of the temple. He walked along the northern portico toward the far eastern side of both temple and city.

He looked down into the Kidron Valley below. Directly across from him, below the Mount of Olives was the location of the death of the first Christian martyr, Stephen. That repulsive troublemaker had vomited vile accusations against the Jews before the Sanhedrin. His inflammatory rhetoric caused a mob to drag him out and punish him for blasphemy.

When you call people stiff-necked, uncircumcised, betrayers and murderers, is it any surprise you get stoned? He had it coming. He deserved every rock that pummeled his flesh and cracked his bones.[12]

That first martyrdom launched the Great Persecution in Jerusalem. Unfortunately for Apollyon, it also scattered the followers of the Nazarene and their outrageous message of hate and bigotry throughout the empire. But the Watcher had finally gotten that annoyance mostly under control with his visits to the seven cities of Asia and to Rome itself.[13]

He now jogged across the eastern roof, called "Solomon's Porch," to the southeast corner of the temple. This was the infamous "pinnacle of the temple," from where one could look down upon the entire Temple Mount, as well as the city of Jerusalem.[14]

This was the location that the Sanhedrin, led by high priest Ananus, had taken a different James, James the Just, brother of the Nazarene, and cast him down eighty feet to the bottom of the Kidron Valley. James failed to die, so they finished their task by stoning the ornery little mimic.[15] James had repeated the very same invectives as Jesus and the others martyred before him. They had all pronounced a curse upon the temple and claimed Jesus would return on the clouds to judge them. Again, well-deserved retribution on these naysayers. Didn't Yahweh's own law prescribe an eye for an eye?[16]

Apollyon thought that murdering the last leader of the wretched cabal of Christians in the capital would be a symbolic victory, but it didn't stop them, which frustrated the Watcher to no end. He had sent emissaries to the four corners of the earth to hunt down all twelve apostles of this sectarian cult and inspire their deaths—every last one of them. He got them all, except old Thunderhead on Patmos, now impotent in his exile. Apollyon thought he had cut off the head of the enemy snake, but it just kept growing a new head.

And he calls me Leviathan. He smirked with satisfaction. Well, now he was going to show them who was the king serpent after all.

He turned to gaze down upon the Temple Mount. The entire complex consisted of, first, the outer court, called the Court of Gentiles. This huge public space was walled in with surrounding columned porticos. It was an imperfect rectangle with each wall just under a thousand feet long and over fifty feet high. This was where the general populace could enter to buy their sacrifices and engage in temple activities.[17]

The inner court housed the holy temple. It was roughly in the center of the Court of Gentiles, with its own protective walls and gates. In terms of sacred space, this was one step closer to God's presence. Gentiles could not enter this area, under pain of death. The holy temple area was almost five hundred feet long and two hundred feet wide, with its own inner and outer courts. The outer court was the Court of Women, beyond which women could not go. The inner court, the Court of Priests, was where sacrifices were made.[18]

Eighty years ago, Herod the Great had initiated the rebuilding of the Second Temple as a replacement for the temple that had previously been destroyed by the Babylonians six hundred years earlier. It had taken half a century of labor, and only recently was completed, long after Herod's death. Herod had outdone Solomon with lavish expenditures and elaborate decoration, all to overcome the fact that he had been hated by the people of Israel. Though he had been the king of the Jews, he had not been a Jew himself. Furthermore, he had been a tyrant who sought the approval of Caesar over the approval of God. He had caused so much trouble during his reign that after his death, Caesar split up Herod's kingdom into tetrarchies with each of his three sons over them. The three sons that were *not* murdered by their father, Herod the Great Tyrant.

I will miss that son of a mule, thought Apollyon. *That willful king. I could not have done all this without him.*[19]

Judea had always been a thorn in the side of Roman rule, and Jerusalem, a focal point of inflexibility within the empire. Normally, Rome allowed local religious preferences to remain for conquered nations. The only requirement was to elevate Caesar over the pantheon. The Jews, with their fierce devotion to monotheism, were unwilling to yield to such idolatry, and thus the unending civil unrest.

That civil unrest was coming to a head, as Jewish sects fought amongst themselves for control of society, and groups of brigands and bandits increased in size and influence, calling for revolt against Rome. And now that so many thousands of workers were unemployed with the completion of the temple, their idleness was fertile ground for the seeds of uprising.

Yet the one thing that united them all against Rome was this single solitary temple. And that temple, that stinking tomb, still stood as a baneful reminder to the Watcher of the covenant between Yahweh and his people.

Apollyon, the god of *this* world, had all of Jerusalem in his control, *except for the temple*.

For some unknown reason, Yahweh had not left his house yet. So Apollyon would have to wait. In the meantime, he would continue to feed the flames of persecution. He turned his gaze to the southern entrance of the temple, the Huldah Gates, where some of his minions were doing just that.[20]

CHAPTER 23

Simon bar Giora stood on the stone platform before the Huldah Gates at the southern entrance of the holy temple. He awaited the sound of the shofar trumpets that would announce the commencement of the sacrifice inside the temple behind him.

Jerusalem was astir with civil unrest. The expectation of Messiah was in the air, but all Simon could sense was a growing chaos. As captain of the Jerusalem Temple Guard, his duty was to protect the purity and integrity of the holy temple precinct. He knew that maintenance of sacred space and holy ritual was the one source of hope for a society increasingly unhinged. The rule of law was the only antidote to the poisonous chaos of anarchy that was infecting his society. He hoped that today's conclusion to the sacred festival would help bring some stability back into the growing madness.

A Galilean by birth, Simon was part of the ruling class of Judea, and now thirty-five years old. He chose to join the Temple Guard instead of becoming a Pharisee. He was devout in his convictions, but he had always felt that the priesthood was more talk than action. They spent too much time and energy quibbling over petty doctrines amongst themselves—the Pharisees, the Sadducees, the Essenes, and the Zealots—rather than achieving real action and reform in Israel. As captain of the Temple Guard, Simon felt that he performed real and active service to God, protecting the temple and maintaining order and law.[1]

His lieutenant, John bar Levi, thirty four-years old, stood obediently beside him with a dozen guards at the ready. John was from Galilee as well. He was so zealous for his hometown, that everyone called him by its name, Gischala. He was a man of the people, with a strong dislike of the ruling class. Simon met him during training for the Temple Guard. They became fast friends because of their mutual hatred of Roman occupation, though for different reasons. Simon hated the Romans for their excessive taxes and

154

political oppression. John hated them because their rule over Judea kept Israel from her calling of being ruled by God alone.

Simon had risen quickly in the ranks because of his integrity of character and commitment to principle. He followed the rules and enforced them with strictness. He appointed John as his chief lieutenant because of John's political acumen that Simon lacked. They were a team that protected the temple with both zeal and strategy.

It made Simon feel like Judas Maccabeus, also known as Judah the Hammer, the hero of the Feast of Temple Dedication they were now celebrating. Simon was nicknamed Simon the Hammer by his guards because his zeal for following the law of Moses reminded them of the Maccabean leader.

Two hundred years ago, Judas and his Maccabean brothers had delivered Israel and the temple from the Greek king, Antiochus Epiphanes. That pagan ruler had defiled the holy temple by building in it a pagan altar to Zeus, upon which he offered abominable sacrifices. He tore down the walls of Jerusalem, outlawed circumcision and forced Jews to eat swine, forbidden by Torah. Judas led the people in a successful revolt that defeated the pagan occupiers, and cleansed the temple of its Gentile desecration.[2]

This feast now celebrated that historical victory.

How appropriate too was the punishment Simon was about to administer to the criminals that were stretched out before him on the pavement. Their backs and chests were exposed, hands strapped to posts, ready for flogging. He gripped his scourge with righteous indignation. Ten villains matched with ten guards, carrying ten whips for punishment. These offenders had blasphemed the temple with their public denunciation and condemnation of the priesthood as being corrupt.

The priesthood is corrupt, thought Simon. *But you don't damn them in public and you certainly do not damn the holy temple of God. These Christians deserve what they are about to get.*

Christians. They had preached their message of hate before this very temple. They called for the destruction of the house of God and, like those pagans of old, had even denied circumcision and the dietary laws of Torah—parroted claims of their ridiculous so-called Messiah, a crucified, dead carpenter. And all while claiming to be true Jews. Punishing them during a feast that dedicated that temple was powerful, symbolic irony. Those who defile the temple deserve holy discipline and correction.[3]

The sun had just set on the horizon. Torches lit up the Huldah porch for the citizens who had gathered around to watch the flogging of the Christians.

Inside the inner court, on the corner of the holy temple, a priest blew the shofar trumpet, a ram's horn used for special announcements. It could be heard for miles.

In homes all throughout the city, individual oil lamps were lit in honor of what was going on inside the holy place of the temple. The menorah, a huge candelabra with seven branches, was lit in memory of the temple lights that were snuffed out before the historic Maccabean victory.[4]

A band of priestly musicians led a chorus in singing the Hallel Psalms of David for remembrance. Their joyous praise carried through the entire temple area with the accompaniment of lyre, flute, cymbal and drum.

> *I will offer to you the sacrifice of thanksgiving*
>> *and call on the name of Yahweh.*
> *in the courts of the house of Yahweh,*
>> *in your midst, O Jerusalem.*
> *Praise Yahweh![5]*

On the temple porch, Simon heard the sound of the trumpet and announced to the crowd of hundreds watching them, "Hear, O Israel, these criminals have been found guilty by the Sanhedrin of defiling the temple with their words and actions. See now the chastisement of Yahweh!"

He turned to his guards and yelled, "Commence with the punishment!"

The ten of them, including Gischala, relaxed their scourges behind them, wooden batons with a dozen leather whiptails, several feet long. Each of the leather tails was knotted at their ends for more effect.

> *Out of my distress I called on Yahweh;*
>> *Yahweh answered me and set me free.*
> *Yahweh is on my side; I will not fear.*
>> *What can man do to me?[6]*

They snapped their wrists and began to flog their victims with thirty-nine lashes, one-third on the chest, two-thirds on the back. Forty was the maximum required by Torah for such infractions. Stopping short by one lash was their way of being careful not to break the law of God by overdoing their punishment.[7]

Simon's flogging was not so cautious. He used a Roman scourge, called a scorpion, that included bits of metal and glass tied into the end knots of the leather cords.[8] The reason for this was because he was punishing the leader of the group, Joshua bar Annas, a man in his late fifties, with a white Moses-like beard and wild-flowing hair.

Joshua would stand in the street, like some kind of self-proclaimed prophet, spewing his bitter words of spite as the others would stand around and proselytize for their cult.

He must be made an example of—with equal enthusiasm.

Yahweh is on my side as my helper;
I shall look in triumph on those who hate me.[9]

In the Court of Priests of the holy temple, priests took ten bullocks, two rams and fourteen lambs from the animal pens for the sacrifice of the feast. They led them to the slaughter area.[10]

They laid hands on the animals. Sacrificial daggers were used to cut their throats. Other priests would catch the flow of blood in silver bowls. Those bowls were carried up to the large altar of sacrifice, forty eight feet square, fifteen feet high, made of unhewn stone for holiness. The priests poured the blood at the base of the four horns of sacrifice on each corner of the altar.[11]

The priestly singing continued to echo through the temple area like a sacrifice of praise.

The stone that the builders rejected
has become the cornerstone.
This is Yahweh's doing;
it is marvelous in our eyes.[12]

Simon's temple guards became weary as they completed the thirty-nine lashes on the Christian offenders. Flogging was hard on the arms of the punishers. It was even harder on the torsos of the punished, now covered with red, black and blue bruises, many of them broken open and bleeding. All of the Christians wept beneath the brutal, searing pain.

Joshua bar Annas was much worse off than his followers. Because of the metal and glass tipped cords, his back and chest were ripped up like a plowed field. But as Simon scourged him, with each hit, the old man cried out, "Woe is Jerusalem!"

It made Simon angry. *Woe is Jerusalem. Woe is Jerusalem? How dare he continue the very proclamation for which he was being punished!* Simon increased the fury of his scorpion tail.

But when Joshua had fallen unconscious from the pain, Simon's enthusiasm waned. He saw the white of bone showing through some of the old Christian's bloody wounds.

He stopped after thirty or so lashes. The rules allowed him to if he saw the victim might not live.[13]

He noticed Gischala looking at him with a cocked eye of disapproval. Perhaps he had overdone it.

Save us, we pray, O Yahweh!
Blessed is he who comes in the name of Yahweh!
We bless you from the house of Yahweh.
Yahweh is God,
and he has made his light to shine upon us.[14]

In the inner court, the sacrificial animals were butchered, cleaned and flayed of their skin. The pieces of flesh were salted for purity and taken up to the altar to be offered in the great fire upon it. The smoke of the sacrifice rose to the sky.[15]

At the Huldah Gate, the sweat and blood of the Christian victims dripped through the cracks of the stone floor and mixed with the blood of the martyrs who had been slain before them in days and years past. Slain for the Word of God and for the witness they had borne. The prayers of the souls beneath the altar rose before God like incense.

Joshua, now conscious, was the most audible. "O Sovereign Lord, holy and true, how long before you will judge and avenge our blood on those who dwell on the Land?"[16]

Oh shut up, you braying donkey, thought the unseen form of Apollyon, licking the blood from the pavement. *Spare me your victimhood.* He stood with disgust and made his way to the pinnacle of the temple above him.

At that very moment, in the inner court, a strange series of events occurred that were considered by many of the priesthood to be omens of the future. First, the sacrificial fire on the altar suddenly increased in intensity. Not the flames, but the brightness of its light. It burned so bright, it seemed like the light of day. The priests had to turn away their eyes. This lasted for a half hour before returning to normalcy.

During that half hour, the last heifer to be brought for sacrifice fell to the ground groaning in pain. Heifers were young cows that have yet to be impregnated. It had been a fat animal, so the priests did not realize that it was in fact pregnant. It gave birth right there in the slaughter pen. But instead of producing a calf, it actually gave birth to a lamb. The priests were in awe of the miracle and wondered what it could mean.

Before they could figure it out, the gate to the inner court of sacrifice, a huge, bolted and fortified brass door that took twenty men to move, simply blew wide open.

One of the former high priests, Ananus ben Ananus, had seen this all happen from his post by the colonnade in the inner court. He concluded with awe that these were miracles of Hanukkah. He told those around him that the bright light of the fire was Yahweh participating in their festival of lights. The newborn lamb was most likely a reference to God's miraculous provision for sacrifice, and the open gate was an invitation of happy offering to the masses.[17]

Ananus was dead wrong.

Apollyon cackled with delight from his lofty perch, as an earthquake rumbled the foundations, and a rushing wind blew out of the inner court. It was followed by a voice as of a great multitude that said, "Let us remove ourselves henceforth."[18]

The Watcher muttered, "So that was where that sniveling little prince, Michael, had been hiding. The cowardly archangel." As the protector prince of Israel, Michael's absence left Yahweh's house wide open for plunder.

Apollyon mused over the true meaning of the omens misunderstood by Ananus. The brightness of the fire was not joy, it was judgment. The newborn freakish lamb from the young heifer was not provision, it was symbolic reference to their rejection of the virgin born Lamb of God.[19] And the open gate was a premonition of invitation to God's enemies to bring desolation.

And in case idiots like Ananus didn't catch the point, Yahweh spelled it out in audible words.

Apollyon proclaimed with victory, "He left his house. He left his house." The strong man could now plunder that house at will. He looked up to heaven and said sarcastically, "I thank thee, Yahweh, for your bountiful gifts from above."[20]

CHAPTER 24

As Apollyon approached the temple and its fortification, he mused over the words of the Nazarene so many years ago. He had spoken of how an unclean spirit left a person as they would a house, only to return with seven spirits more evil than itself, to enter and dwell therein. He could not help but grin as he quoted the Nazarene's words aloud with relish, knowing he was heard on high. "And the last state of that person is worse than the first. So also it is with this evil generation."[1]

He thought to himself, *These spirits are but a taste of my intent. Wait until they swallow my sevenfold swarm from the Abyss.*

The Beautiful Gate that led into the inner temple area was made of richly ornamented Corinthian brass, befitting the main gate of the holy place. The double doors were so huge it took twenty men to open them. And when they did, the invisible Apollyon strode into the Women's Court like a proud warlord overlooking his newly conquered treasure.[2]

Of course, he hadn't conquered the deity. Not yet. But he could fantasize. *One day. One day I will ascend to heaven above the stars of God. I will set my throne on high. I will sit on the mount of assembly in the far reaches of the north. I will make myself like the Most High.*[3] The Nazarene had called his aspirations delusional. But were they really? All through history, Apollyon had secured the power of kings, pharaohs and emperors of the world. Of course he could never usurp the heavenly throne of Yahweh above the waters.[4] But here he was taking over the earthly counterpart to that throne. And the spiritual truth did resound throughout the cosmos: *on earth as it is in heaven.*

The Women's Court was about two hundred feet square, lined with colonnades. This was as far as women could go in Yahweh's patriarchal system. Only males could enter into the next courtyard for sacrifice.

When I destroy this people and their despicable religion, I'll replace their covenant with a more gender-inclusive religion. A better place for women and goddesses. Like the good old days, when I had Israel worshipping Asherah and Astarte. Oh, how I miss Jezebel and those wives of Solomon.

Apollyon walked briskly up through the Nicanor Gate into the Court of Priests, where the sacrifices were made on the huge stone-horned altar. It was here that the temple proper now stood with all its marble, in all its gold-gilded glory.

Finally, this is mine. All mine.

Yahweh had abandoned his house, but why?

Whatever the reason, he was gone. And now Apollyon would enter the most sacred of spaces in all the earth, the only place he was never allowed to go. And now it would become *his* holy place, *his* Garden of Eden.

The temple was symbolic of a new Garden of Eden, God's original terrestrial paradise, now long buried beneath the volcanic magma of Mount Sahand.[5] To be more precise, the Garden of Eden was designed as God's original temple on earth that was a mere shadow of his true temple in heaven.[6] And now the temple here in Jerusalem, at the very center of the earth, was spiritually linked to that heavenly temple of Yahweh above the waters. *As above, so below.* The priests, who alone were allowed in here, walked in the midst of God's earthly presence as Adam once did in the Garden. And what they did down here echoed up there. *On earth as it is in heaven.*[7]

As Apollyon sauntered through the sanctuary, he felt positively delighted, knowing that he was defiling Yahweh's holiness as a rapist would a woman's virtue. To take the analogy one step further, he was then turning his victim's children into prostitutes.

These ignorant whores have no idea whose house they now serve. Apollyon smiled again. *Who their new pimp is.*

The metaphor was arousingly appropriate. The priesthood was his harlot; the high priest, his false prophet; and the ruling Jewish aristocracy, a scarlet beast of apostasy upon which the harlot rode. That Beast of the land of Israel was allowed its authority by the Beast of the sea of Rome. And it spoke with the voice of the dragon. Apollyon's voice.[8]

He thought of the high priest's garments worn in the Holy Place but stored in the Antonia under Roman control. Delicious humiliation.[9] His imagination wandered to the inner reality behind the outer façade. He pictured the high priest as a harlot arrayed in the blue, purple and scarlet of both temple and priesthood. Like them, the harlot was adorned with precious metals and jewels. She drank from a golden cup as from an altar. But the blood of sacrifice on her lips was the sweet taste of the martyred Christians. The high priest had on his forehead a golden plate engraved with the words *Holy to Yahweh*. But as Apollyon's slut it should actually read, "Babylon the Great, mother of prostitutes and of the land's abominations."[10]

Oh well, same thing, he thought.

He looked to the back of the holy place and saw the large veil of linen tapestry guarding the holy of holies. Its colorful images of golden cherubim were embroidered against the backdrop of the stars of heaven on Babylonian colors of blue, scarlet and purple. He saw the long sewn-over rip in the curtain, where it had been rent from top to bottom. He would never forget that cursed moment on Golgotha that opened the holy place to the Gentiles—when the Nazarene repossessed the lands from the gods of the nations, and began drawing in his elect from all tribes and nations of the earth.[11]

"Damn you, Nazarene," he whispered with all the hatred in his soul. Messiah had stolen his property.[12]

But now, Apollyon was returning the favor. He was taking Yahweh's house and his priesthood. *My whorehouse, my harlot.* He grinned malevolently as he marched up to the sacred curtain, took a deep breath, and parted the veil.

The holy of holies: the most sacred place of Yahweh's own presence in all of Israel. Only the high priest could enter the holy of holies, and only one time a year, during the annual Day of Atonement. Apollyon mused over it all. If the priest failed to perform his duties exactly according to Yahweh's obsessive tedious details, he would be struck dead by their intolerant god of temper tantrums.[13]

But not any more, he thought. *Now that I am in charge.*

Apollyon pranced around like a poet, singing, "When the landlord's away, the thief will play."

The small room was completely empty. Like a hollow heart. In days of old, it had within it two fifteen-foot-tall golden cherubim statues with wings spread out protectively over where the ark of the covenant lay, like the cherubim protecting the Garden. But both ark and guardian images were long gone, lost to history when the Babylonians destroyed the city and temple centuries ago.[14]

Nevertheless, Apollyon thought it poetic justice that the very throne of Yahweh would be missing along with the fleeing juvenile divinity. An absence that left wide open the foundation stone upon which the ark of the covenant used to rest. Tradition held that the foundation stone, called *Even ha-Shetiyah* in Hebrew, was the center of the world, the navel of the earth. It was the location of the creation, as well as the covenantal rock upon which Abraham sought to sacrifice Isaac. Jews considered it not only the connection between heaven and earth, but the spiritual cornerstone of the temple, as Isaiah had written, "Behold, I lay a foundation in Zion, a stone, a tested stone, a precious cornerstone, of a sure foundation."[15]

The foundation stone was also a gateway to the Abyss. It covered a shaft that led down to the waters of chaos below the earth. And through those waters was the underworld. Of the few earthly openings to the Abyss, the foundation stone in the temple provided the only unhindered access directly to Tartarus, the lowest depths of Hades. Tartarus was where the primeval Watchers, the ancient ones, were imprisoned along with those the Nazarene led captive after his resurrection. And Apollyon was sure as Hades going to use that to his benefit.[16]

He bent down and looked at the foundation stone. A signet finger ring was embedded within the rock—a golden ring with a beryl stone engraved with the seal of Solomon, the son of David. The archangel Michael had given the ring to Solomon, as a symbol of authority over spiritual principalities and powers, a promise of messianic hope. Silly fables had grown up around the incident. One legend went that Solomon used the ring to force demons to help him build the temple. Exactly the kind of foolishness humans were prone to manufacture. But Apollyon let it fester in the imaginations of men, because any amount of deception would benefit his cause.

The truth was, Solomon's seal was the key to the Abyss.[17]

Oh, have I plans for you, my precious signet, he thought, as he opened his tunic, pulled down his pants, and proceeded to relieve himself upon the ring and foundation stone, then on the floor all around him.

"Ahhhhhh," he sighed, feeling like a dragon king marking his territory. *Next stop, the crown of my new temple.*

Apollyon walked upon the cedar roof of the temple, and up to its edge, gabled with golden spikes like a crown. He looked down from his hundred-and-fifty-foot-high perch upon the entire temple complex, the heart and soul of the Mosaic covenant. Atonement, sacred space, the tangible location of God's presence. The temple had unified the chosen people and their worship of Yahweh as nothing else did. Before King David had secured Jerusalem as the holy city and his son Solomon had built the temple, there had been the tabernacle, a temporary, mobile version of the temple. During those days, Apollyon and his allies, Ba'al, Asherah, Molech and others, had managed to create widespread idolatry amongst the Jews on "high places," localized altars of worship in towns and villages all around Palestine. But when the temple was built on Mount Zion, Yahweh was able to exert his tyrannical control over Jews as never before, by centralizing the location of his house. And he did it through the priesthood as his sacred toadies. But now, those toadies licked the boots of Apollyon.[18]

The Watcher looked up to heaven and muttered, "And now, I have your mountain, Nazarene. And with it, the key to the Abyss."

• • • • •

Simon bar Giora raised his sword over his head in defense.

Gischala's gladius clashed against his, inches from Simon's brow.

Temple guards were Jews, but their weaponry was Roman. Simon and Gischala were equals, newly at odds. Allies turned against one another?

Instantly, Gischala swung down low.

Simon twisted his weapon down to guard his right side. Another clang of steel. Simon felt his arm shudder. Gischala was strong—and swift.

That one was too close. Simon responded with force.

He released a volley of attacks on his opponent, pushing him back toward a stone wall.

Simon was fast and relentless. Gischala shifted to defensive responses, barely keeping up. The tables had turned.

Simon found an opening and swiped across Gischala's torso. The light Herodian armor was minimal. The leather ripped, but Simon saw no flesh. "Getting tired?" taunted Simon.

Gischala didn't respond. His face tight in concentration, he kept his enemy's blade from cutting him through.

But then their swords froze against each other in a moment of equalized force. Blade against blade.

That was when Gischala spun his wrist, twirled his arm in a circular twisting motion, and somehow locked into Simon's sword and handle, yanking it right out of his hands. The sword flew against the stone wall yards away with a clang.

Simon was stunned. But his wits snapped back quick enough to avoid the sweeping arcs of Gischala's blade. He darted and dodged, weaponless, eyes on his sword by the wall, too far away. A javelin against another wall was closer.

Gischala grinned diabolically and shouted, "Now look who's tired!"

This time, Simon kept silent. Reserving all his energy for survival.

Swing, dodge. Thrust, dodge.

A voice behind them shouted, "Captain Giora!"

Gischala froze and looked to the doorway.

Simon kept moving, leapt and rolled to the wall, picking up the javelin. He spun around and pointed the weapon at Gischala.

The voice was that of the high priest Ananus. Beside him was the Pharisee, Joseph ben Matthias, newly arrived from Rome.

Ananus said distastefully, "This room smells like a loin cloth."

Simon gave a glance at Gischala. "Sparring does build up a sweat, my lord. We apologize for the odor."

The warriors lowered their weapons, clasped wrists in mutual honor.

Simon said to Ananus, "How can I help you, my lord?"

Ananus placed his robe sleeve against his nose to avoid the smell. But he moved it to talk. "You know Joseph ben Matthias."

Simon bowed to the Pharisee. Gischala joined him.

Joseph barely acknowledged them. His was a noble family of reputation in Jerusalem. Hasmoneans with a lineage back to the Maccabees. Simon thought the Pharisee looked arrogant, like a king among subjects. His well-coifed hair and beard, his perfectly pressed robe. A man of wealth and privilege, protected by lowly men like Simon and Gischala. He didn't like him. And he knew Gischala well enough to know he despised the aristocrat.[19]

Ananus said, "Get cleaned up. I need a guard. I understand the Christian agitator you punished the other day is out on the streets again. I want to see for myself."

Gischala said, "That deranged old man? We whipped him to a pulp, near death."

Simon gave Gischala a scolding look. It was nothing to brag about.

Ananus responded, "Evidently, he is still alive. Unless witnesses saw a phantom."

Simon said to Ananus, "I will lead a small company myself, sir."

"There is no need," replied Ananus. "You and your lieutenant will be enough. I am no longer the ruling high priest, after all."

"But, sir," protested Simon, "all members of the Sanhedrin are potential targets of the Sicarii these days. Especially outside the temple grounds." The Sicarii were a conspiracy of assassins who kidnapped ruling class nobles or killed them with hidden daggers.[20]

Ananus said, "Do I not have the best protection with you, Captain?"

Gischala jibbed, "We were just debating that very question, sir."

Simon shook his head and changed the subject. "Where is the agitator?"

Ananus said, "On the porch of the Huldah Gates."

"That is where we flogged them."

Gischala threw in, "Symbolic defiance."

Joseph interrupted, "The high priest is not speaking to you, Lieutenant."

Simon saw Gischala's eyes burn with anger. He touched his subordinate's shoulder reassuringly, and to stop him from saying anything he would regret. "Forgive me, my lord. I allow him to speak freely."

Ananus said, "And he's right. These Christians are diabolically clever with their propaganda. Meet us at the Huldah Gates."

Simon said, "My lord, we will be ready in minutes."

Ananus held his robe to his nose as the two priests turned to leave. "Do wash up first."

The two temple guards picked up their sparring weapons.

Simon muttered to Gischala, "You have to show me how to do that move with the sword."

Gischala smiled. "Only if you show me how to be patient with these pompous snobs."

CHAPTER 25

The midday sun burned overhead with a brightness that seemed to uncover every shadow. The pavement outside the Huldah Gates had few patrons engaged in temple duties. It was like that shortly after a feast. Most residents had to get back to their daily duties of survival: going to market, building, trading, farming and shepherding in the fields.

Six men came out through the gates onto the large stone porch entrance of the temple. Ananus, Joseph, and two other curious priests guarded by Simon and Gischala, who were well armed with a small shield, sword and javelin each.

They found the agitator, Joshua, standing and preaching by the southeast corner yet again, beneath the pinnacle of the temple.

Simon had expected a crowd of followers and fools to be gathered around him. But there were none. Not even those seeking amusement. The old man stood there croaking out his calumnies with a hoarse voice, stooped in pain, blood seeping through the tunic on his bandaged back and chest. But no one was listening. The masses completely ignored him and went about their day.

"Perhaps he is a phantom after all," said Ananus.

"He is a madman," said Joseph.

Simon muttered, "It looks like the people got our message from his stripes."

"Be quiet," said Ananus. "I want to hear his madness."

They all listened. Simon and Gischala scanned the surrounding area for suspicious activity.

Joshua spoke through his pain, that clearly hampered his every movement. At times, he looked as if he might even fall over.

He had been calling scribes and Pharisees a brood of vipers who would not escape being sentenced to Gehenna. He had condemned them for murdering the prophets and his messengers, and made the proclamation that judgment would come upon this generation.[1]

It was at that moment that Simon realized he was reciting someone else's words, not merely proclaiming his own words. Just whose words, he was not sure.

Joshua said, "See, your house is left to you desolate! For truly I say to you, there will not be left here one stone upon another that will not be thrown down!"[2]

There it was. The threat of destruction of the temple. *Blasphemy*, thought Simon. He felt more justified in what he had done to this miscreant. He was fed up with these Christians and their heresies.

The heretic paused for a second, cringing in pain. He looked over and saw the group of six watching him.

But he didn't look *at* them, he looked *behind and above* them. He looked like he was watching a ghost. A very tall ghost.

Simon gripped his sword and looked behind the men. There was nothing there. No one there. Then why did he feel a chill go down his spine? Why did he feel like he too was being watched?

Joshua returned to his diatribe. "When will these things be? And what will be the sign of his coming and of the end of the age? Jesus said, 'See that no one leads you astray, for many will come in my name, saying I am the Messiah, and they will lead many into apostasy.'"[3]

Simon was all too familiar with that political reality. It seemed like the entire land was full of would-be messiahs gathering gangs of outlaws and trying to claim royal heritage. He and Gischala had to arrest a number of them already. Talk about insanity. Those fools with their messianic delusions contaminated the Roman culture. But not merely the Jews. Even Romans had their own prophecies about a coming king who would rule the world.[4]

Joshua continued to shout. "And you will hear of wars and rumors of wars! But the end is not yet. For nation will rise against nation, and kingdom against kingdom!"

Simon thought of the Pax Romana, peace of Rome. Never had there been such a peace in all the earth until now. The catchwords of the day were 'peace and security,' but he knew that would be the perfect opportunity for sudden destruction to come upon them.[5] Of course, peace did not necessarily mean justice. The Jews, among many other captive nations, were unwilling slaves of this so-called peace. And that was why there were indeed rumors of war boiling over in Judea. But none of this was prophetic. It sounded more like this Joshua was doing what the Jewish writers of apocalyptic literature often did, proclaim what was going on around them as if it were a prophecy from the past.[6]

It was the same thing with the famines and earthquakes Joshua next "predicted" as birth pains leading to the end. Sure, there had been quite a few earthquakes recently in Asia. And plenty of famines as well. He remembered the great famine in the days of Claudius before Nero. But again, these were all past, not future. Was that the point? Predicting present calamity?[7]

Joshua continued to struggle through his jeremiad. "Then they will deliver up the Christians to tribulation and put us to death, and we will be hated by all nations for the sake of the name of Jesus! And many will fall away in apostasy and betray one another and hate one another. But the one who endures to the end will be saved!"[8]

Well, that is certainly happening, thought Simon. *Christians are hated the world over. But can you blame the world? The Nazarene sect condemns anyone who doesn't convert to their ways and they use incendiary rhetoric. You can't expect to rattle a bear cage and then cry victim when your arm is bitten off.*

Joshua continued to preach to the empty air. "And this good news of the kingdom will be proclaimed throughout the whole world as a testimony to all nations. And then the end will come."[9]

The Pharisee Joseph had been listening closely as well. He had been to Rome and saw how the apostle Paul and his religious indoctrination had indeed reached the farthest corners of the Roman Empire, the whole world to them. He remembered that Paul had spoken of similar things before he was beheaded: the wrath to come, the end was near.[10]

The end of what?

What Joshua said next hit Joseph with particular interest. "So when you see the Abomination of Desolation spoken of by the prophet Daniel, standing where it ought not to be, when you see Jerusalem surrounded by armies, know that her desolation has come near! And let those who are in Judea flee to the mountains. For there will be great tribulation, such as has not been from the beginning of the world until now, no, and never will be! A time like Jacob's Trouble!"[11]

Joseph knew the scroll of Daniel well. He had studied it in the synagogue with much anticipation. The Seventy Weeks of Daniel.

Over six hundred years ago, Jerusalem and the first temple of Solomon had been destroyed by the Babylonians. The prophet Daniel had foretold that the Jews would be allowed to restore and rebuild the holy city and its temple. That occurred seventy years later. But then Daniel prophesied that there would be seventy *weeks* of years from the time of that decree until the Anointed One, a king who would "finish the transgression of Israel, put an end to sin, and atone for iniquity." This Messiah would "bring in everlasting righteousness, seal up both vision and prophecy, and anoint the Most Holy."[12]

Seventy weeks of years before Messiah. Seventy weeks of years was seventy times seven, or four hundred and ninety years. The decree to rebuild both Jerusalem and temple was about four hundred and ninety years ago. It was no wonder to Joseph why there was so much unrest, and so many Jews ready for revolt. Many were expecting Messiah to free them from Rome. From Zealots to Essenes to many in the priestly class. Yes, even *Joseph* was expecting Messiah.[13]

But what if the king they were expecting was not who they had expected? What if God's Anointed One was not a Jewish king, but a Roman? Cyrus the Persian had been so. Why not again? Were the Jews simply kicking against the goads?[14]

And the last part of the prophecy foretold that the people of that coming king would destroy the new city and its temple. He remembered Daniel's words: "On the wing of abominations shall come one who makes desolate, until the decreed end is poured out on the desolate."[15]

That was the Abomination of Desolation. The unclean monstrosity that this demented provocateur had just claimed would be fulfilled in armies surrounding Jerusalem. There was only one army in the world capable of achieving that kind of siege in this time of history: Rome. Joshua was predicting that Rome was God's instrument of desolation on Jerusalem. But would not Rome be judged?[16] It wasn't a new idea. Yahweh had done this many times in the past. He used the godless Assyrians to punish Israel, and then he punished the Assyrians. He used the Babylonians to punish Israel, and then judged them as well.[17] As a Pharisee, Joseph believed in the providential control of God over history. Why not this possibility as well?[18]

Joseph would be careful to keep that crazy interpretation to himself. It was so crazy, there just might be something to it.

The Christian's pained and trembling voice brought Joseph's attention back to the present. "Immediately after the tribulation of those days the sun will be darkened, and the moon will not give its light, and the stars will fall from heaven, and the powers of heaven will be shaken. Then will appear the sign of the Son of Man in heaven, and all the tribes of the land will mourn!"[19]

Joseph and Ananus gave each other a knowing look. The two other priests murmured angrily. They knew exactly what that poetic terminology meant. The shaking of the heavens and earth, the failure of the sun, moon and stars was all figurative language that the Hebrew prophets used to describe the collapse of earthly regimes, and the heavenly spiritual powers behind them. Jeremiah used the same symbols to describe the destruction of the First Temple by the Babylonians. Isaiah used the same symbols to describe the fall of Babylon and of Judah. Ezekiel used the same symbols for the destruction of Egypt.[20]

By saying that all the tribes of the land of Israel would mourn, this firebrand was saying that it would be the ruling class of the Herods and the priesthood whose "lights would be put out" like the sun, moon and stars. It was their power that would be destroyed—the ruling class of Ananus the Sadducee and Joseph the Pharisee.

"How dare he," grumbled Ananus. The former high priest stared at the agitator. Joseph could tell he was ready to pull out his own dagger and kill the traitor.

Then Joshua topped off his outrageous insult with a high-handed blasphemy. "And you will see the Son of Man coming on the clouds of heaven with power and great glory!"[21]

Joseph saw Ananus tremble with anger. This idolater just ascribed deity to the dead Nazarene. There was nothing more offensive to the high priest's holy ears. The language of cloud comings was reserved for the gods. And in the holy Scriptures, Yahweh alone came on the clouds to judge a city or nation. Joseph saw how the Christians tried to deify Jesus, exaggerating the place of Daniel's throne-sitting 'Son of Man' to Yahweh's level![22]

Such delusions were offensive, outrageous, intolerable.

Seditious.

Joseph remembered that Ananus had killed James the Just for saying these same things just a few years earlier. Had him cast from the very pinnacle of the temple that towered above them right now.[23]

Ananus whispered to Simon, "Apparently, this charlatan has not learned his lesson. Arrest him again. Let us see if he has a fear of heights."

"Wait," said Joseph. He held Simon back and whispered to Ananus, "Consider your actions carefully, my lord."

Ananus gave him a confused scowl. The other priests quietly listened.

Joseph said, "Look around. Who do you see?"

"No one," said an impatient Ananus. "Just people doing their business and ignoring this fool."

"Exactly. The man is spouting nonsense and profanities. And nobody listens. If you punish him for such buffoonery, you only draw attention and give it meaning. You give them reason to listen."

Ananus was now following him.

Joseph grinned deviously. "If you let a madman rant and rave, it only reinforces the notion that what he says is madness. It annoys the people and they learn to tune him out."

Ananus grinned in return. "A fool allowed to cry persecution proves he is not being persecuted."

"Besides," added Joseph, "the man is demon-possessed. He keeps preaching after he is beaten near to death. You would have to finish him to stop him. And that would only create sympathy for the enemy."[24]

Ananus looked at Simon. "Was this the same drivel you previously arrested him for?"

"Indeed. He is reciting the exact same sermon, over and over."

Joseph added, "He is quoting the Nazarene from a generation ago, recorded in their propaganda that they memorize."[25]

Ananus said, "Let us leave this fool to curse the light."

As they turned to leave, Simon heard the words of Joshua fade into the distance behind him. "When you see all these things, know that he is near, at the very gates. Truly, I say to you, this generation will not pass away until all these things take place!"

Those last words grabbed hold of Simon: *this generation.* The Nazarene had prophesied these things a generation ago. They were now at the end of that generation, just as he had said. So the prophecies were not projected backward after all. They were occurring just as he had said, before the generation to which he spoke would die off.[26] *Well*, thought Simon, *even false prophets eventually get lucky.*

It was at just that moment that everyone's guard was down. The priests and their soldiers had been insulted by a pathetic clown who had wasted their time. They were about to return to the temple complex through the southern gates. None of them, not even Simon, were prepared for what happened next.

Twenty men walking in the thin crowds around them—twenty men whom they had not noticed—suddenly pulled hoods up over their faces, and ran to encircle the small group of six.

Gischala noticed them first. He hissed, "Sicarii."

As the men encircled them, Simon stepped close to Ananus, raised his shield and held out his javelin.

Two against twenty. He knew he shouldn't have yielded to the high priest's impatience earlier. He knew he should have brought more guards.

But now it was too late.

The Sicarii were fast. They didn't carry obvious weapons. They used secreted daggers in their cloaks for their dirty deeds.

They had already moved in for the kill.

Joseph was attacked first. He surprised his attacker by disarming him and dropping him to the ground in pain. Joseph now held his enemy's dagger in defense.

Impressed, Simon corrected himself, *Three against twenty.*

Still bad odds.

"Joseph!" he barked, and pulled his sword from its sheath, tossing it to the Pharisee.

Joseph caught it and used it to take down another attacker.

A woman screamed. The platform quickly emptied of its few innocent bystanders.

Gischala had gone on the offensive. He took out one assassin through the gut. His shield blocked another's slashing dagger.

Simon defended Ananus. He cut a dagger out of the hand of one of the attackers. The wounded assassin ran away.

Four down, sixteen to go.

The other two priests were in the open. They were yanked away from the circle of defenders by six Sicarii.

Simon could not help them. His priority was the high priest. But at that moment he realized that this was a kidnapping. The Sicarii killed some priests and kidnapped others for ransom.

They dragged the two priests away.

Joseph was blocked from helping them.

One of the priests had gotten loose and ran back to Simon and Gischala. Two Sicarii tackled him.

But then Gischala's javelin pierced one of the assailants.

The other one realized that Joseph was going to get him. So he slashed the priest's throat and ran away.

These dirty thugs had decided to kill those they could not kidnap.

Joseph reached the priest, whose lifeblood was spilling out through his gaping throat.

Gischala screamed like a banshee and cut down three Sicarii in a mad fury of blows.

Simon took down two others.

The last three Sicarii saw they were now outplayed. They bolted and joined their fleeing comrades in crime.

Gischala started after them.

"Gischala!" yelled Simon.

He stopped.

"We must get the high priest to safety."

Gischala looked back into the street as the last of the assassins melted away into the labyrinth of Jerusalem alleyways.

Gischala burned with rage. He grumbled, "Cowards."

He and Joseph surrounded Simon and Ananus, and the four of them moved to the gates, just as a squad of twenty temple guards arrived.

Simon barked to his men, "See if any of the attackers are alive."

Ananus said to Simon, "Bring me to the Hall of Hewn Stone. I need to call a counsel of Sanhedrin."

CHAPTER 26

The Hall of Hewn Stone was located in the northwestern wall of the temple complex near the Antonia. It was called by this name because its stones were hewn by iron tools, and it was used for political and judicial activities. Other parts of the temple, used for religious ritual, were built using unhewn stones. Since metals were used in implements of war, they could not be used on God's house of holiness.[1]

Because the Hall was involved in both political and civil matters as well as religious and cultic, it had two entrances, one to the temple area and one to the upper city outside its walls.

Apollyon owned both city and temple. So this would be a crucial room of decision for his plans; a war room for his harlot and false prophet.

From his perch above the high priest's central throne, he looked out upon the gathering of seventy leaders of the Sanhedrin. A pathetic lot of greedy, power-hungry cutthroats. Most of them having sold their souls and betrayed each other to achieve their ambitions. And all in the name of God.

"Thou shalt not take the name of the Lord thy God in vain." Ha.

The priesthood had become a labyrinth of political power plays and double-crossing treachery outdone only by the Herods in their own rule over Judea. In fact, the priesthood was in bed with the Herods, so it was all one big, syphilitic orgy of incestuous fornication. The way Apollyon liked it.

These are my people, he thought. *My beast of the land of Israel.*

Simon stood guard with Gischala and several others at the entrance to the Hall of Hewn Stone. They watched the Roman procurator, governor of Judea, enter from the city side with several of his legionary escort.

He was a small man, with a well-groomed appearance that showed fastidious attention to detail. Clean shaven, closely cropped dark hair, graying at the edges. He wore a pure white toga with purple bands, tightly wound and perfectly draped in place. His large personality and presence overshadowed his size, as he held himself like the emperor, chin held high, looking down upon everyone else from his lowly height.

Simon and Gischala followed the procurator and his personal bodyguards down the hallway and into the deliberation room. Simon was preoccupied with his responsibilities for tonight. It was the last day of the feast. Most of the city would be gathered in the temple area for worship and sacrifice. Herod Agrippa II and his retinue would be there as well, which required extra security for the young ruler and his sister Berenice. As tetrarch over Galilee and this region, Agrippa garnered the limited title of king. But all of it was problematic because of what they had just discovered from interrogating their captured Sicarius.

They arrived at the hall. It was full of elders, scribes, Pharisees and Sadducees. Ananus had managed to persuade the high priest to convene a greater Sanhedrin meeting. Though Ananus was no longer the high priest, he still wielded considerable political clout with his own faction of interests in the community. Lesser Sanhedrins of only twenty-three members were all that were necessary for adjudicating most civil and political matters. The greater Sanhedrin of seventy was required for more important matters related to capital cases, the holy temple, and the greater commonwealth of Judea.[2]

This was a most important assembly.

The crowd of ruling class Jews quieted down in nervous silence when they saw the procurator. It was not a normal thing for unclean Romans to be allowed in the presence of the holy community. But these were desperate days. And most of the Sanhedrin were Hellenists, Herodians and Roman collaborators anyway.

The little Roman governor looked around the room during the uncomfortable silence. It was laid out in a semicircle of seventy chairs with the high priest at the midpoint on his own throne. He shook his head with contempt and addressed the crowd in Greek, the common tongue. "I am Gessius Florus. Nero Caesar has newly appointed me as procurator of this parched and godforsaken armpit of the world called Judea." He looked straight at Ananus, who sat near the throne of the high priest. "Unlike my predecessor, I am not so easily swayed by money, property or whining."[3]

Ananus looked away angrily. Simon knew he had worked the previous procurator, Lucceius Albinus, to cater to his interests. But there was a new boss in town. Ananus would have to start all over, groveling anew.

Joseph knew Florus was exaggerating. Of course he had a price. All Romans had a price. This was just a form of flexing his muscle to get a higher one.

Florus looked to the high priest on the throne. "And you are…?"

Yeshua stood from his seat and responded with apprehension, "My lord procurator, I am the high priest, Yeshua ben Gamaliel. Welcome to this assembly. I am sure you will agree that our problem is of mutual interest with Rome."[4]

Florus waved his hand impatiently. "Sit down." Sounds of grumbling disapproval came from the seventy. He looked around the room again. "Please do get to the point. I know you Jews like to bicker forever over excruciating minutiae."

Joseph noticed the high priest give a questioning glance at Ananus. Florus now knew who was in real control behind the scenes.[5]

Simon knew they were in for hard times ahead with this tyrant-in-training.

Joseph watched the procurator closely, looking for any way in to the man's psyche. His one chance was the fact that Florus' wife was good friends with Nero's wife, the empress—and converted confidante of Joseph.[6]

He glanced at Ananus, who just wanted to appease the damned Roman.

Florus said impatiently, "I haven't all night."

Yeshua cleared his nervous throat and said, "Ananus ben Ananus, one of the high priesthood, can explain the issue best for us." He looked to Ananus, the real control.

Ananus stood and bowed respectfully to Florus. "Procurator. I appreciate your forthrightness. It brings a refreshing air of sincerity to—"

Florus interrupted him. "Flattery wastes my time, priest."

"Forgive me, my lord." Ananus bowed again.

Florus sighed.

Ananus said, "To the point, several of us priests were attacked today by Sicarii. I was rescued by my guards, but one other priest was killed and another kidnapped. We have just received from them their demands."

"Which are…?" pushed Florus.

"Prisoner exchange for ten of their men imprisoned for theft, banditry and murder."[7]

Florus was incredulous. "One for ten? Clearly a Jewish calculation. Is the 'one' a tax collector?" He was clearly impressed by his own humor.

"With due respect, procurator," said Joseph, "this is an increasing problem in Judea. Ransom payments only encourage more kidnapping."

"Then kill the ten prisoners instead," said Florus. "It's worked for me."

"We only have the power of the sword with approval from you."[8]

"True enough," said Florus. He appeared to be thinking of a way to avoid responsibility. "Then don't do it in public. So I won't know." He smiled victoriously.

Joseph asked, "May I speak freely, procurator?"

"Please do," said Florus with raised brow.

Simon thought, *And he will kill you if you insult him.*

Joseph stepped out onto the open floor, as if taking charge.

Simon thought, *This Pharisee is ambitious.*

Joseph said, "The Sicarii are not the only gadflies buzzing in the face of Judea…and Rome. They are kidnapping and murdering priests and Herodians because they consider us 'collaborators with Rome.' The Zealots still cry, 'No king but god,' in defiance against Caesar, and are calling for an uprising. Add to these the rogue cults with their impostor messiahs, and the growing gangs of robbers, bandits and brigands. These are no longer gadflies, they are a hornet's nest, and this country is in imminent danger."

Florus said with contempt, "Do you hold Rome responsible?"

"I do not. But I beg of you to consider the practical implications. In this room are members of the priestly and ruling class, many of whom are Herodians, Hellenists, friends of Caesar. We have all sought to maintain peace and obedience to the authority of Rome. The simple fact that you as a Roman have been allowed into this holy chamber is evidence of our serious intentions. If the people found out, they might riot."[9]

Florus added sarcastically, "Especially should they hear that my belly was full of swine from dinner."

Hushes of offense could be heard amidst the seventy.

Joseph continued, "Now, it is true, as you said earlier, that we Jews bicker amongst ourselves to a fault. With this, I will readily agree. We have a history of struggling with our God and with ourselves."[10]

More mumbling of outrage sounded in the crowd. Florus shook his head. It only proved his accusation.

"But consider this: the many factions of our people have been in constant conflict for as long as I can remember. But in this moment, on the importance of halting an uprising, we are in perfect agreement. It is in Caesar's best interest to work with this Sanhedrin in our fight to bring unity amongst our people. If Rome suppresses the unrest with unilateral force, in complete disregard of the ruling class, it will only serve to feed the flames of revenge."

Florus said, "Dead men do not avenge."

"True," said Joseph, "but their deaths inspire the living to revolt. If you work with this Sanhedrin, it only helps Rome."

Florus glared at Joseph. He walked up to him, staring him in the eye. He was not weak like the others.

Florus smiled and looked up at the high priest. "I like this one. He demonstrates a rare trait amongst you Jews: intelligence." The rest of the Sanhedrin grumbled at the insult. But then Florus turned cold and calculated. "What is your offer, Pharisee?"

Joseph said, "It is not mine to make. I defer to the high priest." He bowed and looked expectantly at Yeshua.

The high priest swallowed nervously under Florus' glare. "We caught one of the assassins today, and interrogated him. He admitted that the Sicarii had made an alliance with the Zealots and a certain rebel leader, called 'the Egyptian,' who claims to be the Messiah."

Florus asked, "The Egyptian? Why does that sound familiar to me?"

Yeshua replied, "Ten years ago, when Felix was procurator, the Egyptian rose up in Jerusalem with a force of four thousand men. He claimed he was Messiah. Felix captured or killed most of the rebels, but the Egyptian escaped."[11]

Florus shook his head. "My incompetent predecessor."

Yeshua said, "The Egyptian has returned and rebuilt his forces to several thousand again. But that is not the only concern of this meeting. After interrogating our captive Sicarius, we have just discovered a plot to assassinate King Agrippa and his sister Berenice tonight at the final evening of the feast. We believe the Egyptian may be planning a coup against Agrippa."

"I will crush this Egyptian insect and his forces," said Florus.

Ananus, the real voice behind the throne of the high priest, interrupted. "Forgive me, procurator, but that is exactly what you should not do."

Florus flashed him a look of anger.

Ananus continued, "Allow us, my lord, to lead this operation. With the back-up support of some of your troops, of course. In this way, we will protect Rome from any implication of excessive force in Jewish affairs. You give no cause to the rebels to revolt." Ananus paused with a smile. "And you let us bicker amongst ourselves."

He would prefer we kill ourselves, thought Simon.

Florus asked, "Who would lead this mission? I will not tolerate another bungling amateur mucking up the works."

Ananus gestured behind the procurator. "May I introduce our suggested leader of the operation, the captain of the Temple Guard, Simon bar Giora."

Simon stepped forward and bowed.

Florus looked Simon up and down with a skeptical eye.

"He rescued me today from twenty assassins," said Ananus. "And he has successfully captured or killed three hundred criminals in conspiracy plots this year alone."

"Three hundred is not the same as three thousand," said Florus.

Simon said, "My lord procurator, I hail from Galilee. I know these factions well. I know how they think and how they fight. I will bring them in or kill them, as the case may require."

Ananus said, "His reputation is impeccable."

Florus kept looking at Simon as he spoke to the high priest. "Very well. But if you disappoint me, priest, I will come in with an iron fist and I will complete the task using any means necessary. Am I understood?"

Simon wanted to cut this imperious Roman pig's throat.

"Yes, procurator." Yeshua nodded. "Thank you for your benevolence and trust."

"I have no interest in benevolence," said Florus. "Nor do I trust Jews. But I am practical. And in the interest of practical strategy, keep this secret. Do not tell the king of this conspiracy, or you will no doubt fail to surprise his enemies."

The hall filled with mutterings of shock.

Ananus said, "But my lord, surely you do not suggest we allow the king to face jeopardy unknowingly?"

Florus glanced at Simon with a wry look. "If your captain is as skilled and of impeccable reputation as you say, then I assume the king will hardly be in jeopardy."

Simon's stomach sank.

Florus concluded, "Besides, what the king does not know will be of little notoriety to you. Now, I leave you to your petty religious squabbling."

He turned and marched out of the room.

All eyes turned to Simon.

Joseph stepped up to him and said, "I will assist you in any way I can."

Simon knew this was not going to be easy. He considered Joseph a grandstanding bootlicker to Ananus. However, too much was at stake for him to fail. He responded, "I need all the help I can get." He then looked to Ananus. "Sire, might you secure Joseph a seat with the royal retinue of Agrippa for that evening? He could operate as a secret bodyguard."

"Unbeknownst to Herod," responded Ananus. "I like that."

Seeing Joseph's face go pale, Simon thought, *He probably regrets his offer of help now.* Joseph would be placed right next to the target of the assassins. Defending the deplorable Agrippa was not an honor; it was more like a punishment. But if Joseph tried to back out of it, he would look weak and self-preserving. He quietly accepted the responsibility.

Out of my hair and into danger, thought Simon with amusement.

Apollyon, who had been watching it all and whispering in the ears of those he owned, was satisfied with the effect.

The spiritual kindling has been set, he thought. *And now I go to get the torch to light an out-of-control inferno that will make the Great Fire of Rome look like child's play in comparison.*

He left for a quick journey into the far reaches of the north.

CHAPTER 27

One hundred miles north of Jerusalem, Mount Hermon rose nine thousand feet above the mouth of the river Jordan in the land of Bashan. Apollyon stood in the ruins of an ancient temple on the face of the mountain looking down on the land. *His* land. From the earliest of ages, gods lived on mountains. The ancient ziggurat temples like the Tower of Babel were man-made cosmic mountains where gods came down to assemble and meet with humanity. The "mount of assembly" on these mountains was the seat of divine power in the cosmos.

The mighty Watcher's eyes pooled with tears of anger. He gritted his teeth to hold back his fury. Mount Hermon had been the mount of assembly for the Watchers of the nations ever since the primeval days of Noah. It was there where the first satanic strategy of the fallen Sons of God had been spawned. The Nephilim were their progeny with the daughters of men. They were the mighty ones of old, and they began the War of the Seed of the Serpent with the Seed of the Woman. It was the perpetual war against Messiah that lasted until this very day.

Hermon was also called "the mountain of Bashan," because it stood over the land of Bashan, which meant "the Place of the Serpent." In the same way that Mount Zion in Jerusalem was Yahweh's holy mountain, so this Hermon was Apollyon's holy mountain. In a spiritual sense, the struggle for control of this entire land of Israel was a struggle between two cosmic mountains, Bashan and Zion, foretold by David in a psalm:[1]

> O mountain of God, mountain of Bashan;
> > O many-peaked mountain, mountain of Bashan!
> Why do you look with hatred, O many-peaked mountain,
> > at the mount that God desired for his abode,
> > yes, where Yahweh will dwell forever?

The chariots of God are twice ten thousand,
> *thousands upon thousands;*
> *the Lord is among them; Sinai is now in the sanctuary.*
You ascended on high,
> *leading a host of captives in your train*
> *and receiving gifts among men,*
even among the rebellious, that Yahweh God may dwell there.[2]

Sinai was Yahweh's first cosmic mountain that was replaced by Zion with the Messiah king David.

> *I have installed my king upon Mount Zion, my holy mountain.*[3]

Ten miles below in the foothills of this range the infamous holy grotto called Panias loomed at the mouth of the Jordan River. Its subterranean passage led to the infamous Gates of Hades. When the Nazarene stood at those gates in the foothills of that mountain of Bashan he said he would build his congregation, Mount Zion, upon the ruins of that rock of Mount Hermon.

Apollyon turned from glaring at that site of tragedy and peered into a secret temple tunnel that led into the heart of the mountain, a great cavern that hosted the assembly of the gods. Or at least, it used to. When the Nazarene stormed the Gates of Hades, he conquered the principalities and powers, those gods of the nations, and destroyed the mount of assembly inside Hermon. And when he ascended, he led his train of captives—those freed and those now in chains—from Hades and into Hades. The Watchers he dragged into the Abyss and down into the lowest parts of the underworld, called Tartarus, where they were imprisoned to await judgment. There was no chance for their escape—until now.[4]

One of the bound Watchers defeated in that battle was the mighty storm god Ba'al. The Nazarene confiscated Ba'al's war hammer, named Yagrush, or "Driver," a primordial weapon of devastating power, and used it upon the mount of assembly.[5] The cavern caved in, burying their unholy of unholies beneath a mountain of collapsed rock.

But the Nazarene had made the mistake of leaving behind Ba'al's hammer in the rubble. Apollyon was here to dig it out.

He began moving boulders and rocks, tunneling his way through the debris of the collapsed cavern.

CHAPTER 28

The final day of the Festival of Dedication was called a solemn assembly. It ended the celebration with fasting and prayer. The people gathered in the temple grounds while the priests led them in lamenting Israel's collective sin and beseeched Yahweh for protection. This was done in memory of the temple's original desecration by that abomination of desolation, Antiochus Epiphanes.

The entire outer court was flooded with thousands of pilgrims standing, kneeling, and prostrate—some dressed in sackcloth and ashes—praying, wailing or mournfully silent.[1]

"A waste of words and tears to an unfeeling, unhearing god," said Apollyon. He stood on the edge of the temple roof, watching the crowd below him swarm like a hive of insects. He looked up in the sky. A star shone in the shape of a sword hanging over the city. Another glorious portent of what was about to happen.[2] "But you're a little off, Yahweh," said Apollyon. "It won't be a sword that brings this desolation." He raised Yagrush, the war hammer of Ba'al and caressed it. Made of heavenly metal, its huge head was twice the size of a Watcher's skull. It took two hands to swing this long-handled battle mace, and it could do some mighty damage in heaven and on earth. Apollyon was about to answer these Jewish prayers with a big surprise. He was going to turn this holy day of lament into an unholy day of terror. He turned and walked down into the heart of the temple.

Simon stood near the colonnade, eyes searching the crowd for hints of subterfuge. Some of his men stood guard in the midst of the masses. Others were undercover as mourning citizens. They were trying to find the ten secret assassins in the crowd that their captive told Simon about.

Their targets would be here soon.

Gischala looked above them at the walls of the Antonia fortress towering over them. He could see Roman legionaries on watch along the walls looking down spitefully upon the faithful. He saw one of the guards spit down into the crowd. He longed for an arrow at that moment. He was quite a good aim with a bow.

It was a good thing no one else had seen it, for such profanity could cause a riot. Years ago, under Claudius Caesar, a Roman soldier had raised his battle skirt and made a gaseous release toward the temple during a Feast of Unleavened Bread. It caused a riot that resulted in ten thousand dead. These Romans were soulless, thoughtless fools without a care for the consequences of their blasphemy.[3]

The shofar horn blew from the corner of the temple in the inner court.

"Gischala," said Simon. "They are here."

The captain and his lieutenant made their way through the crowd toward a royal canopy staged for the king and his entourage near the Golden Gate.

Apollyon heard the shofar as he walked down the stairwell into the holy place of the temple. *What a satisfying irony*, he thought with a grin. The shofar was a ram's horn used as a call to worship. But these fools had no idea that it was doubling as a call to war. Apollyon was on his way to the holy of holies where he would use Ba'al's hammer to smash open the foundation stone, confiscate the Seal of Solomon and use it to unleash the imprisoned Watchers from the Abyss.

"I can't wait to see the look on the Nazarene's face," he said to himself, "when we take back our territories and return the land to idolatry." Back to the good old days of worshipping Ba'al, Asherah and Molech here in the land of Israel. "My land," he muttered.

The Golden Gate was the main entrance of the temple opening into the eastern Kidron Valley below the Mount of Olives. Jewish tradition taught that the Messiah would enter this gate, thus making it a favorite of the Herods for entry during such significant festivals.[4] Twenty temple servants pushed open the enormous, ornamented double gates.

Simon and Gischala continued to scan the crowd desperately in search of intended assassins. They knew some of the plan from their interrogations, but not all of it.

The gate finished opening, and a royal Herodian parade entered.

An obese herald with a booming voice announced, "King Herod Agrippa the Second, the pious! Patron of the holy temple of God! His sister, Princess Julia Berenice!"

A retinue of male servants carried an ostentatiously decorated Roman carriage inside, guarded by a company of Herodian soldiers and accompanied by a reluctant Joseph ben Matthias. He had a secreted weapon, but that didn't protect him from the danger he was walking straight into because of Simon's strategic maneuver to put him there.

King Agrippa, aged thirty-seven, sat on the portable throne next to his sister Berenice, a year his younger, his closest counselor and confidante. They were both young looking, royal and beautiful.

So beautiful was Berenice to Simon, down in the crowd, that he could not take his eyes off of her. Bedecked in gold jewelry, she wore a bright, colorful gown. Her hair was raven black, swept around a golden tiara, with soft, pale skin.

Gischala smirked knowingly at his superior's admiration. He leaned in and whispered to him, "Are the orders to protect royalty or gawk at them?"

Simon gave him an annoyed side glance.

But then Gischala saw Berenice notice Simon as the entourage passed. And he saw in her piercing, gray eyes a sparkle of recognition, a smile of connection. He long suspected there had been something going on between these two for the past year, since Simon became captain of the Guard. But Simon would never admit it. And it would make no sense for either of them, a royal princess or a lowly temple guard, captain though he was.

"Let's go, Gischala," said Simon. They followed the parade over to the regal canopy where Agrippa and Berenice were seated amidst their attendants in the roped-off and heavily guarded area. Joseph stood next to them and the other Herodians, his eyes suspiciously darting around.

The large, square space had a plush, red carpet over the stone. The portable throne remained the seating-place for king and princess. Four poles at each corner normally held a canopy over the entire retinue in case of rain. Tonight was so clear that a banner had replaced the canopy, enabling the sovereign to see the bright constellations overhead. The banner wrapped around the poles, displaying the royal colors and emblem of Herod.

Something didn't feel right to Simon. He looked around the crowd, full of standing patrons now, as they were about to prepare for a new round of prayer led by the high priest from the temple walls.

He had his men placed and ready for what they knew was about to happen. But what did they *not* know?

There were only two priests taking care of the holy place inside the temple as the rest of the priesthood engaged the congregation outside. Apollyon had entered the holy place, snapped the necks of the two priests, and made his way toward the holy of holies. He passed the large menorah candlestand, shaped as a symbol of the Tree of Life, and blew out the flames. "So much for the 'light of the world,'" he said with a gleeful grin into the dead air. "I prefer darkness."

He shoved over the golden table of showbread. It smashed to the floor, throwing the daily bread on the stone in profane uncleanness.

He stopped at the incense altar with its wisp of heavenly aroma drifting toward the ceiling. He regurgitated from his stomach and vomited onto the censer, turning the smoking sweet savor into an acidic putrid stench more fitting to his taste.

He smirked at the thought of his unholy vandalism. It was nothing compared to what was coming. He eyed the holy of holies and sauntered up to the veil swinging his hammer with a whistle.

Simon continued to scan the crowd of worshippers in the temple grounds. The most important strategy in uncovering conspiracy is to look for anything out of the ordinary. Anything, no matter how small, that might escape detection could be the very thing that might lead to pulling the veil off of hidden criminal intention.

The analogy echoed in his mind. *Pulling off the covered veil.*

The canopy.

Simon spun around to face the royal platform. Despite the fact that there was legitimate reason for its lack of presence tonight, the canopy's absence was out of the ordinary. A canopy shielded the king from above.

Simon looked up at the two levels of Solomon's portico above and behind the entourage. He had posted four Herodian guards among the pillars. None of them were there.

He turned to Gischala. "The portico. They're in the portico."

Gischala turned his gaze to the portico, searching.

Simon said, "I'll take the second floor."

Gischala responded, "I'll get the third."

They bolted off through the crowd toward the staircase of the portico.

Inside the temple, Apollyon stood before the large, purple temple veil covered with images of cherubim. He thought of the guardians of Eden, with their divine, whirling swords. He said, "Where are your protectors, now, Nazarene?"[5]

He opened the curtain and stepped inside.

"Well, it's about time, you got here, slug. We've been waiting for an eternity." Apollyon froze. The insult came from the mouth of Uriel, one of three archangels standing guard around the foundation stone, armed and ready. He was the smallest of the archangels, but the loudest of their mouths. His words could enflame the anger of any Watcher, and often did.

Beside Uriel were Gabriel and Michael, the prince of the host and guardian of Israel. The three of them looked like a mismatched gang of misfits to the Watcher. Small, blond and fair-skinned Uriel; sinewy, dark-skinned Gabriel; and the tall, muscular and handsome Michael.

Uriel added, "How stupid do you think we are, Apollio?" Another of the little angel's tactics: making fun of his enemies' names. "Or should I say, 'How stupid can *you* be?'"

Apollyon felt the flush of realization. The abandonment of the temple by the spirit of Yahweh, the curious absence of the angels until now. It had been too easy. He should have caught it. It wasn't cowardice on their part. It was a ruse. The oldest trick in the art of war. Withdrawal deceives the enemy to follow into an ambush.

These angels were going to imprison him with the Watchers.

"Not today, godlickers," said Apollyon.

He dodged through the curtain back into the holy place.

"Go," said Michael to the others, drawing his sword. "I'll guard the stone."

Uriel said to Gabriel, "If I take him down, you better not take the credit."

Gabriel retorted, "When have I ever taken credit for your lucky shots?"

Uriel winced. "*Lucky* shots? I have more skill in my little finger..."

"Enough," barked Michael. "He's getting away."

Gabriel and Uriel engaged in perpetual sibling rivalry that annoyed Michael no end. He often felt like a reluctant mediator for petty squabbles. The mature older brother. He shook his head and said a prayer. "I know you are teaching me patience, Lord."

In the human realm, the high priest, Yeshua ben Gamaliel, stepped out from the main gate of the temple, called the Beautiful Gate, and stood on the steps. Surrounded by priests and guards, he raised his hands to the air, and the crowd quieted down.

Simon broke out onto the second level of the portico from the stairs. Gischala kept running up to the third level.

Simon saw two dead guards lying on the ground. In the distance, an archer was looking down on the temple grounds. *Is there another one on the third floor above?*

At the temple gate, the high priest said with a loud voice, "Let us beseech Yahweh on behalf of our holy city, in memory of the Maccabees and their cleansing of the temple!"

A series of trumpets blew to announce the beginning of prayer.

At that moment, under the cover of loud music, a dozen Sicarii near the royal canopy made their move. They withdrew their assassin daggers and ran toward the king's throne from all corners.

Inside the holy place of the temple, Gabriel and Uriel split up looking for Apollyon. Their enemy's tactic was obvious. Watchers were stronger creatures than archangels. It might take two or three of them to subdue the god of this world. By splitting the angels up, Apollyon was weakening their offense.

But they had no other choice.

Gabriel held his sword tightly and checked the curtains on one side of the holy place. Uriel withdrew his double swords and used them to part the drapes on the other side. He was a master of two-handed sword play. His fighting skills and verbal bravado made up for whatever disadvantage his small size bestowed.

Uriel called out to Gabriel, "In the days of Jared, at the Tigris River in Shinar, when we saved Enoch from a horde of Nephilim."[6]

Gabriel scrunched his face with confusion as he pulled aside another curtain with nothing behind it. "I remember that incident. What about it?"

"I killed six Nephilim and you killed four. But you tried to take the credit for the last one." Uriel stabbed through a curtain. His blade hit stone.

Gabriel rolled his eyes. "You're trying to accuse me of taking credit from you almost three thousand years ago?"

"It's not that long ago for our kind."

Gabriel looked over at Uriel with incredulity. "You only killed that giant *after* I disarmed him."

"But I did kill him."

"We both did."

It was an argument that would most likely go on forever, unless they could get Yahweh to make a ruling.

Uriel teased, "And then you dropped your sword."

"I did not drop my sword. Several Nephilim hit me at the same time. You know that, Uriel. Stop provoking me."

"Okay, big brother. But you did try to take credit."

Their bickering had distracted them. Gabriel did not see the Watcher behind the large pillar. As the angel turned back to the curtains, he was blindsided by a war hammer that swung around with mighty force and knocked him clear across the room into unconsciousness.

Uriel shouted, "GABRIEL!"

Apollyon darted out the entrance of the temple.

Out on the temple grounds, the Sicarii approached Agrippa with their daggers. But a dozen of Simon's undercover guards were ready for them. They strong-armed, tripped, or blocked each one of the approaching assassins. They did so with restraint, trying not to draw too much attention in the busy crowd. The guards pretended to help the attackers who had fallen, but secretly slid their own daggers into their guts and throats.

The guards' collisions and counterattacks were all choreographed to look like accidents or mishaps to head off a public panic. The bodies were left on the ground as if praying prostrate.

Up in the portico, however, two assassins, on two different floors, armed with bows, nocked their death arrows, then aimed them at the royal targets.

On the third floor, Gischala had snuck up on the archer and was able to surprise him from behind. He slit the archer's throat and pulled the dead assassin behind the colonnade out of sight.

Inside the holy place, Uriel rushed over to Gabriel, lying broken before the holy veil. As divine beings, angels could not die. But as created beings with heavenly flesh, they could still feel pain and be harmed, especially by heavenly weapons. Angel flesh healed faster than human, but it would take some time before Gabriel's body, crushed by the war hammer, would regenerate.

"I'm so sorry, Gabriel. If it weren't for my loud mouth, you wouldn't have been distracted."

Gabriel came back to consciousness. He groaned in pain, "Take him out."

Uriel said, "For you, brother, anything," and bolted after the fleeing Watcher. These two were truly like brothers. They engaged in constant competition. But when it came to danger, they fought with perfect harmony and would sacrifice themselves for each other in a wing beat.

The temple trumpets released their second fanfare.

On the second floor of the portico, the archer had already drawn. Simon was too far away. He threw his dagger at the archer. It missed him. It hit the column that he was hiding behind. Chips of stone struck the archer and distracted his aim as he released.

The arrow went astray and hit one of the corner posts of the royal box. It had to be a miracle. Of all the thousands of people filling the outer court, the fact that a random arrow would hit a single post had to be a true miracle.

People close by saw the arrow hit, and looked up in shock. Joseph promptly broke the arrow off and hid it. Without evidence, a riot was diverted, the king and princess saved.

For the moment.

Up on the third floor, the archer took off. Simon raced after him like a panther on its prey.

Gischala swung down from the railing above onto the second floor. He landed with a roll and dashed off after Simon and his quarry.

The assassin was fast. He reached the end of the long colonnade and jumped down the stairs.

Simon barely kept up with him. He was worried he would lose him in the crowded masses.

Gischala caught up with Simon. They broke out into the crowd that now began to follow the high priest in prayer. Some kneeled, some laid prostrate, most stood in prayer.

Simon and Gischala automatically split apart and circled in on the fugitive assassin as he darted and dodged his way to the southern gates of the temple complex.

Simon reached the gates and broke out onto the open porch outside the temple. Gischala joined him. They saw the runner escape down the closest alley. Simon said, "Take a horse," and he sprang after the assassin on foot.

Uriel raced out onto the temple porch in search of Apollyon. He stopped at the top of the stairs when he saw the Watcher waiting for him in the courtyard, war hammer held firmly in his two hands by its long handle. The few human priests performing their duties in the courtyard could not see or hear the heavenly beings, because they were not allowed to.

Uriel walked with deliberation down the steps to meet his enemy next to the large altar of sacrifice. He said, "You're going to pay for pounding my friend."

Apollyon was unphased by the threat. He said sarcastically, "Are you two bickering lovers?" He turned a diabolical grin. "You really should consider it, Uriel. Forbidden fruit provides the most intense taste."

Uriel made it to the foot of the stairs. He was mere yards away from his opponent. He twirled his swords in preparation for battle. "I think the Romans are far too flattering with their depictions of you." He was referring to the sculpted, handsome masculinity of the Roman myth that did not match the form Apollyon had chosen to take: that of an eight-foot tall scrawny androgynous creature.

Uriel added, "Are you supposed to be a man or a woman?"

"Whatever I choose to be, angel. I am chaos."

"Well, either way, you're an ugly freak."

"You of all persons should know," replied Apollyon. "Looks can be deceiving. And distracting."

The Watcher swung his mighty hammer.

Simon sprinted into the dark alley after the fleeing assassin. He rounded a corner and caught sight of his target climbing a wall. An earthquake occurred that almost made the assassin fall. Simon ignored the rumbling and made his way to the wall.

When he got on top of it, he recognized the neighborhood. He knew the actual course of the alleys that the assassin was taking. He knew it circled around to the right.

So he climbed onto the roof of the house he was at and ran across a series of rooftops on his way to where the alley would lead.

When he reached his destination, he saw the assassin just below him. He jumped to a lower level roof and then to another. His last jump brought him to the ground, mere yards behind the assassin.

But the fugitive was fast. Simon wasn't sure he could actually catch him. He was already exhausted.

But as they turned a corner, the assassin stopped in his tracks.

Gischala sat on his horse just ahead, smiling, sword drawn.

The assassin turned back toward Simon, who now approached him, trying to catch his breath with great effort. The killer considered his odds were much better with his exhausted chaser. He drew a knife and a sword on Simon.

Simon said through gasping breaths, "I have to ask. Please tell me you are a race runner. Because you are the fastest scoundrel I've ever chased."

The assassin said nothing. He simply attacked.

Simon drew his sword and met him with equal ferocity.

Even so winded, Simon was a formidable warrior.

The assassin was a better archer and runner than a swordsman.

Simon spun his wrist, then wedged his blade into the angle of his adversary's sword. He launched it out of the assassin's hands into the clearing yards away—the move Gischala had taught him after their sparring.

Simon looked to Gischala and said proudly, "It worked!"

Gischala said, "Am I not an excellent teacher?"

The assassin swiped at Simon with his dagger. He dodged with ease, grabbed the knife arm and shoved the killer up against the wall. He smashed the killer's hand against the mud brick. The dagger dropped.

Simon head-butted the assassin, who stood dizzied and weak-kneed under his grasp.

Simon leaned in and whispered with anger, "Where is the Egyptian?"

The assassin remained mute.

Gischala stepped up and placed his sword at the assassin's Achilles tendon at the back of his foot. He said, "I won't kill you. I'll cripple you for life, so you can crawl on your belly, begging for alms."

Simon smirked. He could see in the assassin's face that it would be mere moments before they had the information they sought.

In the holy of holies, Michael had felt the earthquake caused by Apollyon's war hammer outside. He had felt it once more, and prayed for his fellow prince, Uriel. His preternatural hearing discerned the sound of Uriel's double blades striking out at his opponent in the courtyard. But when he heard the sound of the blades cease, he knew the battle was over. But he couldn't tell who was the winner. Until he heard the victory cry of the Watcher bellowing into the sky. And all his hopes were dashed.

Apollyon was coming. Michael could not let the Watcher release the ancient ones.

Though the prince of Israel was the mightiest of the archangels, and was close to Apollyon's equal, it would still be a difficult task to capture him. The Watcher had become powerful as the god of this world. Michael needed an edge of advantage. He chose the element of surprise.

Apollyon burst through the temple entrance and marched his way back into the inner temple. He trained his sights on the holy of holies, where Michael stood behind the veil protecting the foundation stone.

But Michael was not behind the veil as the Watcher expected. He was hiding outside the holy of holies—where he could ambush the Watcher from behind. He stepped out from the darkness and swung his sword with all his strength to cut off Apollyon's head.

But the Watcher heard the swoosh of the arc and ducked.

The blade clipped off some of Apollyon's stringy hair, but not his head.

And he simultaneously swung his war hammer around at his attacker.

Michael backed up. The weapon missed him by an inch. It would have pulverized his skull.

But now the Watcher was off balance. Michael thrust his sword and connected with his enemy's chest. The blade went in deep. Apollyon cried out in pain. He couldn't swing the hammer, but he could use it to ram Michael in the face.

The archangel flew backward and hit a pillar with pounding force. The ceiling above shuddered.

Michael blacked out for just a moment. When he came to, the pain resounded through his whole head and back. His nose and facial structure was broken. Blood poured from his nose. Through blurry, bloody vision, he saw the Watcher making his way toward the veil, sword still embedded within his chest.

Gabriel, lying incapacitated before the veil weakly grabbed Apollyon's leg. The Watcher kicked him into unconsciousness and kept going.

Michael had to keep fighting. Everything was at stake. He stumbled over to the sacred curtain, wiping the blood from his face, and pushed his way into the holy of holies.

He arrived just in time to see Apollyon swing the hammer down upon the foundation stone, breaking it in half and dislodging the Seal of Solomon from the rock. Another earthquake rumbled the foundation, followed by a gush of putrid air from the opening. It was like sucking the breath of the Abyss into the lungs of the temple—the breath of desolation.

Apollyon now withdrew the sword from his chest with a growl of agony and threw it at Michael. The angel dodged the flying blade, but lost his footing because of his dizzying concussion.

Apollyon picked up the signet ring and placed it on his finger.

Michael could not allow him to escape into the Abyss. He lunged for the Watcher. But he was too late. He landed at the opening to see Apollyon descending, disappearing into the darkness below. The cackling laughter of the Watcher was engulfed in the dead silence of the deep.

He would find his way to Tartarus, use the signet ring of the Son of David—the key to the Abyss—to free the ancient ones.

Michael staggered out of the holy of holies and found the unconscious form of Gabriel on the ground. He almost passed out from the pain in his body. He steadied himself, knelt down, and reached into his comrade's cloak. He pulled out a small, simple, but secret weapon: Gabriel's trumpet.

When Apollyon returned with his army of escaped principalities and powers, Michael would be healed and ready to meet them—with an army of ten thousand times ten thousand of Yahweh's heavenly host, the Sons of God.

He put the trumpet to his lips and blew with every breath left in him.

Though the populace of Jerusalem did not hear the angelic trumpet, some of them were allowed a glimpse of what happened next in the heavenly realm. The night clouds above parted and the display of an angelic army was seen, riding horses and flashing chariots in fully-armed formation. Yahweh's heavenly host had answered the call.[7]

CHAPTER 29

Several miles from Jerusalem, in a secluded mountain hideaway, a gathering of four hundred armed Sicarii and Zealots listened to a tall charismatic orator with a booming voice speaking from atop a large altar-like stone. His hair was dark, long and wild. His eyes, hypnotic; his skin, olive, otherworldly. He carried himself with a kind of theatrical emotion that incited the rebels. He was larger than life.

He was the Egyptian.

He spoke with a conviction that seemed to penetrate the souls of his hearers. "Sixty years ago, the Romans instituted a census of our land. This blasphemous act was nothing but a pretense for slavery, for only God alone can number his people for ownership. Judas the Galilean and the Pharisee Zaddok were the only ones with the zeal for righteousness to stand up to this tyranny and revolt for the nation's liberty. And then after them, Judas' sons, James and John. There was Theudas, Amram, Eleazar ben Dinai and others.[1]

"They believed God alone was to be their ruler and lord. 'No king but God,' was their war cry, 'no god but God!'[2] They preferred death to slavery, and were willing to die for their wives, their children, their country, their God! They looked forward to this day. They sought the Messiah and eagerly desired the deliverance of Israel from the hands of our evil oppressors! They longed for the Day of the Lord, that day of vengeance, when Yahweh would return to Zion and bring in everlasting righteousness, to heal the sick and set the captives free! Well, I tell you, that day has arrived."[3]

He paused dramatically to let the implications sink into his listeners. The silence carried an eerie stillness. Everyone held their breaths together, as if by command from this mesmerizing leader.

He continued, "If we Galileans, we Zealots, we Sicarii can only put aside our differences…and join together under *my* leadership, I will lead us to the hoped-for victory! I will crush the Romans!"

The men cheered.

"I will enter triumphantly into the holy city of Jerusalem, and I will take possession of the temple away from the corrupted hands of the Herodian priesthood!"

More cheers.

The Herodians were well known to be puppets of Rome, without loyalty to Israel. The Egyptian's messianic self-implications were clear. He didn't need to say it. It was more powerful to imply.

"So I echo the words of those who have gone before us: 'No king but God! No king but God!'"

The men chanted, "No king but God! No king but God!"

The Egyptian strutted around like a cock in the moonlight, enflamed with religious hatred for Rome.

But then he froze and his countenance dropped into a stare. The crowd turned around to see what the Egyptian was staring at behind them.

Three warriors on horses dressed in Herodian armor stood on the small ridge overlooking the gathering. They were Simon, Gischala and Joseph peering down upon the Zealots like wraiths of doom.

Simon called out, "Hear me now, Zealots! I am Simon bar Giora, captain of the Temple Guard! You are all under arrest for conspiracy and sedition against Rome!"

The Egyptian crowed with a boisterous confidence, "And just who exactly is going to bring us into custody?"

A few laughs rang through the crowd.

Suddenly, eight hundred Herodian guards and Roman legionaries appeared all around the gathering from out of the dark night. They looked down from their superior position upon the vulnerable gathering.

The mocking stopped.

Simon was relieved by what happened next. To a man, the so-called Zealots laid down their arms in immediate surrender. The Egyptian stood speechless at the lack of defense.

Simon and Gischala smiled at each other. These converts to the cause proved to be less zealous than their pretentious leader had believed. Their devotion to their cause was superceded by their instinct for survival in the face of certain slaughter. Simon's tactic had worked. They had quenched burning coals before they had the opportunity to break out into a fire.

Their success illustrated the truth to Simon that it takes more than political discontent, emotional zeal and a charismatic leader to create an effective result. It takes true believers—and real strategy.

· · · · ·

Simon led Gischala down the wet, mossy stairwell into the prison deep below the Sanhedrin Hall of Hewn Stone. The Herods had been saved, a riot diverted, and a coup crushed. And all of it beneath the unknowing gaze of the masses. Simon was proud of the strategic expertise of his temple guards, and of his lieutenant Gischala at his side. Now, they were on their way to interrogate the Egyptian. Because of their large numbers, half of the captured Zealots had been imprisoned in the Antonia and the other half, almost two hundred of them, had been locked up here.[4] Their voices echoed in the dank atmosphere, so they kept their volume low.

Gischala said, "Princess Berenice certainly looked ravishing tonight in the temple."

Simon didn't respond.

Gischala watched him closely, then added, "I was thinking of ravishing her myself."

Simon stopped and held the torch menacingly, glaring at Gischala.

The lieutenant was undeterred. He said sarcastically, "Have I trod into territory of some personal interest to you, my captain?"

Simon smirked, turned, and continued down deeper into the earth.

"Simon, I have been your colleague and ally for years. You withhold nothing from me, save this one area."

"Apparently," said Simon, "a wise decision on my part."

"Well then, you are not very effective, my friend. I can read you like a scroll. And I say you have a passionate affection for the princess."

Simon shook his head with a chuckle. "Those are not my scrolls you are reading. Perhaps you should be more concerned with reading the Zealots and their relentless need to find the Messiah."

"You mean create one," said Gischala. The two of them had often debated the issue of Messiah and the longed for deliverance of Israel from her spiritual exile.[5] Simon believed the prophets, Gischala questioned them. Promises of a messianic age seemed too obscure and malleable in the hands of self-proclaimed deliverers.

Simon repeated the same arguments he had made many times before: "The existence of so many false messiahs only serves to illustrate that there is a real one to come."

"It illustrates the *hope* for a real Messiah," said Gischala. "And I certainly do not disapprove of the hope for what life would be like without the imperial beast of Rome and her harlot, the priesthood. But hope is not the same as reality."

A tortured scream echoed through the tunnel and stopped them at the foot of the stairs. It was blood curdling. A male voice, though it sounded as if all masculinity had been stripped from it.

Simon and Gischala looked at each other for a response.

A rat scurried in front of them and entered the dungeon hall, lit by torches like a tunnel into Hades. They saw legionaries lining the walls all the way to the cluster of cells where the hundreds were kept.

But their destination was in cell block one.

Another scream sent chills down Simon's spine. He bristled with anger and marched quickly past the long row of legionary guards.

Finally he reached the cell and ignored the guard saluting him. He stormed inside.

The Egyptian was chained up against the stone wall, spread-eagle, his body covered in smoking blackened burns. He wept from the pain.

The torturer stood back with surprise at Simon's entrance. He was a grungy disgusting beast holding a sizzling red-hot poker.

Simon glanced to his left and saw Joseph ben Matthias standing off to the side. "Who ordered this?" he demanded.

Joseph said, "Not I."

Simon looked back at the torturer. He stepped closer, glaring into the little wretch's eyes. The poker dropped to the ground with a clang. Simon grabbed the creature's throat and led him to the entrance of the cell. He threw him choking out into the hallway.

At just that moment, Agrippa arrived at the door with armed bodyguards, and said to Simon, "I am afraid it was I who ordered this." He walked pompously inside, nodding to Joseph, then Simon and Gischala. He wore a more casual robe and tunic, without his jewelry.

Simon bowed. "My lord, is it really necessary?"

Agrippa said, "Well, let us see." He walked up to the Egyptian. "So, you think you are Messiah?"

The Egyptian glared defiantly at Agrippa.

Agrippa shook his head. "Don't they all." He looked intensely into the Egyptian's eyes and shook his head with contempt. "Fanatics."

The Egyptian spoke up. "You call us fanatics. Because we are zealous for our cause."

Agrippa asked, "What kind of cause is worth following that promises nothing but certain defeat?"

"The purity of the holy temple."

"Purity? The temple stands firm. Caesar allows us freedom to worship God as we choose."

"Herods are Caesar's whores."

Agrippa exploded with a backhanded slap to the Egyptian's face. "You are all the same," said the king. "Causes without compromise. Dreams without reality. Words without power."

The sound of troops marching down the hall made everyone turn.

Gessius Florus entered the room with a centurion and several bodyguards. Everyone bowed submissively as he strode around the room, his chin held high.

Agrippa said, "Procurator, the Egyptian is at your disposal."

Simon looked with surprise at Agrippa. "But my lord, I thought this was our jurisdiction."

Florus stepped up into Simon's face. He whispered venomously, "Jurisdiction? Tell me something, Captain, what kind of jurisdiction does a pack of filthy sand rats exercise in an empire ruled by gods? If I had my way,

I'd burn this infectious slum of a city to the ground. Be glad Nero Caesar is more gracious than I."

Florus brushed past Simon and walked up to the Egyptian. Without a moment's thought, Florus drew a dagger and slit the Egyptian's throat.

The Zealot gasped and choked on his blood.

Simon and Gischala looked at each other with shock.

Joseph did not seem surprised.

Florus asked Herod, "Where are the other prisoners?"

"Further down the hall."

"Procurator," interrupted Simon, "my lieutenant and I were there. We arrested the followers. They surrendered immediately without a fight."

Florus said, "Are you saying they are not guilty?"

"They are guilty of rash emotions, but I can assure you, these are not serious revolutionaries. They gave up without a fight. If you crucify them, it may instigate another riot."

Florus responded, "That is why I do not intend to crucify them." He turned to his centurion. "Put them to the sword immediately."

The centurion left the cell.

Simon yelled, "NO!"

Three legionaries grabbed him from behind and held him.

He struggled to get free.

Gischala was held by two others.

Simon yelled again, "Procurator, do not do this! I beg of you!"

They all heard a command down the hall, followed by the sound of swords hacking prisoners to death with iron and steel.

Screams of pain and cries for mercy made Simon's knees weak. The soldiers held him up against the wall. Florus stood before Simon and wiped his bloody dagger on the captain's cloak. Simon asked, "What have you done with the other prisoners in the Antonia?"

Florus said nonchalantly, "I killed them before I came here."

Simon tried to struggle out of the soldier's grip, but they held firm. He wanted to kill the procurator. And he would have if he had the chance. He didn't care what happened to him now. This was barbarism.

Simon looked to Joseph for support. He was silent.

He then looked to Gischala, who was unwilling to fight back. They were outnumbered. It would mean sure death.

The last sounds of the dying drifted into the cell.

Simon stared defiantly at Florus.

Florus then said to him, "And now to this matter of your involvement in the revolt…"

"What are you talking about?" Simon asked.

"Do not equivocate with me, traitor." Florus pulled out his dagger again and pointed it at Simon's left eye.

Simon was filled with confusion. How could he possibly be considered a part of the revolt?

Florus flicked the knife on Simon's cheek and drew blood.

The procurator said, "It seems your undercover operations have corrupted you, Captain Giora. Your opposition against one faction of rebels merely serves to disguise your sympathies for another. Remember the Sicarii? The Galileans?"

"That is a lie!" yelled Simon. The accusations sounded to him like a bizarre nightmare.

Florus said, "Eliminate rivals, consolidate power. Quite a strategy."

Simon turned to Agrippa. "Sire? Tell him, this is madness."

But Agrippa watched Simon with an accusing silence.

Simon's head swirled. *How can this be happening? Who manufactured these lies?* He looked to Gischala. The guards had drawn their blades and placed them at Gischala's chest.

Florus turned to Gischala. "You know him well. Does he tell you everything?" Gischala hesitated. "Does he tell you his secrets? Whom he hates, whom he loves?"

Then Gischala glanced reluctantly at Simon. "No, sire."

"So much for loyal Herodians," said Florus.

Agrippa said with a heavy heart, "Simon, I trusted you. You betrayed the royal family. And the holy temple."

"I am innocent!"

"You are a traitor!" barked Florus. "And a conspirator against Rome. Tomorrow, you will be executed." He turned to the guards. "Strip him down and lock him up."

Two guards obeyed their order. With his hands and ankles chained, wearing only his undergarment, Simon was led down the hallway to the holding cell by the guards.

When they arrived, all three of them were appalled at the sight. Hundreds of dead Jews in several large cells lay in heaps of bloody carnage. Some were pierced through, others, hacked of life and limb. An unimaginable slaughter. Simon could barely look at the pile of corpses.

One of the guards turned and vomited.

Simon looked down at his bare feet, where blood pooled into a drain.

The other guard opened the door.

Simon crumbled as if weakened in defeat.

The lead guard, a rather muscular one, tried to be respectful. "I'm sorry, Captain, but it's an order."

Simon mumbled words of regret.

The guard leaned down closer. "What did you say?"

Simon burst up with both chained fists into the guard's jaw, cracking it and sending him to the floor unconscious.

The other guard drew his sword.

But Simon wrapped his arm chains around the blade and yanked it out of the guard's hands. He used it as a bludgeon to knock the guard out onto the floor.

Then he reached down to get the keys.

CHAPTER 30

Herod's palace was an opulent marble paradise of Hellenist architecture nested within the southern portion of Herod's more functional military fortress on the far western edge of Jerusalem.

King Agrippa and his household resided behind these protective walls of stone. Princess Berenice's royal bath chamber reflected the design of a typical Roman bath, with a colonnade of pillars surrounding the large central steaming spring.

That steam now enveloped the room as Berenice completed sponging her velvety, soft skin. She was proud of how she had painstakingly kept the look of her youth as she had grown older. Women her age were considered far past the age of fertility and even desirability among many men. But not her. In some ways, men desired her more because she offered a maturity to complement her beauty that made her a challenge to conquer. But she made sure that every yielding on her part resulted in an exchange of something to her benefit. She knew that in this world, she had to use what she had, and she was not going to squander her God-given gifts.[1]

Thus, her three previous marriages, gratefully now behind her, had helped to advance her and her brother's influence. Her first marriage was to the brother of the Roman governor of Judea under the emperor Claudius. Her second was to her uncle, from which her brother Agrippa had received his present kingdom. Her third could be considered contrived theater to distract the public from the vicious rumors of an incestuous relationship with her brother.[2]

She no longer cared what the public thought they knew about her. She lived above their petty moral conventions anyway.

She considered marriage a necessary public evil to accomplish her political ambitions. What she privately treasured was the abandon of forbidden romantic passion. To have what was not hers to have.

She rose from the bath and her maidservant wrapped a muslin robe around her. She let down her hair and walked over to a bench to sit down.

"Leave me," she told her maidservant.

Berenice heard the soft footsteps of the woman exit the room. A tear of regret ran down her cheek.

She was too absorbed in her sadness to hear the stealth figure approach her from the mist.

She sensed his presence too late. A hand went firmly over her mouth, stifling her attempt to scream. She tried to wriggle free, but her assailant's hands and arms were strong.

And familiar.

She relaxed.

He released her.

"Simon."

In a breath, they came together, kissing passionately, hungrily. She had been having a secret affair with Simon even before he had been made captain of the Temple Guard. They had met in one of the infamous Herodian parties for which she and her brother had become known. At first, her interest in him was shallow. She was drawn to the raw brutish strength of a warrior. Their difference of station required secrecy. But as time progressed, it became harder for her to choose another lover. Simon's strength was so much more than mere physical masculinity. He was a true leader of men. She feared that she had made the mistake of falling in love.

But here she was. Here they were.

She pulled away. "I overheard my brother preparing the guards to arrest you. I could not get word to you in time."

"You should not have tried such a foolish thing."

"How did you escape?"

"With God's help. But they're not far behind."

She led him out of the bath and into her private chambers that opened onto a large patio veranda. The moon lit a beautiful view of the city below.

Berenice asked, "Where will you go?"

"Where can I go? There is nowhere to hide."

"My brother has spies everywhere." She looked at his belt. "Give me your dagger."

He eyed her questioningly.

"Give me your dagger," she repeated impatiently.

He handed it to her.

She grabbed a part of her hair at the end, and cut off a small tuft. She handed him back the dagger, reached on her table of jewelry and accouterments, then picked up a small leather strap. She wrapped it around the tuft, creating a kind of locket of her hair. She handed it to him.

He held it with fondness.

She looked up at him and reached her hand to touch the cut on his cheek. It was crusted with dried blood.

He stopped her. Grabbed her wrist firmly. His softness turned hard. "Why would Agrippa do this? Does he know about us?"

"I don't know."

The maidservant's voice interrupted them from the misty steam around them. "Princess Berenice?"

Simon slipped silently out of sight behind a pillar.

The maidservant approached Berenice.

The princess said angrily, "I told you to leave me alone."

"Forgive me, your grace. Your brother is looking for you."

"Well, don't tell him you found me."

The maidservant nodded obediently and whisked away.

Simon stepped out from behind the pillar.

Berenice said, "My brother exercises the power of a tyrant with the temper of a slave. But he would lose too much by such duplicity in accusing you after you deterred an assassination attempt."[3] Simon's secret protection that night did not stay secret for long.

Simon looked away. "Duplicity is the heart of Herodian breeding."

"Do you think my brother's lies affect my love for you?"

"Berenice, you have been a Herod. You will be a Herod." He paused grimly. "I am expendable."

"How dare you suggest that I could ever betray you. I would as soon betray myself."

They heard the sound of guards arriving at her doors. Berenice pulled her robe around her. The sound of a hurried knock on the door made her jump. She turned back to Simon. He was gone.

"You may enter," she said toward the door.

The doors burst open to Gischala and a guard of six others, who stayed by the entrance.

"Lieutenant Gischala. You storm my residence without permission."

Gischala looked around the room, expecting to find something—anything. Or someone. "Your highness, your brother told me to find you. He has appointed me the new captain of the Temple Guard." He bowed to her.

She turned cold as ice. "What does he want?"

"Simon bar Giora has escaped."

"Of what concern is that to me?"

He approached her, slowly, cautiously, not wanting to frighten her. "It is our belief that Simon may have had some…interest in you."

"What kind of interest?" Her surprise appeared genuine. She was a masterful actress. She had been all her life.

Gischala walked past her out onto the veranda. He looked to see if there was anyone climbing down the walls. "Whatever he may have appeared to be to you, he is a fanatic who was secretly involved in revolutionary activity against the Herods."

Her eyes went wide with shock.

He continued, "Revenge against Agrippa will be his primary instinct. As his sister, you are a potential target. And believe me, your highness, a fanatic will do anything to accomplish his directive. Even betray those closest to him."

Simon hid behind a pillar, not far from the both of them. He had his blade held ready.

Gischala said, "It broke my heart to testify to your brother of Simon's secret alliance with the Zealots."

Simon almost made a sound upon hearing the egregious lie. It was Gischala who had betrayed him. It was Gischala who had sought to murder him in prison. Simon had trusted this man with his life. They had served together, worked together. But it was all a lie. A lie that unraveled Simon's soul. How could he have failed to see it all these years? How could he have been so fooled? It was all Simon could do to keep himself from stepping out and confronting his betrayer.

Gischala sighed. Then he said, "Oh, how our loyalty and devotion can blind us to the truth."

Berenice was stone cold. She baited him. "How fortunate for the city that such a capable lieutenant was ready to step into the role he left vacant."

Gischala kept glancing around the room. "Are you alone, Princess?"

Berenice stiffened. Did he know? Could he feel it?

He walked up to her, his eyes looking over her with hunger. The soldier turned seductive. "This is a dangerous time. Such a worthy and beautiful noble like you is a precious national treasure. You should not be…left alone. I would be honored to be your personal bodyguard."

She stared him right back in the eye, unmoved. "Your flattery is hardly persuasive, Captain. I will be all right…left alone."

He kept staring at her, trying to draw her out. He could not. "Well, then. Until you change your mind, princess." He then bowed, left the room with his soldiers in tow and closed the door.

She heard them march away down the hall. She sighed as if she had held her breath the entire time.

Simon slipped out from behind the pillar.

He approached her to hold her one last time. But he stopped short.

The doors kicked open to Gischala with sword in hand.

Simon drew his weapon. He marched toward his traitor and unleashed a furious series of blows that pushed Gischala backward.

Gischala met each attack with well-placed defense.

Simon hissed, "I trusted you."

"You shouldn't have."

But instead of renewing his attack, Simon surprised his nemesis; he ran. He pushed through the doors and bolted down the hall.

Gischala yelled out, "Guards!"

Berenice could hear the sound of guards chasing after the fugitive.

Gischala brought her back to the moment. "Fear not, Princess. No one need ever know of your illicit liaison with that coward." He stepped closer, making her tremble with fear. "We both know how violently jealous your brother can be."

He smirked at her.

Oh, how she loathed this creature with everything in her.

He ran off after Simon, leaving Berenice to break down in weeping. Like she had never wept before.

Gischala ran through the royal hallways. He saw guards running around like idiots, trying to find the fugitive. He had evaded them.

Gischala slid to a stop by an open door. He looked into the room, empty, unused. Nothing to hide behind. But there was an open balcony.

He ran to it and looked over, just in time to see Simon climbing down the sixty-foot wall into the courtyard, where a herd of horses were tied up.

Gischala turned and ran back into the hallway, yelling, "He's in the courtyard, you fools! He's at the horses!"

He raced for the stairs.

Down in the courtyard, Simon unleashed as many horses as he could and scattered them before jumping up onto his steed.

He was already well on his way into the streets by the time Gischala and his men arrived and were able to give chase.

Simon took alleyways, hoping to avoid too many people, and hoping to lose his pursuers. He knew these back streets like his own hand.

But so did Gischala.

Gischala burst out of the palace gate and saw Simon take a turn far down the street. He spread his men out to try to box his fugitive in, surround him.

Simon dodged behind a wall as two guards rode past him, shouting, "Clear!" to their captain. He launched out in the opposite direction.

But when he broke out from hiding, he was by the theater, and there were many patrons filling the streets.

A guard shouted, "There he is!"

Simon's route was blocked by citizens. He didn't want to hurt any innocents, so he did the only thing he could do: charge the two guards coming his way. He kicked his horse and yelled.

The guards saw him coming at them like a banshee from the Gates of Hades. At the last second, they pulled their horses out of the way. Simon barreled right through where they had been.

Gischala then saw Simon charging for a gate. But it wasn't to the southern Essene Gate, the obvious choice. That was the closest exit out of the city. Instead, he was making for the northern district of the New City. That gate was twice the distance from here. But unlike the constricted valley outside the Essene Gate, the New City Gate opened up into a vast wilderness with infinite possibilities to hide.

Simon made his way to the northern New City gates. It was a quarter mile ahead, and Gischala was close on his tail. It was a straight shot through less inhabited areas than the lower city. Simon knew that Gischala had only one chance to catch him.

Gischala began yelling, "Shut the gates! Shut the gates!"

The sentries rushed to the gate mechanism and turned it. The huge doors began to crank shut. They were armored to withstand battle, so if Simon didn't make it in time, he would be trapped inside, or worse, crushed to death.

Simon heard Gischala yelling, "Archers! Archers, fire!"
Simon was moments away.
The archers started launching their missiles at him. The closer he got, the easier the shot. But a moving target was not so easy.
The gates were almost shut. Arrows whizzed by Simon. He kicked his steed harder and the horse seemed to jump right through the small opening of the gate—just before the doors slammed shut with a bang, leaving Gischala and his men on the other side.

Gischala shouted, "Open the gates! Open the gates, you fools!"

But he knew it was too late. By the time those gates were open, Simon bar Giora would be gone, like a phantom in the night.

Gischala cursed his nemesis. To be so close to capturing Simon only to have him elude his grasp was intolerable. He had planned this coup for a year. Ever since Simon had been promoted to Captain of the Guard over Gischala, he had lost his respect for his compatriot in arms. Simon wasn't nearly as devout in his religion as Gischala was. In fact, the self-righteous captain was more concerned about politics and taxes than about the holiness of the temple. The reason he was chosen over Gischala's superior religiosity was purely profane and political. Berenice had begun an affair with him a year ago when he was a rising star. Simon had tried to hide it from Gischala, but he had suspected it all along. And recent events proved he was right. That despicable vixen got her lover promoted. Simon wasn't the only one upon whom Gischala was planning vengeance. But right now, Simon was the focus of his rage.

He spoke to the air as if that coward could hear him. "When I find you, Simon bar Giora, I will kill you. For the glory of God."

PART THREE

Apocalypse

CHAPTER 31

Rome
May, AD 65

It had been six months since Nero's first wave of persecution against the Christians in Rome. That massacre had been effective in eliminating two of the key apostles and hundreds of the most influential of the fanatics. Over the next few months, the Christians withdrew their public presence. Some of them left the city to take their chances elsewhere. Some went underground. But that did not stop the emperor from his police actions against the illicit religion that threatened the state.

Alexander had heard that in cities all across the empire, Christians who refused the imperial cult of Caesar were economically boycotted and stripped of public standing. In some cases, they were arrested and shipped to Rome to await their fate in Nero's diabolical theater of the arena. In Rome, Severus engaged in occasional night raids on secret Christian gatherings in search of key leaders. The emperor had ordered the prefect to step up his search-and-capture efforts. Neronia, the special games that occurred every five years, was upon them, and Nero was planning something big.

Severus was right, thought Alexander. While they had watched the first punishment of the Christians in the arena, the prefect had told him, "It gets easier the more you see." What initially offended Alexander's sensibilities became less outrageous over time, a kind of numbness. And the more he participated in helping Severus find insurrectionists, the more he felt that his protection of his people the Jews was justified. In his opinion, for every Christian they arrested, another Jew was saved. Still, it angered him to be forced into making such a terrible moral choice.

Months earlier, when Severus had arrested Cassandra Laetorius during the Christian purge, he made her his household slave instead of condemning her to the arena. Alexander was surprised to find that the prefect did not use her to satisfy his carnal appetite. It was most unlike Severus. He had saved her from the circus executions and sought to use her for information on the Christians, much as he had used Alexander for information on the Jews. As master, he had every right to her body, but for some reason unknown to Alexander, he refrained from it. And when Cassandra refused to divulge information regarding the Christians, Severus eventually pulled back from interrogating her. Instead of beating her, he stopped questioning her. No doubt she would have been willing to die without giving up her secrets, but this young woman was a storehouse of inside knowledge because of her relationship with the now-dead apostles. For Severus to fail in coercing her could only mean that there was a secret between them. Did she have some kind of power over the prefect? Was she a sorceress? If it was that bad, he could just kill her and make it go away.

The obvious possibility was that she was being used as a concubine for Severus' son, Thelonius. He had noticed a tenderness in the young man toward her, but it was respectful, not sexual. He did not display intimacy in his interactions with her. And it would not need to be a secret anyway. If Thelonius were using Cassandra for his gratification, he would most likely have boasted about it. Alexander knew that father and son had not been converted to Cassandra's faith, because of their ongoing activities. So why were they so deferential to her?

He didn't have time to keep thinking about such things. He was on a mission for Severus right now, secretly following a small group of Christians as they crossed the bridge from the Trans-Tiber into Region X. An informant had told Severus of a secret meeting of seditious activity by these Christians. They scurried down Long Street past the newly rebuilt Circus Maximus and turned right onto the Ostian Way that led out of the city.

Clever, thought Alexander. *They are meeting outside the city limits. It is too easy for gatherings to be noticed within Rome. They are probably meeting in some camp.* Since the persecution began, Christians had stopped meeting with the Jews in the synagogue. They were becoming more separate in their identity, which Alexander thought was a good thing. That would keep other Jews from being drawn into their net.

They passed the Ostian Gates. The road traffic at this hour and this distance from town was nothing.

The several cloaked Christians stopped on the road and looked around as if to see if they were being followed.

Alexander ducked behind a bush and watched them run off the road. When he caught up with them, he saw that they were far more inventive than he had thought. They were meeting where no one would have expected them to be: the catacombs, a network of underground tombs connected with tunnels just outside the city limits. *Not clever*, thought Alexander. *Brilliant*.

There were catacombs beside every major road that led out of the city. Family mourners would bring the bodies of their deceased loved ones down into resting places carved out of the rocklike stone beds. After a year or so, when the flesh had fully decayed from the bones, family members would return to the tomb, to lay the bones in an ossuary, or small stone burial box, upon one of the shelves of their family crypt. Because of the never-ending supply of the dead, the catacombs kept expanding over time. Mourners could get lost down there if they were not careful to note their routes.[1]

There was more than a little irony here, thought Alexander. *Meeting in a tomb of death to celebrate their belief in a resurrected Messiah.*[2] He turned back to town to report the location to Severus, who was waiting on the Palatine with a squad of fifty Praetorian guards ready to make arrests.

Alexander, Severus and his squad arrived at the catacomb entrance within the half hour, armed for action. They dismounted their horses and prepared to enter the tombs.

"Have they no respect for the dead?" whispered Severus.

Alexander whispered back, "Desperate times, desperate tactics."[3]

"I suppose you are right. They *have* eluded us successfully with this ploy—until now." Severus drew his sword and gestured to his soldiers to follow him quietly.

They entered the dark rock tunnel into the earth. Torches were posted for the Christians to find their way, and for the Praetorians to track them down as easy prey.

It gets easier the more you see. He had become numb to their suffering. Their persecution no longer repulsed him. And here he was hunting Christians with almost as much fervor as Severus. Was he that toad in the boiling pot? He pushed the thought out of his head.

As they went deeper within, Alexander mused over another irony. He smelled the stench of decaying bodies in the tombs they passed at the same time as he heard the faint sound of joyful singing deep within.

They sang a lot, these Christians. Cheerful in the face of their tribulation. It struck him as if they were mocking death to its face. The words of the prophet Hosea came to his mind. "O Death, where is your victory? O Death, where is your sting?" They really believed their revolutionary claims with all their heart.

The singing got louder. They were closer. Alexander could hear the words now. It was a psalm of David. A messianic psalm. He knew it well.

> The LORD says to my Lord:
>> "Sit at my right hand,
> until I make your enemies your footstool."
> The LORD sends forth from Zion
>> your mighty scepter.
>> Rule in the midst of your enemies.
> The Lord is at your right hand;
>> he will shatter kings on the day of his wrath.
> He will execute judgment among the nations,
>> filling them with corpses;
> he will shatter chiefs over the wide earth.
> He will drink from the brook by the way;
>> therefore he will lift up his head.[4]

He wagged his head with sadness. These poor souls just didn't know how to compromise. They didn't know how to keep alive like Alexander did, and all his fellow Jews, who learned how to manipulate Roman law to their benefit and protection.

Why couldn't they declare allegiance to Caesar with their lips, while holding their true convictions in their hearts? Even if they had just pulled back on their message about the dead Nazarene and stopped criticizing the temple and the sacrifice, they could have averted the riots. And maybe Jews might have even listened to them. But they brought all this upon themselves by their own self-righteousness. Alexander felt strangely sorry for them.

Severus put up his hand. The line of soldiers stopped.

Alexander looked ahead into the darkness, hoping to see something.

The sound of footsteps running away from them confirmed his suspicions. Severus bolted after the fleeing lookout, followed by Alexander and the others. They turned a corner and saw a lighted area further down. The singing had stopped.

The Christians knew they had been discovered.

But it was too late. The Praetorians were upon them.

Alexander arrived to find a cavernous area large enough for the gathering of the fifty Christians still there. A few had fled deeper into the maze, chased by some of the soldiers.

But the bulk of them had accepted their fate.

The lead soldier clubbed an old man, who fell to the floor unconscious. As a screaming woman moved to protect him, the soldier smashed her in the head with the butt of his sword handle. Alexander heard her skull crack under the force. She fell to the ground unconscious, blood gushing from her wound.

Shock tactics, thought Alexander. Meant to shut down any attempt at defense. And it was totally unnecessary.

"Enough, soldier," said Severus. "They're not resisting."

They are not fighters, these Christians. They are more like...well, like stupid lambs.

The Christians stood with their hands out in surrender, void of weapons. The soldiers lined the exit, blocking any retreat. And Severus announced, "You are all under arrest for sedition against Caesar."

A different thought occurred to Alexander. Sometimes the most dangerous of enemies were the least obvious. Armed insurrectionists were a tangible evil readily dispatched. Sedition of the soul was not always visible and thus could fester unchecked in the body politic, like a plague that spreads invisibly among the people. Ideas had consequences. Ideas changed society and fueled revolutions. Christian ideas were subversive of both Judaism and Rome.

Had this sectarian faith become like a plague?

Alexander noticed two elders, each holding babies in their arms, dripping wet with water. He saw a large bowl of water on the table before them. Baptism. They were baptizing members of their household. Alexander was familiar with the rite, as it had become a distinctly Christian sign of covenantal inclusion into their community. Jews had circumcision for their badge of membership. Christians, always trying to distinguish themselves counter to the Jews, had chosen baptism as covenant sign.[5]

Severus gestured to a couple of his soldiers. They responded by moving in and taking the infants from the elders' hands.

Two women screamed and tried to protect their babies. The soldiers held them back with strong arms.

Severus proclaimed, "You are unfit to parent these children with your seditious superstitions. They are now wards of the state."

"Nooooo," cried one of the women. Both of them held their hands out toward their children in a hopeless grasp.

The soldiers took the children away.

Alexander cringed at the tearful weeping of the mothers. Memories of his wife assaulted him. Her outreached arms in the burning house. Her look at him before she died in the flames. He pushed the memories out of his mind to focus on the present.

As the fifty captives were chained, soldiers took the opportunity to harass and beat the surrendered men and women. Such humiliation was part of the process of stripping prisoners of their dignity, the ultimate end of which would be the arena.

One of the women cried out after being hit across the face. It was a foreign phrase unknown to Roman ears, but all too familiar to his own.

"Maranatha!"

Severus stopped the soldier. He asked the woman, "What did you just say?"

"Maranatha," she answered.

"What does that mean? What is that language?"

The soldier holding her raised his hand to strike her. She cringed and closed her eyes.

Alexander said, "It's Aramaic."

The soldier withheld his strike.

"It means, 'Our Lord, come.'"[6]

Severus looked with disdain upon the woman. "Do you think your god is going to help you if you disobey Caesar, the ruler of the gods?"

Alexander walked around the cavern, looking at the walls. They must have been meeting here for a long time, because there were painted murals of their devotion on the rock face.

One of the frescoes was of a clean-shaven "Good Shepherd" carrying a lamb, a common image of their savior, and a symbolic contrast with Hercules. Another was of their Christ entering the holy city seated on a humble donkey, a mockery of the imperial triumphal entry—made more acerbic by the fact that the holy city was not Jerusalem, but Rome! A larger fresco illustrated a divine council of the gods with Caesar enthroned in the center, but in this case, the council was the twelve disciples and Jesus was in the place of Caesar. They were all adorned in royal Roman purple, and depicted in imperial position, face forward. Jesus struck the exact position and look of Caesar that Alexander had seen in the imperial mosaics of the palace. These Christians may have been peaceful when it came to their resistance, but they were engaging in a war of images that Alexander considered of more far-reaching effect.[7]

And it would damn them before Nero's court.

"Alexander!" Severus' shout brought him out of his artistic musings. He jerked a look at Severus pointing to the corner.

Alexander saw a small pile of parchments burning against the wall.

Evidence.

He ran over to the corner and stomped out the flames.

He then reached down and picked up the parchment.

The Christians were led out of the catacombs as Severus joined Alexander in the torchlight, examining the charred remains in his hands.

"More propaganda?" asked Severus.

"Yes," muttered Alexander. "But look at this."

He showed Severus the parchment pieces.

"See how each of the pieces are numbered? This one is number one, this one, thirteen, and then seventeen and eighteen."

"What does it mean?" asked Severus.

"I am not sure."

Severus caught the eye of the last Roman pulling a female captive away. "Soldier. Bring her here."

The soldier obeyed.

Alexander said, "It looks like these are all pieces of a single scroll that was cut up and numbered."

"Was the rest of it burned up?" asked Severus.

"No. There is not enough here to constitute an entire manuscript."

"Where is the rest of it?"

"I don't know."

The soldier holding the woman awaited his orders.

Alexander said, "This is like none of their previous propaganda."

Severus said, "What do you mean?"

"It is overwrought with symbols and coded language. From what I can see here, it has a warfare motif."

"Coded war intelligence?" said Severus.

"More like apocalyptic literature, but different."

Apocalyptic literature was a genre of writing made common in the Second Temple period. When the prophet Daniel and later writers claimed to speak for God under the oppressive regimes of other nations like Babylon or Greece, they would often cloak their condemnation of their oppressors in heavily symbolic language to protect themselves and their message.[8]

"Yet in some places, it is very explicit," said Alexander. "Listen to this. 'From Jesus Christ the faithful witness, the firstborn of the dead, and the ruler of kings on earth. To him be glory and dominion forever and ever. Behold, he is coming with the clouds, and every eye will see him, even those who pierced him, and all tribes of the land will wail on account of him.'"

Severus could not believe it. "They are still claiming this Jesus redivivus is returning to conquer Caesar and rule the earth."

Alexander added, "And they are more bold about it."

As Alexander saw it, the Romans were the ones who "pierced" Jesus with crucifixion. And there was only one ruler over all the kings and tribes of the land, and that was Caesar.

This was subversive propaganda.

Severus turned to the Christian woman, trembling in her simple robe. Most of the Christians were from the poor class. It seemed to appeal to the impoverished who sought comfort in their lack of station and power in this world. Predictable slave morality.

Severus asked her, "Where are the other pieces of the manuscript?"

She was too afraid to respond. He grabbed her hair and yanked her head back. She yelped.

"Do not try my patience, Christian."

She quivered. "I-I don't know."

His stare alone struck fear into the poor woman's eyes.

She added, "The scroll was cut into pieces and numbered. The pieces were separated and sent to other gatherings of Christians."

"Which ones?"

"No one knows."

"So that no one gathering has the complete manuscript if caught," said Alexander. "Clever."

"Seditious," corrected Severus. "I believe we may have just uncovered another conspiracy, Alexander." He was referring to the Pisonian Plot to assassinate Nero that had recently been uncovered and crushed. "That is why they were trying to burn the evidence. We need to find the other pieces."

Alexander said, "I need to read these fragments more closely to see if I can decrypt its message."

Severus grinned. "I know just the person to help you."

CHAPTER 32

Alexander and Severus sat in the prefect's home on the northeast side of the city. They waited for Cassandra's response as she read through the parchment fragments. It was the first time in months that Severus had sought to enlist her help in deciphering anything related to the Christian predicament. But why did the prefect think she would help them at all?

Alexander didn't trust the woman. She knew much more than she let on. But the truth was, as much as he had become numb toward Christian suffering, her presence became like a stone in the sandal of his conscience. A constant reminder of the very personal reality of his moral compromise to survive. The Christians suffered the wrath of Rome so that the Jews would not. They shared a disdain for each other.

"I have never seen this manuscript." She put the parchment pieces down on the table. "It must have been written after you enslaved me."

"Surely gossip finds its way," Severus said. "Even among servants."

"You have me on a tight chain, my lord. I have lost my previous access to the congregation of Christians in the city. And as you know, they have been unable to meet with the Jews in their synagogues."[1]

Severus sighed. "But surely you are familiar with the imagery and symbolism, are you not?"

"No more than Alexander."

"I need an inside believer's understanding."

She said, "Without the fuller context of the rest of the manuscript, we cannot really be sure of anything."

She was playing them. Alexander just knew it.

Severus said, "Cassandra, I do not expect you to provide me with information that will lead to the arrest of your fellow Christians."

Again, thought Alexander, *why is he not beating it out of her?*

Severus continued, "But I have a deal to offer you. An opportunity for mutual benefit. Measure for measure."

She continued to eye him with suspicion.

"For every insight into these manuscripts that you can give me, I promise I will use my authority to release a Christian of your choosing from the Tullianum."

That struck Alexander as brilliant. It was a kind of prisoner exchange. Though he doubted Cassandra would compromise herself. She was too rigid.

But she appeared to be considering it.

Severus added, "You are not helping me against your own people. You are helping me to understand your sacred text."

Her skeptical silence appeared to be changing in her eyes.

"Is that not what you want? For me to understand your message, your 'good news'? Who knows, maybe I will convert if it is persuasive."

Cassandra smirked. "I beg of you, my lord, do not patronize me."

Alexander thought she had gall to say such a thing. But Severus did not respond with anger. Instead, he awaited her answer.

Finally, she said, "And how can I know that my lordship will keep his promise?"

"I will bring you with me to the prison and you can be sure to see them off yourself."

"And how will I know you won't send an order to arrest them again after we leave?"

"You won't. I can only give you my word. You must take the risk and trust me, Cassandra. You must trust a man whom you no doubt despise in your heart."

She looked off into the distance with a wrinkled brow that betrayed a troubled heart. Alexander thought that it was the perfect negotiation on Severus' part. If he got her to trust him, even in this little exchange, they would be on their way toward decoding the letter.

She looked at the manuscript pieces again. "The beginning of this first piece, let us call it fragment one, has been burned. But he writes to seven congregations in the province of Asia."

She's doing it, thought Alexander. *She accepted the offer. Measure for measure.*

The Christians were connected in one vast network of separate assemblies, spread out and diverse, yet united under the authority of their apostles. But as far as Alexander knew, all those apostles were dead. The only true unifying authority was their crucified rebel Messiah, proclaimed risen from the dead in the scroll.

"So who really is this Jesus the Christ?" asked Severus.

"He is Jesus the Christ," said Cassandra.

Severus rolled his eyes. "You really believe he is risen from the dead and hiding out somewhere with an army?"

"No," she replied. "He *is* resurrected, but he is not hiding out anywhere on earth. His weapons are not of this world. And he fights not against flesh and blood, but against principalities and powers and rulers in the heavenly places."[2]

Severus smirked and shook his head at what he apparently perceived as the poor woman's gullibility. She seemed so mature, so elegant, until she opened her mouth about her religious beliefs. Was she protecting the true identity of a rebel usurper and his plans for insurrection? Or did she really believe her dead Nazarene was coming back?

Cassandra continued, "You may not believe my interpretation, but it is what we believe. And that is one Christian to be freed."

"Agreed," said Severus. He picked up fragment one to find details. "Then who is this person who claims to have had this vision?"

"I told you, I don't know. I never saw this letter before today. His greeting was in the burnt portion."

Severus looked frustrated to Alexander. The physician remained silent, watching her closely.

The prefect read from the fragment, "'Write therefore the things that you have seen, those that are and those that are to take place after this.' Could these be battle plans cloaked as prophecy?"

She answered, "Or prophecy cloaked as battle plans."

Severus considered her words. But his mind was racing. "What about these beasts?" said Severus.

"That's two," she said. "Two insights, two Christians released."

Severus' jaw tightened. But then he nodded and continued, "These other fragments seem to speak of two beasts, one from the land and one from the sea with seven heads. What do you think they represent?"[3]

"Well," she said, "the sea is a symbol of chaos. Canaanite myth says that the sea dragon of chaos is Leviathan, and he has seven heads. Could it be a reference to chaos taking over the world?"

Very cunning, thought Alexander. *She is not lying, she is merely suggesting other interpretations to steer Severus away from the Hebrew one.* Yes, Leviathan was the sea dragon of chaos in Canaanite literature. But this was not Canaanite literature, it was Hebrew literature. And Jews had their own meaning for Leviathan that ultimately tied into the Serpent of the Garden, the satan. This Beast imagery had a precedent, and it was in the prophet Daniel, which she had either deliberately ignored or was ignorantly unaware of. Which was it?[4]

Severus began to ask her, "It says here..."

She interrupted him, "That is my third insight for a third Christian."

Severus closed his eyes to keep his calm. "Three. Now, it says here, 'Let the one who has understanding calculate the number of the Beast, for it is the number of a man, and his number is six hundred and sixty six.' Alexander and I have seen graffiti on Roman walls that have testified to this same number. But I cannot figure out any man's name that adds up to that number using gematria."[5]

Cassandra shrugged. "The writer does call it a mystery."

Alexander thought, *But that has nothing to do with whether or not she knows the answer.* His sympathy for her quickly dissipated as he figured out that her suggestions were manipulative, deceptive.

Severus kept going, "Another passage, 'The seven heads are seven mountains on which the woman is seated.' Is that Rome? Rome has long been known to be the 'city on seven hills' from time immemorial."[6]

She seemed doubtful. "They could be seven successive empires. The prophet Daniel used language like that."

So she is familiar with Daniel's vision, thought Alexander. He was right, she was not letting on what she really knew. She was not outright lying, she was telling half-truths, which were more effective in drawing attention away from the *full truth*. Alexander thought Severus had surely been bewitched by her enchanting poise and beauty. The prefect was foolish to trust this captive Christian. Of course she would protect her own people, just as Alexander had protected his.

He felt conflicted. Could he blame her? After all she and her fellow cult members had suffered? That stone in the sandal of his mind was annoying.

Severus now eyed her suspiciously. "Cassandra, how is it that you, a woman and a shipping merchant, are so educated in these things?"

"My lord, Jesus and the apostles taught that women are equal heirs of God's kingdom. We are allowed to study and learn of God's word along with men."[7]

Severus raised his brow with amusement. "Next thing you know, you Christians will be freeing your slaves and making love to barbarians."

"My lord, slaves and barbarians are also equal heirs in the kingdom of God."[8]

"Bizarre," said Severus.

"That is my fifth insight." Cassandra smiled, satisfied with her presumed gain. "And a fifth Christian to be freed."

Severus nodded, turned back to the parchment and got back on target. "It talks of 'the Great City,' Babylon, and the mysterious harlot who carries its name. But Babylon is currently an insignificant province of Parthia. Is this literally the city of Babylon or is it a symbol of something else?"[9]

Cassandra glanced at Alexander. "As Alexander knows, Babylon is an eternal enemy of Israel. In the time of Daniel, the great king Nebuchadnezzar invaded Israel, and took them into captivity. We call it the exile, and it marks the low point of Jewish history out of which deliverance is awaited. Some would say Babylon is literal in this letter. That she will one day return to power." She looked to Alexander for approval.

"*Some* would say," repeated Alexander with a tinge of spite. "But what do *you* say?" He could no longer let her lead Severus down the wrong path like a tongue-wagging dog. "I think I know what you would say...were you safe and alone with your fellow Christians."

She looked at him with surprise.

He continued like a rabbi in a synagogue. "Since you are familiar with the prophet Daniel, whom we both know our esteemed Severus is *not*, then let me educate him on what both you and I know." Alexander could see her swallow nervously. He had her. "Daniel wrote of the same terrifying beast with ten horns who came out of the sea. That beast represented a fourth kingdom on the earth."[10]

Severus looked surprised.

"And that fourth kingdom beast was so important to Yahweh's prophecy that he repeated it in another dream vision to Nebuchadnezzar himself. He foretold the same four kingdoms in history, Babylon, Medo-Persia, Greece…and Rome. Exactly as history has played out. The beast with seven heads and ten horns in this apocalypse is the same beast with ten horns in Daniel: It is the Roman Empire that tramples and rules as a mixed kingdom of iron and clay."[11]

Severus broke in. "Your prophet Daniel foretold the rule of Rome?"

"Yes, prefect. And he also claimed that Messiah would come like a stone cut without hands that would hit Rome in its feet and crush all kingdoms. To take dominion over the earth."[12] Alexander suddenly thought he may have said too much. He knew the Christians claimed that the Nazarene was that messianic stone, though the Jews did not.

He quickly changed the subject. "There is only one great city that, I quote, 'has dominion over the kings of the earth,' and from which 'the merchants of the earth have grown rich from the power of her luxurious living.'" Alexander was now quoting from fragment seventeen and eighteen as he read them. "There is only one city that God would call his people out of, 'lest you take part in her sins,' that are 'heaped high as heaven.' Only one 'great city that is clothed in fine linen, in purple and scarlet of imperial royalty, adorned with gold, with jewels and with pearls.' One city in which 'was found the blood of the prophets and saints and all who have been slain on earth,' those Christians who were martyred in the arena. That city is Rome. Rome is mystery Babylon."[13]

Severus looked at Cassandra to gauge her reaction. She remained silent, incriminating herself.

Alexander quoted as if he were Lucan the Poet, "'Fallen, fallen is Babylon the great! She is a dwelling place for demons, a haunt for every unclean spirit, a haunt for every unclean bird, a haunt for every unclean and detestable beast.' And *that* is exactly the view that Christians like Cassandra have spoken of Rome, an unclean dwelling place for demons."[14]

Cassandra would neither confirm nor deny it.

Severus responded, "In Cassandra's defense, all those things could be true of a future kingdom of a revived Babylon as well."

Alexander would not be stopped. "Except for the fact that the seven heads of the dragon are the seven mountains of Rome, upon which the harlot is seated." He read from fragment seventeen now. "'And those seven are also seven kings, five of whom have fallen, *one now is*, the other is yet to come.' The Beast is both a king *and* a kingdom." He paused for dramatic effect, then said, "There have been six Caesars or kings of Rome. The previous five have fallen: Julius, Augustus, Tiberius, Caligula, Claudius. The sixth king 'now *is*': his name is Nero."[15]

Severus said, "So you are suggesting that Nero Caesar and his kingdom is this so-called Beast?"

Alexander said, "None other."

Severus protested, "But we talked about this before, Alexander. Nero's name does not add up to six hundred and sixty-six. It's one thousand and five."

"In Greek," said Alexander. "These Christians may write in Greek, but they think and conspire in Hebrew. And in Hebrew, the number of Nero Caesar's name is six hundred and sixty-six."[16]

He let it sink in.

Then he found one of the pieces of parchment and read from fragment thirteen, "It says here that the Beast makes war on the saints of God, his holy ones, by taking them captive and slaying them. If that is not Nero's persecution of the Christians, I don't know what is."[17] Alexander could see it making sense to Severus. Perfect treasonous sense.

He completed his triumphal speech while holding up the parchments. "Nero is the Beast of this declaration of war, and Rome is his seven-headed dragon. The mark of the Beast is the Roman imperial cult, the authority under which the world engages in commerce throughout the empire. Rome is the one

234

who 'pierced' their Messiah with crucifixion. Rome is the object of this Christian insurrection, and Nero is the target of an assassination plot."[18]

"Impressive," Severus muttered. He glanced again at Cassandra, who looked guilty at being caught in deception. "But then we are right back to the original question: who is this Jesus impostor, and where is his seditious insurrection hiding?"

"If Cassandra knew, she would not tell us anyway," said Alexander. "Because her goal here has not been to tell you the truth, but to tell you half-truths to mislead you and protect the Christians."

Severus seemed to listen closely.

Alexander saw his opportunity for boldness. "Forgive me, my lord, but in light of this Christian sedition and assassination plot, why have you treated this woman with such partiality and indulgence all these months? Does she have some secret claim on you? Is she blackmailing you?" He saw the shock of his question appear in Severus' eyes.

The vigile prefect turned red with anger. He grabbed Alexander and shoved him up against the wall.

Alexander filled with confusion—and fear. What had he uncovered?

Cassandra watched, wide-eyed and helpless at the escalation.

"You fool," hissed Severus. "She is the reason why my son is here today, and not burned alive in the Great Fire of Rome."

Alexander's mind raced, trying to understand.

"He was trapped at the emporium, buying the herbs for *your* medicine that I agreed to because I was hiding my own shame."

Alexander swallowed.

"She knew who he was, but she took him on a boat instead of leaving him to die. She risked her life to save his. That is why I treat this woman with 'indulgence,' as you call it. Because I am grateful. As you should be grateful that I am indulging you right now." Severus released his grip and stepped back, trying to calm himself.

The implications hit Alexander, making him reel. Everything that had confused him suddenly became clear, but in a way he had never imagined. He said, "My lord, I didn't know."

"No, you didn't." Severus turned away, covering his shame.

Alexander now knew why the prefect had been so troubled. Thelonius had been saved by a Christian. Saved by one of the very people Severus was hunting down to destroy. If anyone found out, they might begin to doubt his loyalty to Rome, and then he would lose everything. His son, his position, his life. It must have created a cognitive dissonance in him. One that he had sought not to resolve, but to suppress.

And suppress it, he did.

Severus said, "We will inform Tigellinus of this new development."

Alexander saw him look at Cassandra.

"After we release six Christians from prison."

CHAPTER 33

An imperial guard led Severus and Alexander through the huge villa of Domus Aurea, the Golden House, just off the western slope of the Palatine Hill. It was the newly rebuilt palace of the emperor, but to Alexander, it was like a small city.

The main palace entrance opened onto a vast atrium surrounded by porticos of marble with gold leaf trimming. They walked past a huge bronze statue a hundred and twenty feet tall in the center of the square. Called the Colossus Neronis, it depicted Nero as the sun god Sol Invictus, and sparkled brightly in the rays of the morning sun. He had done it. The emperor had fashioned his image of self-deification.[1]

Alexander mused how muscular and fit the statue's form was, how unlike Nero's own portly and flabby mass with his spindly legs. It never ceased to amuse him how grandiose the Caesars saw themselves, and yet how human they actually were.

A single phrase of derision came to Alexander's mind: *abomination of desolation*. It was only two decades earlier that Caligula tried to set up a statue of himself as a god in the holy temple in Jerusalem, only to cause a mass riot of desolation. Centuries before that, Antiochus Epiphanes had set up such a statue as well as a pagan altar of sacrifice in the holy temple. His abominable deeds brought about the Maccabean overthrow of that pagan emperor. This statue of idolatry proved that Nero had the same self-delusion as his predecessors. But would he have their madness and audacity to abominate the Jerusalem temple?[2]

They passed through several large meeting rooms with stuccoed and ivory ceilings embedded with jewels. It was the kind of extravagant excess that Alexander deplored. The people of the city suffered in poverty and sickness as their emperor squandered mountains of wealth.[3]

Surrounded by such conspicuous decadence, Alexander thought, *Violence and empire are not the only signs of tyranny.*

They stepped outside and walked through a rolling meadow toward Nero's Pool, a man-made lake with a ship anchored in the middle. It was a large flatbed barge where Nero allowed Tigellinus to host orgies. Prostitutes, wine, strong drink and herbal sorcery, called *pharmakeia*, were plentiful, provided by the royal coffers, with much thanks to the plundered citizens.[4]

Tigellinus' reputation for encouraging Nero's depraved lusts was legendary. They would often travel the streets at night in disguise, just to bed harlots, then beat up and stab men, and rob others' shops. They would abuse freeborn boys and seduce married women. Tigellinus had once persuaded Nero to rape the vestal virgin Rubria. Though it repulsed Severus, he knew it was his superior's way of ingratiating himself to the emperor through shared perversion. He wondered what more Nero would expect of him, should he achieve his imperial task and assume his reward of Praetorian rank.[5]

They found the boatman at the edge of the lake. Severus gave him a message. "This is a matter of utmost urgency. For the eyes of Prefect Tigellinus only."

"Yes, my lord." The boatman left them on the shoreline and hurried his way to the barge on the lake.

Tigellinus sat soberly watching a ceremony on the barge. Normally, he enjoyed his parties with abandon, but not this one. This one was a wedding celebration. Nero was marrying again. He continued to engage in activities that Tigellinus thought would only debase his majesty in the eyes of the public. Needless to say, Poppaea was not present with the entourage of naked whores and boy-loves, sycophants and royal bootlickers. Of course, there was nothing wrong with imbibing the emperor's depraved and violent fantasies in private. Tigellinus would help him do so all the time. And there was certainly no problem with Caesar having multiple wives.

But this wife was a man. Tigellinus knew that publicly marrying the freedman Pythagoras was strategically foolish. Homosexual coupling was for satisfaction of lust, not marriage. Roman matrimony ensured legal offspring and legitimate family inheritance, which was the survival of civilization. A marriage of males provided neither. For the emperor to model such insanity was dangerous. Should the populace seek to emulate it, they would no longer need to beware the barbarians at the gates. Rome would be committing suicide.[6]

Tigellinus had had his share of boy-loves, and even felt the surge of male dominance over others with his own homosexual dalliances, but this was ridiculous.

The bride played the woman with makeup, adorned in dress and veil, standing beside his imperial bridegroom, before a priest of Apollo babbling religious tripe. They turned to kiss each other and the royal entourage applauded. Tigellinus took a gulp of wine to numb himself.

The bride in female garb was Nero.

Another foolish decision on the emperor's part. Of course, there had to be a dominant and a submissive, a male and a female in behavior. Nature dictated such things. But again, that was for the privacy of the bedroom, not for the emperor to adorn himself in public as a woman! That only served to weaken his image as imperator. Women, after all, did not rule the world.[7]

And then, to top off the litany of madness, Nero had nuptial torches and the wedding couch in the open on the barge for everyone to watch the consummation of the marriage.[8]

Disgusting, thought Tigellinus, and he finished his cup of wine. The criticism of Senator Piso was not far off the mark after all. Maybe Nero *would* ruin Rome as Piso had openly argued. The emperor had no prudence, no discretion for hiding his perversions. He *was* a kind of beast.

A messenger tugged at Tigellinus' sleeve. "Prefect, an official awaits you on the shore. He claims a certain urgency."

Tigellinus glanced at the parchment. It read: LUCIUS AURELIUS SEVERUS. *Thank the gods*, he thought. *I can leave this Neronian madness.* He turned to a stately Tribune beside him. "You will want to come with me," he said, grabbing another goblet of wine from a nearby tray.

Severus and Alexander watched Tigellinus carried back to the shore on the crossing boat with a group of his fellow degenerates. Alexander wondered how the prefect might respond to their bad news of conspiracy. He hoped the messengers would not be blamed for their message, but rather rewarded in this time of great distrust and fear.

Just last month, a vast conspiracy to assassinate Nero in a coup d'état was uncovered by chance. It led to a purge of Nero's administration and an opportunity for Tigellinus to eliminate some of his rivals, including his co-prefect, Rufus.

Then it was discovered that a trusted Tribune and a centurion, in conspiracy with several high-ranking individuals, were planning to assassinate Nero at the circus, where he was most vulnerable. The goal was to replace him with a leading senator, Calpurnius Piso, who would then marry a female relative of Nero and thus secure the continuance of the Julio-Claudian line of Caesars.

But a loyal servant caught wind of the Piso Plot and informed the emperor, which led to a string of arrests, uncovering a vast conspiracy that included significant senators, equestrians, Praetorians and even the famous poet Lucan, as well as Nero's old philosopher tutor, Seneca. By the time the investigation was done, seventeen people were exiled, nineteen were beheaded or forced to open their own veins in suicide, and five were exonerated of wrongdoing.[9]

Of particular interest to Severus was the tribune Subrius Flavus and his confession of masterminding the plot. He was the first to conspire and the last to be uncovered. Nero was astonished that so high an official would violate his military oath. The emperor personally questioned the tribune.

Flavus replied tellingly, "I began to hate you when you murdered your mother and wife, became a chariot-driver, an actor, and an arsonist." Perhaps Severus' theory about Nero's involvement in the Great Fire was not so crazy after all.[10]

The most suspicious cases of punished conspirators were the famous poet Lucan and Tigellinus' co-prefect, Faenius Rufus. Nero was artistically envious of Lucan, so it required little imagination to guess his fate. Regarding Rufus, Alexander had learned from Severus that Tigellinus had been seeking every opportunity to ruin Rufus and take sole control of the prefecture. It all seemed a bit too convenient that Tigellinus would spearhead the inquiry that led to the execution of Rufus as a traitor to the throne.[11]

But now, by fate or by machination, Tigellinus had what he longed for: the undivided ear of Caesar and sole authority of the Praetorian Guard. And Nero was consumed with phobic thoughts of disloyalty everywhere. The breadth of the conspiracy involving so many in the ruling class and in the military must have shaken the emperor to the core.[12]

But surely, Severus would put all that cloak and dagger politics behind him now as Tigellinus stumbled out of the boat with his fellow travelers. The prefect's arms were around two young boy-loves, barely pubescent, his goblet, spilling over with wine. He slapped their behinds and they ran ahead.

Beside Tigellinus was another playboy, a tribune, judging by his white purple-bordered tunic. He was a handsome rascal, in his late twenties, with his arms around two naked whores, carrying his drink.

Alexander averted his eyes, for want of modesty.

Tigellinus said, "Severus, have you met Titus Flavius, son of Vespasian? He achieved some mighty victories over the barbarians in Germania and Britannia. And some mighty victories of indulgence and revelry on this very pool."

Titus smirked with pride and released the whores, who walked ahead toward the Golden House.

"My lords," said Severus, bowing.

But Tigellinus and Titus just passed Severus by, and kept walking. Severus and Alexander exchanged glances.

Severus called after Tigellinus, "My lord, where are you going?"

The Praetorian kept walking. He gave a gesture to follow him. "Haven't you heard, Severus? That obsessive Caesar of ours has just married Pythagoras, and as celebration, he started Neronia early this year. He is anxious to perform like a lowly musician in the competition, among other delights of the arena. Come, tell me on the way. We have to prepare for the theater tonight."[13]

Alexander and Severus caught up with him.

Severus said, "This is a matter of utmost urgency, my lord."

"Well then, speak urgently."

Severus added, glancing at Titus, "And privacy."

"Severus, Titus toured Greece with me and the emperor's entourage. You may speak freely."[14]

Severus and Alexander kept up with the drunken Tigellinus and Titus. Alexander kept dutifully silent, but Severus said, "Alexander and I have uncovered another plot against both Nero and Rome."

Tigellinus stopped and gave him a serious look.

Titus listened in curiously.

Severus quivered in his voice. "We have reason to believe that the Christians may be plotting an insurrection."

Tigellinus rolled his eyes. "Christians?" He said it as if in jest.

"Yes. Do you remember the propaganda we found last year? Well, there's more. And this time it appears more aggressive."

"What are the Christians going to do, befriend the lions in the arena and turn them on the emperor? Or attack us on their bloody knees whilst praying without weapons?"

Severus had known that it would come to this. He pulled out the parchment pieces. "We have discovered coded military correspondence. And I believe they have a leader and army hidden somewhere in waiting. They claim their Messiah is resurrected and ready to enter Rome to destroy it."

"And you believe that?" scoffed Tigellinus. "Once a man dies and the earth drinks up his blood, there is no resurrection. Read your Aeschylus."[15] He stumbled on with Titus.

"Prefect, there is a leader somewhere who *claims* to be the risen Messiah. And if they believe the lie, these fanatics are like the Zealots in Jerusalem. They'll fight to the death for their religious superstitions."

Tigellinus stopped again. That one got his attention. He and Titus shared a knowing look. They were very familiar with the hotbed of fanaticism brewing in Judea by the so-called Zealots and other messiah cults. Severus had a point. It didn't matter what was *actually* true, it only mattered what fanatics *believed*. And those beliefs, as insane or ludicrous as they were, could create uprisings and overthrow regimes if not stomped out.

Severus added, "They have endured much violence as peaceful martyrs without fighting back. But that only means they have lulled Rome into unguardedness."

Alexander could tell that Tigellinus was weighing the options of how to deal with this annoyance.

Tigellinus walked on again. "I'm sure the Christians will wait a few more days before they lead the barbarian hordes through the gates. Bring your evidence before Caesar at the Golden House *after* the Games. He will be in a better mind to consider it."

"Thank you, my lord."

"Now, if you will excuse me, I have to sober up to hear the *vox dei* in the theater tonight."

Vox dei meant "the voice of god." He was referring to Nero's scheduled performance in the music and singing competition. But Alexander could tell the alcohol had let slip a subtle edge of sarcasm in the Praetorian's words. Alexander remembered that Severus had often heard Tigellinus voice his displeasure with the emperor debasing his image with such frivolity. But then again, Severus' mistress had been an actress, so his disdain was often restrained by the embarrassment of his own hypocrisy.

Alexander knew that tonight the emperor would sing. And Tigellinus would applaud, reluctantly but vigorously.

CHAPTER 34

The massive stone Theater of Pompey, located in the northern part of Campus Martius, was the largest of its kind, with the capacity to hold twelve thousand patrons. It had survived the Great Fire and was Nero's favorite place to perform because of its grandiosity.[1]

Flavius Titus found it ironic that this also happened to be the location of the assassination of Julius Caesar, the first emperor of Rome. *A fitting platform for Nero's august fate*, he thought as he sat in the prime senatorial seats, watching a boring musical performance onstage. Behind that stage was a large portico where the infamous tyrannicide took place.

At twenty-five years of age, with a tribuneship and military victories on his roster of experience, Titus felt confident in his current station. He had just divorced his wife for her familial connections to one of the Pisonian conspirators. She wasn't guilty, but Titus was intent upon his political ambitions. He must allow no appearance whatsoever of his true sentiments toward Nero. He despised him.[2]

Titus' family, the Flavians, had earned their noble status and wealth through their own hard labors, rather than through inheritance and pedigree. His father, Flavius Vespasian, now fifty-six years old, exemplified that self-made gusto by distinguishing himself through military exploits assisted by Titus. He was appointed a governor of the African Province, and had earned a seat on Nero's recent tour of Greece.[3]

Because of his undistinguished background, Vespasian lacked the refined sense of manners that Titus had developed. His father spoke his mind too freely, paraded his mistress too openly, and failed to support Nero's elevation of the arts. Nero became angry with Vespasian for failing to sit through complete stage performances and falling asleep during the emperor's own playing. In predictable display of that reputation, Vespasian sat beside Titus this very moment, snoring away as the musicians played onstage.[4]

Titus elbowed his father in the side. The old man chortled and shook awake, giving a look of confusion at his mistress beside him, a rather plain-looking woman, now in her late thirties, named Antonia Caenis. She had begun her life as a slave in the imperial court of Claudius, and had won the heart of Vespasian many years ago with her wit and work ethic. She was a self-made mistress to match his self-made nobility.[5]

During an intermission in this insufferably long evening of entertainment, Tigellinus approached Titus and Vespasian. "The loyal Flavians," he said. "How goes your evening of amusement?"

Titus quipped, "Not nearly as amusing as this morning."

Tigellinus winked at him.

"I have seen better," said Vespasian off-handedly. "Though I must say, it is a remedy for my insomnia."

Tigellinus smiled. He shared Vespasian's contempt for the stage.

"In fact, Caenis and I were just on our way out. I have had enough."

"Oh, you cannot leave," said Tigellinus. "The emperor is next, after the break." He pointed to the exits, guarded by contingents of Praetorians. "Caesar strongly suggests that no one leave the performance."

Vespasian replied, "Ah. Enjoyment upon pain of death, I see."

Tigellinus smiled again. The old curmudgeon was a refreshing break from artifice. He said, "I wanted to ask you two seasoned leaders a question. What do you know of Judea?"

Vespasian blurted, "That desert wasteland? Jews are restless and incorrigible. They remind me of the mules I bought and sold to repay my debt. You can beat them, even get them to stay in line. But you'll never break their spirit."[6]

"Father," complained Titus, "must you remind us of your past humiliation?"

"There is no shame in being a muleteer, son. I learned much that has helped me in my leadership." The lowly status of mule trading, coupled with the disgrace of debt, never seemed to embarrass the old codger.

Titus turned back to Tigellinus. "Is not Gessius Florus the procurator over Judea?"

"Unfortunately so," said Tigellinus. "And Caesar is beginning to think he made a mistake in appointing him."

Vespasian said, "Florus is a jackal."

Tigellinus replied, "He seems to be taunting the mules rather than keeping them in line."

"What do you mean?" asked Titus.

"There is rising unrest in the land. Bands of rebels. Word of revolt. Rumors of a Messiah warrior to lead them against Rome. And now that their holy temple has finally been completed, there are thousands of Jews out of work, despondent and idle. It's a cauldron of hot pitch, and Florus seems intent upon lighting it on fire."[7]

"How so?" asked Titus.

"He's provoking the Jews. Extorting money from them, offending their religious practices, favoring the Greeks in law and trade."[8]

Vespasian said, "Then replace him."

Tigellinus leaned in and whispered, "That is not possible. His wife is good friends with the empress."[9]

Titus glanced over to see Poppaea in discussion with some senators at a distance. He muttered, "The entrenchment of jobbery and corruption."

Vespasian said, "Can you not use Cestius to restrain him?" Cestius Gallus was the Roman governor of Syria, just north of Israel.

Tigellinus sighed. "We have tried. Cestius arrives, brings order, and calms him—for a time. But as soon as Cestius returns to Syria, Florus returns to taunting the Jews."[10]

Titus did not seem happy with where this was leading. "Why do you seek our opinion in the matter?"

"Because Caesar may soon be requiring the skills of Vespasian the Muleteer to harness those stubborn mules, the Jews."[11]

A pall went over the Flavians' faces.

The sound of clacking boards alerted everyone to return to their seats for the evening's finale.

Nero entered the stage, and the audience gave him a standing ovation. He quieted them down to make his announcement.

"My dearly beloved people, the judges have awarded me this 'crown of eloquence' in advance for this noble competition." Applause from the crowd forced him to wait a moment before proceeding. "But I must reject the offer and return it, for I do not seek the partiality of private interest nor the favor of the senate. I seek to meet my competitors on equal ground. To acquire an honestly earned distinction by the conscientious award of the judges. Let me not be judged on station. Let me be judged on merit alone."

The crowd broke out again in applause. Titus closed his eyes at the lies he was hearing. On second thought, Nero was so disconnected from reality, he probably believed what he was saying. The man was that chronically deluded.

Vespasian noticed the people around him nervously outdoing one another in extending their acclamation. No one wanted to be the first to stop clapping for the emperor. Especially in view of the menacing looks of a special corps of Augustan soldiers watching them.

The sycophantic applause finally died down.

"My lords," Nero said, "of your kindness, give me ear." He then began to play his lyre and sing a song. He would still win the prize at the end of the competition, as he always did, by "free and unanimous approval" of the judges.[12]

Nero's lyrics were gibberish, and his music mere noise in the ears of Titus as he sat quietly, considering the implications of looming war in Judea.

CHAPTER 35

The musical and theatrical competition of Neronia was followed by gymnastics and chariot racing the next two days. But this year, that trinity of games was augmented by an encore performance, a personal favorite of the emperor. He called it fatal charades.

Fatal charades consisted of the public execution of criminals in the arena presented as scenes from myths of brutal punishment and torture. Convicted criminals were taken from prison and dressed up as characters in plays whose suffering was reenacted for the entertainment of the masses. But in this case, the suffering was real; the punishment was not pretend acting.[1]

It was Nero's way of breathing new life into the repetitious nature of slaughter in the arena. Investing it with drama and thematic meaning raised it above the mundane. This was appropriate because justice to him was a transcendent notion of the gods. Everything became theater to Nero. Everything had to be larger than life, even death.

Though Circus Maximus was rebuilt, Nero continued to use his personal circus in the Vatican Gardens for these executions because of their connection in the public mind.

Today, the arena was packed with citizens of all stripes anxiously awaiting a cathartic bloodletting. Today's criminals had the perverse distinction of incendiarism, mischievous superstition, impious atheism and imperial treason—Christians again.[2]

Titus and Vespasian had seats of distinction in the imperial box just behind Nero with his spy glass, Tigellinus and several senators.

Titus noticed Poppaea's absence. He knew that the empress had no taste for such indulgent excess. It wasn't that she disapproved of the punishment of criminals, but only in the public spectacle and bloodlust.

Nero was clearly agitated because she was not here. So in her place, he brought along Pythagoras, his new "spouse," who, as their wedding had revealed, would play the male to Nero's female in the bedroom.[3]

Titus mused to himself, *Even the most powerful of tyrants secretly long for the release of surrender to another's control. Even if just for a moment.* Why would someone with the status of a god have the primal need for salvation by another? Why was all the power in the world not enough to satisfy?

It seemed as if human nature carried within itself a dark hole of emptiness. Plebeians sought to fill the void with religion. The privileged, with wealth and power. But wealth and power only created an even larger pang of hunger that viciously refused to be satiated. He felt it in his own ambitions, not to mention his adventures of depravity.

But strong drink and fornication were child's play. The most invigorating experiences in his life had been the slaying of men in battle. Killing another human being, and thereby holding another's destiny in one's hands, made one feel like a god. Life was the ultimate mystery and essence of a being, so taking that life was the ultimate power. Killing victims in the arena, however, was a parody of that transcendence.

Titus' thoughts were interrupted by Nero's spouse Pythagoras spying him with a wink. Titus made a slight shake of his head to stop that wildfire from igniting.

"Titus!" The call came from Nero. "Come up here. You'll want to see this more clearly."

Titus and Vespasian had already endured the previous masquerades of massacre and were planning to leave. They both thought the blood theater was a mistake. Over the past few months, Nero had been tormenting these pathetic religious freaks with such excessive enthusiasm that it was creating a backlash in the populace. Fewer patrons had shown up for this spectacle than ever before. Criticism could be heard in the streets. The Christian martyrs were becoming sympathetic victims to many. But one could not defy Nero's wishes without dire consequence, so Flavian father and son swallowed their pride and joined the emperor.[4]

Currently, a moment of intermission had arrived as Christian slaves cleaned up the arena floor of their dead comrades' remains. The previous charade had been that of Actaeon and his punishment from the goddess Artemis. The myth went that Actaeon had offended the Great Mistress of the Animals. So she transformed him into a stag and set his own hunting dogs into a wolven frenzy that tore him to pieces.

Since the Christians were known for their frequent hostile rhetoric against Artemis, it was a fitting mockery when Nero affixed stag horns to the heads of dozens of Christians and then released a pack of ravenous wild dogs upon them in the arena.

The scenario had caused Nero to belly laugh at the silliness of the victims running around like a bunch of clowns with horns on their heads, who were then torn to pieces by the dogs. Nero cruelly mimicked their blood curdling screams and cries for mercy. "Save me, please! Maranatha! Come, Lord Jesus! Ahhhhhhhh!"[5]

The dogs, having had their fill of flesh, were chased back into their gated kennels. As the slaves cleaned up the carnage, another charade was performed at the opposite end of the circus. Two planks were extended from the roof of the porticos a good hundred feet above.

"Come, Titus," said Nero with childish excitement. "It's the myth of Icarus!" Icarus was the young boy, who, using artificial wings made by his father, Daedalus, flew too close to the sun and plummeted to his death. Christians were given fake wings on their backs and were pushed off the planks to fall to their death a hundred feet below.

The crowd started to chant, "Haters of the human race! Haters of the human race!"

Nero held out his emerald concave lens for Titus. "Look through my spyglass. You can see them hit and their brains and blood splatter all over."

The emperor's childlike enthusiasm repulsed Titus. But he looked through the lens. He saw a winged man shoved off the plank, fall silently, head first, and hit the dirt just as Nero had described—a splattering of blood and gore.

Nero barked out, "Oh! That one just landed on his head! What did it look like up close? Was it gruesome?"

"Tragic myth," Titus muttered and handed the lens back to Nero.

"If you think of it," Nero said, "this is poetic justice. I understand Christians worship the sun. And just like Icarus, that worship backfires on them and draws them to their own demise."

"I hear their deity has the head of an ass," Titus replied. "I wonder how that might work with your poetic license."[6]

"Excellent idea," said the emperor. "I wonder if I could have them raped by mules." He thought for a moment, his mind searching for creative new ways of torture.[7]

The depravity of this beast knows no bounds, thought Titus.

On the arena floor, a character dressed as the god Mercury came out with a red-hot iron, poking the victims to make sure they were dead. He was followed by another character dressed in black as Pluto, god of the underworld, to finish off the live ones with a mallet, then drag their bodies back to the feeding trough of the wild animals.[8]

And there was still more of this dreadful masquerade to tolerate.

Nero clapped his hands gleefully. "The myth of Dirce! The myth of Dirce!" This myth told of Dirce, the vindictive wife of Lycus, king of Thebes. When Zeus had impregnated Dirce's niece Antiope, Dirce hated her and treated her cruelly. Later, when Antiope's twin boys had grown to adulthood, they revenged their mother and killed Dirce by tying her hair to the horns of a wild bull, who then trampled her to death.

Titus saw several bulls break out of the open gates of the arena. In perfect imitation of the myth, naked Christian women were tied by their hair to the horns of the stomping beasts. They were crushed beneath the hooves.[9]

One of the women's scalp had ripped off her skull and she flew around into the path of the bull. The horns gored her, and Titus saw Nero jump and clap his hands with excitement.

The crowd responded with painful shock.

Morbid curiosity, thought Titus. *They are drawn to what repulses them.* Yet he, too, felt the allure.

The fatal charade grande finale of the evening was the Daughters of Danaus. As the story went, the Danaids were fifty daughters betrothed in diplomacy to fifty sons of the king of Egypt. On their wedding night, forty-nine of the daughters murdered their husbands. The daughters were ultimately forced into Tartarus for an eternity of punishment by filling up a bath that leaked all its water.[10]

Though such a punishment was not conducive to the requisite terror of the arena, Nero made some adjustments in the scenario. Since he was a lover of all things Egyptian, he drew from other punishments in Tartarus that were listed in sacred texts like the Egyptian *Book of the Dead*.[11]

The horrific spectacle played out like a scene of Virgil's Aeneas in Hades. A long string of women, as well as men forced to dress as women, were lined up along the circus roadway. They all carried water vases upon their heads, impersonating the Danaids in the underworld.

On one side of the arena, a very large wheel made of bronze and wood, twenty feet in diameter, rolled down an artificially constructed ridge. A dozen Christians were tied to the wheel spokes, and the wheel was set on fire. The wheel then followed its path onto the racetrack where it rolled down the line of Danaids, crushing them beneath its massive bronze tread. When the wheel hit the end of the track, its flaming structure crossed a line of pitch that snaked around the other side of the track to a large pool of the black liquid. Standing in that pool of pitch were more Christians on stakes, awaiting their comeuppance.

As the pitch lit on fire, it soon found its way down the stream to its destination, creating a lake of fire that consumed screaming victims in a parody of eternal torment.[12]

Nero stood and applauded with vigor. The rest of the audience followed suit dutifully with an ovation of their own, though without enthusiasm to equal the emperor's.

Titus saw many of the patrons walking out in disgust and protest. He knew that a turning point had occurred, and if Nero did not respond appropriately, one day he would find himself on the receiving end of his own fatal charade.

CHAPTER 36

Nero barged into his bedroom, where Poppaea had been napping. Her pregnancy was nearing six months. "Wake up, wife!" he barked. "Must you sleep the day away like a sloth?"

She rubbed her eyes, visibly angry. "I can think of nothing more slothful than days of grotesque amusement."

He trembled, then broke out into a tantrum. "I want you by my side in public!"

"Would that you could carry a child in your belly. You might reconsider your irritation."

"You could just as well have relaxed in a chair, watching the games with me."

"You know how I feel about the games." She sat up with a sigh, tired of this old fight.

"Yes, I do. The entire populace knows how you feel about the games. And it is affecting their attendance and loyalty. They see their empress does not support her emperor, so it discourages them."

Her eyes grew wide with anger. "They are discouraged because of the foolish excess of their emperor in his fatal charades."

"My excess?" he spit out. "What about yours? Gilding the shoes of your passenger mules with gold? Bathing in the milk of five hundred asses? And you speak of *my* excess!"[1]

"It is required to maintain my beauty," she countered. "Beauty that *you* so rigorously demand."

Nero's eyes filled with fury. "What I demand is that you do your part to encourage the populace to support the welfare of the state."

She eyed him right back. "The populist sentiment of pity for the Christians is due to the impression that they are being sacrificed, not for the welfare of the state, but to the ferocity of a single man."[2]

Nero hauled back and punched Poppaea in the face. She fell to the floor, her nose gushing blood. "I will show you my ferocity, you ingrate."

He kicked her in the belly. She grunted and gurgled on her blood.

"I…" He kicked her again.

"Will…"And again.

"Not…" Each word followed by a kick.

"Tolerate…" She lay unconscious.

"Insolence!" He kept on kicking. His chest heaved with frenzy.

He felt overtaken. As if he was not in control, as if he was a mere instrument of his own fury. He could not stop kicking her.

But finally, he did, shocked at his outburst.

He stood silently staring at her prostrate form. He knelt down and looked with sudden pity upon her. His eyes filled with tears as he reached out and gently pulled back the hair covering her face.

She was dead.[3]

"My Sabina," he whispered. "I am so sorry. I am so sorry."

His trembling hand traced the soft skin of her cheek.

"But you provoked me."

He was interrupted by a knock on the door. A Praetorian guard said, "My lord, Caesar, Tigellinus arrives with an urgent matter."

Nero wiped his eyes dry, stood to his feet, and left the room. His loyal Praetorian needed him. He would clean up this mess later.

Nero burst through the entrance of a private anteroom where Tigellinus awaited him with Severus and Alexander.

Tigellinus looked concerned. "My lord, are you well?"

At first, Nero looked confused. Until he saw everyone looking at his hand and lower tunic, splashed with blood.

Nero brushed it off casually. "Oh, this. I just got carried away."

Everyone was quite familiar with Nero's tendency to get carried away. Alexander assumed there was some lazy servant lying bleeding somewhere in the palace.

"What is so urgent, my Tigellinus, that requires my attention?"

Tigellinus nodded to Severus, who handed the emperor some parchment pieces. Nero looked at them. Then Tigellinus said, "This is secret correspondence we have uncovered that indicates a possible insurrection. It is written in code that Alexander here has helped to decipher."

"A Jewish insurrection?" Nero said.

Tigellinus corrected him. "A *Christian* insurrection."

"Christian?" Nero's face scrunched up. "Please, Tigellinus, spare me the comedy. I was just arguing with Poppaea about the exact opposite reality. I think there may be no more Christians left in Rome because I have exhausted their numbers in the arena."

Tigellinus corrected him, "In Rome, sire. Yes."

Nero gave him a curious look.

Tigellinus looked at Alexander. "Let the Jew explain."

Alexander swallowed. It was a frightening proposition to speak in the presence of Caesar. "Those parchments are incomplete. But we have deciphered enough to know that the Christians are calling for your assassination and for the arrival of a hidden messianic army."

Nero was incredulous. "Is this that Jesus redivivus myth again?"

"Yes," Alexander said, "but we believe it is code for some warrior leader ready to attack. Exactly where, we do not know for certain. It is true that there is no Christian threat in Rome, or all of Italy for that matter. Their numbers are too small. But in other parts of the empire it is a different matter. That letter was written and circulated amongst the Christians in Asia. They have an influential presence there. They may not be able to attack Rome, but what about an uprising in Roman colonies?"

"Who wrote this?" said Nero. "Find him and interrogate him."

Alexander demurred. "Unfortunately, we do not know who wrote it, my lord. The letter is partially destroyed, and they have cut it up into pieces to avoid being discovered."

Nero sat down in his throne chair. He thought for a moment. "Do you know to which cities in Asia the letter was sent?"

Alexander nodded slightly. "Some of them, my lord. Ephesus, Smyrna, Pergamum and others. Seven of them. They may even have the other pieces of the letter in their possession. If you send a security detail, they may be able to confiscate the rest."

"No," said Nero. "That would be foolish. Trumpeting my intentions. They would scurry into hiding like cockroaches. I have a better idea." He looked at Severus. "I commission you to find the rest of this letter on a secret mission to Asia. Use the Jew to decipher it. Go undercover as a spy." He held the parchment up. "Just find the author of this propaganda and his impostor messiah, and kill them both."

Severus countered, "But Caesar, what if they do have an army?"

"I will give you a dispatch, granting you authority over a cohort or legion if needed."

"Yes, my lord," said Severus, crestfallen.

Nero said, "Fear not, Severus. If you are successful, I will grant you senatorial status. How does that sound to your downcast little heart?"

"I am unworthy, my lord," said Severus.

"Yes, you are," said Nero. "So, find this author and his phantom messiah...and *prove* yourself worthy."

"Yes, Caesar." Severus gave him the customary stiff-handed salute with pride.

Alexander knew that this would inspire Severus more than anything. One usually had to own large amounts of property and have large amounts of money to become a senator, not to mention the right family connections. But imperial exceptions could be made. Caesar's simple decree could ignore all of that and place Severus into the upper echelons of power where he needed to be to achieve his ultimate goal of Praetorian prefect. Assuming that by then, Tigellinus had moved on in the world or to the next.

Alexander felt dread penetrate his soul with Nero's commission to Severus. His entire world had just turned upside down.

CHAPTER 37

Aegean Sea
off the coast of Asia Minor

Cassandra leaned on the railing of her own merchant ship and looked out upon the horizon of an endless sea stretching out before her under a full moon. The ship was called a *corbita*, a swift commercial sailing vessel. Corbitas were the workhorses of the sea. They were built sturdy to carry multiplied tonnage of shipping goods, but also speedy to maximize profit and outrun pirates. This ship was a hundred feet long and propelled by a large, single-square sail with a smaller bow sail for added maneuvering. Her dozen crew members were mostly asleep belowdecks, with a few on watch and keeping the course. Except they weren't her crew members anymore, and this was no longer her ship.

When Severus enslaved Cassandra, he took control of her property and appropriated it for his own purposes. His current purpose was the imperial mission to find the rest of the subversive apocalypse and report back to Nero. He was accompanied by Alexander and a small group of twenty-five bodyguards, who lay sleeping belowdecks. Severus had decided against bringing a detachment of legionaries because it would draw too much attention and he would lose the strategic advantage of spying. Instead, he had chosen stealth and covert operation.

Cassandra looked up at the stars above shining with divine brightness. Then out on the dark ocean highlighted by glimmering moonlight. She glanced down at the soft waves cresting at the edge of the moving ship. The waters below were dark, foreboding, calling her. Severus and Alexander were asleep in a small cabin enclosure at the stern for the captain and passengers. She had slipped out unnoticed with her own purpose this evening.

After prayer and consideration, Cassandra had decided to kill herself by jumping off the ship to drown in the deep. She considered self-sacrifice to be her only option to save Christians from further persecution. She had tried to misdirect the Roman vigile by giving fallacious interpretations of the apocalypse, but Alexander had called her out. He knew enough to not allow her to continue her holy deception.

Her bargain for release of Christians with each bit of information had been futile. She had rescued six from prison so far, and might be able to free dozens more. But at what price? The cost of leading her captor to hundreds more that would be tortured or killed? And the more Severus understood the apocalypse, the more he would help Nero to persecute more Christians. And she would have been party to achieving that demonic goal. Severus had held back from abusing her only because she had saved his son's life. But she knew that could not last forever. His devotion to Nero would inevitably outweigh his gratitude to her.

They had traveled a thousand miles from Rome to Asia Minor in about six days under a strong headwind. They were at the end of their long journey and nearing their first target city, Ephesus, a major port and communications center for Asia—as well as Cassandra's residence in years past. Once there, she would be called upon to betray her friends and loved ones with whom she had grown in Christ for so many years. She would not let that happen.

She remembered Demetrius, the son of Apollos, fellow traveling preacher with the apostle Paul. Demetrius was her age and a dark-skinned Egyptian like his father. They met when they were both seventeen. She had admired the young man greatly. He had followed after his father with a bold witness for Christ, but when Apollos moved on to minister across the Mediterranean, Demetrius stayed behind in Ephesus, making it his home. He had asked Cassandra to marry him, but she turned him down because she wanted single-minded devotion to the kingdom of God. A spouse and children during the Great Tribulation would be a far greater danger for everyone involved.

She hadn't seen Demetrius in over a decade. She had avoided the city full of memories. What had happened to him? Like her, he would be twenty-nine by now, probably married. She wouldn't be able to face him, knowing she had helped Severus in any way. She had no other choice. She could not help a Roman murderer hunt Christians.

But she could die to protect them.

The choice was easy. She had already died to herself many years ago when she gave her life to Christ Jesus. She had nothing to lose and everything to gain. She would merely be uniting with her brothers and sisters who had already been martyred for Christ.

She climbed the rail to plunge herself into the depths. She glanced up at the stars again and whispered a prayer, "Come quickly, Lord Jesus. Save your people, vindicate your martyrs and judge your enemies." She saw a bright shooting star falling to the earth.

How beautiful. How appropriate.

She closed her eyes, felt the soft evening breeze on her face, and released her grip on the rail.

Suddenly, she felt a tug on her robe. She did not fall into the water. A hand had grabbed her cloak. A strong hand. She was pulled back onto the ship. The shock of it all made her dizzy and she fainted. But it was only for a moment. When she opened her eyes again, she stared up at a face that she did not recognize.

It wasn't Severus or Alexander, it wasn't a crew member or one of Severus' guards. He had a bright shining face, almost like bronze. He was handsome and clean shaven with dark hair, dark eyes, and muscular build.

She panicked and lost her breath at his frightful appearance. As he knelt beside her, she raised her arm in protective fear. But his peaceful face and compassionate eyes calmed her. Somehow, she knew he wasn't hostile. She lowered her arm. He had strange armor beneath his cloak. She had never seen it before. It wasn't Roman or Hebrew.

"Who are you?" she whispered.

"My name is Gabriel."

"Gabriel," she repeated with wonder. "Like the archangel."

"Exactly like the archangel." He smiled.

"Do you mean…?" Her eyes widened, moonlike. "Are you…?"

"I stand in the presence of God. And I was sent to speak to you."

She stared at him, silently and in shock, her mouth open.

"Cassandra Laetorius, do not cast yourself into the sea. For Yahweh has a plan for you. You are to bring salvation to many."

"But how?" she said. "If I stay alive, I will not bring salvation but death…to many."

Gabriel said, "This is what the Lord says, 'You must help Severus to understand the apocalypse.'"

She could not believe what she heard. "But the more he understands, the more he will persecute. You know the atrocities this man has already committed. He is an agent of Nero Caesar and a murderer of Christians."

"He is God's chosen servant to save the Christians. For this reason Yahweh has raised him up, that his Word may be proclaimed in all the land."

The contradiction could only be resolved to her with one possibility. "Will Severus become a Christian?" she asked.

"That is not your concern. You need only obey the Lord and leave the results to God."

She remained perplexed. "But we do not have the complete apocalypse, and what we do have, I do not fully understand."

"All will be revealed in due time. Only trust in the Lord wholeheartedly and lean not on your own understanding. Help Severus find the apocalypse and decipher it."

"Why do you not simply explain it to me right now? That would be easier, would it not?"

"Your journey is necessary to the accomplishment of God's will, and to the perfection of your souls."

She sighed. "Perfection" meant maturity. Paul had often told her that the kingdom of God was marked by suffering, but it was suffering through which God perfected his people. It suddenly struck her just how selfish her suicide would have been.

Another thought came to her, one that sent a chill through her. Paul had also warned about the satan disguising himself as an angel of light to deceive the elect.[1]

Her heart beat faster. Was she being deceived? Tricked into helping the enemy by a vague appeal to "God's will?" She narrowed her eyes. "How do I know you, Gabriel, are not merely one of Severus' men disguised to fool me? Or worse, a lying spirit?"

"Because Jesus Christ has come in the flesh," he said. "He is the uniquely begotten Son of God, sent as a propitiation for the sins of the world. Who is the liar, but he who denies Jesus is the Christ? That is the antichrist, he who denies both Father and Son."[2]

Paul had taught that no one could say Jesus was Lord except by the Holy Spirit. Demons would shudder at Christ, but they would not affirm his authority. She could see in his eyes that he meant what he had said. This messenger was no antichrist. But was he really who he said he was?[3]

The archangel leaned in and said, "You will be allowed to see your true enemy. And when you do, remember my words. Help Severus find the apocalypse and decipher it. In that lies the rescue of a remnant of your people, the hundred-and-forty-four thousand."

Gabriel stood back from her and opened his arms as if in welcome. His whole body began to glow like bright, burnished bronze.

The glare became so strong, it blinded her eyes. She rubbed them and opened them again, only to see he had vanished, and apparently none of the sailors on night duty had seen him. They continued fixing rigging in the dark as if nothing had happened.

What did he mean she would see the enemy? What was this rescue of the remnant? And who were "the hundred-and-forty-four thousand?" Why was he leaving her with so little understanding?

CHAPTER 38

"I will help you find and decipher the apocalypse and I will mislead you no longer."

Cassandra stood before Alexander and Severus in the corbita cabin as the ship sailed into the rising eastern sun. The sound of deckhands awake, performing their early-morning duties, told Alexander they were nearing their destination.

Severus stared at her skeptically. "Why now? After all I've done to your people?"

"Because…" She took a deep breath, as if questioning her decision to speak. "Last night I was visited by an angel of God who told me… Well, he said that you were God's instrument to save a remnant of his people."

Alexander and Severus looked with shock at each other.

Severus grinned with amusement. "Well, I would think God might want to tell me a little about his plans if he expects me to perform his will."

Alexander could not help but grin as well at the sarcasm.

"That's what I thought," she said. "But God does not tend to consult humans for his plans. Especially sinners and unbelievers."

Her implication was not lost on Severus. But he apparently decided to humor her as if she were making sense. "And what if I refuse to be his instrument?"

She said, "As did Pharaoh?"

He raised his brow. Alexander had told Severus the story of the Exodus. He knew the Israelite belief that God used even the godless to accomplish his purposes. God had hardened Pharaoh's heart to display miraculous deliverance of the Jews. God had used the evil Nebuchadnezzar as his servant to punish Israel in exile for her sins. And God had used the idolator Cyrus of Babylon as his "anointed one" to bring Israel back into the Land.[1]

Alexander hated to admit it, but she was right. God's sovereign power could not be thwarted, even by men who thought they were fighting against him. Yet Yahweh would then judge those same godless nations afterward for their own sins. What made the doctor's blood boil was that she had previously accused the Jews of being used by God to crucify Messiah to accomplish his purpose. And she did not hide her hatred for them and her desire to see them cut off and rejected by Yahweh.[2]

Severus brought him out of his thoughts. "Tell me then, Cassandra, if God has such puppet-like control over us all, why does he find fault with any of us? Why should I be punished since I am performing his will?"

She said, "Who are you, O man, to answer back to God? Will what is molded say to its molder, 'Why did you make me like this?' Does not the potter have the right to make out of the same lump of clay, one vessel for honorable use and another for dishonorable use?"[3]

She was obviously quoting some literature, thought Alexander. *Probably her apostle Paul's writings again.* But again, Alexander became annoyed, because this was the same analogy that the Hebrew prophets had used of God. Jeremiah had said Babylon was the clay in his hands used to punish Israel. Alexander was in more agreement with Cassandra than he would ever want to admit.[4]

Severus was not done. "So do you believe that God will punish Nero for what he has done to the Christians by assassinating him?"

Cunning. He was trying to lead her to an admission of guilt.

"Not by the hand of a Christian," she said.

Severus, still amused, looked to Alexander. "What do you think, Alexander? Should I trust her now?"

Alexander shared a look of contempt with Cassandra. He then said, "You can trust me to alert you to any deception I may uncover, my lord."

Severus remained focused on Cassandra. "Well then, since we all have a new pact of trust between ourselves"—his sarcasm remained light—"then I guess our Christian servant will be a bit more talkative than she has been. I look forward to the insight you intend to give us."

To Alexander's surprise, she asked, "Would my lord consider a new exchange, measure for measure? To replace your most gracious previous offer of mutual benefit?"

Severus appeared delightfully curious, disarmed by such boldness. "What exactly were you thinking?"

"May I ask you about your life and beliefs?"

"You want to decipher my life in return for deciphering the apocalypse? You Christians are truly an odd breed."

Alexander jumped in. "It's how they seek to convert others."

Severus said, "That is nothing to be afraid of, Alexander. Unless you have secrets to hide."

"Everyone has secrets, my lord," said Alexander. He tried to give the prefect a look that reminded him to consider his own secrets, ones he had shared with the doctor.

But Severus was too amused to let it bother him.

Alexander concluded the prefect was smitten with Cassandra, which made him vulnerable to her manipulation.

"Fair enough," Severus said. "In the spirit of our new 'openness,' why not? Ask me whatever you like." He qualified, "Within reason."

Cassandra glanced at Alexander. Was that a guilty look or was she hoping he was agreeable? He refused to respond. He merely glared at her, brow wrinkled, eyes narrowed.

"Tell me," she said to Severus, "how did you achieve your current position as prefect of the Vigile Cohorts?"

Severus displayed no suspicion as Alexander watched him. He had a distant look in his eyes as he reminisced about his past. "The previous vigile prefect—his name was Annaeus Serenus—was a friend of Seneca. He was at a banquet with some officers, tribunes and centurions. The entire company was poisoned by mushrooms. All of them died."[5]

Cassandra asked, "Assassination?"

"Never proven," he said. "And I have lived ever since beneath the shadow of suspicion."

"Yet it has not appeared to impede your ambitions," she said. "Did you murder Serenus for your promotion?"

264

Shocked, Alexander looked to see if Severus would respond with anger. But instead, the prefect was smiling at her directness as if impressed. It almost appeared that he welcomed the opportunity to confess.

"No, I didn't murder him. But I wanted to. So his death was a joyous occasion for my ambition. What does your god think of that?"

She responded, "Jesus said if you hate someone, you have murdered them in your heart."

"Well, that makes us all murderers, then."

"Precisely," she said.

He looked incredulous. "It sounds like this savior of yours has one impossible task of redemption."

"With man it is impossible. But with God, all things are possible."

"Why then does he cause so much trouble through his followers and then allow them to suffer for it? That strikes me as capricious. Cruel."

"I could say the same of you," she said.

Severus looked off into the distance. "I *am* a murderer."

Alexander first thought he was talking about his life as a soldier. But something in his eyes said otherwise.

Severus looked at Alexander. "The good physician. You are a Jew. What say you of this religious conundrum? Who can save me from this wretched body of death, under sentence for my deeds?"

Alexander did not answer. His jaw tightened. Sometimes it was his only way of maintaining some shred of control. This Roman Gentile controlled his life, his very body, but Alexander would not allow him to control his spirit.

Severus turned to Cassandra. "What is all the fuss about between you two? You believe in different Messiahs?"

"There is one Messiah," she answered. "Jesus of Nazareth. He was foretold by the prophets, he died for our sins, and rose from the dead. But his own people rejected him, so God has rejected them."[6]

Alexander would stay silent no longer. "That is a lie. The Nazarene did not fulfill the messianic prophecies. Yahweh's promise to Abraham was everlasting, and the Jews are the seed of Abraham."[7]

Severus smiled, leaned back and said with relish, "For being the 'chosen people,' you sure argue a lot over who is actually chosen."

Alexander and Cassandra glared at each other like gladiators competing in the arena.

Severus asked, "Is this what causes the riots in your communities?"

"It is not the Christians who riot," said Cassandra through gritted teeth. "*We* are the victims of Jewish persecution for the sake of the Gospel. As the Lord Jesus predicted."

Hatred burned in her face as she glared at Alexander.

The prefect smirked and said, "So, I guess you are right, Cassandra. We *are* all murderers at heart. Even the both of you."

Guilt washed over her face. She looked away from Alexander in shame. Her lips formed a silent prayer.

Alexander fell silent. He felt foolish that this pagan would be the one to chasten them. So much for being a light to the Gentile nations.[8]

Cassandra said painfully, "My parents were murdered by Jews in the riots under Claudius." Her countenance had fallen.

The men went silent.

Alexander thought, *So that is what drives her bitterness.*

Severus said to her, "Forgiveness is much easier to proclaim than to provide, is it not?"

Alexander could tell that Severus felt bad for her, bad that he had uncovered the flaw of imperfection in the beauty that was enchanting him.

Severus added, "So, tell me, Cassandra, measure for measure, what is this 'gospel' to which you are frequently referring?"

"It is the good news of God's kingdom. The prophet Isaiah wrote about the Messiah, or Christ, which means 'anointed one.' It is Messiah who would speak the words of the prophet: 'The Spirit of the Lord God is upon me, because Yahweh has anointed me to bring good news to the poor; he has sent me to bind up the brokenhearted, to proclaim liberty to the captives, and the opening of the prison to those who are bound; to proclaim the year of Yahweh's favor, and the day of vengeance of our God.'"[9]

"Day of vengeance?" asked Severus.

"Yes. He brings both jubilee and judgment."

"How is it that your deliverer would be a humble woodworker of no political significance, crucified under Pontus Pilate?"

"That was the messianic secret. Everyone expected that the Son of David to come would be a military warrior king. But we misunderstood the Scriptures, for Isaiah said he would be a suffering servant."

Severus glanced at Alexander, who could not hide his rising anger.

"Behold, my servant," Cassandra quoted from memory. "He was despised and rejected by men; a man of sorrows, and acquainted with grief. Surely he has borne our griefs and carried our sorrows; yet we esteemed him stricken, smitten by God, and afflicted. But he was pierced through for our transgressions; he was crushed for our iniquities; upon him was the chastisement that brought us peace, shalom, and with his wounds we are healed. All we like sheep have gone astray – every one – to his own way; and Yahweh has laid on him the iniquity of us all."[10]

Alexander was impressed by Cassandra's command of the Scriptures. But at the same time, she annoyed him with how much of it she quoted when they argued.

Severus said, "That sounds very much like the language of sacrifice to the gods."

"Sacrifice to Yahweh," she corrected. "Like a lamb that is led to slaughter on the altar, so Jesus became a substitute for our sins. The temple, the sacrificial system, was all a shadow that looked forward to the ultimate reality in Messiah."[11]

Alexander knew well enough that Severus understood sacrificial atonement. It was at the heart of all religion. Atonement was the procedure whereby the wrath of the gods was propitiated, satisfied by bloodshed. In essence, redemption was an economic exchange with the deity, like buying freedom for a slave.

Severus asked, "So you are saying that he was an innocent man dying the death of a criminal, thus purchasing the redemption of the guilty?"

"He took our place," she said. "He paid our redemption price. So that if we believe in him, his sacrifice cleanses us of our sins. By God's grace we are forgiven, through faith, and that not of ourselves. It is the gift of God." She paused. "That is the Gospel."[12]

Severus looked at Alexander for his response. He asked with incredulity, "This 'good news' is why the Jews attack Christians?"

The physician took a deep breath to calm himself down. Then he said, "It is not good news to us, my lord prefect. It is offensive. The suffering servant of Isaiah is not an individual. It is Israel, his people. We are the ones who suffer under the yoke of Roman oppression, just as we suffered under the yoke of Babylonian captivity in the time of Isaiah. It is Israel who takes on the suffering, not some individual person."[13]

Cassandra said, "But Alexander, Israel was in exile *for her sins*. The prophet wrote, 'All *we* like sheep have gone astray.' So Israel could not be the servant who is called 'the righteous one" suffering for the guilty. Israel was not innocent or sinless. But Jesus was. Isaiah said he was 'stricken for the transgression of Israel.' He bore the sin of many as the Lamb of God."[14]

Alexander became defensive. "But that passage is a litany of death. Where is this resurrection you trumpet?"

She quoted again, "'After his soul makes an offering for guilt, he shall see his offspring; he shall prolong his days.' How does a dead man see his offspring and prolong his days alive unless he is risen from the dead?"[15]

"It is a figure of speech," Alexander complained.

"For him who has ears to hear," she countered.

Severus jumped in. "You speak of this man, Jesus, as the sacrifice for sins. But what makes a mere man the mediator between God and man?"

"Jesus was no mere man," she said. "He was the Son of God. Isaiah also says, 'Therefore the Lord himself will give you a sign. Behold, the virgin shall conceive and bear a son, and shall call his name Immanuel,' which means 'God with us.'"[16]

Severus became incredulous. "Are you saying that Yahweh had sex with a human to birth his son? Like Zeus with Alcmene?"

"No," she answered. "Because then she could not be considered a virgin. It is a miracle of Yahweh. Mary, the mother of Jesus, conceived through the Holy Spirit. But the only way a mediator could reconcile God and man would be if *he* was both God and man. A God-man. That is what Jesus is: God with us, Immanuel."

Severus nodded, appearing to consider her words with approval.

Alexander protested, "The Hebrew word for that girl in Isaiah is *almah*. Almah means young maiden, not virgin."

"Alexander, is a young maiden not typically a virgin, as Rebekah was, when Abraham's servant found her at the well as an almah?"[17]

His lack of response proved that he knew she was right again.

She surprised him. "But I will grant you that it is true that almah does not always involve a lack of sexual experience."

Where is she going with this? he wondered.

She said, "You are a Hellenist, are you not?"

"Yes."

"Does not your synagogue use the Greek translation of the Torah?" The Greek translation of the Scriptures was made by Jewish scribes in Alexandria, Egypt, generations ago.

"We do," he said reluctantly. Now he knew where this was going, and he was angry at himself for being led into the trap.

"Does not the Greek Torah use the word *parthenos* for the Hebrew *almah*?"

Alexander nodded reluctantly.

"And what does *parthenos* mean, Alexander?"

"Virgin."[18] He rolled his eyes and sighed. "Nevertheless, Isaiah prophesied seven hundred years ago to King Ahaz. Those prophecies related to his own time period, not ours."

She scowled in disagreement. "I am not aware of any child in the time of Isaiah and Ahaz who fulfilled prophecy of being the 'Wonderful Counselor, Mighty God, Father of Eternity, Prince of Peace. Of the increase of his government and of peace there will be no end, on the throne of David and over his kingdom to establish it and to uphold it with justice and with righteousness from this time forth and forevermore.' Jesus is all those things and more.[19] He is the Son of David, the new temple, our Promised Land. Jesus is the Seed of Abraham."[20]

Alexander knew there was no reasoning with this woman. She knew the Scriptures too well. She was so thoroughly convinced of her religious convictions, she would not consider another view. Everything he said only emboldened her. He thought it best to avoid dragging this discussion on.

But he didn't have an answer for her. And that disturbed him deeply.

Severus broke the uncomfortable silence. "Well, that was all too scholarly for my understanding. But if I gather correctly, the identity of this Jesus as the Son of God is quite scandalous to the Jewish mind."

Alexander nodded in agreement.

"Not so for my Roman mind," Severus said. "What is scandalous to the Roman mind is the weakness. How you Christians can envisage a mighty god in the weakness of a criminal crucified beneath the power of mighty Rome is just foolishness."

Cassandra said with resignation, "God chooses the weak of the world to shame the strong. He chooses the foolish to confound the wise."[21]

"A strange god you Christians serve," said Severus. He had watched her closely, as a snake would a bird in a nest. "Cassandra, how is it you come by such scribal knowledge?"

Cassandra sighed and divulged her secret. "I traveled with the apostle Paul during some of his missionary journeys."

Severus reached down and pulled the parchment fragments from a pouch. "So, you worked closely with the provocative apostle of Tarsus whose writings have fueled a movement. And yet, the very words *we* seek to understand are still a mystery to you?"

Good, thought Alexander. *He has not been fully blinded by his obvious attraction to her.*

"Those are not the writings of Paul," she said. "I have never lied to you by saying I was not familiar with this letter. And I did not lie when I said I would help you decipher it with all that I know."

Severus asked, "Where did you meet the apostle Paul?"

"In Corinth," she replied. "But I traveled with him to Ephesus, where I lived for several years."

Severus watched her thoughtfully.

A sailor appeared at the entrance of the captain's quarters. "My lord, land is in sight."

Severus grinned. "Well then, we will soon see how much you believe this angelic vision of yours. It is time you introduce us to the Christian congregation in Ephesus."

CHAPTER 39

Ephesus

The merchant ship docked at the port of Ephesus early in the evening just after the shipping labor went home. Severus had decided to make his bodyguards stay behind, hidden on the ship, in order to maintain a covert presence in the city.

The captain and crew disembarked to find food and sleeping quarters. As they entered the city from the harbor entrance, concealed in their midst were three humbly cloaked figures, who eventually broke away from the group and made their way inconspicuously through the streets.

Though it had been ten years since her last visit, Cassandra had assured them that she had many friends in the congregation here. She maneuvered the streets and paths with a learned caution, avoiding the districts that were more hostile to the Christians. But much had changed. The city seemed like a darker world. Were her emotions mistaken?

They walked past the gymnasium and great theater, as well as a brothel and some temples of various deities. But when they approached the municipal building for the government of the city, Cassandra stopped and stared at the roof of the structure.

"What do you see?" asked Alexander.

"Are we in danger?" Severus rested his hand on his sword hilt hidden beneath his cloak.

"Follow me." She took them down an alleyway, out of the sight of the building. "This entire city is danger," she said. She decided not to tell them what she had seen standing on the roof of the civic building. She wasn't sure she had seen it herself. A tall, great shadow being. Something she had seen before.

271

The words of Gabriel came to her mind. *You will be allowed to see your true enemy.* Is that what he meant? It must have been.

She spoke to them in a hushed voice. "We are in a stronghold of spiritual evil. Principalities and powers of the heavenly places reside here."

Severus whispered, "Seeing angels again, are we?"

"Supernatural evil," she said.

Alexander looked at her.

She could see in his eyes that he was not so skeptical as before. Maybe he had felt the darkness too. Had he seen it?

They turned a corner. Suddenly, Severus stopped them and pulled them back up against the wall.

Moments later, a hooded man turned the corner after them.

Severus grabbed him by the tunic and slammed him up against the brick wall, placing a dagger at his throat. He pulled back the man's hood.

The stranger was bald and had cloudy eyes. His face was full of fear.

Severus said, "The only evil I see here is human evil. This is a stronghold of thieves and ruffians." He turned to the bald man. "I have a good mind to rob you for trying to rob us. Do you have a team waiting to ambush us?"

The bald man shook his head fearfully. He glanced down at the blade against his skin.

Cassandra approached their captive.

Severus said, "Now, how can I trust someone like you? There's only one way to make sure." He pressed the blade deeper. He drew some blood.

Then the bald man caught Cassandra's eye. Hatred filled his face.

Severus noticed. He said to her, "Do you know this rascal?"

"He is not a thief," she said. "He is a magus." She grabbed a clay amulet hanging from a chain around his neck, and yanked it off of him.

"No, no, please!"

He seemed more frightened at her act than at Severus' threat.

Cassandra threw the amulet to the ground and stomped on it, smashing it to pieces.

"No!" the magus cried out.

"I just crushed the source of his courage," she said. "He believes the amulet protects him with magic."[1]

Severus looked into the magus' frightened eyes and let the rascal go.

The bald man scurried away into the crowds out in the street.

Cassandra said, "This city is a viper's den of magic and sorcery that carries more spiritual evil than Roman eyes can see."[2]

Alexander could tell her words were meant for Severus.

Severus responded, "He seemed harmless enough to me."

She said, "He's gone to tell the guilds of magicians and necromancers that I am here. There are hundreds of them."

"What do you mean?" interrupted Alexander.

"When we were in this city with the apostle Paul, he caused great harm to their economic industry of sorcery and idol worship. That magus remembered me. They will hunt us down."[3]

"Why didn't you tell me that?" Severus complained. "I would have killed him."

"Haven't you killed enough?" she said. Her strength was arresting to Alexander. She had transformed from their lowly servant in Rome into a formidable equal here in Ephesus.

Severus appeared speechless. Her words seemed to expose him. He *had* killed so much. He *was* a death dealer.

Yet an angel supposedly told her to help him? Alexander still found it beyond belief.

"Come," she said. "They fear the Christian quarter of the city. We can find refuge there."

"What do they fear?" asked Severus.

"The Angel of Ephesus."

Alexander knew she meant the guardian angel of the city. The demon goddess Artemis may own this city. But angels still guarded Yahweh's people.

Cassandra led them down the alley toward their destination.

They arrived in the Christian quarter on the far eastern edge of the city. It was dilapidated and mostly abandoned.

Cassandra seemed taken aback.

The sun was setting, increasing the shadows around them.

As they walked through the streets, she looked around at the people they passed. She whispered to the men, "I recognize no one."

Severus had been eyeing her closely. He saw her hesitate.

He said, "Leading us into an ambush as well?"

She said, "I have been praying from the day you enslaved me that God would ambush you with his grace."

Severus looked to Alexander for support. Alexander shrugged with resignation and looked nervously behind them. No sorcerers were on their trail yet.

Cassandra led them to a house at the end of the street. "I stayed with these Christians for two years. We will be safe with them."

They walked up to the door. It was a residence somewhat larger than those surrounding it. But just as worn and torn.

Cassandra knocked.

An older lady that Cassandra did not recognize cracked open the door and eyed her suspiciously. She saw the two men behind Cassandra.

"Who are you?"

"My name is Cassandra Laetorius. I'm a shipping merchant. I lived here a few years back with the family of Apollos the Egyptian."

"He left the city ten years ago." The old woman came across as impatient, abrupt even.

"Yes," Cassandra said. "But what of his son, Demetrius? He had stayed behind."

The lady slammed the door on her.

Cassandra was shaken. But she was determined. She knocked on the door again. From inside, they heard the old lady's voice, "Go away. Christians are not welcomed here." Cassandra turned to her comrades with complete surprise. "I do not know what has happened. It seems as if the Christians have left the city."

Severus said, "Or worse."

She didn't want to believe it. "I know it was difficult here, but not..." She could not bring herself to speak the worst. Caesar's condemnation of Christianity as *religio illicita* had reached throughout the empire.

They heard a whistle in the distance. They turned to see the little bald man down the street, holding a torch. He whistled again.

"They found us," said Severus.

Alexander said, "If only you had brought your bodyguards with us."

Severus said, "Nothing but a century of well-armed legionaries can stop a mob like that."

They saw a swarm of citizens with torches join the bald man. He pointed directly at the three of them.

Cassandra also saw the eight-foot tall shadow creature standing above them in their midst. "Demons of hell," she said.

"I believe you this time," said Severus. "We had better run."

Cassandra saw a young boy watching them from an alleyway. He waved at them. "This way," she said, and they took off running down the side street toward the boy.

When they met him, they discovered he was not a child, but a small man, a dwarf of less than four feet in height with a knife scar down a blind left eye. "You are looking for Demetrius?" he asked.

Cassandra nodded. "Yes."

The dwarf gestured to some thick bushes. "Get behind these, they are almost upon you."

Alexander said, "Do you know this man?"

She stared at the knife wound, wondering where it came from. "No," came her reply.

"How then can we trust him?"

"We have no choice." Severus drew his sword, looked the dwarf in his good eye and said, "Little man, I will be close enough to cut you down."

The dwarf smiled eerily.

Severus joined his comrades behind the foliage. He cocked his head, as if wondering about the unsavory background of their battle-scarred helper.

The shouting men came down their street.

The dwarf yelled to them, "They went toward the Magnesian Gate!"

It was the obvious escape route. He *was* helping them.

They saw the torchlights through the thick foliage, and the sounds of a mob of over a hundred chase by.

After the mob was gone, they saw the little face of the smiling one-eyed dwarf appear from around the bush. "It's all clear."

The three of them slipped out into the alleyway, still in the shadows.

Alexander said, "Where can we go?"

Severus said, "When they discover our ploy, they'll split up and search the city. We can't stay here."

The dwarf said, "There is only one place you can go, where criminals are safe."

He looked straight at Cassandra. She knew exactly where he meant. But she didn't agree it would be all that safe.

Before she could respond, she heard two men with torches jogging after the crowd. The three ducked back into the shadows.

The dwarf went out to meet the two men.

Severus peeked out from their hiding place. The two men did not look normal. They jerked and twitched like angry puppets. They did not appear in full possession of their bodies. When they spoke, their voices were not singular, but like an overlap of several voices.

One of them said, "What are you doing, little man?"

The other said, "Hiding something?"

The first one added, "We'll have to cut it out of you."

Cassandra whispered, "They are possessed by demons."[4]

Severus moved to save the dwarf, but he stopped when he saw the little one-eyed man draw a dagger and stab one of them in the belly. He spun around, stabbing the other in the belly as well. The two thugs dropped their torches and doubled over, howling like wounded hyenas, now down to the dwarf's level. He promptly dispatched both by slicing their throats open. They fell to the ground in unison, choking on their own blood, unable to call out for help.

So, he *was* a dangerous brigand of some kind after all.

Severus stepped out to meet the small warrior. The dwarf wiped the blade off on one of the dead men's tunics and offered its handle to Severus.

Severus felt for his dagger in his belt. It was missing. The dwarf had stolen his blade from him. So he was a burglar as well.

The prefect looked back at the little man with surprise, only to be greeted by that toothy smile.

"Who are you?" said Severus.

Alexander butted in with humor, "The Angel of Ephesus?"

Severus smirked. "We had best confirm that with our spiritual Sensitive." It was an obvious jab at Cassandra's angelic visitation.

The dwarf smiled. "Do not expect me to wipe out that mob for you."

"We must go," said Cassandra. "Immediately."

"Where to?" asked Severus.

"The Artemisium."

Both Severus and Alexander had heard of it before. The Artemisium was just north of the city, a half mile from where they were through the forest. The huge temple of Artemis was famous throughout the land for its policy of protective sanctuary for criminals who could make it inside its hallowed pillars.[5]

To Cassandra, it was the very heart of spiritual evil in the city, but it was the only place they would be safe from the lynch mob. After all, if Christians were criminals, then they too were protected by its asylum.

"Godspeed," said the dwarf.

The three jogged over to the tree line for their half-mile journey to the huge acropolis. But before they could even break the tree line, they heard the shout of a group of men coming back from the gates.

"There they are! The Christians!"

Cassandra looked over to see what the dwarf would do.

He was gone.

The three of them bolted into the forest.

There were twenty or so pursuers behind them. Too many for Severus to handle with his sword. They ran on, small branches slapping them in the face, feet slowed by the undergrowth on the forest floor.

They were able to stay just far enough ahead of their pursuers until they were near the end of the forest.

But then they heard voices and saw to their left that they had been outmaneuvered. Another group had run around the forest and was now entering from the west to cut them off.

Cassandra could see the torches getting closer. If the three refugees could not make it to the forest edge before them, they would be surrounded, front and back, by the killing mob.

They pressed on, exhausted, but running for their lives.

The advantage they had was not having torches, so they could not be easily spotted.

But without a light, they also could not see well enough.

Severus did not notice the low-hanging branch that dropped him to the ground with a thud. He felt his nose break, bleeding all over.

Alexander was there. Then Cassandra.

"No," Severus mumbled. He felt dizzy and was starting to pass out. "Leave me. Get to the temple. Save yourselves."

"Quiet," whispered Alexander. "They might hear you."

The trio laid low in the thicket. Everyone was all around now, looking for them. They were encircled by one big dragnet that was getting closer and closer.

Alexander saw Cassandra silently mouthing a prayer. It made him angry how much she prayed. It made him feel out of touch with God.

A single torch was coming their way. They ducked.

The hunter stood alone, as others searched among the trees for their prey nearby. He heard a noise in the brush in front of him. He peered closer.

It looked like someone sitting on the ground.

He was about to yell out that he found something. But before he could, someone grabbed his torch hand. He looked to his left.

It was a red-haired woman. A *woman*?

Before he could figure out what was happening, a dried tree branch slugged him in the face, and he fell to the ground, leaving the torch in the hand of the woman.

Cassandra whispered, "May you find the light of the world."

"Let's go," whispered Alexander.

They reached Severus, who could now stand, but was still dizzy from the concussion. Alexander thought he must be feeling completely ridiculous. Here he was, a hardened warrior incapacitated by running into a tree branch. The mightiest of men were, in the end, still subject to the weakness of human flesh and bone.

They helped hold him steady and began to walk around as if they were one of the hunters looking for the fleeing Christians. And they just walked right through the searching sorcerers to the edge of the forest.

Then, they dropped the torch and ran for it.

The Acropolis was a few hundred yards away.

Alexander kept his eyes on the huge pillared columns lit by evening torches. He heard an arrow whiz by his head.

They were trying to shoot them down.

Alexander and Cassandra just kept running, helping to hold up the staggering Severus. They made it to the bottom of the acropolis and began their steep ascent of steps to the temple top.

Alexander looked back.

The mob of hunters had stopped launching missiles at them, now that they were on holy ground. But they continued to chase them.

The travelers were not safe in the sanctuary yet.

They broke the top of the steps. Only another hundred feet to the acropolis steps, and another fifty steps to the top.

But the mob was already upon them.

Severus found a burst of inner strength.

But it was not enough.

They were tackled at the very foot of the temple steps.

Twenty or so men surrounded them.

The already-wounded Severus was hit from behind with a staff. He dropped to his knees. Take out the strong man first.

Rape the woman next.

One of them cackled like a hyena and danced up to her. He couldn't look in her eyes, but stared off to her left as if trained on a master. Cassandra could smell his rancid breath. It reeked of sulfur. He was clearly not the one controlling his body.

She said, "I am covered by the blood of Jesus Christ."

The demoniac jerked back as if punched in the soul. He flopped around on the ground like a fish out of water.

But then a voice rang out from behind.

"Do not touch them!"

The demoniac stopped flopping. He got up, howled, and ran away into the crowd that parted.

The bald man with cloudy eyes walked up to them. He must have been a leader of this guild of sorcerers. He said, "We want them alive and fully conscious...for now."

Alexander looked up at the bald man, who walked over to Severus and kicked him in the gut. Severus grunted and laid out on the ground.

The bald man kicked him one more time in the head, and the Roman went unconscious. The bald man said, "Bring these scum back to the city."

But before they could do so, everyone was surprised by the sound of a war cry from the top of the steps of the temple.

A mob of a hundred criminals who had been hiding out in the temple now descended the stairs in a fury. They caught the magi and sorcerers like a tsunami wave.

The magi could not withstand the force of hardened killers and thugs, who were evidently more experienced in fighting than they.

The magi melted before the ruffians. The few who were not knocked silly, ran back down the steps.

The ruffians carried Severus, Alexander and Cassandra to safety behind the pillars of the temple of Artemis. The three had been rescued from an angry mob of magicians and sorcerers by a desperate band of refugee thugs and criminals.

CHAPTER 40

Severus awoke from his unconsciousness. Cassandra was attending to his bleeding nose.

Alexander moved in. "Are you with us?"

"Yes," said Severus.

"Good," said Alexander. And without warning, he grabbed Severus' nose between his hands and jerked. Severus heard a crunching sound and almost passed out from the pain.

"I am sorry," said Alexander. "It's best if you don't anticipate it."

"Fair enough," mumbled Severus. His nose pain was less now, and he could breathe through it. "Who saved us?" he asked.

"Jesus did," Cassandra said brightly. "But you'll say it was the refugees of the temple."

Alexander smiled.

Severus leaned up.

Alexander said, "I guess criminals help their own."

They were in the vast interior of the temple of Artemis. A wooden statue of the goddess adorned the far end, attended by priests beneath torchlight. It was huge, carved with loving detail: an elaborate headdress, a zodiac necklace, bulbous packets of magic that looked like many breasts, and in her hands a sacred stone that fell from heaven.[1]

Severus said with a smirk, "Are you sure it wasn't the graven image over there that rescued us?"

Cassandra whispered with a smile, "What would that ugly demoness want with us?"

Alexander threw in, "I think it would be wise if we saved our insults of Artemis for a time when we are not surrounded by her attendants."

Severus sat up.

"Be careful, my lord," said Alexander. "You have a concussion. You need to rest."

Severus ignored the prescription. He looked at Cassandra. "Why did you save me in the forest?"

She didn't answer him.

He said, "And do not say it was because an angel told you to."

She shrugged, looked away. "But he did."

He said, "After being persecuted by Rome, and your people killed in the arena, why, having an opportunity to escape your bondage, did you risk your life and rescue me, your master?"

"You are not my true master," she corrected him.

"Why did you do it?"

She sighed.

Alexander watched her like a hawk.

She said, "Because Jesus did the same for me."

Severus still failed to comprehend this bizarre love for one's enemies, this embrace of martyrdom. It went against everything he believed. It seemed like a suicide pact to him.

He said to her, "This Messiah of yours, I still don't understand his ways. But I thank you, Cassandra."

She replied, "You don't have to understand grace to experience it."

Suddenly, Alexander began weeping.

"What is wrong, Alexander?" she asked.

He gathered his wits. He took a labored breath. "I killed my wife."

It seemed to come out of nowhere. Something she said must have triggered him.

Cassandra said, "But she died in the Great Fire."

He shook his head softly. "I let her die."

She glanced at Severus. So it hadn't come out of nowhere. Everything they had experienced had led up to this.

"I returned to my home before it burned down. I saw her and her lover passed out on the threshold from the smoke." He paused. He could barely say it. "I didn't help them. I let them die. I could have saved her, but I let her die.

I watched the house fall upon them and consume them in flames. And I told myself she deserved it."

Severus and Cassandra remained silently listening.

"But I am the one who deserves it. I deserve the fire. I have betrayed my people and my God. I have sacrificed others for my own survival." Alexander looked at Severus with red eyes. "You said on the ship that we are all murderers."

Severus nodded.

Alexander said, "I am a murderer."

Cassandra placed a comforting hand on his shoulder. "There is atonement, Alexander. Real, transforming forgiveness. The perfect High Priest has come. He was tempted in every way as we have been, but he was without sin. And he entered the heavenly temple by his shed blood as the unblemished Lamb of God." She was speaking the language of Torah. "He rose from the dead to justify us. He is Messiah, Alexander. Stop resisting him. Let him forgive you."

This talk was religious-sounding babble to Severus. Theological symbols and metaphors. It amazed him, but it made no sense to his reason. Symbols and metaphors were just no match for the cold hard reality of flesh and blood, stone and steel, power and dominion.

But for Alexander, everything made perfect sense. His Hellenism had polluted his reasoning with Greek philosophical nonsense. But he was still a Jew, and he lived and breathed the meaning of Torah, temple and land. In one big rush of transcendence, he suddenly understood it all. Not in intellectual cognition, but in a baptism of spirit. A wave of faith washed over him. It felt like he was given a gift. It was not something he had done of himself.

While Severus was completely unaware of what he was witnessing, Cassandra's eyes filled with tears. She knew exactly what was happening.

Alexander said with surprise in his voice, "I believe."

He just knew Jesus was the promised Messiah. The fulfillment of Torah, temple and land.

Everyone stared at each other with a long silence.

Finally, Alexander said to Severus, "I will not help you hunt Christians any longer."

Severus searched his eyes for conviction. It was real. Something had truly changed in this Jew.

"No," said Cassandra. "You must fulfill your duty to Severus."

"What are you saying?" said Alexander. "You have faced life and death to explain Messiah to us. And now you would encourage me to betray that Messiah?"

She smiled. "There is no earthly Messiah for you to betray. That is the delusion of Rome. Severus does not believe Jesus is risen, so he looks for him among the earthly false prophets. He can search all he wants. He will never find Jesus on this earth."

Severus was amused that she had no fear talking right in front of him like this. *Well, if she's right, then she's right, I will be wasting my time on a fool's errand.* And since she was arguing on behalf of staying obedient to Severus, then let her persuade Alexander all she wanted. *But if she is wrong...*[2]

She spoke softly, "Alexander, I believe God has a special purpose for you."

"What?" he said, frustrated.

"I don't know. But I do believe the apocalypse is not what Rome thinks it is. If we help Severus find the rest of it, and decipher it, we will only be deciphering God's will. And God's will cannot be used against us. Find your purpose in the apocalypse."

Alexander searched her eyes for more.

Severus added, with a touch of sarcasm, "And don't forget that angel's advice."

Alexander looked at Severus with surprise. Then a smile spread on the doctor's lips.

At that very moment Severus' finely tuned instincts became aware of what was happening around them. This emotional transformation had so captured his curiosity and attention that he had failed to see the criminals in the temple slowly and quietly descending upon them.

But now, it was too late.

The trio were surrounded by murderers, rapists, thieves and bandits. A good hundred of them. They were dirty, hungry and determined.

They grabbed their three visitors.

Cassandra screamed.

Alexander tried to protect her, but he was held down by four men.

Even as wounded as he was, Severus was able to knock down two men before he was overwhelmed by five others.

The band of criminals used rope to tie up their quarry. They dragged them over to the large statue of the Mother Goddess.

The priests of Artemis stood waiting in their white robes with bejeweled hands and necks, their male gender disguised beneath the effeminate makeup on their faces.

One of them said, "Take them to the Garden of Ortygia."

CHAPTER 41

Alexander looked up at the treetops that passed by in the bright moonlight. He, Cassandra and Severus were carried over the heads of their captors through the grove of terebinths that filled the Garden of Ortygia. There was no struggling, no searching for an out. They were outnumbered and overpowered. And Severus was too wounded with his concussion to be of much help for escape.

They were totally and completely at the mercy of these criminal servants of Artemis.

They arrived at the foot of a huge tree, the branches of which spread out like the legs of a hoary spider.

Alexander saw it was a sacred tree, with a shrine to Artemis—and a stone altar of sacrifice. The thought occurred to him that this timber idol, considered a tree of life to these idolaters, would become a tree of death for him and his companions.

Several priestesses of Artemis welcomed the party as the hostages were pushed to the ground, back to back.

Alexander saw the horns on the four corners of the altar and his mind drifted. He was reminded of the horned altar of the holy temple in Jerusalem. The priest would smear the blood of the sacrifice on the horns. Alexander didn't know if they represented the horns of the sacrificial animals or were a symbol of deity and sacred space. But it struck him as a sick parody of atonement that these pagans engaged in with their false idols.[1]

As a Jew, he had always considered the gods of the pagans as foolish myths that blinded their followers to the Creator. Now he saw them for what they really were: demonic evil.

But it also struck him that those horns in Jerusalem were a refuge of protection for accused criminals in a similar way that the Artemisium was.

He imagined himself before that altar in the promised land, far, far away, grasping the blood-drenched horns, pleading, "Have mercy on us, heavenly father."[2] But there was to be no mercy this evening for the Christian intruders.

"The female first." The High Priestess, a viciously beautiful woman, gestured towards Cassandra, who struggled as the criminals hoisted her bound form onto the horned altar and held her down.

Alexander knew what this was. They all knew what it was. Human sacrifice. And they were to be the victims.[3]

The priestess raised her hands to the sacred tree above her and prayed in a foreign language that Alexander had never heard before.

He felt Severus working on the knots of his bonds at his back. Would it matter?

All he could think of was those two broken infants he had crushed and cut up for Severus so long ago. He never forgot them. Nor the cries and screams of the Christians he had helped to capture for torture. He had denied his complicity in the crimes, rationalized them as a means to the end of saving his own people. But not any more. His repentance had marked a change of heart. But even though Christ had forgiven him of his sins, was this fate the earthly consequence of his actions?

Cassandra saw a tall dark shadow rise up behind the priestess. It looked like the wooden idol in the temple they had just come from. The horned headdress, a multitude of magic pouches on her chest. And it was the creature she had seen on the roof of the agora watching them. She knew at once that this was the demonic principality of Ephesus.[4]

Did the others see it?

The priestess jerked and twitched like a puppet, much like the group of men they had seen from the alleyway in Ephesus. And when the woman opened her eyes, they were pure white. Her pupils were rolled back into her head. She kept praying in a foreign tongue, her voice sounded altered, as if a voice of other spirits were sharing it.

Alexander felt Severus finish loosing his bonds. Their captors did not notice. Alexander's hands were free.

He knew this was his only chance to do something, anything. But they were outnumbered, and he was not a warrior. What could he do?

It was hopeless. But he was not going to sit there and let it happen. Never again. He stood up and bolted for the altar.

The others were too shocked to respond.

He tried to pull Cassandra off the stone.

The priestess began laughing like a hyena.

Four men were upon him, grasping his arms, pulling him away.

Alexander fought against them with every ounce of his strength. "No!" he shouted. "No, No! Take me! Please, take me!"

The four men dragged him back next to Severus.

The priestess returned to her cryptic babbling.

As someone retied his hands behind his back, Alexander felt the complete release of failure. He had done everything he could do, but it was not enough. He would have to accept their fate.

A strange calm came over him as he saw Cassandra, her head turned toward him, on her lips, a prayer. He could barely hear the words. "Though I walk through the valley of the shadow of death, I will fear no evil, for you are with me."

It was the Twenty-Third Psalm of David. He knew it well from his Torah schooling. He used to pray it on the battlefield while tending to the wounded and dying. He realized he had stopped praying it long ago.

Their eyes locked in spirit. He prayed with her. The words came back from the deep recesses of his memory. "For you are with me; your rod and your staff, they comfort me. You prepare a table before me in the presence of my enemies."

In that moment all evil dropped away, and it was only the two of them, Alexander and Cassandra, with the spirit of the living God uniting them before a heavenly throne.

Preparing herself for the kill, the priestess raised a sacrificial dagger above Cassandra's prone form.

Alexander continued to pray. He was not afraid. He would see her again one day. He believed in the resurrection.

But suddenly, a swooshing sound was accompanied by the thud of two arrows plunging into the chest of the priestess. She jerked back against the mighty tree. A third arrow pinned her throat to the trunk.

Alexander looked back for the source of the attack.

As did everyone else.

Several more arrows came out of the night and dropped the other possessed priests.

The criminals took defensive stances. But they had no weapons. They were not allowed in the asylum of the temple.

Twenty shadow warriors jumped out of the dark surrounding the gathering. It was an ambush.

But Alexander wasn't sure who it was. The sorcerers from earlier? Were they now out of the cauldron and into the coals?

These men fought with warrior precision and skill. They used staffs and clubs. They beat and pummeled the criminals into the ground with ease. These were no sorcerers or magicians.

In the midst of the mayhem, Alexander saw the form of the nameless, one-eyed dwarf they had met on the street. The little man scurried up to him and cut his bonds.

"You!" said Alexander.

"Were you expecting an angel?" The dwarf smiled.

"Thank you."

The dwarf finished and moved to cut the bonds of Severus.

Alexander ran to Cassandra and sought to untie her. But he had no blade and the rope was too tight.

The battle was swift. The odds were unfair. The criminals were battered senseless and clubbed unconscious in no time.

The attackers had swords but they did not use them. For some unknown reason they did not kill. They merely pummeled the enemy into a defenseless stupor.

Alexander stood protectively over Cassandra. The hostages had been left unharmed.

In moments, it was all over. Unconscious criminals littered the ground at their feet.

One of the warriors approached Alexander and Cassandra. He had a dagger in his hand.

The other twenty warriors circled them.

Alexander stood between the helpless Cassandra and the rescuing knight. He was a tall, dark-skinned Egyptian with flowing black hair and eyes to match, a wide chin and dimple. He had a rugged handsomeness, probably thirty years of age.

From behind him, Alexander heard Cassandra call out, "Demetrius!"

The stranger responded, "Cassie." It was a shortened version of her name. The way a close friend might say it.

Alexander sighed with relief. *Finally, saved by someone who wasn't going to kill us.* He let Demetrius cut her ropes.

She said to the tall warrior, "I thought you might be dead."

Demetrius said with a smile, "You almost were."

She sat up. "I consider you a guardian angel."

Alexander found himself feeling jealous, intimidated by their masculine savior.

Demetrius asked her, "These with you, are they Christians?"

She glanced at Severus. "They are safe."

Severus nodded with gratitude.

Demetrius turned serious toward Cassandra. "No one here is really safe. The Day of the Lord is coming."

Then they kissed cheeks as old friends would.

"I have missed you, Cassie," said Demetrius.

She said, "And I, you."

Alexander could see there was a deep connection between these two. He butted in, "Where did the dwarf go? If it weren't for him alerting your forces, we would all three be dead right now."

Demetrius turned to Alexander with a confused look. "Dwarf?"

"He didn't tell us his name. He had a battle wound over his left eye. Was he not the one who informed you of our escape from the city?"

Demetrius said with amusement, "We have spies all over Ephesus, but not one of them is a one-eyed dwarf. Catalus, who keeps an eye on the guild of sorcerers, is the one who told me about you. He is not small, and he has both eyes."

Alexander exchanged knowing looks with Severus and Cassandra. Perhaps they had encountered the Angel of Ephesus after all, in supernatural disguise.

She asked Demetrius, "Where do you live now? Are you in hiding?"

"Yes. Five miles south of here in the mountains. I will explain it all later." He turned to his men. "Let us get Cassie and her friends out of here, before these wicked wretches wake up and we are discovered."

The trio found their horses just outside the grove. Severus sent a messenger for his bodyguards to join them. They were already deep into the mountains before the sun came up to expose their deeds in the diabolical garden.

Cassandra walked her horse beside Demetrius. Alexander and Severus were behind them. The bodyguards took up the rear.

Demetrius had been explaining to Cassandra what happened. "The persecution of believers in the city was intensifying. It had the effect of purifying our faith, separating the false converts from the true. But it also threatened the extinction of our entire community. We could no longer wait for the inevitable. So we fled to the mountains and established a free community there."[5]

Alexander joined in. "Why do you say it was inevitable?"

Demetrius answered, "The apostle John brought the mother of Jesus to live in Ephesus many years ago. We realized she would become a symbolic target of violence. We had to protect her. She has since gone home to be with the Lord."[6]

Severus piped up, "I noticed your fighters who rescued us were trained warriors."

Demetrius explained, "They are an elite rescue team of ex-legionaries and mercenaries who converted to the faith. They are called Kharabu. It is an ancient word that means 'clan of the cherubim, guardians of Eden.'"[7]

Severus said, "I thought you Christians were all peaceful."

Demetrius smiled. "We are. But peace has many dimensions. One of them is the protection of others. We only kill in self-defense or in defense of others. It's what the law of God provides. But our goal is to get Christians to safety before God judges a city."

"Like Noah's ark?" said Severus.

"Very good," said Demetrius.

Severus smirked. "I know more of your cult than you may realize."

Demetrius added, "Jesus said that the days before his coming would be like the days of Noah. Destruction would take the wicked by surprise, like a thief in the night. But his faithful servants would be ready."[8]

Severus said sardonically, "Rescue the few, to hell with the rest." He may have been familiar with their beliefs, but he still didn't care for them.

Alexander was impressed by the genius of Demetrius' plan, which only made him more envious as he watched Cassandra's attention toward the tall dark warrior.

"Well then," said Demetrius, "be thankful you are one of the elect today. We just arrived at the ark."

Cassandra saw the village ahead of them, nestled in the folds of the mountain they had been traversing.

"Welcome to Kirkindje."

CHAPTER 42

Alexander had slept long and hard after their perilous experience in Ephesus. Now, safely protected by these Christians, he had become overwhelmed with exhaustion and slept through the night and into midday.

Evidently, Severus had a similar situation, because when Alexander awoke, the prefect was still asleep in their visitor's home.

But Cassandra was not.

"Severus," said Alexander with alarm.

Severus awoke.

"Cassandra is gone." Alexander began putting on his clothes.

Severus got up, shaking himself out of his sleep.

There was no telling how these Christians may have helped their beloved merchant's daughter to escape. She could already be long gone into the mountains by now. They had let their guard down.

Severus strapped on his sword.

If she was really gone, Demetrius' head would roll. He didn't care that Demetrius saved the three of them from certain death at the hands of the Ephesians. He didn't care how hospitable they had been treated by these Christians. It would only make the betrayal deeper.

But the two of them stopped their frantic preparation when they saw Cassandra enter the room with Demetrius.

"It is about time you two are awake," said Cassandra.

Alexander and Severus looked at each other with surprise.

Demetrius held out some papyrus in his hand as Cassandra explained to them, "Demetrius has provided us with more clues to our search. He has some missing fragments of our mysterious apocalypse."

Alexander looked at the gallant Demetrius beside her. What else had their host shared with her? And what secrets had she shared with him?

Severus asked Demetrius, "Why would you help us?"

293

Demetrius said, "We will be helping each other. You have pieces that we do not have."

Severus replied, "Why would you help *me*?" He was, after all, the Roman in the room. An obvious danger to their safety.

"Because I agree with Cassie," said Demetrius, "that you will find something very different from what you are looking for."

Severus said, "Are you so certain?"

"That is faith," said Demetrius. "For him who has—"

"Ears to hear." Severus finished the line with him. "Yes, Cassandra has already said that to me more than once."

Demetrius smiled. "Here's praying you'll grow some ears."

Alexander was barely following the discussion. All he saw was Demetrius' annoying smile at Cassandra. All he heard was that personal nickname he gave her: Cassie. It made him feel like an outsider. Even after all the time he had spent with her on their journey together. Even after his conversion. She had a past with Demetrius that clearly drew them close.

Severus interrupted Alexander's jealous thoughts. "Get to work deciphering, Alexander. We have no time to delay."

Severus had a migraine headache from his concussion and his nose was still sore from its previous break. He spent the remainder of the day resting as Alexander read and discussed their puzzle of papyrus and parchment with the others.

When he awoke, it was night. He felt much better and could hear the other three in the next room still discussing the letter.

When Severus stepped into the room, their talk quickly died down with his presence.

"Good evening," said Demetrius.

Severus saw him put something away in his leather satchel. "I trust you are feeling better."

"Much better," said Severus. "Thank you." He saw the parchment and papyrus on the table before all of them. Then he sat in their circle. "Now, tell me what my ears need to hear." He picked up a piece of papyrus to look at it.

The parchment they had was made of animal skin. This papyrus was made from reeds and glue.

"You need to read what we have, first," said Cassandra. "With our combined fragments, we have most of the first sections of the letter. Here." She handed a burnt piece to him. "Start with the first."

Severus asked, "Do we now know who wrote this?"

"Unfortunately, we still do not have all the pieces," she said. "That one is the burnt fragment that we already had with the missing greeting."

"How many pieces are there to the letter?"

"That is unsure," said Demetrius. "Our fragments stop at eighteen."

Severus spent the next half hour reading closely the fragments in order. A couple sections were missing, but he had a clearer picture now of the content. Clearer, that is, only in terms of what it said.

But not what it meant.

He put the last fragment down. "Well, this is quite a proclamation of destruction. It seems the writer has had a vision of the heavenlies and this Jesus redivivus has convinced him that he will bring a series of judgments upon the land unlike anything ever seen before. Four sets of seven judgments. Seven broken seals, seven sounding trumpets, seven unheard thunders and seven poured-out bowls. That is quite excessive."

Alexander said, "Do not be fooled by your rational Roman mind. You have to think like a Hebrew to understand the symbols. The judgment is severe. But the repetition of numbers and judgments reflects a common technique used by Jewish writers called recapitulation."

"Recapitulation?" repeated Severus.

Demetrius said, "It's a cyclical repetition, a way of saying the same thing in four different ways. The seals, the trumpets, the thunders and the bowls are all referring to the same judgments from four different perspectives. Except we only have three, because John did not reveal what the thunders were. But that's why each have seven elements, and if you look at those elements, they overlap with each other."[1]

"Give me an example," demanded Severus.

"Here." Alexander picked up some of the letter pieces as reference. "The second trumpet and second bowl both talk about the sea. The third trumpet and third bowl talk about wrath upon the rivers and waters. The fourth trumpet and bowl address the sun. The sixth trumpet and bowl call upon the River Euphrates. Babylon falls or is destroyed three different times. But really, only once. Each seal, trumpet and bowl judgment provides a different perspective and adds more detail to the picture as it progresses toward the final judgment. It operates as a kind of spiraling whirlpool of meaning, not a chronological order of events."[2]

Cassandra added, "God often repeats himself when he says something very important. The prophet Daniel is an example. We spoke about this on the ship during our journey here. During the Jewish exile in Babylon, God gave Nebuchadnezzar a dream of a kingly statue made of four different metals. The metals represented each one of four consecutive kingdoms that would unfold in history after Daniel. There was the Babylonian kingdom, the Medo-Persian, the Greek and the Roman kingdoms. Then after Belshazzar succeeded Nebuchadnezzar, God gave Daniel a dream that recapitulated those kingdoms as monstrous hybrid beasts, very similar to these, yet different."[3]

Severus said, "You mean, the lion, the bear, the leopard and the beast with ten horns."

"Yes," she said. "And later, under King Darius, Daniel received another vision from God. A threefold expanding cycle of repetition."[4]

Severus asked, "But what do all the symbols mean?"

"That will take some time," said Alexander. "But we believe there is a key to those symbols in yet another prophet of the exile: Ezekiel. This letter seems to be modeled after the prophecy of Ezekiel."[5]

Severus stood and paced the floor around them. "And you are all still convinced that this Jesus redivivus, who is supposedly bringing these judgments upon the earth, is not an earthly revolutionary in hiding, but your Nazarene rabbi resurrected from the dead, and one day coming back on the clouds of heaven."

They all nodded their heads. Cassandra said, "Yes."

Severus stood beside Demetrius, searching their faces for deception. There was none. He could see these deluded Christians really believed this.

But they were not telling the entire truth to him. And he had an idea of where that truth may be hidden.

Before Demetrius could respond, Severus stepped behind him, pulled his dagger and put it to the man's throat.

Cassandra gasped. Demetrius froze. Though he was a skilled warrior, so was Severus.

Severus reached down and opened Demetrius' satchel at his feet. This was the satchel he had seen Demetrius use to secret something when Severus had entered the room earlier. The prefect slowly pulled out a piece of parchment. It appeared to be another fragment of the apocalypse. "Now, let us see what you have been hiding from me." Careful not to give Demetrius an opportunity for escape, Severus held the dagger tight to his neck and handed the fragment to Alexander. "Read it."

Alexander began, "The revelation of Jesus Christ, which God gave him to show to his servants the things that must soon take place. He made it known by sending his angel to his servant—John."

His voice quivered.

Severus said, "So you do know the author of this letter after all."

"They didn't know," Demetrius said. "I was keeping it from them."

Cassandra and Alexander looked as surprised as Severus felt.

Demetrius added, "Alexander told me you were commissioned with executing the author of the apocalypse. And since they were helping you find him, I didn't want any of you to know."

Another look at their bewildered faces assured Severus that the Egyptian was telling the truth.

Severus said to Alexander, "Keep reading."

Alexander read on in the letter and came to the clincher. "I, John, your brother and partner in the tribulation and the kingdom and the patient endurance that are in Jesus, was on the island called Patmos on account of the word of God and the testimony of Jesus." When he got to that part, Alexander stopped in shock.

Was this the first he had read it?

And then it dawned on Severus. "I remember this man. He survived being boiled in oil. I was there when Nero banished him. This is your apostle John."

He gripped Demetrius' neck tighter. "Thank you for your hospitality. And for your help in identifying the author of this apocalypse, who will no doubt enlighten us as to the true meaning of his symbols and metaphors."

Cassandra said, "Please…do not kill him, Severus."

Alexander added, "Can you blame him for protecting the apostle?"

"Maybe you should have told him about your angel, Cassandra. We could have avoided all this." Severus saw abject fear in her face. *She must still be in love with this Egyptian,* he thought. *That will be useful for me if she ever changes her mind about her God-given mission.*

The prefect released the knife from Demetrius' throat and stood back. "I have decided to spare this man's life. I will bring him with us. Everyone, pack your things. We leave immediately for Patmos."

CHAPTER 43

Caesarea Philippi was an important city of merchant and religious activity at the crossroads of travel near the base of Mount Hermon. It represented the height of the emperor cult as developed by Herod the Great. He spent hundreds of talents of gold to make it a center of Hellenism. Its population was a hybrid mixture of Greek, Roman and Semitic residents. Its religion, a fusion of Greco-Roman polytheism.

But its real power lay just outside the city, a brief walk away to a sacred grotto in the foothills, the cave sanctuary of Pan. Called Panias, the location of this grotto at the bottom of the cosmic mountain Hermon, in the ancient land of Bashan, made it a spiritual nexus. Bashan, that "place of the serpent," had a spiritual heritage that went back to Og of Bashan, the last of the giant Rephaim in the days of Joshua. Bashan became the inheritance of the Jewish tribe of Dan, and the center for Dan's idol worship of the golden calf. This area would forever be the bane of Israel, as prophesied by Jacob, "Dan shall be a serpent in the way, a viper by the path, that bites the horse's heels." Another reference to the ongoing War of the Seed: "He shall crush your head, and you shall strike his heel."[1]

The sacred grotto hosted a cavern from which the headwaters of the Jordan River poured forth like the fount of a demonic Eden. The cave was enveloped in darkness now. At its back end, a large crevice opened up to a deep shaft that dropped away into the Abyss. This doorway to the underworld, called the Gates of Hades, was watched over by an occultic priesthood of Pan, the satyr god of nature and revelry.[2]

But the real secret behind Panias lay in the large, twenty-foot-tall golden statue in the center of the cave interior. It was a satyr god with horns on his head, the torso of a man, and the hairy legs and hooves of a goat. But it wasn't a graven image of Pan. It was an image of Azazel, an ancient fallen one, god of the desert chaos. Azazel was one of the original archons, rebel leaders of the Sons of God who fell to earth at Hermon. The other was named Semyaza. The two of them together led two hundred of those Sons of God to violate the heavenly/earthly divide. They mated with the daughters of men, who gave birth to the unholy seed of the Serpent, the Nephilim. In punishment for their corruption and violence, shared with humankind, Yahweh sent the Deluge. Azazel and Semyaza, along with most of the primeval Watchers, were imprisoned by the archangels, bound in Tartarus until judgment. Seventy Sons of God and their subordinates were left. Those remaining became the gods of the seventy nations who were the children of Noah.[3]

But the Nazarene had imprisoned those seventy at his resurrection and ascension to the right hand of God.

Panias was deserted now. Abandoned. Messiah had exorcised the demons of this unholy temple, stormed the Gates of Hades and descended into the underworld to proclaim his triumph over death.[4] With his ascension, the Abyss had been sealed.

Until now.

At the bottom of that deep rocky shaft, the black waters of the Abyss broke open to an army of divine beings escaping the underworld. Watchers, two hundred of them, released from the bowels of Tartarus. They began to climb the rock walls toward the top of the crevice thousands of feet above. They clawed and pulled their way up through pitch-dark silence toward freedom.

Apollyon led them with the key to the Abyss, the Seal of Solomon, on his hand, a war hammer strapped to his back, and a plan in mind. The horde of Watchers following him had orders to return to their lands of origin and take over their previous identities as the gods of the nations. Ba'al, Asherah and Molech in Israel; Artemis and Mithras in Rome, Zeus and Poseidon in Greece, and the many others would have to step aside and hand their identities over to their primeval predecessors, the ancient fallen ones.

Climbing beside Apollyon toward that steep precipice above were his new captains of dominion, Azazel and Semyaza.

Apollyon snarled, thinking of the cosmic competition he faced. Mount Hermon versus Mount Zion. The Nazarene had destroyed the mountain of

Bashan to replace it with Mount Zion. It had been a declaration of war, a call to *Armageddon.*

Armageddon was a word whose Hebrew origin meant a climactic battle for the "mount of assembly," the seat of divine power on the holy mountain. Armageddon would be a cosmic battle between holy mountains.[5]

Apollyon growled under his breath as he continued his ascent, "You wanted Armageddon, Nazarene. Armageddon you will have."

• • • • •

This story continues with the next novel in the series, *Remnant: Rescue of the Elect.* (www.ChroniclesOfTheApocalypse.com)

See www.Godawa.com for more information on everything by the author Brian Godawa.

If you liked this book, then please help me out by writing an honest review of it wherever you purchased it. It's usually pretty easy. That is one of the best ways to say thank you to me as an author. It really does help my exposure and status as an author. Thanks! — *Brian Godawa*

If You Like This Novel
Get This Free eBook
Limited Time Offer

FREE

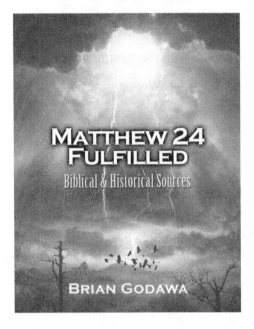

The Research Notes behind the Novel Series
Chronicles of the Apocalypse
By Brian Godawa

Over one hundred pages of Biblical and historical sources, with citations, addressing each verse in Matthew 24.

Download
Free eBook

https://godawa.com/matthew-24/

Get the Theology behind This Novel Series

The Biblical Theology behind Chronicles of the Apocalypse
By Brian Godawa

Brian Godawa reveals the Biblical and historical basis for the Last Days presented in the novel series *Chronicles of the Apocalypse*.

Godawa unveils the biblical meaning of many End Times notions like the Last Days, cosmic catastrophes, the Abomination of Desolation, the antichrist, the Great Tribulation, and more!

Available in eBook, Paperback & Audiobook

https://wp.me/P6y1ub-io8

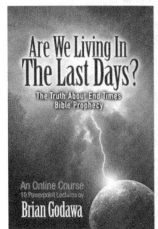

304

GET MORE BIBLICAL IMAGINATION

Get More Biblical Imagination

Sign up Online For The Godawa Chronicles

www.Godawa.com

Insider information on the novels of Brian Godawa

Special Discounts, New Releases,

Bible Mysteries!

We won't spam you.

CHRONICLES OF THE NEPHILIM

CHRONICLES OF THE APOCALYPSE

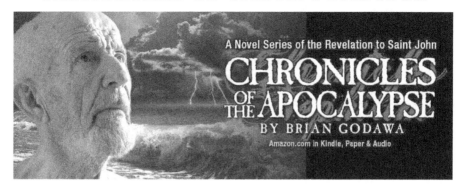

A Novel Series About
the Book of Revelation & the End Times.
A Fresh Biblical View.

www.Godawa.com

CHRONICLES OF THE WATCHERS

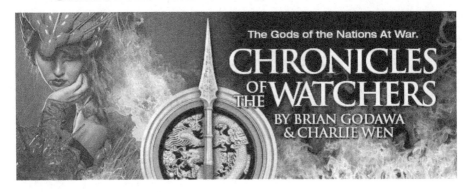

A Series About the Watchers in History.
Action, Romance, Gods, Monsters & Men.
The first novel is *Jezebel: Harlot Queen of Israel.*

www.Godawa.com

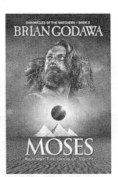

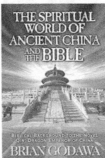
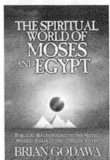

ABOUT THE AUTHOR

Brian Godawa is the screenwriter for the award-winning feature film, *To End All Wars*, starring Kiefer Sutherland. It was awarded the Commander in Chief Medal of Service, Honor and Pride by the Veterans of Foreign Wars, won the first Heartland Film Festival by storm, and showcased the Cannes Film Festival Cinema for Peace.

He previously adapted to film the best-selling supernatural thriller novel *The Visitation* by author Frank Peretti for Ralph Winter (*X-Men, Wolverine*), and wrote and directed *Wall of Separation*, a PBS documentary, and *Lines That Divide*, a documentary on stem cell research.

Mr. Godawa's scripts have won multiple awards in respected screenplay competitions, and his articles on movies and philosophy have been published around the world. He has traveled around the United States teaching on movies, worldviews, and culture to colleges, churches and community groups.

His popular book *Hollywood Worldviews: Watching Films with Wisdom and Discernment* (InterVarsity Press) is used as a textbook in schools around the country. In the Top 10 of Biblical Fiction on Amazon, his first novel series, *Chronicles of the Nephilim*, is an imaginative retelling of Biblical stories of the Nephilim giants, the secret plan of the fallen Watchers, and the War of the Seed of the Serpent with the Seed of Eve. The sequel series, *Chronicles of the Apocalypse*, tells the story of the apostle John's book of Revelation, and *Chronicles of the Watchers* recounts true history through the Watcher paradigm.

Find out more about his other books, lecture tapes and DVDs for sale at his website, www.godawa.com.

NOTES

NOTES

NOTES

NOTES

ENDNOTES — TYRANT: RISE OF THE BEAST

[1] **The coup d'état of Jesus over the powers**: Ephesians 1:20–22; 1 Peter 3:18-22; Colossians 2:15; 2 Corinthians 2:14; Ephesians 4:8-10. The language of "triumphal procession" was based on the Roman military tradition. "It means to 'celebrate a triumph,' or more specifically 'lead in triumph,' as a victorious general leading his army with his defeated enemies in his train…In a manner anticipating the Fourth Gospel's theology of glory, the cross and the ascension are merged into a single thought of triumph. The cross on which Christ died is compared to the chariot in which the victor rode in triumph." James D. G. Dunn, *The Epistles to the Colossians and to Philemon: A Commentary on the Greek Text*, *New International Greek Testament Commentary* (Grand Rapids, MI; Carlisle: William B. Eerdmans Publishing; Paternoster Press, 1996), 168.

Supernatural guardians over God's people: Revelation 1:20; 2:1, 8, 12, 18; 3:1, 7,14; Daniel 10:12-13, 21; Psalm 34:7, Matthew 18:20.

The angel of Ephesus: Revelation 1:20-2:1.

[2] Genesis 3:15; Romans 16:20; Revelation 12:7-12. For a creative depiction of this "War of the Seed" through the entire Bible, see the novel series, *Chronicles of the Nephilim* by Brian Godawa. www.chroniclesofthenephilim.com.

[3] **Divine allotment of the nations under the heavenly Sons of God**: "When the Most High gave to the nations their inheritance, when he divided mankind, he fixed the borders of the peoples according to the number of the sons of God. But the LORD's portion is his people, Jacob his allotted heritage." Deuteronomy 32:8–9.

Heavenly host (Sons of God) as real supernatural entities and gods of the nations: Deuteronomy 4:19-20; 1 Enoch 6-7. For a creative depiction of this primeval fall and territorial allotment, see Brian Godawa, *Noah Primeval* (Los Angeles, Embedded Pictures, 2011) and *Enoch Primordial* (Los Angeles, Embedded Pictures, 2012). For a scholarly defense of the view see Michael S. Heiser, *The Unseen Realm: Recovering the Supernatural Worldview of the Bible*, First Edition. (Bellingham, WA: Lexham Press, 2015).

Watchers as territorial supernatural authorities over mankind: Daniel 4:13, 23; 1 Enoch 20:1. "[the term Watcher] utilizes the arrangements of a human court to picture God's management of the affairs of heaven and earth. An earthly king had watchmen, for instance, who were the eyes and ears whereby he controlled and provided for his realm (see n. 3:2.c). The heavenly king governs his realm by similar means, members of the Council of Yahweh (1 Kgs 22:19–22; Job 1–2; Ps 89:6–8 [5–7]; Jer 23:18) who act as his eyes (2 Chr 16:9; Zech 4:10; cf. 1:9), keeping him informed on the affairs of his realm and seeing that his will is put into effect throughout it." John E. Goldingay, *Daniel, vol. 30, Word Biblical Commentary* (Dallas: Word, Incorporated, 1998), 88.

Israel as Yahweh's allotted people: "When the Most High gave to the nations their inheritance, when he divided mankind, he fixed the borders of the peoples according to the number of the sons of God. But the LORD's portion is his people, Jacob his allotted heritage." Deuteronomy 32:8–9.

[4] **Apollyon as Satan**: "This angel is named only here in Revelation [9:11 as Apollyon], and elsewhere in the OT and early Jewish literature is mentioned only in 4Q280 10 ii 7:"[Cursed be you Angel of the Pit, and Spirit of Abaddon" (Kobelski, Melchizedek, 43–44). While in 4Q280 and related texts these two titles are alternate ways of describing Belial, in Revelation it is not at all clear that the angel of the abyss is a designation for Satan, for he is carefully named elsewhere with a selection of aliases in two different contexts (12:9; 20:2), and neither Abaddon nor the angel of the abyss is mentioned again. The fact that ἄγγελον is articular here, however, suggests that the author expected the readers to be familiar with this

figure, i.e., that the angel of the abyss is none other than Satan-Belial." David E. Aune, *Revelation 6–16, vol. 52B, Word Biblical Commentary* (Dallas: Word, Incorporated, 1998), 534.

"The "Destroyer" in Rev. 9:11 is either the devil himself or an evil representative of the devil; either alternative receives confirmation from Jewish exegetical tradition on Exodus (see below). Rev. 12:3–4 and 13:1ff. are compatible with this conclusion, since there the devil and the Beast respectively are pictured wearing royal diadems and leading evil forces. This is also in line with the same conclusion already reached about the angel's identification in 9:1." G. K. Beale, *The Book of Revelation: A Commentary on the Greek Text, New International Greek Testament Commentary* (Grand Rapids, MI; Carlisle, Cumbria: W.B. Eerdmans; Paternoster Press, 1999), 503.

"The title "angel of the abyss" is not found anywhere else in antiquity except in 2Q280. The demons this trumpet unleashes upon Jerusalem are under the dominion of a king whose name in Hebrew is Abaddon, and in the Greek he has the name Apollyon (9:11b). …The following evidence suggests to me that this "king" is Satan: (1) John describes him both as a "king" as well as "the angel of the abyss" (from which come the demons; 9:1–3). In Scripture, Satan functions as an evil ruler of great power in the fallen world (Mt 4:8; Jn 12:31; 14:30; 16:11; 1Jo 5:19), and even as the ruler of demons (Mt 9:34; 12:24–27; Lk 10:17–18; Eph 2:2; cp. Jub. 11:15; 17:16; 18:9, 12; 48:2–15). In fact, the Bible calls fallen angels (demons) "his angels" (Mt 25:41; Rev 12:9). Later in Revelation, we see Satan appearing as a dragon with diadems, showing his kingship (12:3).

"(2) John refers to him as "the angel of the abyss [ton aggelon tēs abussou]," where the definite article suggests this angel is well-known. Satan is certainly a well-known figure in Scripture and in first-century Judaism. John even mentions him in Revelation four times before now (2:9, 13, 24; 3:9). (3) The symbolic names given to him, "Apollyon" and "Abaddon" (9:11b), both mean "destroyer," which fits Satan's character and work (1Co 5:5; Eph 6:11; Heb 2:14; 1Pe 5:8). This is true even in Revelation where he seeks to destroy Jesus at his birth (12:3–4) and then his saints (12:12–13, 17). Indeed, the name "Satan" means "adversary" which comports with the concept of "destroyer"—since he seeks a legal means to destroy God's people (e.g., 2:9–10). So once again we see Satan's work among the Christ-denying Jews, as per Christ's declaration that their father is the devil (Jn 8:44) and that they are a "synagogue of Satan" (Rev 2:9; 3:9). They are now receiving their just desserts: Satan sends his demon army to sorely afflict them.

"John's Greek abbadōn is a transliteration of the Hebrew ʾbaddōn, which appears in the Old Testament only in the Wisdom literature (Job 26:6; 28:22; 31:12; Ps 88:11; Pr 15:11; 27:20). It also appears four times in the DSS (NIDOTTE 1:226). It means "destruction" and in the LXX is always translated by apōleia ("destruction, annihilation), except in Job 31:12 which translates it apolluein. In Job 31:12 it is the place of destruction, whereas elsewhere it parallels Sheol (Job 26:6; Pr 15:11; 27:20), death (Job 28:22), or the grave (Ps 88:11), and is thus strongly associated with death. The word "Apollyon" is apolluōn in the Greek: it is the present participle of apollumi, which means to "destroy." Like the Hebrew ʾbaddōn it is often used to refer to killing (Mt 2:13; 12:114; 27:20; Mk 3:6; 9:41; 11:18; Lk 11:51; 12:33; 15:17; 17:27; 19:47). Satan himself virtually personifies death in Heb 2:14b: "who had the power of death, that is, the devil" (cp. 1Co 5:5).

"In addition to the designation "Apollyon" referring to Satan as the "destroyer," the term has an "etymological connection" with the name of Apollo the sun god and may therefore allude to him (Smalley 234; cp. Caird 120; Sweet 170; TDNT 1:397; Beagley 54; Ford 152; Morris 128; Lupieri 163; M. Wilson 2002: 305; Boxall 145; Osborne 374). If so, Apollo would serve as a link to the Roman emperor Nero who held Apollo as his patron deity. Suetonius notes that Nero drove a chariot in the games (Nero 24:2) mimicking Apollo. Nero "was acclaimed as the equal of Apollo in music and of the Sun in driving a chariot" (Nero 53)." Kenneth L. Gentry, Jr., *The Divorce of Israel: A Redemptive-Historical Interpretation of Revelation Vol. 1* (Dallas, GA: Tolle Lege Press, 2016), 750-752.

Belial: 2 Corinthians 6:14-15. ""The personification of wickedness, treachery, or the like, as Belial. In most of its OT attestations, bĕliyyaʿal functions as an emotive term to describe individuals or groups who commit the most heinous crimes against the Israelite religious or social order, as well as their acts." S. D. Sperling, "Belial," ed. Karel van der Toorn, Bob Becking, and Pieter W. van der Horst, *Dictionary of Deities and Demons in the Bible* (Leiden; Boston; Köln; Grand Rapids, MI; Cambridge: Brill; Eerdmans, 1999), 169.

Helel ben Shachar: Isaiah 14:12-15. Though many scholars accept this passage as having two referents, one, a historical prophecy to the King of Babylon, and the other, a spiritual allusion to Satan's pre-Edenic fall, David Lowe makes a persuasive argument that it has nothing to do with Satan. See David W. Lowe, *Deconstructing Lucifer: Reexamining the Ancient Origins of the Fallen Angel of Light* (Seismos Publishing 2011).

Mastemah: "Mastemah appears as a noun meaning 'hostility' in OT (Hos 9:7–8) and Qumran writings. In Qumran literature the word is mostly connected with an evil angel (Belial) and in Jub. Mastemah is always a proper name for the leader of the evil angels." J. W. van Henten, "Mastemah," ed. Karel van der Toorn, Bob Becking, and Pieter W. van der Horst, *Dictionary of Deities and Demons in the Bible* (Leiden; Boston; Köln; Grand Rapids, MI; Cambridge: Brill; Eerdmans, 1999), 553.

Satan as ancient serpent and dragon: "And the great dragon was thrown down, that ancient serpent, who is called the devil and Satan, the deceiver of the whole world." Revelation 12:9.

Job 1:6-12; Zechariah 3:1-2. "The Hebrew (satan) means something like "adversary," "prosecutor," or "challenger." It speaks of an official legal function within a ruling body—in this case, Yahweh's council. When Yahweh asks the satan where he has been, we learn that his job involves investigating what is happening on earth (Job 1:7). He is, so to speak, Yahweh's eyes and ears on the ground, reporting what he has seen and heard." Michael S. Heiser, *The Unseen Realm: Recovering the Supernatural Worldview of the Bible, First Edition* (Bellingham, WA: Lexham Press, 2015), 56–57.

Nero as Apollo: "Because he was thought to equal Apollo in music, and the sun in chariot-driving,." Tranquillus, Gaius Suetonius, *The Lives of the Twelve Caesars: Nero* 6:53.

"Many commentators feel that the verse contains a derogatory reference to the Greek god Apollo and those emperors who claimed a special relationship to him. To name the king of the underworld Apollyon would be a cryptic way of saying that an emperor such as Domitian who liked to be regarded as Apollo incarnate was in reality a manifestation of the powers of the underworld. As early as the fifth century B.C., the Greeks had derived the name of Apollo from the same Greek verb as the root of Apollyon. The allusion is strengthened by the observation that the locust was one of the symbols of the god Apollo." Robert H. Mounce, *The Book of Revelation, The New International Commentary on the New Testament* (Grand Rapids, MI: Wm. B. Eerdmans Publishing Co., 1997), 191.

[5] **The Adversary of God's heavenly council ("the satan") is an office appointed by God:** "In four OT passages śāṭān appears as an angelic being…Satan functions as an adversary against God's people either by attempting to seduce them to do evil or by accusing them before God for their sins. But in each case Satan's power is limited and he acts only within God's permissive will. (Job 1-2, Zechariah 3:1)" D. P. Fuller, "Satan," ed. Geoffrey W. Bromiley, The International Standard Bible Encyclopedia, Revised (Wm. B. Eerdmans, 1979–1988), 340.

[6] **Israel as adulterous harlot with idols**: Ezekiel 16:15-59; Ezekiel 23; 2Kings 17:7-17; Jeremiah 3:1-11; Hosea 1-2.

Yahweh vomiting out Israel: "But you shall keep my statutes and my rules and do none of these abominations, lest the land vomit you out when you make it unclean, as it vomited out the nation that was before you." Leviticus 18:26–28.

[7] **Satan's fall from heaven was not in the Garden, it was in the ministry of Christ**: "In Revelation 12, we see the origin of the notion that one third of the angels fell to earth with Satan at his fall. The only problem is that this event did not occur before the garden of Eden in a cosmic rebellion, it happened at the birth of Jesus Christ! Revelation 12:1-6 describes an apocalyptic parable of the cosmic war of the Seed of the Serpent (a dragon of chaos) and the Seed of the Woman (Israel/the Church). It describes one third of the angelic stars (Watchers?) joining Satan with the swipe of his serpentine tail. The dragon and his minions seek to devour the male seed (offspring) of the woman, but they fail and the child becomes king. And then the passage tells of a heavenly war:

Revelation 12:7–10 Now war arose in heaven, Michael and his angels fighting against the dragon. And the dragon and his angels fought back, 8 but he was defeated, and there was no longer any place for them in heaven. 9 And the great dragon was thrown down, that ancient serpent, who is called the devil and Satan, the deceiver of the whole world—he was thrown down to the earth, and his angels were thrown down with him. 10 And I heard a loud voice in heaven, saying, "Now the salvation and the power and the kingdom of our God and the authority of his Christ have come, for the accuser of our brothers has been thrown down, who accuses them day and night before our God." Most Christians believe this is a reference to Satan's fall before the Garden of Eden incident, where he takes one third of the angels in heaven with him. But a closer look at the context reveals that this is not the case at all, but rather the opposite. The war in heaven does not happen before the Garden, it happens at the time of the incarnation of Messiah on earth! The woman (Israel) gives birth to a male child (Messiah, v. 5), who the dragon (Satan) seeks to devour (from Herod's slaughter of the innocents all the way to the Cross). That Messiah ascends to the throne in authority after his resurrection (v. 5; Eph 1:20-22), during which time that woman (Israel) flees to the wilderness (time of tribulation under the Roman Empire)." The war in heaven we see cannot be before the Garden because it says that the throwing down of Satan occurs with the coming of the kingdom of Christ! (v. 10). He is thrown down to earth and then seeks to kill the Christ (v. 13). Satan then seeks to make war with the rest of her offspring (God's people) which we see in history.

"Revelation 12 is an apocalyptic parable that is describing the incarnation of Messiah, his ascension to the throne of authority over all principalities and powers, and his suppression of Satan's power as the Gospel goes forth into the world." Brian Godawa, *When Giants Were Upon the Earth: The Watchers, the Nephilim, and the Biblical Cosmic War of the Seed* (Embedded Pictures, 2014), 149-150.

[8] **Christ claiming the nations as his inheritance:** Psalm 2:8; Isaiah 2:1-5. For a fictional portrayal of this victory of Jesus Christ over the principalities and powers see Brian Godawa, *Jesus Triumphant* (Los Angeles, Embedded Pictures, 2015).

Christ's triumphal procession, with victory over the powers: Colossians 2:15 [15] He disarmed the rulers and authorities and put them to open shame, by triumphing over them in him.

Ephesians 4:8–10 [8] Therefore it says, "When he ascended on high he led a host of captives, and he gave gifts to men." [9] (In saying, "He ascended," what does it mean but that he had also descended into the lower regions, the earth? [10] He who descended is the one who also ascended far above all the heavens, that he might fill all things.)

1 Peter 3:21–22 [21] Jesus Christ, [22] who has gone into heaven and is at the right hand of God, with angels, authorities, and powers having been subjected to him.

Ephesians 1:20–22 [20] that he worked in Christ when he raised him from the dead and seated him at his right hand in the heavenly places, [21] far above all rule and authority and power and dominion, and above every name that is named, not only in this age but also in the one to come. [22] And he put all things under his feet.

[9] "Satan is called "the ruler of this world" (Jn. 12:31, 14:30-31, 16:11), in 2 Cor. 4:4, "the god of this world." In Eph. 2:2 he is called the "prince of the power of the air, the spirit that is now working in the sons of disobedience." In fact, when Jesus was tempted by the satan in the desert, he offered Christ all the kingdoms of the world for his own "domain and glory; for it has been handed over to me, and I give it to whomever I wish" (Luke 4:6). It seems as if the satan is the only Watcher god in authority over the nations, like he has all the power." Brian Godawa, *When Giants Were Upon the Earth* (Embedded Pictures, 2014), 289." Much tradition identified Satan as the angel of Rome, thus adapting the angels-of-the-nations idea to the situation of Roman world-hegemony. Since Rome had conquered the entire Mediterranean region and much else besides, its angel-prince had become lord of all other angel-princes of the vanquished nations. This identification was already explicit at Qumran, where Rome and the Romans (the "Kittim" of the War Scroll) are made the specific allies and agents of Satan and his host. Similarly in the New Testament, Satan as the 'archon of this world' (John 12:31; 14:30; 16:11) or 'god of this aeon' (2 Cor. 4:4) could scarcely avoid being identified as the special patron of Rome." Walter Wink. *Naming the Powers: The Language of Power in the New Testament* (The Powers : Volume One) (Kindle Locations 405-409). Kindle Edition.

[10] **Christianoi and Caesariani as titles:** Clinton E. Arnold, *Zondervan Illustrated Bible Backgrounds Commentary: John, Acts., vol. 2* (Grand Rapids, MI: Zondervan, 2002), 319.

[11] **The Artemesium**: Colin J. Hemer, *The Letters to the Seven Churches of Asia in Their Local Setting* (Grand Rapids, MI; Cambridge, U.K.; Livonia, MI: William B. Eerdmans Publishing Company; Dove Booksellers, 2001), 48-49.

[12] Mark 3:17.

[13] **Ephesus as financial center of Asia Minor**: "Broughton describes the temple of Artemis as 'the biggest bank in Asia.'…it is clear that Artemis of Ephesus exercised a great deal of influence on the economic activity of both Ephesus and Asia Minor in our period, and greatly contributed to the financial welfare of the region." Paul Trebilco, "Asia," in *The Book of Acts in Its First Century Setting: The Book of Acts in Its Graeco-Roman Setting*, ed. David W. J. Gill, Conrad Gempf, and Bruce W. Winter, vol. 2 (Grand Rapids, MI; Carlisle, Cumbria: William B. Eerdmans Publishing Company; The Paternoster Press, 1994), 325-326.

[14] **Description of the goddess Artemis and her connection to Apollo**: Paul Trebilco, "Asia," in *The Book of Acts in Its First Century Setting: The Book of Acts in Its Graeco-Roman Setting,* ed. David W. J. Gill, Conrad Gempf, and Bruce W. Winter, vol. 2 (Grand Rapids, MI; Carlisle, Cumbria: William B. Eerdmans Publishing Company; The Paternoster Press, 1994), 317-18.

The bulbous objects on Artemis: "The meaning of the rows of bulbous objects on the chest of Artemis has proved a mystery to interpreters. Some early Christian interpreters identified them as female breasts and saw this as an expression of a fertility motif. This interpretation has not been generally accepted because of the differences in shape. Numerous other ideas have been suggested such as eggs, grapes, nuts, and even steer testicles. The latter view has a number of prominent adherents because in some of the ancient religions, mutilated body parts were attached to the cultic image of a deity. The most convincing explanation yet has recently been offered by Sarah P. Morris, Steinmetz professor of classical archaeology and material culture at UCLA, who concludes that the bulbous objects are comparable to leather goatskin pouches, called kurša, known from Hittite practices. These little bags were filled with magical material and used as fetishes. She observes that the Hittite tutelary deities associated with the kurša were often associated with protecting people and places and were frequently invoked in oaths and called upon in magical rites. She suggests that an ancient Anatolian cult image at Ephesus, to which rows of such bags were attached, was the predecessor to the image of the Ephesian Artemis. As such, the bags functioned as symbols for fecundity, spiritual power, and protection." Clinton E. Arnold, *Ephesians (Zondervan Exegetical Commentary on the New Testament)* (Zondervan, 20102), 45.

[15] **Shortly take place**: Apollyon is mocking the Apostle John's words in Revelation 1:1, but he realizes it is soon going to happen.

"When a writer says that an event will shortly and speedily come to pass, or is about to take place, it is contrary to all propriety to declare that his statements allow us to believe the event is in the far future. It is a reprehensible abuse of language to say that the words immediately, or near at hand, mean ages hence, or after a long time. Such a treatment of the language of Scripture is even worse than the theory of a double sense. Milton S. Terry, Biblical Hermeneutics: *A Treatise on the Interpretation of the Old and New Testaments* (New York: Phillips & Hunt, 1883), 495-496.

[16] **These words that John preaches are directly from**: 2 John 7; 1 John 4:2–3.

[17] **Heretics that John wrote against**: "Who is the liar but he who denies that Jesus is the Christ? This is the antichrist, he who denies the Father and the Son." 1 John 2:22.

For information on Cerinthus from early church father's writings: Irenaeus, *Against Heresies* 3.3.4; Eusebius, *Church History* 2.28.2; Irenaeus, *Against Heresies* 1.26.1; Dionysius, quoted in Eusebius, *Church History* 2.28.4.

"Irenaeus claims that the Gospel of John was written as a response to the errors taught by Cerinthus and the Nicolaitans. Clement of Alexandria (Strom. 2.20; 3.4) attributed the heretical movement of the Nicolaitans to the misunderstanding of the followers of Nicolaus of Antioch." - David E. Aune, *Revelation 1–5, vol. 52A, Word Biblical Commentary* (Dallas: Word, Incorporated, 1998), 149. "Eusebius records that the heretic Cerinthus taught an earthly kingdom of sensual pleasure ("the gratification of appetite and lust; i.e., in eating, drinking, and marrying") to follow the resurrection (Eusebius, Hist. Eccl.

3.38.)" Robert H. Mounce, *The Book of Revelation, The New International Commentary on the New Testament* (Grand Rapids, MI: Wm. B. Eerdmans Publishing Co., 1997), 368.

"One example was the Cerinthians. Cerinthus appears in early writings of the church as a kind of arch nemesis to the Apostle John. If the account of Irenaeus is accurate, which is by no means certain, considerable tension existed between the two. On one occasion, the story goes, John walked into a public bath-house and, finding Cerinthus already inside, he turned and hastened out the door, declaring, "Let us fly, lest even the bath-house fall down, because Cerinthus, the enemy of the truth, is within." [*Irenaeus against Heresies*, 3.3.4]

"Since John lived in Ephesus, perhaps the conflict was inevitable. Whether the incident actually happened or not, the members of the church in Ephesus were barraged with assaults on the teaching of the Gospel. Cerinthus presented a twisted version, close enough to be confusing, different enough to draw people away.

"He claimed revelations supposedly written by a great apostle and insights which he maintained were given him by angels. Trained in the wisdom of the Egyptians, Cerinthus taught that Jesus was an ordinary human being, the natural son of Joseph and Mary. Though he believed Jesus was a righteous and wise man, Cerinthus asserted that Jesus was not God. After his baptism, Christ descended on Jesus in the form of a dove and through Jesus performed miracles and taught about the supreme God, the Father. Before the crucifixion, the non-corporeal Christ left Jesus, who then suffered and died, later to rise again.

"Cerinthus founded a sect named Cerinthian, after himself, and pursued a life devoted to the "pleasures of the body." Comparison of John's epistles with the teachings of Cerinthus indicates that correcting the false teaching was at least in the back of John's mind as he wrote. For example, the statement that anyone who "denies that Jesus is the Christ" is a liar might well have been written to counter the Cerinthian claim that Christ came to Jesus and then left him." Don Enevoldsen, *The Harlot and the Bride*, unpublished book (Don Enevoldsen, 2014), 81.

[18] **These words that John preaches are directly from**: 1 John 2:18; 2:22; 5:19; 2:28.

[19] **Accuser of the brethren**: Revelation 12:10.

Satan bound in the ministry of Jesus: (Matthew 12:27-29). In Rev 20:2-3, binding the satan is described as stopping his ability to "deceive the nations."

Drawing all men to himself: John 12:32.

[20] **Drawing all nations to Mount Zion**: Isaiah 2:1-4.

The messianic mountain that would grow to fill the earth: Daniel 2:35, 44-45.

[21] **Children of the devil**: John 8:44.

Prince of the power of the air: Ephesians 2:2.

Satan's inability to accuse Christians: 1Peter 5:8; Revelation 6:9-11; 12:13-17; 13:7-8; 20:4-6.

Regarding Satan's ability to persecute the Christians while not being able to prosecute: we see this reality in Revelation 12:10 when Satan the accuser of the brethren was thrown down by Christ's ministry, death, resurrection and ascension. Kenneth Gentry writes.."During his ministry, Jesus associated his lifting up (his death on the cross, Jn 12:32–33) with the casting out of Satan (Jn 12:31). And as instruments of Satan, the Jews were responsible for his being "lifted up" to death. For as the Lord warned: "Behold, we are going up to Jerusalem; and the Son of Man will be delivered to the chief priests and scribes, and they will condemn Him to death" (Mt 20:18).26 Of note, when speaking to the Pharisees while in the temple (Jn 8:20), Jesus declared in John's Gospel: "When you lift up the Son of Man, then you will know that I am He" (Jn 8:28). And just a few verses later Jesus associated Satan with those same Jews when he proclaimed: "You are of your father the devil" (Jn 8:44). Returning to John 12:31, we should recognize that the "now [nun]" shows that Satan's casting out results from Christ's cross-resurrection work. But again, Satan's casting out by Christ's death-resurrection parallels and gives theological meaning to Jerusalem's destruction as a dramatic and important redemptive-historical effect of his cross-resurrection work…

"Ancient Jewish literature often focuses on Satan's legal, accusatory function, not only in the well-known biblical passages in Job 1:6–12; 2:1–6; and Zechariah 3:1–2, but elsewhere (1 En. 40:7; 1 En. 36:25:12; Apoc. Zeph. 6:17; Jub. 1:20; 17:15–16; 18:99–100). For instance, Zechariah 3:1 reads: "then he showed me Joshua the high priest standing before the angel of the LORD, and Satan standing at his right hand to accuse him.''...

"As a result of the linked AD 30 ascension and the approaching AD 70 destruction, the "accuser of our brethren" is thrown down. The result is that those whom he persecutes overcame [enikēsan] him because of the blood of the Lamb and because of the word of their testimony. Nikaō can mean to overcome "in a legal action". Regarding Satan, the brethren "overcame [enikēsan] him" legally before God's throne, just as Jesus overcame Jewish and Roman charges and sat down on the Father's judicial throne (3:21). The aorist enikēsan speaks of their victory as if already fully accomplished, for in God's sovereign plan it is certain (cp. 13:8; 17:8). "The victory of Satan over believers is both earthly and temporary (cf. 13:7), while their victory over him is final and eternal"...

"As the humiliated dragon-devil comes down, we see him having great wrath, knowing that he has only a short time (12:12c). Here the "great red dragon" (12:3b) who could cast down the stars (12:4) exhibits "great wrath" after he is cast down (12:9, 10, 13). He does this because he now knows "that he has only a short time." As a result of his defeat in heaven he no longer has access to God's throne to accuse God's people; he now will only be able to do his work on earth. Stuart (2:260) argues that this refers "to the triumph of the church over the persecuting Jewish power.... For Satan, in this sketch of regressive action, is represented as specifically concerned with the church in Judea, where Christianity had its origin." Since Satan was legally defeated in heaven at Christ's ascension (which defeat eventually led to Israel's AD 70 judgment), he had only a short time as John writes. We will see that the woman must flee only for "a time and times and half a time" (12:14). It is important for Satan to crush out the remnant of Israel, that is "the Mother Church, the Church of Jerusalem, which, as it were, rocks the cradle of Gentile Christianity." Kenneth L. Gentry, Jr., *The Divorce of Israel: A Redemptive-Historical Interpretation of Revelation Vol. 2* (Dallas, GA: Tolle Lege Press, 2016), 177-183.

[22] **Armageddon and the Coming of the Lord**: Revelation 16:16; 19:11-21; 1Thessalonians 4:13-17.

[23] **Terebinth as sacred**: K. Nielsen, "Terebinth," ed. Karel van der Toorn, Bob Becking, and Pieter W. van der Horst, *Dictionary of Deities and Demons in the Bible* (Leiden; Boston; Köln; Grand Rapids, MI; Cambridge: Brill; Eerdmans, 1999), 850.

Tree of Life: "The name therefore may have been at first the embodiment of the thought that the Evangelist occupied in the service of the true God that position which they occupied in that of the Ephesian goddess, that he was the witness of the Truth, of which her worship was a counterfeit'...To the shrine of Artemis we must now turn. There are apparent analogies here with the 'tree of life', the 'paradise of God' and other concepts relevant to the Apocalypse. Two passages in the literary sources describe the foundation of the holy place of Artemis as a tree-shrine." Colin J. Hemer, *The Letters to the Seven Churches of Asia in Their Local Setting* (Grand Rapids, MI; Cambridge, U.K.; Livonia, MI: William B. Eerdmans Publishing Company; Dove Booksellers, 2001), 42-44.

Royal parks as sacred gardens: "The idea of the royal park in which the king walked passes easily into that of a sacred enclosure in whose innermost heart the deity was present...We may venture to see a series of partial parallels implicit in the background of the passage: the tree of life in the garden of Eden, the tree-shrine in the asylum of the goddess, and the cross, as Roberts placed it, in the paradise of God." Colin J. Hemer, *The Letters to the Seven Churches of Asia in Their Local Setting* (Grand Rapids, MI; Cambridge, U.K.; Livonia, MI: William B. Eerdmans Publishing Company; Dove Booksellers, 2001), 41-51.

[24] **Sorcery and magic at Ephesus:** Clement of Alexandria, *The Stromata* 5.8.

The Ephesian Letters of Magic: "Closely related to worship of Artemis was the practice of magic, especially the world famous *Ephesia Grammata*, the Ephesian Letters. They were actually six mystical words, inscribed, according to Eustathius, a Greek bishop of the twelfth century, on the feet, the girdle and the crown of the statue of Artemis. The words were believed by many to carry magical powers for everything from healing to financial success to making people fall in love. They were renowned throughout the ancient world for almost as long as the temple of Artemis existed. Sale of copies of the letters was a significant part of the income of the city. The letters were not the only form of magic, however. A brisk business trafficked in all kinds of magical scrolls and charms. It is perhaps significant that the earliest use of the Greek word mageia, or sorcery, is attributed to Heraclitus, an Ephesian of the fifth century B.C." Don Enevoldsen, *The Harlot and the Bride*, unpublished book (Don Enevoldsen, 2014), 80.

"The fame of Ephesus for the practice of magic was enhanced by the widely known "Ephesian Letters" (Ephesia Grammata) in antiquity. They were six magical words (or names) used in spoken charms or inscribed on amulets. Our first record of them comes from the fourth century BC. They were used for their power to ward off demonic spirits. One ancient writer refers to people who were "wearing fine Ephesian charms in little sewed bags." As mentioned earlier, these bags may well be the bulbous objects of fetish material on the chest of the Ephesian Artemis. Plutarch claims that magicians instructed those possessed by spirits to repeat to themselves the magic words in the proper order to drive out tormenting demons. A couple of ancient sources relate a story of an Ephesian wrestler competing in the games at Olympia wearing the Ephesian Letters as an amulet on his ankles.[49] He was winning at his event until the amulet was removed and then experienced three successive losses. Such a story would have become proverbial around Ephesus as a demonstration of the power and effectiveness of the Ephesian Letters. The connection of Artemis to these magical practices is also borne out by the fact that she is called upon repeatedly in the invocations of magical texts." Clinton E. Arnold, *Ephesians (Zondervan Exegetical Commentary on the New Testament)* (Zondervan, 20102), 48.

[25] **The Nicolaitans:** Revelation 2:6, 14-15. "The Nicolaitans are not merely a subgroup in the church who were more lenient toward pagan religion and society. In the letters their thought is called a teaching (Gk didachē;. 2:14, 15, 20, 24), and they may have claimed inspiration for this teaching (2:20). Their leaders may have called themselves apostles (2:2) and prophets (2:20), and been actively seeking disciples. They were permissive about both eating meat offered to idols and immorality…The Nicolaitans appear to have gnostic tendencies. Irenaeus (Haer. 3.11.1) states that the Nicolaitans had disseminated doctrine similar in kind to the gnostic heresy of Cerinthus." Duane F. Watson, "Nicolaitans," ed. David Noel Freedman, *The Anchor Yale Bible Dictionary* (New York: Doubleday, 1992), 1107.

[26] **Hymenaeus, Alexander and Philetus**: 2Timothy 2:17-18; 1Timothy 1:20.

[27] **Christianity as "The Way"**: Acts 9:2; 19:9, 23; 24:14, 42.

[28] **Asylum of Artemis as criminal refuge**: Colin J. Hemer, *The Letters to the Seven Churches of Asia in Their Local Setting* (Grand Rapids, MI; Cambridge, U.K.; Livonia, MI: William B. Eerdmans Publishing Company; Dove Booksellers, 2001), 49.

[29] **This description comes from** Revelation 2:1-7.

CHAPTER 2

[1] **Claudius' expulsion of the Jews**: Acts 18:2. This occurred in A.D. 49 "Because the Jews at Rome caused continuous disturbances at the instigation of Chrestus [Christ], he expelled them from the city." Suetonius, *Claudius* 25.4. See also Dio Cassius, *Roman History* 60:6. A similar expulsion of the Jews was ordered by Tiberius in A.D. 29. See Philo, *Embassy* 159–61; Suetonius, *Tiberius* 36. Clinton E. Arnold, *Zondervan Illustrated Bible Backgrounds Commentary: John, Acts., vol. 2* (Grand Rapids, MI: Zondervan, 2002), 397–398.

[2] **Citizenship in heaven:** Philippians 3:20, Ephesians 2:19-20.

[3] **Paul's Thorn in the Flesh**: 2 Corinthians 12:7 So to keep me from becoming conceited because of the surpassing greatness of the revelations, a thorn was given me in the flesh, a messenger of Satan to harass me, to keep me from becoming conceited.

"The majority of interpreters, from Tertullian onward (Pud. 13), take the thorn to be some form of physical illness. In favor of this view is the metaphor of a thorn, the connection in ancient times between demonic manifestations and physical illness, and the structure of the 2 Corinthians 12:7–10 passage imitating the narratives of a healing miracle." Gerald F. Hawthorne, Ralph P. Martin, and Daniel G. Reid, eds., *Dictionary of Paul and His Letters* (Downers Grove, IL: InterVarsity Press, 1993), 379.

"A physical ailment, however, seems more likely here, though the lack of details forbid a proper diagnosis. Physical infirmities that seem to fit the situation are malaria, Malta fever, epilepsy, convulsive attacks, and chronic ophthalmia.

"Many of these physical disabilities also affect the eyesight and it seems probable that even Paul himself experienced difficulty with his vision—this could very well be caused by his thorn in the flesh. Paul took advantage of various amanuenses to do the actual writing of at least some of his epistles. A mentioned amanuensis of Paul is Tertius who wrote down the book of Romans and added his own greeting to the church in Rome (Rom 16:22). Other times we see Paul adding a salutation with his own hands (1 Cor 16:21; 2 Thess 3:17) as opposed to physically writing the entire epistles. Paul even wrote in large print as noted in Gal 6:11. Other evidences of poor vision can be found earlier in the epistle to the Galatians. Paul says that because of physical infirmity he preached the gospel to the Galatians at the first (Gal 4:13). Some have speculated that the physical infirmity was a disease which affected his eyesight and the higher altitude in Galatia would have been better for him, especially if the disease was malaria. And only two verses later Paul states that the Galatian church would have plucked out their own eyes and given them to him if it were possible (Gal 4:15). Another example of Paul's poor eyesight is found in Acts 23:3-5. Paul was in the Sanhedrin at this point and referred to the high priest as a "white-washed wall" and those who stood by him asked why he was insulting the high priest. Paul responded by telling them that he did not realize that the man was the high priest. Though Paul, previously being a Pharisee, would have been able to recognize the high priest quite easily. Yet at this point he seemed unable to identify the high priest, even though the high priest would have stood out because he wore special garments and accessories. For a former Pharisee to have not recognized him is likely explained through understanding that Paul was not able to see him properly—giving weight to theories of trouble with his vision." The Blue Letter Bible: https://www.blueletterbible.org/faq/thorn.cfm

[4] **Pantomime and actresses in the Roman Empire**: "In time, pantomime, mime's child, came to rival its parent. Because Roman pantomime can best be described as interpretive dancing to the music of a singer or chorus, it might be considered more modern dance than drama… Unlike mime, pantomime took either a serious or comic tone. The texts were mainly reworked tragedies and mythologies. Also unlike mime, only one player, the saltator, danced all the parts while the chorus sang the lines. Late in the Empire, erotic subjects and female dancers entered the repertoire.

"Pantomime was always more popular with the upper classes. But even though it was the favorite art of the Roman Empire, it fell to accusations of immorality and evil influence. Noble men and women owned and used pantomimists for their personal pleasures." Paul Kuritz, *The Making of Theatre History* (New Jersey, Prentic Hall, 1988), 57.

[5] **Wormwood and Myrrh as abortifacients**: John M. Riddle, *Contraception and Abortion from the Ancient World to the Renaissance* (Harvard University Press, 1994) 48.

Abortion in ancient Rome: "Accordingly, among surgeons' tools there is a certain instrument, which is formed with a nicely-adjusted flexible frame for opening the uterus first of all, and keeping it open; it is further furnished with an annular blade, by means of which the limbs within the womb are dissected with anxious but unfaltering care; its last appendage being a blunted or covered hook, wherewith the entire fœtus is extracted by a violent delivery. There is also (another instrument in the shape of) a copper needle or spike, by which the actual death is managed in this furtive robbery of life: they give it, from its infanticide function, the name of ἐμβρυοσφάκτης, the slayer of the infant, which was of course alive. Such apparatus was possessed both by Hippocrates, and Asclepiades, and Erasistratus, and Herophilus, that dissector of even adults, and the milder Soranus himself, who all knew well enough that a living being had been conceived." Tertullian, "A Treatise on the Soul," in *Latin Christianity: Its Founder, Tertullian*, ed. Alexander Roberts, James Donaldson, and A. Cleveland Coxe, trans. Peter Holmes, vol. 3, *The Ante-Nicene Fathers* (Buffalo, NY: Christian Literature Company, 1885), 206.

[6] **The Stoic on when personhood begins at first breath**: Susan Dowsing, *Contraception and Abortion in the Early Roman Empire: A Critical Examination of Ancient Sources and Modern Interpretations*, Master's Thesis (University of Ottawa, 1999), 87-88.

[7] **The Hippocratic Oath**: "I swear by Apollo Physician, by Asclepius, by Health, by Panacea and by all the gods and goddesses, making them my witnesses, that I will carry out, according to my ability and judgment, this oath and this indenture…I will use treatment to help the sick according to my ability and

judgment, but never with a view to injury and wrong-doing. Neither will I administer a poison to anybody when asked to do so, nor will I suggest such a course. Similarly I will not give to a woman a pessary to cause abortion." Hippocrates. *Ancient Medicine. Airs, Waters, Places. Epidemics 1 and 3. The Oath. Precepts. Nutriment.* Translated by W. H. S. Jones. *Loeb Classical Library 147.* Cambridge, MA: Harvard University Press, 1923.

[8] **Abortion was not a crime in Rome, despite the Hippocratic Oath**: Michael J. Gorman, *Abortion and the Early Church: Christian, Jewish, and Pagan Attitudes in the Greco-Roman World* (Downers Grove, InterVarsity Press, 1982), 21-22.

"The most desirable form of human life": Aristotle, *Politics* 7.1.1 [1323a]

[9] **The personhood of the preborn in the Old Testament**: Exodus 21:22–24 "When men strive together and hit a pregnant woman, so that her children come out, but there is no harm, the one who hit her shall surely be fined, as the woman's husband shall impose on him, and he shall pay as the judges determine. But if there is harm, then you shall pay life for life, eye for eye, tooth for tooth." In truth, there was not universal agreement amongst the Jews as to the interpretation of this passage. Some believed it did confer value upon the unborn at conception, but others agreed with the Stoic belief that the baby was not ensouled until birth and therefore had much less legal status. For Scriptures that indicate a soulish relationship with God while in the womb see Psalm 139:16; Luke 1:41.

For the debate within Jewish circles see Michael J. Gorman, *Abortion and the Early Church: Christian, Jewish, and Pagan Attitudes in the Greco-Roman World* (Downers Grove, InterVarsity Press, 1982), 33-45.

[10] **Motives for abortion in ancient Rome including convenience and body shape**: Michael J. Gorman, *Abortion and the Early Church: Christian, Jewish, and Pagan Attitudes in the Greco-Roman World* (Downers Grove, InterVarsity Press, 1982), 14-15.

Ovid, *Amores, Book 2,* Elegy XIV, Ovid criticizes Roman women using abortion to avoid the unpleasantries that pregnancy brought into their lives, from its effect on physical beauty to the inconvenience and burden of responsibility and suppression of fun. Titled: "To his Mistress, who endeavoured to make herself miscarry."
http://www.perseus.tufts.edu/hopper/text?doc=Perseus%3Atext%3A1999.02.0069%3Atext%3DAm.%3A book%3D2%3Apoem%3D14

[11] **Infant exposure**: "An infant could be abandoned without penalty or social stigma for many reasons, including an anomalous appearance, being an illegitimate child or grandchild or a child of infidelity, family poverty, parental conflict (*ob discordiam parentum*) or being one of too many children. Sometimes they were given to friends, but more often than not they were abandoned to the elements, and death resulted from hypoglycemia and hypothermia. Sometimes the infant was devoured by the dogs that scavenged public places. It was likely however, that the *expositi* were rescued from these fates and picked up by slavers. Abandonment generally occurred in a public place, where it was hoped that the infant could be taken up by some wealthy person. A well-traveled street called the *Velabrum*, where oil and cheese merchants worked, and the vegetable market in the Forum (*Olitorium*), with *columna lactaria*, or nursing columns, were two favored locations for placing sucklings. Such an infant was considered a *res vacantes* (an unclaimed thing) and legally could be claimed. If picked up by wealthy persons, the child could become a slave, a play companion for another child, a pet (*delicia*), or a prostitute; it could be sold for begging purposes after mutilation or become a truly adopted child, a treasured alumnus. Most adoptions, however, were not of abandoned infants but of a close relative, a *propinquus*, because adoption commonly was used for purposes of succession or inheritance, to keep wealth within a biological family."

A.R. Colón with P.A. Colón, *A History of Children: A Socio-cultural Survey Across Millennia,*(Westport, Greenwood Press, 2001), pp. 104-106.

[12] **Christians and infant exposure**: "In many instances Christians rescued exposed infants, baptized them, and brought them up with the aid of community funds." Will Durant, *Caesar and Christ: A History of Roman Civilization and of Christianity from Their Beginnings to A.D. 325* (Story of Civilization) (Simon and Schuster, 2011), 1040, Scribd.com. See also, Michael J. Gorman, *Abortion and the Early Church: Christian, Jewish, and Pagan Attitudes in the Greco-Roman World* (Downers Grove, InterVarsity Press, 1982), 47-62.

[1] **Paul quotes from Romans**: Romans 11:25–28 [25] a partial hardening has come upon Israel, until the fullness of the Gentiles has come in. [26] And in this way all Israel will be saved, as it is written, "The Deliverer will come from Zion, he will banish ungodliness from Jacob"; [27] "and this will be my covenant with them when I take away their sins." [28] As regards the gospel, they are enemies for your sake. But as regards election, they are beloved for the sake of their forefathers.

[2] **Paul's recommendation not to be married in view of the present tribulation**: 1 Corinthians 7:26–29 [26] I think that in view of the present distress it is good for a person to remain as he is. [27] Are you bound to a wife? Do not seek to be free. Are you free from a wife? Do not seek a wife. [28] But if you do marry, you have not sinned, and if a betrothed woman marries, she has not sinned. Yet those who marry will have worldly troubles, and I would spare you that. [29] This is what I mean, brothers: the appointed time has grown very short. From now on, let those who have wives live as though they had none.

[3] **Peter quotes from**: 2 Peter 3:9-15.

[4] **Heavens and Earth and the covenants**: "In chapter 2, "Biblical Creation and Storytelling," I argued that the establishment of covenants by God is spoken of in the Bible in figurative terms of the creation of the heavens and earth. After all, the Jews' entire existence and reality was interpreted through their covenant with God, so it makes perfect ancient Near Eastern sense to speak of it in the big picture terms of heaven and earth.

"God describes the creation of His covenant with Moses as the creation of the heavens and the earth (Isa. 51:14-16). The creation of Israel through deliverance and Promised Land was likened to God hovering over the waters and filling the formless and void earth (Deut. 32:10-12), separating the waters from the dry land (Exod. 15:8, 16-17), establishing the sun and moon, and defeating the mythical sea dragon of chaos to create His ordered world (Psa. 74:12-17; 89:6-12; Isa. 51:9-14).

"If the creation of a covenant is spoken of as the creation of heavens and earth, and the ruling powers are referred to as sun, moon and stars, then what would the destruction of those powers be but the destruction of the heavens and the earth, including the fall of those astronomical symbolic entities? And what was the embodiment of that covenant but the holy Temple in the holy city of King David?

"The first time that Jerusalem and the Temple was destroyed in 586 B.C. by the Babylonians, the prophets used the language of decreation to express the covenantal violation of Israel. The destruction of the Temple and exile of the Jews through God's providence was likened to the destruction of the heavens and earth and a return to a pre-creation chaotic state, a reversal of Genesis 1 language:

Jer. 4:23-26
I looked on the earth, and behold, it was without form and void;
and to the heavens, and they had no light.
I looked on the mountains, and behold, they were quaking,
I looked, and behold, there was no man,
and all the birds of the air had fled.
I looked, and behold, the fruitful land was a desert...
For this the earth shall mourn,
and the heavens above be dark.

Isa. 24:1-23
Behold, the LORD will empty the earth and make it desolate...
The earth shall be utterly empty and utterly plundered...
The earth staggers like a drunken man;
On that day the LORD will punish
the host of heaven, in heaven,
and the kings of the earth, on the earth...
Then the moon will be confounded
and the sun ashamed.

"In the same way that the first temple destruction was earth-shattering in its covenantal impact, so the second destruction of Jerusalem and the holy Temple in A.D. 70 was of equal spiritual significance in God's covenantal relations with Israel. It was the shaking of the heavens and earth with a punishment of the host of heaven, both astronomical and political/spiritual. This is a perfect example of C.S. Lewis' "myth become fact," an apologetic of God's Word being true.

"In the year A.D. 66, revolutionary Zealots and other factions had fueled a revolt against their Roman occupiers. The leaders of Israel had rejected Jesus of Nazareth as being the Messiah, but they knew the calculations of Daniel's prophecy (Dan. 9:24-27). The 490 years were up. Messiah would arrive, crush the Roman pagan oppressors and establish the long-awaited eternal Kingdom of God (Dan. 2:44-45) on earth.

"The destruction of the Old Covenant order would be likened to the destruction of the heavens and the earth.

"In Hebrews 12:18-22, the writer tells us that God shook the heavens and the earth when He established His covenant with Moses on Sinai. But then in verses 23-24 he says that the New Covenant is a heavenly city of God on the Mount Zion of the heavenly Jerusalem, far superior to the Mosaic covenant. Then he concludes that the end of that Old Covenant is near because a new shaking of the heavens and earth is coming, and that shaking is the establishment of the New Covenant.

> Heb. 12:26-28 At that time His voice shook the earth, but now He has promised, "Yet once more I will shake not only the earth but also the heavens." This phrase, "Yet once more," indicates the removal of things that are shaken — that is, things that have been made — in order that the things that cannot be shaken may remain. Therefore let us be grateful for receiving a kingdom that cannot be shaken.

"J. Stuart Russell answers the relevant question, "What then, is the great catastrophe symbolically represented as the shaking of the earth and heavens?"

"No doubt it is the overthrow and abolition of the Mosaic dispensation, or old covenant; the destruction of the Jewish church and state, together with all the institutions and ordinances connect therewith… the laws, and statutes, and ordinances."

"The book of Hebrews was written before A.D. 70, when the Temple was destroyed. So the physical embodiment of the Old Covenant was still on earth even though the New Covenant had been inaugurated by the death and resurrection of Christ. It was not until the Temple was destroyed that the New Covenant was considered fully inaugurated. They were living in a transition period between covenants during the years of A.D. 30-70.

"This is why the writer of Hebrews says, "In speaking of a new covenant, He makes the first one obsolete. And what is becoming obsolete and growing old is ready to vanish away" (Heb. 8:13). Notice how the author says that the Old Covenant was becoming old and obsolete but was not yet replaced. That is because the incarnation of the old heavens and earth, the Jerusalem Temple, was not yet destroyed at the time of his writing. The Old Covenant was the heavens and earth that was shaken and replaced by the New Covenant, which is the eternal kingdom that will never be replaced or shaken." From Brian Godawa, *God Against the gods: Storytelling, Imagination and Apologetics in the Bible* (Los Angeles, CA: Embedded Pictures Publishing, 2016), 128-133.

See also: "Appendix: The Day of the Lord in 2 Peter" in Brian Godawa, *End Times Bible Prophecy: It's Not What They Told You* (Los Angeles, CA: Embedded Pictures Publishing, 2017).

[5] **Paul quotes about the Lord's Coming and the Lawless One from**: 2 Thessalonians 2:1–9 [1] Now concerning the coming of our Lord Jesus Christ and our being gathered together to him, we ask you, brothers, [2] not to be quickly shaken in mind or alarmed, either by a spirit or a spoken word, or a letter seeming to be from us, to the effect that the day of the Lord has come. [3] Let no one deceive you in any way. For that day will not come, unless the rebellion comes first, and the man of lawlessness is revealed, the son of destruction, [4] who opposes and exalts himself against every so-called god or object of worship, so that he takes his seat in the temple of God, proclaiming himself to be God. [5] Do you not remember that when I was still with you I told you these things? [6] And you know what is restraining him now so that he may be revealed in his time. [7] For the mystery of lawlessness is already at work. Only he who now restrains it will do so until he is out of the way. [8] And then the lawless one will be revealed, whom the

Lord Jesus will kill with the breath of his mouth and bring to nothing by the appearance of his coming. [9] The coming of the lawless one is by the activity of Satan with all power and false signs and wonders,

[6] **Cassandra quotes Jesus**: Matthew 24:14 And this gospel of the kingdom will be proclaimed throughout the whole world as a testimony to all nations, and then the end will come.

The same Greek word for "whole world" (*Oikoumene*) in Matthew 24:14 is used in these passages to mean the Roman Empire:

Romans 1:8 because your faith is being proclaimed throughout the whole world.

Luke 2:1 Now it came about in those days that a decree went out from Caesar Augustus, that a census be taken of all the world.

Acts 11:28 And one of them named Agabus stood up and foretold by the Spirit that there would be a great famine over all the world (this took place in the days of Claudius).

[7] **Paul quotes from Jesus and Romans**:

Matthew 24:14 And this gospel of the kingdom will be proclaimed throughout the whole world as a testimony to all nations, and then the end will come

Romans 5:3–4 [3] Not only that, but we rejoice in our sufferings, knowing that suffering produces endurance, [4] and endurance produces character, and character produces hope.

Jesus, Paul and Scriptures promised us persecution:

2 Timothy 3:12 Indeed, all who desire to live a godly life in Christ Jesus will be persecuted.

1 Thessalonians 3:4 For when we were with you, we kept telling you beforehand that we were to suffer affliction, just as it has come to pass, and just as you know.

John 17:14–15 [14] I have given them your word, and the world has hated them because they are not of the world, just as I am not of the world. [15] I do not ask that you take them out of the world, but that you keep them from the evil one.

John 15:18–20 [18] "If the world hates you, know that it has hated me before it hated you. [19] If you were of the world, the world would love you as its own; but because you are not of the world, but I chose you out of the world, therefore the world hates you. [20] Remember the word that I said to you: 'A servant is not greater than his master.' If they persecuted me, they will also persecute you. If they kept my word, they will also keep yours.

[8] **Claudius' expulsion of the Jews**: Acts 18:2. This occurred in A.D. 49 "Because the Jews at Rome caused continuous disturbances at the instigation of Chrestus [Christ], he expelled them from the city." Suetonius, *Claudius* 25.4. See also Dio Cassius, *Roman History* 60:6. A similar expulsion of the Jews was ordered by Tiberius in A.D. 29. See Philo, *Embassy* 159–61; Suetonius, *Tiberius* 36. Clinton E. Arnold, *Zondervan Illustrated Bible Backgrounds Commentary: John, Acts., vol. 2* (Grand Rapids, MI: Zondervan, 2002), 397–398.

CHAPTER 4

[1] **A map of all the Jewish quarters in Rome at this time**: James D. G. Dunn, *Beginning from Jerusalem (Christianity in the Making, vol. 2)* (Eerdmans Publishing, 2008), 871. See the map in this book on page xii for its context within this story.

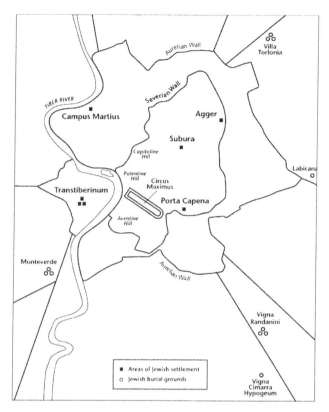

Rome, Showing the Location of Jewish Communities

[2] **Games of Caesar's Victory**: Stephen Dando-Collins, *The Great Fire of Rome: The Fall of the Emperor Nero and His City* (Da Capo Press, 2010), 121.

"What of circuses? Under Augustus there had been sixty-six days of public games every year. Nero increased the total by several days and made the spectacles more elaborate. A new wooden amphitheatre was built in the Field of Mars. An arena yawned open to reveal a magic wood filled with exotic animals. An artificial lake was created to display aquatic beasts. Bears and hippopotamuses appeared. Senators, equestrians and guardsmen battled wild beasts in the arena. A naval battle was staged, Athenians against Persians. Gladiators were carried off in amber-studded coffins. Four-camel chariots raced in the circus. Actors playing Daedalus and Icarus flew across the stage – and one crashed to earth, spattering Nero with blood. Food-parcels were distributed to spectators, and vouchers to claim corn, clothes, gold, silver, precious stones, pearls, paintings, slaves, oxen and mules, wild beasts, even whole farms, tenement-blocks or merchant-ships." Faulkner, Neil (2012-09-30). *Apocalypse: The Great Jewish Revolt Against Rome AD 66-73* (Kindle Locations 356-362). Amberley Publishing. Kindle Edition.

[3] **True religion as rescuing widows and orphans**: James 1:27.

Yahweh adopted Israel on Mount Sinai: Romans 9:4-5.

Israel as God's possession: Deuteronomy 7:6-8.

[4] **Roman marriage laws:** "Augustus passed the Lex Iulia de adulteriis coercendis ("Julian law on restraining adulterers") in 18 BCE, as part of his program of moral reform…If he was of low social status and the pair were caught in the woman's matrimonial home, the husband could kill him (but he could not kill his wife, or else he would be liable for homicide). The husband must then divorce his wife without

327

delay, or he could be subject to a charge for lenocinium, pimping." Thomas Hubbard, Ed., *A Companion to Greek and Roman Sexualities* (England, Blackwell Publishing, 2014), 79.

CHAPTER 5

[1] **On Merkavah Mysticism (Also spelled: Merkabah):** "Merkabah mysticism "is used to refer to an esoteric, visionary-mystical tradition centred upon the vision of God seated on the celestial throne or Merkabah" (Morray-Jones 1992, 2). "Its essence is not absorbed contemplation of God's true nature, but perception of his appearance on the throne, as described by Ezekiel, and cognition of the mysteries of the celestial throne-world.... God's preexisting throne, which embodies and exemplifies all forms of creation, is at once the goal and the theme of his mystical vision" (Scholem 1954, 44). The term Merkabah ("throne-chariot") is not used in the text of Ezekiel but is first used in reference to Ezekiel's vision in Sirach 49:8 (cf. 1 Chron 28:18; see Sirach) and also frequently in the scrolls from Qumran." J. Laansma, "Mysticism," ed. Craig A. Evans and Stanley E. Porter, *Dictionary of New Testament Background: A Compendium of Contemporary Biblical Scholarship* (Downers Grove, IL: InterVarsity Press, 2000), 727–736.

[2] **On the Colossian link to Laodicea:** "Laodicea, as the principal centre of the district, may have been the source of the cosmological speculation affecting the Colossian church, and the identification of its Jews with Gentile society may naturally have fostered an accommodation to pagan thought-form." Colin J. Hemer, *The Letters to the Seven Churches of Asia in Their Local Setting* (Grand Rapids, MI; Cambridge, U.K.; Livonia, MI: William B. Eerdmans Publishing Company; Dove Booksellers, 2001), 184.

The false teaching of both Colossae and Laodicea involved mysticism, Jewish regulations, and ascetic abstinence from food and sex: Colossians 2:16–23 Therefore let no one pass judgment on you in questions of food and drink, or with regard to a festival or a new moon or a Sabbath. These are a shadow of the things to come, but the substance belongs to Christ. Let no one disqualify you, insisting on asceticism and worship of angels, going on in detail about visions, puffed up without reason by his sensuous mind, and not holding fast to the Head, from whom the whole body, nourished and knit together through its joints and ligaments, grows with a growth that is from God. If with Christ you died to the elemental spirits of the world, why, as if you were still alive in the world, do you submit to regulations— "Do not handle, Do not taste, Do not touch" (referring to things that all perish as they are used)— according to human precepts and teachings? These have indeed an appearance of wisdom in promoting self-made religion and asceticism and severity to the body, but they are of no value in stopping the indulgence of the flesh.

On the Colossian heresy: "C.Arnold has argued that magic and folk religion mixed together with Jewish cultic observances and mystery cult initiation were served up as a gumbo that some of the converts in Colossae consumed... I am inclined to agree with F.O. Francis, Dunn, and T.J. Sappington that we seem to be dealing with some sort of esoteric and mystical Jewish philosophy, perhaps lightly influenced by Greek philosophy, not some sort of largely pagan philosophy to which has been added a few marginal Jewish elements." Ben Witherington III, *The Letters to Philemon, the Colossians, and the Ephesians : A Socio-Rhetorical Commentary on the Captivity Epistles* (Grand Rapids, MI: Wm. B. Eerdmans Publishing Co., 2007), 110.

On Metatron: "The etymology and meaning of the name Metatron is not yet clear, but there appear to be two main sides to his character. He is the "Angel of the Lord" or "Prince of the Presence," a Name-bearing angel (Ex 23:21) who mediates and to some extent embodies the divine Glory... However, some texts relate how the famous Enoch was transformed in the course of his ascent into an angelic figure and go on to identify Metatron with the transformed Enoch (e.g., 3 Enoch 7–15)." J. Laansma, "Mysticism," ed. Craig A. Evans and Stanley E. Porter, *Dictionary of New Testament Background: A Compendium of Contemporary Biblical Scholarship* (Downers Grove, IL: InterVarsity Press, 2000), 729.

[3] **True prophets stood in the divine council of Yahweh**: Jeremiah 23:16–18, 21-22 [16] Thus says the LORD of hosts: "Do not listen to the words of the prophets who prophesy to you, filling you with vain hopes. They speak visions of their own minds, not from the mouth of the LORD. [17] They say continually to those who despise the word of the LORD, 'It shall be well with you'; and to everyone who stubbornly follows his own heart, they say, 'No disaster shall come upon you.' " [18] For who among them has stood in the council of the LORD to see and to hear his word, or who has paid attention to his word and

listened?...[21] "I did not send the prophets, yet they ran; I did not speak to them, yet they prophesied. [22] But if they had stood in my council, then they would have proclaimed my words to my people, and they would have turned them from their evil way, and from the evil of their deeds.

For more on the prophetic authority of experiencing Yahweh's divine council: Michael S. Heiser, *The Unseen Realm: Recovering the Supernatural Worldview of the Bible*, First Edition (Bellingham, WA: Lexham Press, 2015), 232-239; H. Wheeler Robinson., "The Council of Yahweh," *Journal of Theological Studies*, 45 (1944) 151-157; Frank M. Cross, Jr. "The Council of Yahweh in Second Isaiah," *Journal of Near Eastern Studies*, Vol. 12, No. 4 (Oct., 1953), pp. 274-277.

[4] **On the earthquake of AD 60**: "The remarkable words of Tacitus which describe the disaster he dates in AD 60: "In the same year, Laodicea, one of the famous Asiatic cities, was laid in ruins by an earthquake, but recovered by its own resources, without assistance from ourselves" (Ann. 14.27.1). This was evidently unusual, and the pointedness of Tacitus' remark suggests that the case was notorious." Colin J. Hemer, *The Letters to the Seven Churches of Asia in Their Local Setting* (Grand Rapids, MI; Cambridge, U.K.; Livonia, MI: William B. Eerdmans Publishing Company; Dove Booksellers, 2001), 193.

On the banking of the city, the gold, the black wool and eye salve: Colin J. Hemer, *The Letters to the Seven Churches of Asia in Their Local Setting* (Grand Rapids, MI; Cambridge, U.K.; Livonia, MI: William B. Eerdmans Publishing Company; Dove Booksellers, 2001), 195-199.

[5] On the language used in this paragraph see Revelation 3:14-22.

CHAPTER 6

[1] **The Great Fire of Rome in ancient sources**: Tacitus, *The Annals* 15.38-45; C. Suetonius Tranquillus, *Lives of the Twelve Caesars, Volume 6,* Nero 38; Cassius Dio, *Roman History*, 62.16-17.

[2] **Vigiles as night guards and firefighters**: Gregory N. Daugherty, "The Cohortes Vigilum and the Great Fire of 64 AD," *The Classical Journal*, Vol. 87, No. 3 (Feb. - Mar., 1992), 231.

[3] **The spread of the Great Fire**: Tacitus, Cornelius; J. C. Yardley; Anthony A. Barrett (2008-06-12). *The Annals: The Reigns of Tiberius, Claudius, and Nero* 15:38 (Oxford Worlds Classics) (p. 356). Oxford University Press. Kindle Edition.

[4] **Lack of water for the Great Fire**: Stephen Dando-Collins, *The Great Fire of Rome: The Fall of the Emperor Nero and His City* (Da Capo Press, 2010), 76-84.

[5] **Creating back-fires as fire fighting**: Stephen Dando-Collins, *The Great Fire of Rome: The Fall of the Emperor Nero and His City* (Da Capo Press, 2010), 129.

[6] **"We have our authority" to start fires**: Tacitus, Annals 15:38; Stephen Dando-Collins, *The Great Fire of Rome: The Fall of the Emperor Nero and His City* (Da Capo Press, 2010), 127.

CHAPTER 7

[1] **The great earthquake and its effect on Philadelphia and its region**: Tacitus, *Annals* 2.47.3–4; Dio Cassius, *Histories* 57.17.8.

Philadelphia's name change to Neocaesarea: Colin J. Hemer, *The Letters to the Seven Churches of Asia in Their Local Setting* (Grand Rapids, MI; Cambridge, U.K.; Livonia, MI: William B. Eerdmans Publishing Company; Dove Booksellers, 2001), 157.

[2] **Dionysus was the patron deity of Philadelphia**: Colin J. Hemer, *The Letters to the Seven Churches of Asia in Their Local Setting* (Grand Rapids, MI; Cambridge, U.K.; Livonia, MI: William B. Eerdmans Publishing Company; Dove Booksellers, 2001), 158.

[3] **Synagogue of Satan in Philadelphia**: Revelation 3:9.

⁴ **No king, but Caesar:** The Jews and their leaders considered Caesar to be their king, with the saying, "No king, but Caesar" (John 19:15). This was the basis of the Jewish revolutionaries' counter saying, "No king but God." Martin Hengel, *The Zealots: Investigations into the Jewish Freedom Movement in the Period from Herod I Until 70 A.D.* (Edinburgh, T&T Clark, 1989), 108.

⁵ **Shut door as excommunication of Christians:** "The shut door has been understood to refer to the excommunication of Christians from the synagogue according to the Twelfth Benediction issued by the Jews at the Council of Jamnia in A.D. 90. However, this benediction only formalizes the earlier practice of local synagogues, which excommunicated those who professed Jesus," Clinton E. Arnold, *Zondervan Illustrated Bible Backgrounds Commentary: Hebrews to Revelation., vol. 4* (Grand Rapids, MI: Zondervan, 2002), 274.

⁶ **Inscribing names of patrons on temple pillars:** A common activity throughout the ancient world. Clinton E. Arnold, *Zondervan Illustrated Bible Backgrounds Commentary: Hebrews to Revelation., vol. 4* (Grand Rapids, MI: Zondervan, 2002), 275–276.

⁷ **The necropolis in Sardis:** "On the west of Sardis is a necropolis, a "great ancient cemetery," which was "imposing and oddly magical when viewed from the city of Sardis". This noteworthy feature of Sardis probably forms the local backdrop to Christ's rebuke of the church when he complains: "I know your deeds, that you have a name that you are alive, but you are dead" (3:1c)." Kenneth L. Gentry, Jr., *The Divorce of Israel: A Redemptive-Historical Interpretation of Revelation Vol. 1* (Dallas, GA: Tolle Lege Press, 2016), 353.

Soiled garments as spiritual metaphor: Revelation 3:4 Yet you have still a few names in Sardis, people who have not soiled their garments.

Alive, but dead, spiritually: Revelation 3:1 "I know your works. You have the reputation of being alive, but you are dead."

⁸ **Triumphal entry language:** Revelation 3:4 and they will walk with me in white, for they are worthy.

⁹ **The history of Sardis and its fall to Cyrus of Persia:** "Almost all the commentators have recognized local allusion in this and the following verse to the two famous occasions when the citadel of Sardis had fallen through lack of vigilance." Colin J. Hemer, *The Letters to the Seven Churches of Asia in Their Local Setting* (Grand Rapids, MI; Cambridge, U.K.; Livonia, MI: William B. Eerdmans Publishing Company; Dove Booksellers, 2001), 144.

Strengthen what remains: Revelation 3:2 Wake up, and strengthen what remains and is about to die."

¹⁰ **The unfinished temple of Artemis at Sardis:** Also of historical significance is the fact that Sardis was the site of a great temple of Artemis which was never finished. It was begun under the rule of Alexander the Great (334 BC) but was abandoned. Then it was restarted in 175 BC, but stopped once again. Thus, it stood as an imposing, albeit unfinished, structure. This probably explains why Christ would rebuke the Sardian Christians by "I have not found your deeds completed" (3:2b)." Kenneth L. Gentry, Jr., *The Divorce of Israel: A Redemptive-Historical Interpretation of Revelation Vol. 1* (Dallas, GA: Tolle Lege Press, 2016), 353.

Incomplete deeds: Revelation 3:2 "for I have not found your works complete in the sight of my God."

¹¹ **On citizenship in Greek cities and erasing names from public registry:** "Greek cities in the ancient world maintained a list of citizens in a public register. When someone committed a criminal action and was condemned, he lost his citizenship and his name was then erased from the register. This action, using the same Greek verb exaleiphō, is attested by several ancient authors and inscriptions (Dio Chrysostom, Or. 31.84; Xenophon, Hell. 2.3.51.)." Clinton E. Arnold, Zondervan *Illustrated Bible Backgrounds Commentary: Hebrews to Revelation., vol. 4* (Grand Rapids, MI: Zondervan, 2002), 272–273.

¹² **Christ comes like a thief:** Revelation 3:3 If you will not wake up, I will come like a thief, and you will not know at what hour I will come against you.

Erasing names from the book of life: Revelation 3:5 The one who conquers will be clothed thus in white garments, and I will never blot his name out of the book of life. I will confess his name before my Father and before his angels.

CHAPTER 8

[1] **Nero in Antium during the Great Fire:** Tacitus, *The Annals* 15.39; Stephen Dando-Collins, *The Great Fire of Rome: The Fall of the Emperor Nero and His City* (Da Capo Press, 2010), 131-136.

[2] **Nero's behavior in the competition**: Suetonius, *Lives of the Twelve Caesars*, Nero 23.

[3] **Nero equated with Apollo:** Suetonius, *Lives of the Twelve Caesars*, Nero 53; Cassius Dio, *Roman History*, 61.5; 63.19.5.

[4] **Nero's obsession with the arts, theater and stage:** Cassius Dio, *Roman History*, 63.9-10; Suetonius, *Lives of the Twelve Caesars*, Nero 20; 41.1; 49:1; Tacitus, *The Annals* 14.14.1; 14.20; 14.15; 14.21.1; 16.4.

"He had not the black-hearted malignity of Domitian, the love of wickedness for its own sake; nor was he a monster of extravagance, like Caligula. He was a painstaking stage-hero, an operatic emperor, music-mad, trembling before the pit, and making that tremble too,- what a commonplace citizen of our day would be, crazed by the reading of modern poets and fancying himself bound in every-day life to imitate the characters of some romantic fiction. Every day Nero proclaims that Art is the only thing to be taken seriously; that all virtue is a lie; that the real gentleman is he who shamelessly avows his shame; that the great man is he who can intelligently abuse all, ruin all, squander all." Ernest Renan, trans. Joseph Henry Allen, *The Antichrist: The Period From the Arrival of Paul in Rome to the End of the Jewish Revolution* (Boston, Roberts Brothers 1897), 117-118.

Plato's theory of beauty through contemplation of the body ultimately leading to the ideal form of beauty in heaven: Plato, *Symposium* 210-212.

[5] **Tigellinus sought to undermine Faenius Rufus:** Tacitus, *Annals* 14.57.1; 15.50.

CHAPTER 9

[1] **"First of Asia":** William Ramsay, *The Letters to the Seven Churches of Asia and Their Place in the Plan of the Apocalypse* (London, Hodder and Stoughton, 1904), 255. Robert H. Mounce, *The Book of Revelation, The New International Commentary on the New Testament* (Grand Rapids, MI: Wm. B. Eerdmans Publishing Co., 1997), 73.

Smyrna and its metaphor of the victory crown: Colin J. Hemer, *The Letters to the Seven Churches of Asia in Their Local Setting* (Grand Rapids, MI; Cambridge, U.K.; Livonia, MI: William B. Eerdmans Publishing Company; Dove Booksellers, 2001), 70-76.

The faithfulness of Smyrna to Rome, and the building of the imperial temple: "As early as 195 [BC], when Antiochus was still at the height of his power, Smyrna built a temple and instituted a worship of Rome; this bold step was the pledge of uncompromising adherence to the cause of Rome, while its fortunes were still uncertain. After a century, when a Smyrnaean public assembly heard of the distress in a Roman army during the war against Mithridates, the citizens stripped off their own clothes to send to the shivering soldiers. The faithfulness of Smyrna to this alliance was a just ground of pride to the city, and was fully acknowledged by her powerful friend. Cicero expressed the Roman feeling that Smyrna was 'the city of our most faithful and most ancient allies.' And in 26 A.D. the Smyrnaeans argued before the Senate that the new temple to be dedicated by the Commune of Asia to Tiberius should be built in Smyrna, because of their faithful friendship dating from a time before the East had learned that Rome was the greatest power in the world ; and they were preferred to all other cities of the Province.'" — William Ramsay, *The Letters to the Seven Churches of Asia and Their Place in the Plan of the Apocalypse* (London, Hodder and Stoughton, 1904), 254.

See also: Colin J. Hemer, *The Letters to the Seven Churches of Asia in Their Local Setting* (Grand Rapids, MI; Cambridge, U.K.; Livonia, MI: William B. Eerdmans Publishing Company; Dove Booksellers, 2001), 70-75.

Revelation uses these epithets, "first and last" and "crown of life" of Christ: Revelation 2:8 "And to the angel of the church in Smyrna write: 'The words of the first and the last, who died and came to life." Revelation 2:10 "Be faithful unto death, and I will give you the crown of life." Colin J. Hemer, *The Letters to the Seven Churches of Asia in Their Local Setting* (Grand Rapids, MI; Cambridge, U.K.; Livonia, MI: William B. Eerdmans Publishing Company; Dove Booksellers, 2001), 60-65, 70-71.

[2] **Start of the Imperial Cult under Augustus:** J. W. van Henten, "Ruler Cult," ed. Karel van der Toorn, Bob Becking, and Pieter W. van der Horst, *Dictionary of Deities and Demons in the Bible* (Leiden; Boston; Köln; Grand Rapids, MI; Cambridge: Brill; Eerdmans, 1999), 712-714.

"Recent studies have demonstrated how quickly the imperial cult grew in the empire from the time of Augustus through to the principates of Claudius and Nero. See Bruce W. Winter, "B. The Imperial Cult," in *The Book of Acts in Its First Century Setting: The Book of Acts in Its Graeco-Roman Setting*, ed. David W. J. Gill, Conrad Gempf, and Bruce W. Winter, vol. 2 (Grand Rapids, MI; Carlisle, Cumbria: William B. Eerdmans Publishing Company; The Paternoster Press, 1994), 93.

"Lord of the Whole Universe," "Nero, Zeus," "Son of God, Savior.": Kenneth Gentry, Jr. *The Beast of Revelation* (Tyler, TX: Institute for Christian Economics, 1989, 1994), 57-67; S.R.F. Price, "Gods and Emperors: The Greek Language of the Roman Imperial Cult," *The Journal of Hellenic Studies*, Vol. 104 (1984), pp. 79-95.

[3] **Cybele's lions**: William Ramsay, *The Letters to the Seven Churches of Asia and Their Place in the Plan of the Apocalypse* (London: Hodder and Stoughton, 1904), 258. "[Cybele] is depicted in statues either on a chariot pulled by lions or enthroned carrying a bowl and drum, wearing a mural crown, flanked by lions." "Cybele," Ancient History Encyclopedia, http://www.ancient.eu/Cybele/

[4] **Synagogue of Satan as Jews rejecting Messiah**: Revelation 2:9 The slander of those who say that they are Jews and are not, but are a synagogue of Satan.

Revelation 3:9 those of the synagogue of Satan who say that they are Jews and are not–but lie.

See also Romans 2:17-29; Galatians 5:1-4, 12.

[5] **Torah religion as slavery in light of the New Covenant**: Galatians 4:8-10; Romans 6:16; 2Peter 2:15-19.

[6] **The letter X used to abbreviate for Christianoi**: R.C. Sproul, "What Does the X in Xmas Mean?" http://www.ligonier.org/blog/why-is-x-used-when-it-replaces-christ-in-christmas/

[7] **The economic suffering of Christians at Smyrna**: Revelation 2:9.

"Jesus first assures the Christians in Smyrna that he knows what they are going through. Believers have apparently lost their jobs or their businesses are being boycotted, hence depriving them of material support." Clinton E. Arnold, *Zondervan Illustrated Bible Backgrounds Commentary: Hebrews to Revelation., vol. 4* (Grand Rapids, MI: Zondervan, 2002), 263.

"Because the church at Smyrna refused to participate in the imperial cult, they no doubt endured economic sanctions as well." C. Marvin Pate, *Writings of John: A Survey of the Gospel, Epistles, and Apocalypse* (Zondervan, 2011), 599.

[8] **Tattoos forbidden in the Torah**: Leviticus 19:28.

[9] Revelation 2:10 "Be faithful unto death, and I will give you the crown of life."

CHAPTER 10

[1] **The extant of the Great Fire**: Tacitus, *The Annals* 15.40

[2] **Poppea's vanity bathing in asses' milk**: "The extremes of luxury indulged in by this Sabina I will indicate in the briefest terms. She caused gilded shoes to be put on the mules that drew her and caused five hundred asses that had recently foaled to be milked daily that she might bathe in their milk. For she bestowed the greatest pains on the beauty and brilliancy of her person, and this is why, when she noticed in a mirror one day that her appearance was not comely, she prayed that she might die before she passed her prime." Cassius Dio, *Roman History*, 62.28.1.

[3] **Nero's physical description:** Suetonius, *Lives of the Twelve Caesars, Nero* 61.

[4] **Poppaea's scandalous past:** Plutarch, *The Parallel Lives*, Galba, 19; Tacitus, *The Annals* 13.45; Suetonius, *Lives of the Twelve Caesars*, Nero 35.

[5] **Josephus in Rome during the Great Fire:** Flavius Josephus, *The Life of Flavius Josephus*, 13-16. Flavius Josephus, *The Antiquities of the Jews*, 20.195

[6] **The Designation of Israel as Palestine:** "A. Palestine The use of the name Palestine for the region W of the Jordan Rift (Cisjordan) became popular in the time of the British Mandate (1918–1948; after World War I Iraq, Transjordan, and Palestine were mandated to the British, while Syria and Lebanon were placed under French control). It is not so used in the Hebrew OT. In Ex. 15:14; Isa. 14:29, 31, Heb *pelešet* (AV "Palestina") should be translated "Philistia" (cf. RSV, NEB). In Joel 3:4 (MT 4:4) the term is clearly used for the coastal region of Philistia. Gk *Palaistinē* does not occur in the NT.

"Jerome spoke of "the land of Judea, which is now called Palestine" (In Ezechiel 37:17, quoted by F.-M. Abel [GP, I, 313], who said that this usage became official in the Roman and Byzantine Chancellery, and even included the southern portion of Transjordan)." G. A. Lee, "Palanquin," ed. Geoffrey W Bromiley, *The International Standard Bible Encyclopedia, Revised* (Wm. B. Eerdmans, 1979–1988), 633.

"Palestine is derived from the name Pelishtim or "Philistines." The Greeks, familiar primarily with the coastal area, applied the name "Palestine" to the entire southeastern Mediterranean region." Timothy Trammel, "Palestine," ed. Chad Brand et al., *Holman Illustrated Bible Dictionary* (Nashville, TN: Holman Bible Publishers, 2003), 1237.

"Originally a designation for the southern coastal strip where the Philistines had settled in the twelfth century B.C., Palestine became the name for the entire region. The ancient Greek historian Herodotus was the first to use Palaistinē, the Hellenistic form of Philistia, in the inclusive sense. After the suppression of the Bar-Kochba revolt in A.D. 135 the Roman emperor Hadrian expunged the name Provincia Judea and substituted Provincia Syria Palaestina or simply Palaestina (Palestine)." Paul J. Achtemeier, Harper & Row and Society of Biblical Literature, *Harper's Bible Dictionary* (San Francisco: Harper & Row, 1985), 740.

[7] **Nero consulted the Sibylline oracles:** Tacitus, *The Annals*,15.44; Stephen Dando-Collins, *The Great Fire of Rome: The Fall of the Emperor Nero and His City* (Da Capo Press, 2010), 159-160.

[8] **Nero's building plan for Rome with wider streets and better construction**: Tacitus, *The Annals* , 40-43.

[9] **Nero's goal to rebuild Rome as Neropolis**: Suetonius, *Lives of the Twelve Caesars*, Nero 55; Cassius Dio, *Roman History*, 62.16; Stephen Dando-Collins, *The Great Fire of Rome: The Fall of the Emperor Nero and His City* (Da Capo Press, 2010), 154.

The connection July 19 with a previous fire that destroyed Rome in 390 B.C.: Tacitus, *The Annals*, 15:41.

The rumors of Nero's involvement in the conflagration: Cassius Dio, *Roman History*, 62.16; Tacitus, *The Annals*, 15.39-40.

[10] **Nero's weak and husky voice**: "Although his voice was weak and husky, he began to long to appear on the stage." Suetonius, Lives of the Twelve Caesars, *Nero* 20.1.

CHAPTER 11

---

[1] **Carried the rubble to the marshes of Ostia**: Stephen Dando-Collins, *The Great Fire of Rome: The Fall of the Emperor Nero and His City* (Da Capo Press, 2010), 150-151.

[2] **Tigellinus sought to undermine Faenius Rufus**: Tacitus, *Annals* 14.57.1; 15.50.

[3] **Rumors and blame of arson on Nero**: Suetonius, *Lives of the Twelve Caesars*, Nero 38; Cassius Dio, *Roman History*, 62.16-18.

[4] Cassius Dio, *Roman History*, 62.18.

[5] **The Jewish quarter in the Trans-Tiber untouched by the Great Fire, and possible suspect for arson:** "It was the Transtiberim region, with its effective fire break of the Tiber itself, which escaped the devastation of the fire. As argued below, it is assumed that it was in this area that a good number of Christians lived, and this fact strengthened the argument that the Christians should be blamed for the fire." Andrew D. Clarke, "Rome and Italy," in *The Book of Acts in Its First Century Setting: The Book of Acts in Its Graeco-Roman Setting,* ed. David W. J. Gill, Conrad Gempf, and Bruce W. Winter, vol. 2 (Grand Rapids, MI; Carlisle, Cumbria: William B. Eerdmans Publishing Company; The Paternoster Press, 1994), 464.

"What influenced Nero at this juncture to select the Christians as his victims can only be conjectured. Possibly the suspicions of the Roman crowd had fallen upon the Jews, the objects at once of their detestation and contempt, as being incendiaries, partly because their own Ghetto across the Tiber was one of the few uninjured quarters of the city." George Edmunson, *The Church In Rome In The First Century An Examination Of Various Controverted Questions Relating To Its History, Chronology, Literature, And Traditions* (New York, Longmans Green, 1913), 127.

"By the 40's, during the reign of Claudius, Christianity had made steady inroads into Rome, though it is speculated that even by Nero's time its followers numbered not more than 3,000. Early members of the faith had mostly been Jews, living in Rome's Jewish community over in the regio XIV, the Transtiberum." Gilbert, John (2015-02-27). *Parallel Lives, Parallel Nations Volume Two: A Narrative History Of Rome & The Jews, Their Relations And Their Worlds* (161 BC-135 AD) (p. 277). Kindle Edition.

[6] **Jews performed sacrifices at the Jerusalem Temple on behalf of Caesar**: Flavius Josephus, *The Wars of the Jews*, 2.409-410 (2.17.2).

The Christian rejection of the temple in Jerusalem: Matthew 23:37–24:2 [Jesus said,]"O Jerusalem, Jerusalem, the city that kills the prophets and stones those who are sent to it! How often would I have gathered your children together as a hen gathers her brood under her wings, and you were not willing! See, your house is left to you desolate. 39 For I tell you, you will not see me again, until you say, 'Blessed is he who comes in the name of the Lord.' Jesus left the temple and was going away, when his disciples came to point out to him the buildings of the temple. But he answered them, "You see all these, do you not? Truly, I say to you, there will not be left here one stone upon another that will not be thrown down."

Ephesians 2:18–22 For through him we both have access in one Spirit to the Father. So then you are no longer strangers and aliens, but you are fellow citizens with the saints and members of the household of God, built on the foundation of the apostles and prophets, Christ Jesus himself being the cornerstone, 21 in whom the whole structure, being joined together, grows into a holy temple in the Lord. In him you also are being built together into a dwelling place for God by the Spirit.

Acts 17:24–25 The God who made the world and everything in it, being Lord of heaven and earth, does not live in temples made by man, nor is he served by human hands, as though he needed anything, since he himself gives to all mankind life and breath and everything.

Acts 7:48–50 Yet the Most High does not dwell in houses made by hands, as the prophet says, "'Heaven is my throne, and the earth is my footstool. What kind of house will you build for me, says the Lord, or what is the place of my rest? 50 Did not my hand make all these things?'"

"Persecution occurred when Christians challenged the symbols of ethnic solidarity so sharply that they placed themselves beyond the tolerance-limits of the Jewish community." The Jews, therefore, seek capital punishment for any who speak against or defile the temple, not only in Jeremiah's day (Jer 26:7–8, 11; Ant. 10:6:2 §89–92) but also in the first century (Ac 6:14; 21:26–30; 24:6; 25:7–8; t. Sanh. 13:5; t.

Ros. Has. 17a; t. Ber. 9:13b). Thus, Bauckham notes that the "controversy about the temple was evidently the occasion for the first major persecution of Christians (Acts 6–8). Kenneth L. Gentry, Jr., *The Divorce of Israel: A Redemptive-Historical Interpretation of Revelation Vol. 2* (Dallas, GA: Tolle Lege Press, 2016), 85.

[7] **The Jewish laws that the Christians apparently were rejecting**:

SABBATH: Jesus fulfills the Sabbath and becomes the Sabbath rest for believers: Hebrews 4:1-13.

Christian alteration of the Sabbath to the first day of the week: 1Corinthians 16:1-2; Acts 20:7.

Jesus abolishes the sabbaths and dietary restrictions of the the old covenant: Colossians 2:16–17 Therefore let no one pass judgment on you in questions of food and drink, or with regard to a festival or a new moon or a Sabbath. These are a shadow of the things to come, but the substance belongs to Christ.

Jesus abolished the dietary restrictions of Mosaic Law: Mark 7:18–23 And he said to them, "Then are you also without understanding? Do you not see that whatever goes into a person from outside cannot defile him, since it enters not his heart but his stomach, and is expelled?" (Thus he declared all foods clean.) And he said, "What comes out of a person is what defiles him. For from within, out of the heart of man, come evil thoughts, sexual immorality, theft, murder, adultery, coveting, wickedness, deceit, sensuality, envy, slander, pride, foolishness. All these evil things come from within, and they defile a person." See also Peter's vision, Acts 10:9-33.

Circumcision: Circumcision is derided in the New Testament as no longer the sign of covenant with God: The entire book of Galatians is all about this very issue. Paul then concludes,

> Galatians 5:2–6 Look: I, Paul, say to you that if you accept circumcision, Christ will be of no advantage to you. I testify again to every man who accepts circumcision that he is obligated to keep the whole law. You are severed from Christ, you who would be justified by the law; you have fallen away from grace. For through the Spirit, by faith, we ourselves eagerly wait for the hope of righteousness. For in Christ Jesus neither circumcision nor uncircumcision counts for anything, but only faith working through love.

See also Romans 2, where Paul discredits circumcision as inferior to faith and ineffective without it. Circumcision is no longer the boundary marker of being God's people. He then concludes: Romans 2:28–29 For no one is a Jew who is merely one outwardly, nor is circumcision outward and physical. But a Jew is one inwardly, and circumcision is a matter of the heart, by the Spirit, not by the letter. His praise is not from man but from God.

See also Romans 4 that downplays circumcision as an expression of faith, which is the true mark of covenant inclusion. Circumcision was merely the outward sign.

Baptism as the new covenant sign replaces the old covenant sign of circumcision: Colossians 2:11-13; Acts 2:36-39; Romans 6:1-10.

Christian teaching denied the signs of covenant inclusion claimed by Jews as circumcision, Sabbaths, and dietary laws: "Therefore let no one pass judgment on you in questions of food and drink, or with regard to a festival or a new moon or a Sabbath. These are a shadow of the things to come, but the substance belongs to Christ." Colossians 2:16–23. See also Galatians 2:21-3:14; Romans 4.

[8] **Tacitus writes of the Christians and how the Romans saw them**: "Christus, the founder of the name, had undergone the death penalty in the reign of Tiberius, by sentence of the procurator Pontius Pilatus, and the pernicious superstition was checked for a moment, only to break out once more, not merely in Judaea, the home of the disease, but in the capital itself, where all things horrible or shameful in the world collect and find a vogue. " Tacitus, *The Annals*, 15.44.

[9] **Suetonius writes of the Jewish riots caused by Christian preaching**: "Since the Jews constantly made disturbances at the instigation of Chrestus, he expelled them from Rome." Suetonius, *Lives of the Twelve Caesars*, Claudius 25.4.

Acts 18:2 confirms the expulsion of the Jews.

"No king but Caesar" was a common phrase uttered by Jews: John 19:15. It was countered by the Zealots who proclaimed "No king but God." Martin Hengel, *The Zealots: investigations into the Jewish freedom movement in the period from Herod I until 70 A.D.* (Edinburgh: U.K., T. & T. Clark, 1989), 108.

[10] See Chapter 2 endnotes for information about Christians and abortion and infant exposure.

[11] **Roman acceptance of homosexuality, lesbianism, and pederasty:** "Roman society seems to have inherited widespread homosexuality from Greece in the second century B.C. It occurred in all forms (pederasty, male prostitution, mercenary catamites, adult mutuality, and lesbianism)." James B. De Young, *Homosexuality: Contemporary Claims Examined in Light of the Bible and Other Ancient Literature and Law* (Grand Rapids, MI: Kregel Publications, 2000), 257.

Jesus' statements against same-sex and same-sex marriage in the first century: Matthew 19:4–6; Matthew 11:23–24.

New Testament condemnation of same-sex behavior during the first century: Romans 1:24–32 Therefore God gave them up in the lusts of their hearts to impurity, to the dishonoring of their bodies among themselves, because they exchanged the truth about God for a lie and worshiped and served the creature rather than the Creator, who is blessed forever! Amen. For this reason God gave them up to dishonorable passions. For their women exchanged natural relations for those that are contrary to nature; and the men likewise gave up natural relations with women and were consumed with passion for one another, men committing shameless acts with men and receiving in themselves the due penalty for their error. And since they did not see fit to acknowledge God, God gave them up to a debased mind to do what ought not to be done. They were filled with all manner of unrighteousness, evil, covetousness, malice. They are full of envy, murder, strife, deceit, maliciousness. They are gossips, slanderers, haters of God, insolent, haughty, boastful, inventors of evil, disobedient to parents, 31 foolish, faithless, heartless, ruthless. Though they know God's righteous decree that those who practice such things deserve to die, they not only do them but give approval to those who practice them.

1 Corinthians 6:9–10 Or do you not know that the unrighteous will not inherit the kingdom of God? Do not be deceived: neither the sexually immoral, nor idolaters, nor adulterers, nor men who practice homosexuality, nor thieves, nor the greedy, nor drunkards, nor revilers, nor swindlers will inherit the kingdom of God.

See also: 1 Timothy 1:8–11; 2 Peter 2:6–10; Jude 7.

[12] **Roman homosexuality and pedophilia**: "Sex with adolescent males was among the socially approved sexual options for a Roman man. On the whole, however, a Roman man's sexual relations with adolescent males were restricted to slaves and prostitutes. Sex with a free-born Roman youth, like sex with a freeborn Roman woman other than one's wife, would have constituted the crime of stuprum—a broad category of forbidden sexual behavior." Thomas K. Hubbard, ed., *A Companion To Greek And Roman Sexualities* (Oxford, Blackwell,), 117.

[13] **The charges against the Christians of sex orgies, cannibalism, superstitious magic and hatred of the human race during Nero's day**: "The offences with which the Christians were charged under Nero appear to have been, according to Tacitus, of the same character as those of which Pliny the Younger speaks in his famous letter from Bithynia to the Emperor Trajan, as the 'crimes adhering to the name,' and which we find described in the writings of the second-century Christian Apologists, perhaps more succinctly than any other by Athenagoras (about 177 A.D.), who writes. 'Three things are alleged against us: Atheism, Thyestean feasts, Oedipodean intercourse.' The refusal to take part in the ceremonies or to recognise the gods of the national religion constituted the crime of Atheism. The secret assemblies, the bringing of children to them for the rite of baptism, the words of consecration in the Holy Eucharist, the salutation with 'a holy kiss,' were travestied by the enemies of Christianity into charges of murder, cannibalism, and promiscuous intercourse, which were accepted as true by public opinion already in the days of Nero, and which still remained a fixed article of popular belief and execration when Tertullian wrote his 'Apology' about a century and a half later. These were the *flagitia* to which Tacitus attaches the epithets *atrocia* and *pudenda*, abominations horrible and shameful.

"Jews who, when Christianity began to be first preached, scattered abroad false reports of the Gospel, such as that "Christians offered up an infant in sacrifice, and partook of its flesh;" and again, "that the professors of Christianity, wishing to do the 'works of darkness,' used to extinguish the lights (in their meetings), and each one to have sexual intercourse with any woman whom he chanced to meet." Origen, "De Principiis," in *Fathers of the Third Century: Tertullian, Part Fourth; Minucius Felix; Commodian; Origen, Parts First and Second*, ed. Alexander Roberts, James Donaldson, and A. Cleveland Coxe, trans. Frederick Crombie, *vol. 4, The Ante-Nicene Fathers* (Buffalo, NY: Christian Literature Company, 1885), 585.

"That the Christians were also condemned for the crime of 'magic' may be inferred from the fact that their religion is styled by Tacitus a most pernicious superstition - *abilis superstitio* - and by Suetonius a strange and maleficent superstition - *superstitio nova ac malefica* - (the word *maleficus* having juristically the special signification of a magician or sorcerer), and the punishment in the Vatican Gardens was that specially assigned to those convicted of practising magical arts.

"The crime of 'hatred of the human race,' however, was the charge which included all these other accusations, and henceforth during the succeeding centuries was to render the mere name of Christian a sufficient ground for summary." *The Church In Rome In The First Century: An Examination Of Various Controverted Questions Relating To Its History, Chronology, Literature And Traditions* (New York, Longmans, Green and Co., 1913), 135-136.

"Thoroughly alarmed now, the authorities began to zero in on the Christians' activities. Previous reports were confirmed, new evidence turned up. They held secret meetings and performed strange rites, and they believed in universal love which meant that they were perverts, dedicated to orgies. They " baptized" people by holding their heads under water, and they gathered and had strange meals where they in some way partook in eating their master's flesh and drinking his blood. The reports weren't clear, but it was possible the Christians were cannibals. Moreover, and on an even more important note, these Christians had been busy preaching on the streets about the coming of a divine kingdom and the return of their Master, and how, and here was once again the important part, everything was going to be engulfed in fire as part of some big " Judgment Day." *Gilbert, John (2015-02-27). Parallel Lives, Parallel Nations Volume Two: A narrative history of Rome & the Jews, their relations and their worlds (161 BC-135 AD) (p. 280). Kindle Edition.*

CHAPTER 12

[1] **On the lack of status of Thyatira:** Colin J. Hemer, *The Letters to the Seven Churches of Asia in Their Local Setting* (Grand Rapids, MI; Cambridge, U.K.; Livonia, MI: William B. Eerdmans Publishing Company; Dove Booksellers, 2001), 106; William Ramsay, *The letters to the Seven Churches of Asia and Their Place in the Plan of the Apocalypse* (London, Hodder and Stoughton, 1904), 318-19.

Jezebel at Thyatira: Revelation 2:20-24.

[2] **The story of Jezebel** can be found in 1 Kings 16-21.

[3] **The story of King Josiah and his reforms** can be found in 2 Kings 21-23.

[4] **"Yahweh and his Asherah"** is a common inscription on walls and images found in Israel, the most famous being the image found in Kuntillet 'Ajrûd. Archeological evidence shows that the widespread "folk religion" of the common populace in Israel was riddled with idolatry. This is much different from the official monotheistic religion of the priesthood rooted in Jerusalem. *Did God Have a Wife?: Archaeology And Folk Religion In Ancient Israel* (Grand Rapids, Eerdmans, 2005), 5-7; 162-164.

[5] **On Thyatira guilds and commerce, purple cloth:** "Thyatira was a major inland Asian city in the first century. Standing midway between Pergamum and Sardis on a broad fertile plain, its location made it an ideal commercial center. Many trade guilds were formed that grew to have an influential role in civic life. The city was particularly noted for its local purple dye derived from the madder root. As a result there was a prosperous guild of dyers. Lydia, the businesswoman Paul met in Philippi, was a purple dye seller from the city (Acts 16:14). Syncretism characterized the city's religious life. Outside the city in a sacred precinct of the Chaldeans, there was a shrine of the oriental Sibyl Sambathe. Sometime before 2 B.C. a

locally organized civic cult of Rome and Augustus was dedicated." Clinton E. Arnold, *Zondervan Illustrated Bible Backgrounds Commentary: Hebrews to Revelation., vol. 4* (Grand Rapids, MI: Zondervan, 2002), 269.

Deeper things of Satan: Revelation 2:24.

Trade guilds in Thyatira: The city's most obvious peculiarity was then its unusually large number of influential trade-guilds. Associations of this kind were an ancient feature of community life in Asia, especially in Lydia (cf. Hdt. 1.93). In many cities of the area, including Thyatira, Philadelphia and Hierapolis, they seem to replace the more usual civic tribal structure. Colin J. Hemer, *The Letters to the Seven Churches of Asia in Their Local Setting* (Grand Rapids, MI; Cambridge, U.K.; Livonia, MI: William B. Eerdmans Publishing Company; Dove Booksellers, 2001), 107–108.

[6] The Apostle John's phrases referred in this paragraph:

Liars: 1 John 2:4 Whoever says "I know him" but does not keep his commandments is a liar, and the truth is not in him.

1 John 5:10 Whoever believes in the Son of God has the testimony in himself. Whoever does not believe God has made him a liar, because he has not believed in the testimony that God has borne concerning his Son.

Blind: 1 John 2:11 But whoever hates his brother is in the darkness and walks in the darkness, and does not know where he is going, because the darkness has blinded his eyes.

Antichrist: 1 John 2:22–23 Who is the liar but he who denies that Jesus is the Christ? This is the antichrist, he who denies the Father and the Son. 23 No one who denies the Son has the Father. Whoever confesses the Son has the Father also.

Deceivers: 2 John 7 For many deceivers have gone out into the world, those who do not confess the coming of Jesus Christ in the flesh. Such a one is the deceiver and the antichrist.

Lawless: 1 John 3:4 Everyone who makes a practice of sinning also practices lawlessness; sin is lawlessness.

Children of the devil: 1 John 3:10 By this it is evident who are the children of God, and who are the children of the devil: whoever does not practice righteousness is not of God, nor is the one who does not love his brother.

John 8:44 Jesus: "You are of your father the devil, and your will is to do your father's desires."

Murderer: 1 John 3:15 Everyone who hates his brother is a murderer, and you know that no murderer has eternal life abiding in him.

God is love: 1 John 4:8 Anyone who does not love does not know God, because God is love.

Wicked: 2 John 10–11 If anyone comes to you and does not bring this teaching, do not receive him into your house or give him any greeting, 11 for whoever greets him takes part in his wicked works.

3 John 10 So if I come, I will bring up what he is doing, talking wicked nonsense against us.

[7] **Spiritual compromise at Thyatira**: "Presumably Jezebel argued that a Christian might join a guild and participate in its feasts without thereby compromising his faith. He was initiated into a superior wisdom. He knew the idol was nothing and he could not be defiled by that which did not exist." Colin J. Hemer, *The Letters to the Seven Churches of Asia in Their Local Setting* (Grand Rapids, MI; Cambridge, U.K.; Livonia, MI: William B. Eerdmans Publishing Company; Dove Booksellers, 2001), 123.

The "sexual immorality" of Jezebel was a metaphor of spiritual unfaithfulness to God: "A metaphorical understanding of immorality seems best here. The two charges — eating things sacrificed to idols and committing acts of immorality — are really one charge presented as a hendiadys, expanding the heresy for rhetorical effect." Kenneth L. Gentry, Jr., *The Divorce of Israel: A Redemptive-Historical Interpretation of Revelation Vol 1* (Dallas, GA: Tolle Lege Press, 2016), 390.

[8] **The mark of the Beast was a sign of loyalty to Caesar tied to economic rights**: Revelation 13:16-18.

"But now: What about the Beast's imposing his mark upon men?

"And he causes all, the small and the great, and the rich and the poor, and the free men and the slaves, to be given a mark on their right hand, or on their forehead, and he provides that no one should be able to buy or to sell, except the one who has the mark, either the name of the beast or the number of his name (Rev. 13:16-17). In answering this question we must recall the symbolic nature of Revelation and parallel images within Revelation that seem to be based on an Old Testament practice.

"First, marking men in the service of the Beast is no more a literal mark than marking the servants of the Lamb in the very next scene: And I looked, and behold, the Lamb was standing on Mount Zion, and with Him one hundred and forty-four thousand, having His name and the name of His Father written on their foreheads (Rev. 14:1).

"Second, such marking appears to be a metaphor for dominion and control exerted by the source of the mark. In Revelation 13 no one may buy or sell without the mark. That is, all subjects of the Roman empire are under the dominion of the emperor who effectively holds their livelihood in his hands.

"Third, in that the Beast demands worship (Rev. 13:4, 8), thereby showing his divine pretensions, John presents his pretentious claim to sovereignty against an Old Testament backdrop. This very Old Testament-oriented book is using the mark on the right hand and forehead as a negative image of God's requiring his Law on his people.

"And these words, which I am commanding you today, shall be on your heart…. And you shall bind them as a sign on your hand and they shall be as frontals on your forehead (Deut. 6:6, 8). This is underscored by the previously noted fact that the next verse presents the servants of the Lamb with marks on their foreheads.

"Fourth, any present day mark goes against John's near term timeframe (Rev. 1:1, 3; 22:6, 10), relevance for persecuted first century Christians (Rev. 1:9;3:10; 6:9-11; 12:4-6,17), theme presenting judgment on Israel (Rev. 1:7), and tying the beast to the era of the first seven emperors of Rome (Rev. 17:9-10). Thus, modern searches are anti-contextual.

"Consequently, by this marking imagery John is teaching that the Beast (Nero) will act out his divine pretensions, acting as an absolute sovereign over the lives and fortunes of his subjects. He will no more impose a literal mark upon his subjects than Christ does his. This is dramatic imagery, not literal reality."

Kenneth Gentry, *The Book of Revelation Made Easy: You Can Understand Bible Prophecy* (Powder Springs, GA: American Vision), 62-63.

"This mark of the Beast given in Revelation 13:16 is contrasted with the mark or "seal of God" on the 144,000 in Revelation 7:3 Gentry writes, "Beale (715) is surely correct that this mark "is the parody and opposite of the 'seal' in 7:3-8." The seal shows the fidelity of Palestinian Christians to Christ, thereby marking them out for his safe-keeping, just as the mark of the beast allows his followers to buy and sell to support their lives (13:17). This spiritual parody (a literary feature so common in Rev) is proved in the very next scene just three verses later. There we see the followers of the Lamb, the Judean Christians, with "His name and the name of His Father written [gegrammenon] on their foreheads" (14:1)." Kenneth L. Gentry, Jr., *The Divorce of Israel: A Redemptive-Historical Interpretation of Revelation Vol. 2* (Dallas, GA: Tolle Lege Press, 2016), 277.

Binding the Scriptures to the forehead and hand In the Old Testament: A symbolic reference to having the Word of God rooted in one's mind and applied to everything one does. Deuteronomy 6:6-8 And these words that I command you today shall be on your heart. You shall teach them diligently to your children, and shall talk of them when you sit in your house, and when you walk by the way, and when you lie down, and when you rise. You shall bind them as a sign on your hand, and they shall be as frontlets between your eyes.

The heart of the Nicolaitan heresy: "That Nicolaitanism involves a doubt regarding Christ's true identity which is moving many Jewish-Christians to withdraw from the new faith because of its high christology. We see even in Christ's ministry that many would claim to believe in him only to have Jesus himself reject them (Jn 2:23-25; cp. 6:2, 6:14-15, 26). The text suggests that they apparently are moved

339

to affirm him only because of their personal self-interest which arises due to his miracles (2:23). Others claim to believe in him (8:30–31) only to wholly and vehemently reject him in that very context (8:37, 48, 59), while violently rejecting his claim to be God's Son and divine (8:38, 49–52, 58).

"…In Rev the struggle is not over Jewish identity markers such as circumcision, but over something even more substantial. In fact, it is so deadly that it could be deemed a form of idolatry and equated with sexual immorality (2:14, 20). As noted this struggle regards the identity of Christ, the central, distinguishing doctrine of the Christian church." Kenneth L. Gentry, Jr., *The Divorce of Israel: A Redemptive-Historical Interpretation of Revelation* Vol. 1 (Dallas, GA: Tolle Lege Press, 2016), 399.

[9] **Shining Ones**: "The noun śārîm in Ps 82:7, traditionally rendered as 'princes' or the like, has been construed as the designation of divine beings: 'Shining Ones' (MULLEN 1980:227–245) or 'Shining One' (PAGE 1996:162–164). PAGE (1996:162) interprets the final mēm as having emphatic force and derives the meaning from Proto-Semitic ŚRR, 'to shine'. Ps 82:6–7 would contain allusions to a Canaanite Myth of Cosmic Rebellion." B. Becking, "Shining One(s)," ed. Karel van der Toorn and Pieter W. van der Horst, Dictionary of Deities and Demons in the Bible (Leiden; Boston; Köln; Grand Rapids, MI; Cambridge: Brill; Eerdmans, 1999), 774.

Divine beings in heaven like the Cherubim of Ezekiel 1:7 and the heavenly man of Ezekiel 40:3 are described as "sparkling like burnished bronze." The glorified Jesus in Revelation 1:15 and 2:18 has feet that shine like burnished bronze. The divine being in Daniel 10:6 had a body of beryl, a shining metal, and legs like burnished bronze.

[10] **The bronze statue of Apollo in Thyatira:** "If then the context is of local industry, it seems likely that the local patron-god Apollo Tyrimnaeus is in John's mind. Kiddle renews the old suggestion that this god was represented by a bronze statue in the town (p. 37). Caird (p. 43) refers to the coins where he is depicted grasping the emperor's hand, and suggests that the picture of Christ in the letter was put forward in deliberate opposition to this combination of local and imperial religion. …The recurrence of motifs so reminiscent of the Revelation (e.g. 1:16, 20; 2:1) again prompts the thought that the pretensions of the imperial cult were seen as a Satanic parody of the realities in Christ. The Thyatiran Christians were subject to organized paganism, but the realities of the case were those of Ps. 2, where the Lord was master of oppressive earthly powers. In the 'Son of God' the church had her true champion, irresistibly arrayed in armour flashing like the refined metal from the furnaces of the city. He was the true patron of their work." Colin J. Hemer, *The Letters to the Seven Churches of Asia in Their Local Setting* (Grand Rapids, MI; Cambridge, U.K.; Livonia, MI: William B. Eerdmans Publishing Company; Dove Booksellers, 2001), 116–117.

Heavenly host as interchangeable with stars: There is more than just a symbolic connection between the physical heavens and the spiritual heavens in the Bible. In some passages, the stars of heaven are linked interchangeably with angelic heavenly beings, also referred to as "holy ones" or "sons of God" (Psa. 89:5-7; Job 1:6). See also Job 38:4-7; Neh. 9:6; Psa 148:2-3, 1King 22:29 & 2King 21:5. In Isa 14:12-14 the king of Babylon is likened to the planet Venus (Morningstar) seeking to reign above the other stars of heaven, which are equivalent to the sons of God who surround God's throne on the "mount of assembly" or "divine council" (see Psa 89:5-7 and Psa 82).See H. Niehr, "Host of Heaven," Toorn, K. van der, Bob Becking, and Pieter Willem van der Horst. *Dictionary of Deities and Demons in the Bible DDD*. 2nd extensively rev. ed. Leiden; Boston; Grand Rapids, Mich.: Brill; Eerdmans, 1999., 428-29; I. Zatelli, "Astrology and the Worship of the Stars in the Bible," ZAW 103 (1991): 86-99.

Jesus as the Morning Star/Venus as Morning Star: "To the one who overcomes, Jesus says, "I will give him the morning star." The odd wording reinforces the idea of our joint rule with Jesus over the nations.

"The "morning star" phrase takes us back once more to the Old Testament, which at times uses astral terminology to describe divine beings. Job 38:7 is the best example ("the morning stars were singing together and all the sons of God shouted for joy"). Stars were bright and, in the worldview of the ancients, living divine beings since they moved in the sky and were beyond the human realm.

"The morning star language in Revelation 2:28 is messianic—it refers to a divine being who would come from Judah. We know this by considering two other passages in tandem.

"In Numbers 24:17, we read the prophecy that "a star will go out from Jacob, and a scepter will rise from Israel." Numbers 24:17 was considered messianic in Judaism, completely apart from the New Testament writers. In other words, literate readers of John's writing would have known the morning star reference was not about literal brightness. It was about the dawning of the returned kingdom of God under its messiah. Later in the book of Revelation, Jesus himself refers to his messianic standing with the morning star language: "I am the root and the descendant of David, the bright morning star" (Rev 22:16).

"The wording of Revelation 2 is especially powerful when read against this backdrop. Not only does Jesus say that he is the messianic morning star in Revelation 22:16, but when he says "I will give him [who overcomes] the morning star" (Rev 2:28), he grants us the authority to rule with him." Michael S. Heiser, *The Unseen Realm: Recovering the Supernatural Worldview of the Bible*, First Edition (Bellingham, WA: Lexham Press, 2015), 312–313.

Lucifer as the Morning Star: A popular interpretation of Morning Star as "Lucifer" in Isaiah 14:12-15 has confused many Christians. How can Jesus be the Morning Star and Satan be the Morning Star as well? This is from an unfortunate tradition of mistranslation. David Lowe explains how the word Lucifer was actually a Latin word for the planet Venus, and through tradition, it became believed to be a reference to Satan. But that is not in the text. Lowe writes:

"The entity addressed in Isaiah 14:12-15 has nothing to with Satan or a former angel named Lucifer, and it is time for Christians to break free from this traditional myth. There is a powerful, profound explanation for the taunt song of the former pagan kings delivered to the king of Babylon upon his descent to the pits of Sheol. Because of the power and wealth experienced during his mortal existence, the king of Babylon was filled with pride. He proclaimed he was going to experience postmortal stellar apotheosis, a divine status in the heavens that would rival the status of the Most High God. The punishment for his hubris and oppression he dealt during his life was, instead of an ascent to the remote slopes of Mount Zaphon, a descent to the remote sides of the pits of Sheol. While the kings before him were laid down in relative postmortal splendor, he was regarded as a worthless branch that was cast from the grave as a slain, mangled corpse. The accomplishment of Jesus Christ provides a powerful contrast to the king of Babylon, descending from the heavens in humility and experiencing the ultimate postmortal stellar exaltation – our Morning Star! Lowe, David W. (2011-10-01). *Deconstructing Lucifer: Reexamining the Ancient Origins of the Fallen Angel of Light* (p. 114). Seismos Publishing. Kindle Edition.

Jesus as One-of-a-kind Son of God: "Readers of Psalm 82 often raise a specific question about Jesus. If there are other divine sons of God, what do we make of the description of Jesus as the "only begotten" son of God (John 1:14, 18; 3:16, 18; 1 John 4:9)? How could Jesus be the only divine son when there were others?

"…The Greek word translated by this phrase is monogenes. It doesn't mean "only begotten" in some sort of "birthing" sense. The confusion extends from an old misunderstanding of the root of the Greek word. For years monogenes was thought to have derived from two Greek terms, monos ("only") and gennao ("to beget, bear"). Greek scholars later discovered that the second part of the word monogenes does not come from the Greek verb gennao, but rather from the noun genos ("class, kind"). The term literally means "one of a kind" or "unique" without connotation of created origin. Consequently, since Jesus is indeed identified with Yahweh and is therefore, with Yahweh, unique among the elohim that serve God, the term monogenes does not contradict the Old Testament language.

"The validity of this understanding is borne out by the New Testament itself. In Hebrews 11:17, Isaac is called Abraham's monogenes. If you know your Old Testament you know that Isaac was not the "only begotten" son of Abraham. Abraham had earlier fathered Ishmael (cf. Gen 16:15; 21:3). The term must mean that Isaac was Abraham's unique son, for he was the son of the covenant promises." Michael S. Heiser, *The Unseen Realm: Recovering the Supernatural Worldview of the Bible*, First Edition (Bellingham, WA: Lexham Press, 2015), 36–37.

Jesus as the second Yahweh in heaven: "In Ugaritic mythology, El was the supreme god and Baal was his vice-regent who ruled over the other gods of the council. In the Hebrew Bible, El/Elohim/Yahweh is the creator God, but he also has a vice-regent, the Son of Man/Angel of the Lord who was a visible incarnation of Yahweh who ruled over the divine council (Dan 7). Christians would eventually argue that this "second Yahweh" was in fact the pre-incarnate Messiah, Jesus." Michael S. Heiser, *The Divine*

341

Council In Late Canonical And Non-Canonical Second Temple Jewish Literature (Madison, WI: University of Wisconsin, 2004) 34-41: http://digitalcommons.liberty.edu/fac_dis/93/;

[11] **The allotment of the nations to the Sons of God/heavenlyhost/stars which are the gods of the nations**:

"Deut. 32:8-9 When the Most High gave to the nations their inheritance, when he divided mankind, he fixed the borders of the peoples according to the number of the sons of God. But the LORD's portion is his people, Jacob his allotted heritage.

"The reference to the creation of nations through the division of mankind and fixing of the borders of nations is clearly a reference to the event of the Tower of Babel in Genesis 11 and the dispersion of the peoples into the 70 nations listed in Genesis 10.

"But then there is a strange reference to those nations being "fixed" according to the number of the sons of God. We'll explain in a moment that those sons of God are from the assembly of the divine council of God. But after that the text says that God saved Jacob (God's own people) for his "allotment." Even though Jacob was not born until long after the Babel incident, this is an anachronistic way of referring to what would become God's people, because right after Babel, we read about God's calling of Abraham who was the grandfather of Jacob (Isa. 41:8; Rom. 11:26). So God allots nations and their geographic territory to these sons of God to rule over as their inheritance, but he allots the people of Jacob to himself, along with their geographical territory of Canaan (Gen. 17:8).

"The idea of Yahweh "allotting" geographical territories to these sons of God who really existed and were worshipped as gods (idols) shows up again in several places in Deuteronomy:

Deut. 4:19-20 And beware lest you raise your eyes to heaven, and when you see the sun and the moon and the stars, all the host of heaven, you be drawn away and bow down to them and serve them, things that the LORD your God has allotted to all the peoples under the whole heaven. But the LORD has taken you and brought you out of the iron furnace, out of Egypt, to be a people of his own inheritance, as you are this day.

"Deut. 29:24-26 Then men will say, 'Because they forsook the covenant of the LORD, the God of their fathers, which He made with them when He brought them out of the land of Egypt. They went and served other gods and worshiped them, gods whom they have not known and whom He had not allotted to them.

"Here again, we see a description of the "allotment" of the host of heaven to the pagan nations along with the allotment of Israel to Yahweh as his inheritance. The gentile nations are allotted to the sons of God/heavenly host/false gods of the land, while Israel is allotted to Yahweh and Yahweh allotted to Israel.

"But notice in this passage, there is an equivalency of the sun, moon and stars with the host of heaven, a term used interchangeably with the Sons of God. The sun, moon, and stars were worshipped as gods, and Yahweh is saying that these gods are the ones allotted to the nations. So, this is not a holy host of heaven, but an unholy host of heaven. These sons of God are not in God's heavenly court, they are evil fallen beings from that divine council.

"The demonic reality of pagan gods is expressed further down in the same Deuteronomy chapter 32. The false gods were demons, real spiritual beings that had fallen from God's divine council:

"Deut. 32:16-17 They stirred him to jealousy with strange gods; with abominations they provoked him to anger. They sacrificed to demons that were no gods, to gods they had never known, to new gods that had come recently, whom your fathers had never dreaded." Brian Godawa, *When Giants Were Upon the Earth: The Watchers, the Nephilim, and the Biblical Cosmic War of the Seed* (Embedded Pictures, 2014), 201-202.

Christians will be glorified and transformed to be just like Jesus Christ: 1 John 3:2 Beloved, we are God's children now, and what we will be has not yet appeared; but we know that when he appears we shall be like him, because we shall see him as he is.

Philippians 3:20–21 But our citizenship is in heaven, and from it we await a Savior, the Lord Jesus Christ, who will transform our lowly body to be like his glorious body, by the power that enables him even to subject all things to himself.

Daniel 12:2–3 And many of those who sleep in the dust of the earth shall awake, some to everlasting life, and some to shame and everlasting contempt. And those who are wise shall shine like the brightness of the sky above; and those who turn many to righteousness, like the stars forever and ever.

See also: Rom. 8:29; 2 Cor. 3:18; 2 Pet. 1:4.

[12] **Christians will rule with the rod of iron (replacing Rome's iron rule):** Revelation 2:26–28 The one who conquers and who keeps my works until the end, to him I will give authority over the nations, and he will rule them with a rod of iron, as when earthen pots are broken in pieces.

The winepress of the wrath of God: Revelation 19:15 From his mouth comes a sharp sword with which to strike down the nations, and he will rule them with a rod of iron. He will tread the winepress of the fury of the wrath of God the Almighty.

[13] **Apollyon's mocking here was taken from** 2 Peter 3:3–7 knowing this first of all, that scoffers will come in the last days with scoffing, following their own sinful desires. They will say, "Where is the promise of his coming? For ever since the fathers fell asleep, all things are continuing as they were from the beginning of creation." For they deliberately overlook this fact, that the heavens existed long ago, and the earth was formed out of water and through water by the word of God, and that by means of these the world that then existed was deluged with water and perished. But by the same word the heavens and earth that now exist are stored up for fire, being kept until the day of judgment and destruction of the ungodly.

[14] **Daniel's dream of a metallic statue** destroyed by a cornerstone cut without hands. That stone was Messiah, whose kingdom would grow to fill the earth like a mountain: Daniel 2:31-45.

[15] **Women as prophets:** There are five women prophets mentioned in the Old Testament: Miriam (Exodus 15:20-21), Deborah (Judges 4:4-5), Isaiah's wife (Isaiah 8:3), Huldah (2 Kings 22:14), Nodiah (Nehemiah 6:14). This is obviously not intended to be exhaustive. In the New Testament, as the prophet Joel predicted, "I will pour out my spirit on all flesh; your sons and your daughters shall prophesy" (Joel 2:28), the daughters of Philip (Acts 21:8-9) and Ana (Luke 2:36).

Women as co-inheritors: 1 Peter 3:7 Likewise, husbands, live with your wives in an understanding way, showing honor to the woman as the weaker vessel, since they are heirs with you of the grace of life, so that your prayers may not be hindered.

Women teaching and in authority: 1 Timothy 2:11–14 Let a woman learn quietly with all submissiveness. I do not permit a woman to teach or to exercise authority over a man; rather, she is to remain quiet. For Adam was formed first, then Eve; and Adam was not deceived, but the woman was deceived and became a transgressor.

See also: 1Peter 3:7-6; Ephesians 5:22-33; 1Corinthians 11:3; 14:34-35.

Some scholars argue that there is one woman mentioned as an apostle in the New Testament, Junia (Romans 16:7), but this is highly contested, is not clearly a female name, and does not fit the pattern of patriarchal male leadership in the Old Testament and New Testament.

[16] **Early gnosticism of Cerinthus as explained in this passage**: Gnosticism as full fledged religious alternative to Christianity was not established until the second century. It was mostly derivative of Christianity, a new spin. "The earliest Gnostic known by name is Cerinthus, the antagonist of the apostle John. On the authority of Irenaeus, who quoted Polycarp the disciple of John, there is little doubt that the two met in Ephesus. Cerinthus was a Jew who seemed to have stood between the EBIONITES and Gnostics. From the accounts that have been preserved of Cerinthus and his teaching, it can be gathered that he taught that the world was created not by the Supreme God, but by an inferior power; he also taught a docetic theory of the Incarnation. Caius of Rome, a disciple of Irenaeus, recorded that Cerinthus held there would be a millennium of unrestrained sensuality. Dionysius of Alexandria (ca A.D. 260) confirmed this (R. Law, p. 37). There is the testimony of Irenaeus, that the Gospel of John was written to oppose that form of Gnosticism taught by Cerinthus and, before him, by the Nicolaitans. According to Irenaeus, Cerinthus maintained that the world was made not by the sovereign Power but by some inferior being who was ignorant of the supreme God. He taught that Jesus was not born of a virgin but was the son of Joseph and Mary, born after the manner of other people. After His baptism the Spirit in the form of a dove descended on Him, and before His crucifixion the Spirit left Him. Thus, while the man Jesus suffered and

rose again, the Christ remained impassible as a spiritual being (cf. Mansel, p. 74)."A. M. Renwick, "Gnosticism," ed. Geoffrey W Bromiley, *The International Standard Bible Encyclopedia, Revised* (Wm. B. Eerdmans, 1979–1988), 489.

[17] **Eve was deceived as opposed to Adam:** 1 Timothy 2:11–14 Let a woman learn quietly with all submissiveness. I do not permit a woman to teach or to exercise authority over a man; rather, she is to remain quiet. For Adam was formed first, then Eve; and Adam was not deceived, but the woman was deceived and became a transgressor.

[18] **Woman's desire to usurp her husband's authority:** Genesis 3:16 To the woman he said,…Your **desire** shall be for your husband, and he shall rule over you."

The word for "desire" is the same Hebrew word used for the sin nature in Cain: Genesis 4:6–7 The LORD said to Cain, "Why are you angry, and why has your face fallen? If you do well, will you not be accepted? And if you do not do well, sin is crouching at the door. Its **desire** is for you, but you must rule over it."

In the interest of fairness and balance, the curse also implies male nature as tending toward abusive dominance as opposed to proper leadership: "rule over you."

Leviathan as the sea dragon of chaos: See Brian Godawa, "Leviathan: Sea Dragon of Chaos" scholarly paper https://www.academia.edu/4617559/Leviathan_Sea_Dragon_of_Chaos

"Appearing in only one pre-Biblical text and mentioned six times in the Bible, Leviathan could seem to be a figure of minor importance. However, as a paradigmatic monster and enemy of considerable mythological attire, he outweighs other representatives of chaos and evil. The so-called 'Chaoskampf' constellation or 'combat myth' in which Leviathan plays the role of a threatening, but vanquished enemy, has been functionalized in politics and propaganda from the early 2nd mill. BCE until today, with T. Hobbes' Leviathan (a treatise on the modern state first published 1651) being only one peak in a tremendous 'Wirkungsgeschichte'. The study of this monster thus exemplifies how an ancient Near Eastern mythological concept could travel from one culture to another or adapt itself, within one given culture, to changing historical trends. It illuminates the fluidity in the development of ancient Near Eastern mythological imagination.

"In the Bible, Leviathan is mentioned exclusively in poetic texts, some of which are deliberately archaizing. Ps 74, a communal lament weeping over the profanation of Yahweh's sanctuary by enemies, contains a section which functions as a confessional reminder for the distressed (vv 12–17): Yahweh is king "from of old" (miqqedem, i.e. since primeval times), and his kingship specifically implies helpful dominion over the earth (v 12). This is illustrated by a reference to the 'traditional' victories of Yahweh over the sea (yām), the dragons (pl.) and Leviathan (vv 13–14). As in Ugarit, Leviathan and the dragons are considered as Yam's associates of monstrous appearance; together, the three entities represent the maritime chaos which once had endangered the earth but was then overwhelmed by the creator-god and given as food to wild beasts (or possibly sharks). Yahweh's victory was a necessary prelude to his subsequent organization of the cosmos: the opening of springs and the division of time in day and night, summer and winter (vv 15–17)."

C. Uehlinger, "Leviathan," ed. Karel van der Toorn, Bob Becking, and Pieter W. van der Horst, *Dictionary of Deities and Demons in the Bible* (Leiden; Boston; Köln; Grand Rapids, MI; Cambridge: Brill; Eerdmans, 1999), 512-513.

In Revelation, Satan takes on the identity of Leviathan when he is described as the seven-headed dragon. Revelation 12:3, 9.

CHAPTER 13

[1] **"A calculation anew, Nero his mother slew":** Suetonius, *Lives of the Twelve Caesars, Nero*, 39.

"In the midst of his Latin history, Suetonius records a sample of a Greek lampoon that was circulated after the burning of Rome, which occurred on A.D. 64 "Neopsephon Neron idian metera apektine." The translation of this lampoon is: "A calculation new. Nero his mother slew." G J. C. RoMe notes in the Loeb Classical Library edition of Suetonius' works that "the numerical value of the Greek letters in

Nero's name (1005) is the same as that of the rest of the sentence; hence we a have an equation, Nero = the slayer of his own mother." Ken Gentry, *The Beast of Revelation* (Tyler, TX: Institute for Christian Economics, 1989, 1994), 32.

[2] **Ichthys, the Christian fish symbol**: "The Greek word for fish is 'ichthys.' As early as the first century, Christians made an acrostic from this word: Iesous Christos Theou Yios Soter, i.e. Jesus Christ, Son of God, Savior. The fish has plenty of other theological overtones as well, for Christ fed the 5,000 with 2 fishes and 5 loaves (a meal recapitulated in Christian love-feasts) and called his disciples "fishers of men." Water baptism, practiced by immersion in the early church, created a parallel between fish and converts… When threatened by Romans in the first centuries after Christ, Christians used the fish mark meeting places and tombs, or to distinguish friends from foes. According to one ancient story, when a Christian met a stranger in the road, the Christian sometimes drew one arc of the simple fish outline in the dirt. If the stranger drew the other arc, both believers knew they were in good company." Elesha Coffman (August 8, 2008). "What is the origin of the Christian fish symbol?". *Christianity Today*.

[3] **Alexander quotes from**: Ecclesiastes 4:2-3.

[4] **God's sovereign control over history as paraphrased here:** Job 12:16-25; Proverbs 16:4; Isaiah 45:7; Amos 3:6; Job 2:10.

[5] **Peter's command to obey ruling authorities:** 1 Peter 2:13-17. See also Romans 13:1-7.

[6] **Yahweh's sovereignty described here by Alexander**: Job 12:16–25 [16] With him are strength and sound wisdom; the deceived and the deceiver are his. [17] He leads counselors away stripped, and judges he makes fools. [18] He looses the bonds of kings and binds a waistcloth on their hips. [19] He leads priests away stripped and overthrows the mighty. [20] He deprives of speech those who are trusted and takes away the discernment of the elders. [21] He pours contempt on princes and loosens the belt of the strong. [22] He uncovers the deeps out of darkness and brings deep darkness to light. [23] He makes nations great, and he destroys them; he enlarges nations, and leads them away. [24] He takes away understanding from the chiefs of the people of the earth and makes them wander in a trackless waste. [25] They grope in the dark without light, and he makes them stagger like a drunken man.

Job 42:1–2 [1] Then Job answered the LORD and said: [2] "I know that you can do all things, and that no purpose of yours can be thwarted.

CHAPTER 14

[1] **The Apostle John's letter to Pergamum alluded to in this chapter**: William Ramsay, *The letters to the Seven Churches of Asia and Their Place in the Plan of the Apocalypse* (London, Hodder and Stoughton, 1904), 283.

Colin J. Hemer, *The Letters to the Seven Churches of Asia in Their Local Setting* (Grand Rapids, MI; Cambridge, U.K.; Livonia, MI: William B. Eerdmans Publishing Company; Dove Booksellers, 2001), 83.

[2] **Stages of an ancient Roman trial**: "In a trial, the first stage involved a hearing before the jurisdictional magistrate (the praetor), while the second stage of the trial was an appearance before a court selected from the *centumviri*." David E. Aune, *Revelation 1–5, vol. 52A, Word Biblical Commentary* (Dallas: Word, Incorporated, 1998), 183.

[3] **The "Throne of Satan"**: Revelation 2:13 " 'I know where you dwell, where Satan's throne is. Yet you hold fast my name, and you did not deny my faith even in the days of Antipas my faithful witness, who was killed among you, where Satan dwells.

[4] **Dionysus and Asclepius at Pergamum**: Colin J. Hemer, *The Letters to the Seven Churches of Asia in Their Local Setting* (Grand Rapids, MI; Cambridge, U.K.; Livonia, MI: William B. Eerdmans Publishing Company; Dove Booksellers, 2001), 82.

William Ramsay, *The letters to the Seven Churches of Asia and Their Place in the Plan of the Apocalypse* (London, Hodder and Stoughton, 1904), 284-87.

[5] **Description of Ascleipius**: "Asklepios the Saviour was introduced from Epidauros in a comparatively recent period, perhaps the fifth century. He appears on coins from the middle of the second century B.C. and became more and more the representative god of Pergamum." William Ramsay, *The letters to the Seven Churches of Asia and Their Place in the Plan of the Apocalypse* (London, Hodder and Stoughton, 1904), 286.

[6] **The persecution of Antipas**: Revelation 2:13–14 'I know where you dwell, where Satan's throne is. Yet you hold fast my name, and you did not deny my faith even in the days of Antipas my faithful witness, who was killed among you, where Satan dwells. But I have a few things against you: you have some there who hold the teaching of Balaam, who taught Balak to put a stumbling block before the sons of Israel, so that they might eat food sacrificed to idols and practice sexual immorality.'

Jews performed sacrifices at the Jerusalem Temple on behalf of Caesar: Flavius Josephus, *The Wars of the Jews*, 2.409-410 (2.17.2).

[7] **The Imperial Cult**: Regarding the co-existance of Caesar with the local culture and pantheon, S.F.R. Price writes, "The rule of Rome was represented in marble. But the widespread imperial temples and imperial statues did not form the cold grandeur of an alien authority. The visual expression of the emperor was incorporated into the regular life of the communities through public celebrations (3). The emperor was honoured at ancestral religious festivals; he was placed within the gods' sanctuaries and temples; sacrifices to the gods invoked their protection for the emperor. There were also festivals, temples and sacrifices in honour of the emperor alone which were calqued on the traditional honours of the gods. In other words, the Greek subjects of the Roman empire attempted to relate their ruler to their own dominant symbolic system (235). The imperial cult, like the cults of the traditional gods, created a relationship of power between subject and ruler. It also enhanced the dominance of local elites over the populace, of cities over other cities, and of Greek over indigenous cultures. That is, the cult was a major part of the web of power that formed the fabric of society." S.F.R. Price, *Rituals and Power: The Roman Imperial Cult in Asia Minor* (Cambridge University Press, 1985), 248.

"The language of Augustus Caesar reflected similar concepts of the divinity of their emperor, as the New Testament did of Jesus Christ. Inscriptions on coins and buildings throughout the empire called Augustus, "God, Son of God, Savior." A famous proclamation of Augustus used phrases such as "savior," "god manifest," and "good news [gospel]." The most divine Caesar…we should consider equal to the Beginning of all things…; for when everything was falling [into disorder] and tending toward dissolution, he restored it once more and gave to the whole world a new aura…and who being sent to us and our descendants as Savior…and [whereas,] having become [god] manifest, Caesar has fulfilled all the hopes of earlier times… and whereas, finally, the birthday of the god [Augustus] has been for the whole world the beginning of good news concerning him [therefore let a new era begin from his birth]." Stanley E. Porter, "Paul Confronts Caesar with the Good News," Stanley E. Porter, Cynthia Long Westfall, Ed., *Empire in the New Testament* (Wipf and Stock, 2011), 172-3.

Richard A. Horsley, *Jesus and Empire: The Kingdom of God and the New World Disorder* (Minneapolis, MN: Fortress Press, 2003) 23.

[8] Christians were called atheists by pagan polytheists because they denied the gods: Dio Cassius, *Roman History* 67.14; Eusebius, *Church History* 4.15.18-19.

[9] **Sexual immorality is a metaphor for spiritual infidelity to God**: "A close association is assumed by Judaism to exist between idolatry and sexual immorality (Exod 32:15–16; Wis 14:12–31; T. Reub. 4:6; T. Benj. 10:10. …In the OT, the idolatry of Israel is frequently condemned through the use of the metaphor of prostitution and sexual immorality (Jer 3:2; 13:27; Ezek 16:15–58; 23:1–49; 43:7; Hos 5:4; 6:10). Idolatry is often regarded as the root of all other forms of vice; according to Wis 14:12, "the invention of idols is the beginning of fornication," and Wis 14:27 says "for the worship of the unspeakable idols is the beginning, cause, and end of every evil." …The connection between idolatry and sexual misdeeds in Judaism is taken over by Christianity (Acts 15:20, 29; 21:25; Rom 1:23–25; Gal 5:19f–21; 1 Cor 6:9–11; 1 Thess 1:9 together with 4:3; Rev 22:15)." David E. Aune, *Revelation 1–5, vol. 52A, Word Biblical Commentary* (Dallas: Word, Incorporated, 1998), 188.

[10] **The story of Balaam** can be found in Numbers 22-24. The Moabite Balak sought the pagan prophet, Balaam to curse Israel, but when he tried, Yahweh stopped him. Balaam sought to circumvent Yahweh's

prohibition by counseling Balaak to have his Moabite and Midianite women marry Israelites and thus violate the proscription of Yahweh against intermarriage with cursed and godless pagans. Those pagan wives then spiritually seduced the Israelites away from Yahweh and into idolatry (Numbers 25:1-3) As the apostle Paul wrote, 2 Corinthians 6:14–16 "Do not be unequally yoked with unbelievers. For what partnership has righteousness with lawlessness? Or what fellowship has light with darkness? What accord has Christ with Belial? Or what portion does a believer share with an unbeliever? What agreement has the temple of God with idols? For we are the temple of the living God."

[11] **Antipas quotes from:** Jude 4 and 2 Peter 2:1-3.

The Nicolaitans are most likely equated with the "error of Balaam" that appears to be a kind of antinomianism that is explained in the following New Testament passages, from which the language used in this passage comes: Revelation 2:6; 2:15; Jude 3-16; 2 Peter 2:1-22.

Hemer concludes that "Nicolaitanism was an antinomian movement whose antecedents can be traced in the misrepresentation of Pauline liberty, and whose incidence may be connected with the special pressures of emperor worship and pagan society." Colin J. Hemer, *The Letters to the Seven Churches of Asia in Their Local Setting* (Grand Rapids, MI; Cambridge, U.K.; Livonia, MI: William B. Eerdmans Publishing Company; Dove Booksellers, 2001), 94.

[12] **Antipas quotes from**: 2 Peter 2:4, 17; Jude 6, 12-13. These Biblical passages are drawing their language from: 1 Enoch 100:11; 80:2; 80:3; 67:5-7; 101:4; 80:6; 46:6; 46:6.

Watchers cast into Tartarus: Jude 12-16: 2 Peter 2:4-11, 17; Genesis 6:1-4. 1 Enoch 1-16 (Book of the Watchers) is an extended amplification of the Genesis 6 passage. My novel series *Chronicles of the Nephilim* recounts the story of the Fall of the Watchers in *Enoch Primordial* and *Noah Primeval*.

[13] **The rebellion of the angels led by Azazel and Semyaza**: 1 Enoch 9:7-9; 10:4-13. Their story is fictionalized in the novel, *Enoch Primordial*, book 2 of *Chronicles of the Nephilim* (Embedded Pictures Publishing, 2014).

[14] **The white stone judgment**: "He who has an ear, let him hear what the Spirit says to the churches. To the one who conquers I will give some of the hidden manna, and I will give him a white stone, with a new name written on the stone that no one knows except the one who receives it." Revelation 2:17.

"The word for "stone," psephos, occurs only twice in the New Testament, the other place being Acts 26:10, where Paul confessed that he cast his vote, or stone, against the saints when he persecuted them before his conversion. This use of the word to describe a ballot or a means of casting a vote occurs numerous times in ancient literature. Sometimes it refers to elections. Other times the description is of the voting by a jury in a trial. Ovid described it: "It was an ancient custom of that land to vote with chosen pebbles, white and black. The white absolved, the black condemned the man. (Ovid, *Metamorphoses* 15.1)."

Don Enevoldsen, *The Harlot and the Bride*, unpublished book (Don Enevoldsen, 2014), 111.

[15] **The apotheosis (divinization) of Julius Caesar**: "In 44 B.C. Caesar was assassinated in the Roman Senate House. Not long afterwards the same Senate issued an official decree declaring the deification of Caesar. His adoptive son and successor Octavian received the name of *Divi Filius*, in Greek *Huios Theou*, in English 'Son of God'. In 27 B.C. Octavian received the honorary title of Augustus, in Greek Sebastos, 'worthy of honour'. These two names, Son of God and Augustus, belonged thenceforth to the regular stock of imperial titles." Ethelbert Stauffer, *Christ and the Caesars: Historical Sketches* (Wipe and Stock, 2008), 208.

The power of naming: Ramsay writes, "He who knows the right name of a demon or divine being can become lord over all the power that the demonic being possesses, just as he who knows the name of a man was considered to possess some power over the man, because the name partakes of reality and not merely marks a man's personality, but is almost identified with it." William Ramsay, *The letters to the Seven Churches of Asia and Their Place in the Plan of the Apocalypse* (London, Hodder and Stoughton, 1904), 308.

[16] **Antipas quotes from**: Jude 14-15, which is quoting 1 Enoch 1:9 "Behold, he will arrive with ten million of the holy ones in order to execute judgment upon all. He will destroy the wicked ones and

347

censure all flesh on account of everything that they have done, that which the sinners and the wicked ones committed against him." James H. Charlesworth, *The Old Testament Pseudepigrapha, vol. 1* (New York; London: Yale University Press, 1983), 13–14.

[17] **Antipas' martyrdom in the brazen bull**: Antipas' martyrdom in the bronze bull is legendary and linked to the altar of Zeus, but I moved it to the altar of Caesar because of the higher likelihood that the "Throne of Satan" is referring to the imperial cult.

"The legend appears in later hagiographers (Simon Metaphrastes, the Bollandists) that he was slowly roasted to death in a brazen bull during the reign of Domitian." Robert H. Mounce, *The Book of Revelation, The New International Commentary on the New Testament* (Grand Rapids, MI: Wm. B. Eerdmans Publishing Co., 1997), 80.

[18] **On the Brazen Bull**: "The story of the brazen bull is this. It was made by Phalaris at Agrigentum; and he used to force men to get into it, and then by way of punishment light a fire underneath. The metal becoming thus red hot, the man inside was roasted and scorched to death; and when he screamed in his agony, the sound from the machine was very like the bellowing of a bull. When the Carthaginians conquered Sicily this bull was removed from Agrigentum to Carthage. The trap door between the shoulders, through which the victims used to be let down, still remains." Polybius, Histories 12.25(Medford, MA: Macmillan, 1889), 101.

[19] **Ancient Roman court trials**: "In a trial, the first stage involved a hearing *in iure*, i.e., before the jurisdictional magistrate (the praetor), while the second stage of the trial was the *iudicium centumvirale*, i.e., an appearance before a court selected from the *centumviri*." David E. Aune, *Revelation 1–5, vol. 52A, Word Biblical Commentary* (Dallas: Word, Incorporated, 1998), 183.

Beheading was the normal punishment for capital criminals who were Roman citizens.

CHAPTER 15

[1] **Charm is deceitful and beauty is vain**: Proverbs 31:30.

[2] **Peter wrote 2 Peter near AD 64 while in Rome**: "The style and teaching of 2 Peter suggest strongly that it was written toward the end of Peter's life. It must have been written after A.D. 60 or so if 2 Peter 3:1 is a reference to 1 Peter. Peter was in Rome, as we have seen, in A.D. 60, and again at the time of his death in A.D. 64–65. He may have been there also when he wrote 2 Peter, therefore, although we cannot be sure." Clinton E. Arnold, *Zondervan Illustrated Bible Backgrounds Commentary: Hebrews to Revelation., vol. 4* (Grand Rapids, MI: Zondervan, 2002), 154.

[3] **Apocalypse or "revelation of Jesus Christ"**: 1 Peter 1:7, 13.

"Coming of Christ" in Peter's letter: 2 Peter 1:16; 3:4, 12.

Parousia: "is used technically for the visit of a ruler or high official…The imperial period with its world ruler or members of his household, if it did not increase the cost, certainly invested the parousia of the ruler with even greater magnificence." Gerhard Kittel, Geoffrey W. Bromiley, and Gerhard Friedrich, eds., *Theological Dictionary of the New Testament* (Grand Rapids, MI: Eerdmans, 1964–), 860.

[4] **Jews rejection of Messiah and by extension, Messiah's people**: "Revelation's overarching theme is Christ's judgment upon Israel for having him crucified (1:7; cp. 5:6, 9, 12; 13:8). But we should understand that this also involves Israel's persecuting his people who are united with him (14:1a; cp. 17:14; 19:14), have his name upon them (14:1b; cp. 22:4), follow him wherever he goes (14:4b, 13; cp. 7:17), and bear his testimony (6:9; 11:3; 12:11) as his "witnesses" (17:6b). "Jesus had already foreseen this analogy between himself and believers" (Reicke in Bammel and Moule 1984: 146) as indicated in Mt 10:17-25//; Mt 24:9-11//. John's Gospel recognizes this identifying of the Lord with his servants: "Remember the word that I said to you, 'A slave is not greater than his master.' If they persecuted Me, they will also persecute you" (Jn 15:20). (See additional discussion at 1:7.)" Kenneth L. Gentry, Jr., *The Divorce of Israel: A Redemptive-Historical Interpretation of Revelation Vol. 2* (Dallas, GA: Tolle Lege Press, 2016), 436-437.

The rejection of the Jews by Yahweh: Jesus' parable of the tenants and the vineyard, concludes, Matthew 21:38–45 But when the tenants saw the son, they said to themselves, 'This is the heir. Come, let us kill him and have his inheritance.' 39 And they took him and threw him out of the vineyard and killed him. 40 When therefore the owner of the vineyard comes, what will he do to those tenants?" 41 They said to him, "He will put those wretches to a miserable death and let out the vineyard to other tenants who will give him the fruits in their seasons." 42 Jesus said to them, "Have you never read in the Scriptures: " 'The stone that the builders rejected has become the cornerstone; this was the Lord's doing, and it is marvelous in our eyes'? 43 Therefore I tell you, the kingdom of God will be taken away from you and given to a people producing its fruits. 44 And the one who falls on this stone will be broken to pieces; and when it falls on anyone, it will crush him." 45 When the chief priests and the Pharisees heard his parables, they perceived that he was speaking about them.

[5] **The end of all things is at hand**: 1 Peter 4:7.

Salvation ready to be revealed in the last time: 1 Peter 1:3.

Last days in the first century: 2 Peter 3:3.

The Day of the Lord: 2 Peter 3:10.

[6] **The new covenant of Jeremiah referred to by Peter**: Jeremiah 31:31–34 [31] "Behold, the days are coming, declares the LORD, when I will make a new covenant with the house of Israel and the house of Judah, [32] not like the covenant that I made with their fathers on the day when I took them by the hand to bring them out of the land of Egypt, my covenant that they broke, though I was their husband, declares the LORD. [33] For this is the covenant that I will make with the house of Israel after those days, declares the LORD: I will put my law within them, and I will write it on their hearts. And I will be their God, and they shall be my people. [34] And no longer shall each one teach his neighbor and each his brother, saying, 'Know the LORD,' for they shall all know me, from the least of them to the greatest, declares the LORD. For I will forgive their iniquity, and I will remember their sin no more."

The Last Days occurred in the first century during the time of Christ: Hebrews 1:1–2 Long ago, at many times and in many ways, God spoke to our fathers by the prophets, 2 but in these last days he has spoken to us by his Son, whom he appointed the heir of all things, through whom also he created the world.

Hebrews 9:26 But as it is, he has appeared once for all at the end of the ages to put away sin by the sacrifice of himself.

1 Peter 1:20 He was foreknown before the foundation of the world but was made manifest in the last times for the sake of you

Acts 2:16–17 But this is what was uttered through the prophet Joel: 17 " 'And in the last days it shall be, God declares, that I will pour out my Spirit on all flesh...

1 Corinthians 10:11 [11] Now these things happened to them as an example, but they were written down for our instruction, on whom the end of the ages has come.

Hebrews 10:24–25 [24] And let us consider how to stir up one another to love and good works, [25] not neglecting to meet together, as is the habit of some, but encouraging one another, and all the more as you see the Day drawing near.

The Last Days: "One of the first things a Christian must learn in interpreting the Bible is to pay attention to the time texts. Failing to recognize the proximity of a prophetic event will distort its intended meaning. The New Testament clearly states that the "end of all things" was at hand for those who first read 1 Peter 4:7; that is, the Old Covenant with its types and shadows was about to pass away. The Book of Hebrews opens with two verses that put the timing of certain eschatological events into perspective: "God, after He spoke long ago to the fathers in the prophets in many portions and in many ways, in these last days has spoken to us in His Son, whom He appointed heir of all things, through whom also He made the world" (Heb. 1:1–2). Prior to the coming of Jesus, God spoke via dreams, prophets, written revelation, and types. Through the New Covenant God "has made the first obsolete. But whatever is becoming obsolete and growing old is ready [lit., near] to disappear" (8:13).

349

"The New Covenant is better than the Old Covenant because the blood of Jesus is better than the blood of animals (Heb. 7:22; 8:6). In addition, the way God communicates with His people has changed. For example, under the Old Covenant no man could look upon the face of God and live (Ex. 33:20). At the dawning of the New Covenant, however, God was no longer hidden. He had taken on human flesh in the person of Jesus Christ...

"God spoke in this new way "in these last days." The last days were in operation in the first century when God was manifested in the flesh in the person of Jesus Christ! Those Hebrew Christians who read the letter addressed to them were being told that an important covenantal era was about to end, the era of "the fathers in the prophets." The proof that the last days had come was that God "has spoken in His Son." The last days are not way off in the distant future. The end came to an obsolete covenant in the first century.

"In A.D. 70 the "last days" ended with the dissolution of the temple and the sacrificial system. A similar pronouncement is made in 1 Peter 1:20: "For He was foreknown before the foundation of the world, but has appeared in these last times for the sake of you." Gordon Clark comments on what Peter means by "these last times": " 'The last days,' which so many people think refers to what is still future at the end of this age, clearly means the time of Peter himself. 1 John 2:18 says it is, in his day, the last hour. Acts 2:17 quotes Joel as predicting the last days as the life time of Peter." Gary DeMar, *Last Days Madness: Obsession of the Modern Church, Fourth revised edition* (Powder Springs, GA: American Vision, 1999), 37–38.

[7] **The passage he reads** is from 2 Peter 3:7-13.

[8] **Day of the Lord:** Many Christians assume that the Day of the Lord is a phrase that always refers to the Second Coming of Jesus at the End Times, or to the Final Judgment at the end of time. But this is not the Biblical meaning. In the Bible, it is a generic term that is used any time that God judges a city, a people, or nation. Here are examples from the Bible that illustrate this wide usage. Notice that they all refer to actual historical events of the past that already occurred, *not* a future Coming of Christ.

Oracle Against Edom between 597 BC and 586 BC: Obadiah 15 "For the **day of the LORD** draws near on all the nations. As you have done, it will be done to you."

"Jeremiah's oracle against Edom (Jer. 49) contains verses 14–16, 9, which are the same as Obadiah 1b-4 and 5. Jeremiah's oracle is not dated, and the rearrangement of verses suggests he is quoting Obadiah. That the prophets are contemporaries is likely, Jeremiah taking up his colleague's words—both perhaps speaking in the interval between the Babylonian attacks of 597 and 587–586 B.C." John H Walton, Zondervan Illustrated Bible Backgrounds Commentary (Old Testament): *The Minor Prophets, Job, Psalms, Proverbs, Ecclesiastes, Song of Songs, vol. 5* (Grand Rapids, MI: Zondervan, 2009), 93.

Oracles against Jerusalem and Judah being judged in 701 BC or 586 BC:
Zeph. 1:7 Be silent before the Lord GOD! For the day of the LORD is near, ...14 Near is the great day of the LORD, Near and coming very quickly; Listen, the **day of the LORD**! In it the warrior cries out bitterly. 15 A **day of wrath** is that day.

Destruction of Jerusalem in 586 BC:
Joel 1:15 Alas for the day! For the **day of the LORD** is near, And it will come as destruction from the Almighty... 2:1 Blow a trumpet in Zion, And sound an alarm on My holy mountain! Let all the inhabitants of the land tremble, For the **day of the LORD** is coming; Surely it is near.

Amos Prophecies Israel's Northern kingdom destruction by the Assyrians in 701 BC: Amos 5:18 Woe to you who desire **the day of the LORD**! Why would you have the day of the LORD? It is darkness, and not light.

The fall of Babylon to the Medes in 539 BC:
Isaiah 13: 6 Wail, for the **day of the LORD** is near! It will come as destruction from the Almighty.... 9 Behold, the **day of the LORD** is coming, Cruel, with fury and burning anger,

The Fall of Egypt to Nebuchadnezzar in 605 BC:
Jer. 46:1 That which came as the word of the LORD to Jeremiah the prophet concerning the nations. 2 To Egypt,...10 For **that day belongs to the Lord GOD** of hosts, A **day of vengeance**, so as to avenge Himself on His foes;

The Fall of Egypt in 605 BC:
Ezekiel 30:3 For the day is near, the day of the LORD is near; it will be a day of clouds, a time of doom for the nations.

Stoicheia: In every place that *stoicheion* shows up in the New Testament it means elementary principle rudiments of a worldview, sometimes a godless worldview (Col. 2:8), but more often the elementary principles of the Old Covenant law described as a "cosmos" (Gal. .4:3; 9; Col. 2:20; Heb. 5:12).[8]

Remember how the cosmic language of creating heavens and earth was used to describe the cosmic significance of God establishing a covenant? And remember how in the Old Testament, the destruction of covenants, nations, and peoples was described in *decreation* terms as the collapsing of the universe?

That is the case in these passages as well, with the term "cosmos" being used metaphorically for the "universe" of God's covenantal order as embodied in the Old Covenant laws of Jewish separation: Circumcision, dietary restrictions and Sabbaths. Paul is telling his readers that the *stoicheion* of the Old Covenant *cosmos* are no longer over them because the people of God are under new *stoicheion*, the elementary principles of faith (Gal. 4:1-11).

Peter means the same thing. When he says that the heavens will pass away and the *stoicheion* will be burned up, he is claiming that when the Temple in Jerusalem is destroyed, it will be the final passing away of the Old Covenant cosmos, along with all the elementary principles tied to that physical sacramental structure, the laws that once separated Jew and Gentile. The new cosmos is one in which both Jew and Gentile "by God's power are being guarded through faith for a salvation ready to be revealed in the last time" (1 Pet. 1:5).

Leithart, Peter J. *The Promise of His Appearing: An Exposition of Second Peter.* Moscow, ID: Canon Press, 2004, p.101. Bauckham argues that "The heavenly bodies (sun, moon and stars) is the interpretation favored by most commentators," for *stoicheion*. But then we are right back to the sun, moon, and stars as figurative language of covenantal elements. Bauckham, *2 Peter, Jude*, 316. But I doubt this interpretation because the clear words for "heavenly bodies" are not *stoicheion*, but *epouranios soma* (1 Cor. 15:40-41).

[9] **The apostle Paul saw the Roman empire as "all the world."** It is common in the Bible to refer to the Roman Empire as "all the world" (*oikoumene*) which meant the known inhabited world under Rome's power. Luke writes that when Caesar ordered a census of the Roman Empire, he made a decree that "all the world (*oikoumene*) should be registered" (Luke 2:1). Jesus said that the Gospel would be proclaimed "through all the world (*oikoumene*) as a testimony to all the nations" (Mattew 24:14). When Paul wrote that within his own lifetime, the Gospel "has been proclaimed in all creation under heaven" (Colossians 1:23), and that "the gospel, which has come to you, as indeed in the whole world" (Colossians 1:6) it is an obvious expression of *the inhabited world of the Roman Empire*, not the entire globe as we now know it. He also spoke of the Romans' faith being "proclaimed in all the world (cosmos) (Romans 1:8), which also meant the Roman empire.

"Earlier in his letter to the Colossians, Paul describes how the gospel was "constantly bearing fruit and increasing in all the world [kosmos]" (1:6). The faith of the Romans was "being proclaimed throughout the whole world…Robert Van Kampen, a prophecy author who believes the events outlined by Jesus in Matthew 24 are yet to be fulfilled, writes, "Christ tells His disciples that only after the gospel is preached to all nations, 'then the end shall come.' " Since the Bible clearly states that that the gospel "was proclaimed in all creation under heaven" (Col. 1:23), then the end spoken of by Jesus is a past event for us. Earlier in his letter to the Colossians, Paul describes how the gospel was "constantly bearing fruit and increasing in all the world [kosmos]" (1:6). The faith of the Romans was "being proclaimed throughout the whole world [kosmos]" (Rom. 1:8), "to all the nations" (16:26). These statements by Paul reveal a fulfillment of what Jesus told His disciples would be a prelude to the destruction of Jerusalem. "The Gospel had been preached through the whole Roman world, and every nation had received its testimony, before the destruction of Jerusalem: see Col. 1:6, 23; 2 Tim. 4:17. This was necessary not only as regarded the Gentiles, but to give God's people the Jews, who were scattered among the nations, the opportunity of receiving or rejecting the preaching of Christ." In addition, we learn that Paul was making plans to go "to Spain" (Rom. 15:24, 28). It is possible that a church already existed there. This would mean that the gospel had nearly reached the western border of the Roman Empire in Paul's day." Gary

DeMar, *Last Days Madness: Obsession of the Modern Church, Fourth revised edition* (Powder Springs, GA: American Vision, 1999), 87–88.

[10] **Peter forseeing his own death**: 2 Peter 1:14.

[11] Isaiah 51:15-16.

[12] Jeremiah 4:23.

[13] **What Heavens and Earth means:** When believers hear this phrase, they assume it refers to the literal physical heavens and earth that we call the universe. But this is often not the case in the Bible.

God describes the creation of His covenant with Moses as the creation of the heavens and the earth (Isa. 51:14-16). The creation of Israel through deliverance and Promised Land was likened to God hovering over the waters and filling the formless and void earth (Deut. 32:10-12), separating the waters from the dry land (Exod. 15:8, 16-17), establishing the sun and moon, and defeating the mythical sea dragon of chaos to create His ordered world (Psa. 74:12-17; 89:6-12; Isa. 51:9-14).

If the creation of a covenant is spoken of as the creation of heavens and earth, and the ruling powers are referred to as sun, moon and stars, then what would the destruction of those powers be but the destruction of the heavens and the earth, including the fall of those astronomical symbolic entities? And what was the embodiment of that covenant but the holy Temple in the holy city of King David?

The first time that Jerusalem and the Temple was destroyed in 586 B.C. by the Babylonians, the prophets used the language of decreation to express the covenantal violation of Israel. The destruction of the Temple and exile of the Jews through God's providence was likened to the destruction of the heavens and earth and a return to a pre-creation chaotic state, a reversal of Genesis 1 language:

Jer. 4:23-26
I looked on the earth, and behold, it was <u>without form and void;</u>
and to the <u>heavens,</u> and they <u>had no light.</u>
I looked on the <u>mountains,</u> and behold, they <u>were quaking,</u>
I looked, and behold, there was <u>no man,</u>
and all the <u>birds</u> of the air <u>had fled.</u>
I looked, and behold, the fruitful land was a <u>desert</u>…
For this the <u>earth shall mourn,</u>
and the <u>heavens above be dark.</u>

Isa. 24:1-23
Behold, the LORD will <u>empty the earth</u> and <u>make it desolate</u>…
The <u>earth</u> shall be <u>utterly empty</u> and utterly plundered…
The <u>earth staggers</u> like a drunken man;
On that day the LORD <u>will punish</u>
the <u>host of heaven,</u> in heaven,
and the <u>kings of the earth,</u> on the earth…
Then the moon will be confounded
and the sun ashamed.

In the same way that the first temple destruction was earth shattering in its covenantal impact, so the second destruction of Jerusalem and the holy Temple in A.D. 70 was of equal spiritual significance in God's covenantal relations with Israel. It was the shaking of the heavens and earth with a punishment of the host of heaven, both astronomical and political/spiritual.

In Hebrews 12:18-22, the writer tells us that God shook the heavens and the earth when He established His covenant with Moses on Sinai. But then in verses 23-24 he says that the New Covenant is a heavenly city of God on the Mount Zion of the heavenly Jerusalem, far superior to the Mosaic covenant. Then he concludes that the end of that Old Covenant is near because a new shaking of the heavens and earth is coming, and that shaking is the establishment of the New Covenant.

Heb. 12:26-28 At that time His voice shook the earth, but now He has promised, "Yet once more I will shake not only the earth but also the heavens." This phrase, "Yet once more," indicates the removal of things that are shaken — that is, things that have been made — in order that the things that cannot be shaken may remain. Therefore let us be grateful for receiving a kingdom that cannot be shaken.

J. Stuart Russell answers the relevant question, "What then, is the great catastrophe symbolically represented as the shaking of the earth and heavens?"

"No doubt it is the overthrow and abolition of the Mosaic dispensation, or old covenant; the destruction of the Jewish church and state, together with all the institutions and ordinances connect therewith… the laws, and statutes, and ordinances."[13]

The book of Hebrews was written before A.D. 70, when the Temple was destroyed. So the physical embodiment of the Old Covenant was still on earth even though the New Covenant had been inaugurated by the death and resurrection of Christ. It was not until the Temple was destroyed that the New Covenant was considered fully inaugurated. They were living in a transition period between covenants during the years of AD 30-70.

This is why the writer of Hebrews says, "In speaking of a new covenant, He makes the first one obsolete. And what is becoming obsolete and growing old is ready to vanish away" (Heb. 8:13). Notice how the author says that the Old Covenant was becoming old and obsolete but was not yet replaced. That is because the incarnation of the old heavens and earth, the Jerusalem Temple, was not yet destroyed at the time of his writing. The Old Covenant was the heavens and earth that was shaken and replaced by the New Covenant, which is the eternal kingdom that will never be replaced or shaken.

[14] **The Christians were seen as causing the conflagration because they preached about Christ bringing fiery judgment:** "Looking deeper into the matter uncovered more damning evidence. For in their early zeal, Christians were convinced that not only was their savior and prophet going to return, but that he was going to establish a new order, a new '' kingdom'' on earth. Almost immediately the backs of the Roman authorities went up. What new '' kingdom''? The Empire was the only '' kingdom'' on earth. And there was more damning evidence, too. The Christians had been preaching that the world was going to '' be consumed by fire'', that Rome was going to go down in flames, and that the Christian savior, this mysterious Christos was going to come riding out of the clouds, wielding the sword. This wasn't good, especially since an even closer investigation revealed that this Christos was the same Jesus whom Pilate had had crucified for treason against the state back in the 30' s." Gilbert, John (2015-02-27). *Parallel Lives, Parallel Nations Volume Two: A Narrative History Of Rome & The Jews, Their Relations And Their Worlds* (161 BC-135 AD) (p. 280). . Kindle Edition.

"The incendiarism of which the Christians were accused and of which they made open confession was an incendiarism in will not yet realised, but in their firm and absolute conviction immediately to come, and meanwhile eagerly watched for and desired. In Christian circles this one belief during the early decades of the second half of the first century overpowered all others, and transformed all men's ideas and their outlook upon life, that the second Advent of Christ was at hand, and it would be preceded by the destruction by fire of the world and with it the great city of Rome. In every part of the New Testament there are evidences that the Christians of the period with which we are dealing expected that ' the end of all things ' a would be consummated in their own lifetime, and the Apocalyptic literature of the time dwells not only upon the fire which was to burn up the world and all its wickedness, but also upon the sign that the final judgment was at hand." George Edmunson, *The Church In Rome In The First Century An Examination Of Various Controverted Questions Relating To Its History, Chronology, Literature, And Traditions* (New York, Longmans Green, 1913), 133.

CHAPTER 16

[1] **Description of the Golden House and Nero's statement used in this paragraph**: Suetonius, *Lives of the Twelve Caesars, Nero* 31.

[2] **Nero's identity fusion of Apollo and Sol:** Edward Champlin, *Nero* (Massachussetts, Harvard University Press, 2003), 113-117; 135-138.

Sol as patron of Circus Maximus: Edward Champlin, *Nero* (Massachussetts, Harvard University Press, 2003), 119.

[3] **The images and phrases engraved on minted coins described here can be found in:** Edward Champlin, *Nero* (Massachussetts, Harvard University Press, 2003), 116, 140; C Martin Pate and Calvin B. Haynes, *Doomsday Delusions: What's Wrong With Predictions About the End of the World* (Downers Grove, InterVarsity Press, 1995), 41-42; Suetonius, *Lives of the Twelve Caesars, Nero 25.2.*

[4] **On Nero as head of the four imperial religious colleges:** Emma Buckley and Martin T. Dinter Eds., *A Companion To The Neronian Age* (England, Wiley-Blackwell, 2013), 119.

On Nero as Pontifex Maximus: Tucker, T. G. (Thomas George) (2012-05-17). *Life in the Roman World of Nero and St. Paul* (p. 172), Kindle Edition.

[5] **Nero's dream vision:** This vision that Nero has is fictional, but it is based on the imagery of the red dragon in Revelation 12 the sea beast and land beast of Revelation 13, and the beast and harlot of Revelation 17. The premise I have operated upon here is that Satan loves to deceive by mimicking God's own imagery, to appear as an angel of light (2 Corinthians 11:14). Satan uses the negative monster images of Revelation with a positive spin to Nero who would be seduced by the power. He is not deceiving Nero, he is twisting God's truth to an evil purpose.

For a FREE complete book-length treatment that proves Nero was the Beast of Revelation, see Kenneth L. Gentry, Jr., *The Beast of Revelation* (Texas, Institute for Christian Economics, 1994), access at: http://www.garynorth.com/freebooks/docs/pdf/beast_of_revelation.pdf

[6] **Nero's increased taxes and deprivation of free grain:** Cassius Dio, *Roman History*, 62.18.5.

[7] **Annual atonement drowning in the temple of Apollo:** K. M. Coleman, "Fatal Charades: Roman Executions Staged as Mythological Enactments," *The Journal of Roman Studies*, Vol. 80 (1990), 44-73.

[8] **The Sibylline prophecy about Nero:** "Thrice three hundred years having run their course of fulfillment, Rome by the strife of her people shall perish. Last of the sons of Aeneas, a mother-slayer shall govern." Cassius Dio, *Roman History*, 62.17.4.

Nero's murder of his mother Agrippina: There is no agreement by the ancient biographers on the actual motives of Nero in the murder, but they agree that in some way Agrippina had become hostile to her son: Tacitus, *The Annals*, 14; Suetonius, *Lives of the Twelve Caesars, Nero* 34; Cassius Dio, *Roman History*, 63.

[9] **Nero pillaged the temples of Rome to help pay for the rebuilding of the city:** BBC's "Ancient Rome: The Rise & Fall of an Empire," https://www.awesomestories.com/asset/view/Nero-Rebuilding-Rome-after-the-Fire.

CHAPTER 17

[1] **Nero pillaged the temples of Rome to help pay for the rebuilding of the city:** BBC's "Ancient Rome: The Rise & Fall of an Empire," https://www.awesomestories.com/asset/view/Nero-Rebuilding-Rome-after-the-Fire.

[2] **Nero's statement about fire devouring the world as he lived:** Suetonius, *Lives of the Twelve Caesars, Nero* 38; Cassius Dio, *Roman History*, 58.23.

[3] **Tacitus' bizarre twisting of Jewish history and beliefs marks a significant example of how Romans misunderstood Jews:** "Most authors agree that once during a plague in Egypt which caused bodily disfigurement, King Bocchoris approached the oracle of Ammon and asked for a remedy, whereupon he was told to purge his kingdom and to transport this race into other lands, since it was hateful to the gods. So the Hebrews were searched out and gathered together; then, being abandoned in the desert, while all others lay idle and weeping, one only of the exiles, Moses by name, warned them not to hope for help from gods or men, for they were deserted by both, but to trust to themselves...

"Whatever their origin, these rites are maintained by their antiquity: the other customs of the Jews are base and abominable, and owe their persistence to their depravity... They sit apart at meals, and they sleep apart, and although as a race, they are prone to lust, they abstain from intercourse with foreign women; yet among themselves nothing is unlawful." Tacitus, *The Histories* 5.2-5.

See also: Josephus, *Against Apion*, 1.229, 279, 304 ff.; Justinus, *Epitome of the Philippic History of Pompeius Trogus* 36.2, 12-15; Diodorus Siculus 34.frag. 1, 1-2.

[4] **Josephus describes his visit to Rome and the relational connections of this scene**: Flavius Josephus, *The Life of Flavius Josephus*, 16.

[5] **Definition of genius**: "a. With reference to classical pagan belief: the tutelary god or attendant spirit allotted to every person at birth to govern his or her fortunes and determine personal character, and finally to conduct him or her out of the world. Also: a guardian spirit similarly associated with a place, institution, thing, etc." "genius, n. and adj.". *OED Online*. December 2015. Oxford University Press. http://www.oed.com/view/Entry/77607?redirectedFrom=genius (accessed January 06, 2016).

Tertullian on the Genius as demonic: "Thus, too, is it that to all persons their *genii* [geniuses] are assigned, which is only another name for demons." Tertullian, "A Treatise on the Soul, 39" in *Latin Christianity: Its Founder, Tertullian*, ed. Alexander Roberts, James Donaldson, and A. Cleveland Coxe, trans. Peter Holmes, vol. 3, *The Ante-Nicene Fathers* (Buffalo, NY: Christian Literature Company, 1885), 219.

[6] **Omens interpreted for Nero's reign:** Suetonius writes that some astrologers "had promised him the rule of the East, when he was cast off, a few expressly naming the sovereignty of Jerusalem, and several the restitution of all his former fortunes." Suetonius, *Lives of the Twelve Caesars, Nero* 40.2.

[7] **Tigellinus exploited Nero's fears**: Tacitus, *The Annals* 14.57.

[8] **Relations between Jews and Christians in Rome during Nero:** "As we have already seen (Acts 33.2-3), the outlines of the early years of Christianity in Rome are at best sketchy:
• apartment congregations established through the early ministry of Andronicus and Junia and others (Rom. 16.7), which won Gentile converts in significant numbers;
• disturbances within the Roman synagogues over the messiahship claimed for Jesus by such Jewish believers, resulting in expulsion of those identified as the most significant leaders and troublemakers;
• tensions between predominantly Gentile congregations and Jewish believers returning after the lapse of Claudius' decree of expulsion (14.1; 15.8);
• tensions between those wanting to continue maintaining characteristically Jewish traditions of clean and unclean and those claiming freedom from such scruples (14.1-15.7);
• consciousness of the vulnerability of the small groups to harassment and worse from authorities ever on the lookout for trouble-making factions (12.9-13.7);
• increasing rivalry in regard to Paul during the latter's imprisonment in Rome and in the way the gospel continued to be preached (Phil. 1.15-18);
• the spreading influence of Paul's continuing witness. even despite his chains (Acts 28.16; Phil. 1.12-13);
• increased boldness in the proclamation of the gospel to others (Phil. 1.14)." James D. G. Dunn, *Beginning from Jerusalem: Christianity in the Making Volume 2* (Downers Grove, Eerdmans, 2009), 1068.

[9] **Tigellinus, Poppaea, Aliturius and Josephus are all considered possible candidates of influencing Nero to blame the Christians for the Great Fire**: Leon Hardy Canfield, *The Early Persecutions of the Christians* (New York, Columbia, 1913), 69.

The Jews diverting Nero away from them to the Christians: Regarding Nero's search for scapegoats on which to blame the Roman fires of July, AD 64 (Tac., Ann. 15:41), Gibbon sees the Jews behind Nero's choice of Christians. He notes that the Jews "possessed very powerful advocates in the palace, and even in the heart of the tyrant: his wife and mistress, the beautiful Poppaea, and a favourite player of the race of Abraham." These two suggest to Nero "the new and pernicious sect of Galileans," the Christians…

Clement (1 Clem 6:5) claims that the Neronic persecution was prompted "through envy [dia zēlos pathontes]," which many scholars believe refers to the Jews…

(2) Suetonius (Claud. 25:4; cp. Dio 60:66:6) shows that the Jews were expelled from Rome under Claudius around AD 50 for causing riots in their confrontations with Christians (cp. Ac 18:2; 24:5). The Romans disliked the Jews (Jos., Ap 2:66-92) even declaring that "the Jews regard as profane all that we

hold sacred; on the other hand, they permit all that we abhor" (Tac., Hist 5:4). Tacitus (Hist. 5:5) adds that "the other customs of the Jews are base and abominable, and owe their persistence to their depravity" and that toward the non-Jewish "they feel only hate and enmity." Romans saw the Jews as troublemakers frequently stirring riots in Rome. Such conduct caused the Romans to expel them from Rome on several occasions (Suet., Tib. 36; Tac. Ann. 2:85; Jos. Ant. 18:3:5 §81). The Jews could rightly fear that blame for the AD 64 fires in Rome might fall upon them and would therefore be motivated to deflect attention to the Christians…

Schaff (HCC 1:383) comments that "it is not unlikely that in this (as in all previous persecutions, and often afterwards) the fanatical Jews, enraged by the rapid progress of Christianity, and anxious to avert suspicion from themselves, stirred up the people against the hated Galileans." Kenneth L. Gentry, Jr., *The Divorce of Israel: A Redemptive-Historical Interpretation of Revelation Vol. 2* (Dallas, GA: Tolle Lege Press, 2016), 220-223.

[10] **Christianity as a maleficent superstition:** "'Superstitionis novae et maleficae,'" are the words of Suetonius; the latter conveying the idea of witchcraft or enchantment. Suidas relates that a certain martyr cried out from his dungeon "Ye have loaded me with fetters as a sorcerer and profane person." Tacitus calls the Christian religion "a foreign and deadly [exitiabiis] superstition," Annal. xiii. 32; Pliny, in his celebrated letter to Trajan, "a depraved, wicked (orprava), and outrageous superstition." Epist. x. 97." C. Suetonius Tranquillus, *Suetonius: The Lives of the Twelve Caesars; An English Translation, Augmented with the Biographies of Contemporary Statesmen, Orators, Poets, and Other Associates*, ed. Alexander Thomson (Medford, MA: Gebbie & Co., 1889), Nero 16, Footnote 577 (Kindle Locations 951-954). Kindle Edition.

[11] Christians were called atheists by pagan polytheists because they denied the gods: Dio Cassius, *Roman History* 67.14; Eusebius, *Church History* 4.15.18-19.

Christian refusal to engage in the imperial cult: "You do not worship the gods," you say; "and you do not offer sacrifices for the emperors." Well, we do not offer sacrifice for others, for the same reason that we do not for ourselves,—namely, that your gods are not at all the objects of our worship. So we are accused of sacrilege and treason. This is the chief ground of charge against us." Tertullian, *"The Apology,"* in *Latin Christianity: Its Founder, Tertullian*, ed. Alexander Roberts, James Donaldson, and A. Cleveland Coxe, trans. S. Thelwall, *vol. 3, The Ante-Nicene Fathers* (Buffalo, NY: Christian Literature Company, 1885), 26.

[12] **Christians called haters of the human race:** "Nero substituted as culprits, and punished with the utmost refinements of cruelty, a class of men, loathed for their vices, whom the crowd styled Christians. Christus, the founder of the name, had undergone the death penalty in the reign of Tiberius, by sentence of the procurator Pontius Pilatus, and the pernicious superstition was checked for a moment, only to break out once more, not merely in Judaea, the home of the disease, but in the capital itself, where all things horrible or shameful in the world collect and find a vogue. First, then, the confessed members of the sect were arrested; next, on their disclosures, vast numbers were convicted, not so much on the count of arson as for hatred of the human race." Tacitus, *The Annals* 15.44.

"To the Romans *genus humannni* meant, not mankind in general, but the Roman world—men who lived according to Roman manners and laws; the rest of the human race were enemies and barbarians. The Christians then were enemies to civilised man and to the customs and laws which regulated civilised society. They were bent on relaxing the bonds that held society together; they introduced divisions into families, and set children against their parents; and this end they attained by nefarious means, working on the minds of their devotees by magical arts." William Ramsay, *The Letters to the Seven Churches of Asia and Their Place in the Plan of the Apocalypse* (London, Hodder and Stoughton, 1904), 236.

[13] **Religio illicita and Christianity:** Some scholars claim that there was no general edict issued against the Christians so that the magistrate could pursue it as a police action instead. Bernard W. Henderson, *The Life and Principate of the Emperor Nero* (London, Methuen, 1903), 446; Leon Hardy Canfield, *The Early Persecutions of the Christians* (New York, Columbia, 1913), 33, 60; Gilbert, John (2015-02-27). *Parallel Lives, Parallel Nations Volume Two: A Narrative History Of Rome & The Jews, Their Relations And Their Worlds* (161 BC-135 AD) (p. 272), Kindle Edition.

[1] **Poppaea very likely influenced Nero to protect the Jews:** She was possibly a convert to Judaism. Flavius Josephus, *The Life of Flavius Josephus*, 3§13–16; Flavius Josephus, *The Antiquities of the Jews*, 20:8:11 §195.

[2] **The evidence for Peter's presence at Rome during the Neronian persecution:** "[A] line of indirect evidence lies in the likelihood that Mark wrote his Gospel based on the testimony of Peter while in Rome. Papias reports that Mark was Peter's interpreter and wrote down accurately all that Peter remembered from his experience with Jesus… Since the middle of the second century, Christian writers unanimously concur that Peter visited Rome. In his Letter to the Romans (c. AD 106), Ignatius assumes that Peter had already ministered in Rome. In the Apocalypse of Peter (c. AD 135), Jesus commands Peter to go to "the city of the west," which is undoubtedly Rome. Dionysius of Corinth wrote a letter to Roman Christians (c. AD 170) in which he claims that "Peter and Paul sowed among Romans and Corinthians." And Gaius, Roman presbyter in the early third century (c. 199-217), claims that Peter and Paul founded the Roman church. Towards the end of the second century (AD 170s), Irenaeus says that Peter and Paul preached at Rome and laid the foundation of the church" Sean Joslin McDowell, *A Historical Evaluation Of The Evidence For The Death Of The Apostles As Martyrs For Their Faith* (Southern Baptist Theological Seminary, Dissertation, 2014), 110-112.

"Peter's death can be dated with a high probability in A.D. 64 or 65. See Robinson, Redating, 149, for an argument that 65 is more likely." Richard J. Bauckham, *2 Peter, Jude, vol. 50, Word Biblical Commentary* (Dallas: Word, Incorporated, 1998), 159.

"By the close of the second century these were accepted facts. (1) that Peter and Paul had founded the church of Rome and made Linus its first bishop. This is the statement of Irenaeus, bishop of Lyons, an Asiatic who had visited Rome. If he, as is supposed, was in Rome at the time of the martyrdom of Polycarp, i. e. the middle of the second century, his information must have been due to a much earlier belief. This tradition must consequently be admitted as good. (2) A little later the tombs of Peter on the Vatican and of Paul on the Ostian way were shown to visitors to Rome. This we learn from Eusebius on the authority of Gaius, who may possibly be Hippolytus. (3) That Peter was at Rome, and that Mark embodied his teaching in his Gospel. This, as is well known, is the testimony of Clement of Alexandria. (4) That Peter was crucified and Paul beheaded as Tertullian records. (5) That Peter was, according to Origen who visited Rome, crucified head downwards." F. J. Foakes Jackson, "Evidence for the Martyrdom of Peter and Paul in Rome," *Journal of Biblical Literature*, Vol. 46, No. 1/2 (1927), pp. 74-78.

[1] **On the tradition that John miraculously survived boiling in oil:** "According to an old tradition, St. Peter had been accompanied to Rome by the Apostle John. He too was seized by the police and condemned to be plunged into a cauldron of boiling oil at a spot near the Latin Gate. By what Providence St. John escaped we know not." Herbert B. Workman, *Persecution In The Early Church: A Chapter In The History Of Renunciation* (Jennings and Graham, 1923), 45.

Church father Tertullian wrote: "How happy is its church, on which apostles poured forth all their doctrine along with their blood! where Peter endures a passion like his Lord's! where Paul wins his crown in a death like John's where the Apostle John was first plunged, unhurt, into boiling oil, and thence remitted to his island-exile!" Tertullian, "The Prescription against Heretics," in *Latin Christianity: Its Founder, Tertullian*, ed. Alexander Roberts, James Donaldson, and A. Cleveland Coxe, trans. Peter Holmes, vol. 3, *The Ante-Nicene Fathers* (Buffalo, NY: Christian Literature Company, 1885), 260.

[2] 1 John 2:17–18 And the world is passing away along with its desires, but whoever does the will of God abides forever. Children, it is the last hour, and as you have heard that antichrist is coming, so now many antichrists have come. Therefore we know that it is the last hour.

[3] **The passage Nero quotes is:** 1John 2:18.

[4] **Jews rejection of Messiah and by extension, Messiah's people**: "Revelation's overarching theme is Christ's judgment upon Israel for having him crucified (1:7; cp. 5:6, 9, 12; 13:8). But we should understand that this also involves Israel's persecuting his people who are united with him (14:1a; cp. 17:14; 19:14), have his name upon them (14:1b; cp. 22:4), follow him wherever he goes (14:4b, 13; cp. 7:17), and bear his testimony (6:9; 11:3; 12:11) as his "witnesses" (17:6b). "Jesus had already foreseen this analogy between himself and believers" (Reicke in Bammel and Moule 1984: 146) as indicated in Mt 10:17-25//; Mt 24:9-11//. John's Gospel recognizes this identifying of the Lord with his servants: "Remember the word that I said to you, 'A slave is not greater than his master.' If they persecuted Me, they will also persecute you" (Jn 15:20). (See additional discussion at 1:7.)" Kenneth L. Gentry, Jr., *The Divorce of Israel: A Redemptive-Historical Interpretation of Revelation Vol. 2* (Dallas, GA: Tolle Lege Press, 2016), 436-437.

Who or what is antichrist?: Antichrist is one of the most commonly misunderstood terms by Bible prophecy interpreters. Many evangelicals believe it refers to an individual incarnation of Satan yet to come to power in our day and age. But there is nothing of the sort in the Bible. Gary DeMar explains in his chapter on "Identifying the Antichrist":

"First, we must find a biblical definition of antichrist. The word 'antichrist' appears only in John's epistles (1 John 2:18, 22; 4:3; 2 John 7). "What is taught in these passages constitutes the whole New Testament doctrine of Antichrist."[13] John's description of antichrist is altogether different from the modern image. John's antichrist is Anyone "who denies that Jesus is the Christ" (1 John 2:22).

Anyone who "denies the Father and Son" (1 John 2:23).
"Every spirit that does not confess Jesus" (1 John 4:3).
"Those who do not acknowledge Jesus Christ as coming in the flesh.
This is the deceiver and the antichrist" (2 John 7).

"None of what John writes relates to the modern doctrine of the antichrist as previously outlined. John's antichrist doctrine is a theological concept related to an apostasy that was fomenting in his day. John did not have a particular individual in mind but rather individuals who taught that Jesus Christ is not who the Bible says He is:

"In one word, 'Antichrist' meant for John just denial of what we should call the doctrine, or let us rather say the fact, of the Incarnation. By whatever process it had been brought about, 'Christ' had come to denote for John the Divine Nature of our Lord, and so far to be synonymous with "Son of God." To deny that Jesus is the Christ was not to him therefore merely to deny that he is the Messiah, but to deny that he is the Son of God; and was equivalent therefore to "denying the Father and the Son"—that is to say, in our modern mode of speech, the doctrine—in fact—of the Trinity, which is the implicate of the Incarnation. To deny that Jesus is Christ come—or is the Christ coming—in flesh, was again just to refuse to recognize in Jesus Incarnate God. Whosoever, says John, takes up this attitude toward Jesus is Antichrist.

"Antichrist is simply any belief system that disputes the fundamental teachings of Christianity, beginning with the person of Christ. These antichrists are "religious" figures. The antichrist, contrary to much presentday speculation, is not a political figure, no matter how anti- (against) Christ he might be. The modern manufactured composite antichrist is not the antichrist of 1 and 2 John: "Putting it all together, we can see that Antichrist is a description of both the system of apostasy and individual apostates. In other words, antichrist was the fulfillment of Jesus' prophecy that a time of great apostasy would come, when 'many will fall away and will betray one another and hate one another. And many false prophets will arise, and will mislead many' (Matt. 24:10–11)."[16] In addition, you will not find the word antichrist in the Book of Revelation. This is significant since the John who defines antichrist for us in his first two letters is the same John who penned the Book of Revelation.

"Second, according to the Bible antichrist is not a single individual. John wrote, "Children, it is the last hour; and just as you heard that antichrist is coming, even now many antichrists have arisen; from this we know that it is the last hour" (1 John 2:18). "He calls them just 'Antichrists,' and he sets them over against the individual Antichrist of which his readers had heard as the reality represented by that unreal figure."[18] It is possible that the early church "heard" that one man was to come on the scene who was to be the antichrist. John seems to be correcting this mistaken notion: "John is adducing not an item of

Christian teaching, but only a current legend—Christian or other—in which he recognizes an element of truth and isolates it for the benefit of his readers. In that case we may understand him less as expounding than as openly correcting it—somewhat as, in the closing page of his Gospel, he corrects another saying of similar bearing which was in circulation among the brethren, to the effect that he himself should not die but should tarry till the Lord comes [John 21:18–23].”[19] In a similar manner, the people in Jesus' day had "heard" certain things that were only partially true. Jesus corrected them in their misreading of the Bible (Matt. 5:21, 27, 33, 38, 43).

"Third, whether there was to be only one or many antichrists, John made it clear that "it is the last hour" for those who first read his letters (1 John 2:18). How do we know this? John said, "Even now many antichrists have arisen." And in case you did not get his point, he repeated it: "From this we know that it is the last hour." John did not describe a period of time thousands of years in the future. It was the "last hour" for his contemporaries. Keep in mind that Jesus had told His disciples years before, John among them, that their generation would see the destruction of the temple and Jerusalem (Matt. 24:1–34). John, writing close to the time when this prophecy was to be fulfilled, described its fulfillment in the rise of "many antichrists," that is, many who preach and teach a false religious system, the denial that Jesus had come in the flesh (2 John 7). The apostle's knowledge about coming antichrists was probably taken from Matthew 24:24: "For false Christs and false prophets will arise and will show great signs and wonders, so as to mislead, if possible, even the elect."

"They had heard that "the spirit of antichrist" was coming. For them, "now it is already in the world" (1 John 4:3). Antichrists had arrived. It is inappropriate to look for a contemporary rising political leader and describe him as the antichrist. Such a designation cannot be supported from Scripture. Does this mean that the spirit of antichrist cannot be present in our day? Not at all. It does mean, however, that a figure called the antichrist cannot be alive somewhere in the world today. Having said this, we still must conclude that John had the time prior to Jerusalem's destruction in mind when he described the theological climate surrounding the concept of the antichrist." Gary DeMar, *Last Days Madness: Obsession of the Modern Church* (Powder Springs, American Vision, 1999), 267-270.

For an excellent online article that addresses the Evangelical interpretation and misinterpretation of antichrist, see Joel McDurmon, The Antichrist Hoax," The American Vision website: http://americanvision.org/3670/the-antichrist-hoax/

[5] **Nero quotes:** 1John 2:28.

Parousia: "The term parousia was widely used for the official visit of a potentate. If we accept Wilcken's explanation of the difficult Flinders Petrie Papyrus 2.39e, we may see there an early reference to enforced contributions to a fund for presenting golden stephanoi to officials at their parousiai. Deissmann finds in this practice a background for figurative language in the Pauline and Pastoral epistles: 'While the sovereigns of this world expect at their parusia a costly crown for themselves, "at the parusia of our Lord Jesus" the apostle will wear a crown—the "crown of glory" (1 Thess. 2:19) won by his work among the churches, or the "crown of righteousness" which the Lord will give to him and to all them that have loved His appearing (2 Tim. 4:8)" Colin J. Hemer, *The Letters to the Seven Churches of Asia in Their Local Setting* (Grand Rapids, MI; Cambridge, U.K.; Livonia, MI: William B. Eerdmans Publishing Company; Dove Booksellers, 2001), 74–75.

"The word 'parousia' is itself misleading, anyway, since it merely means 'presence'; Paul can use it of his being present with a church, and nobody supposes that he imagined he would make his appearance flying downwards on a cloud. The motif of delay ('how long, O Lord, how long?'69) was already well established in Judaism, and is hardly a Christian innovation, as is often imagined. The usual scholarly construct, in which the early church waited for Jesus' return, lived only for that future and without thought for anything past (such as memories of Jesus himself), only to be grievously disappointed and to take up history-writing as a displacement activity, a failure of nerve—this picture is without historical basis. The church expected certain events to happen within a generation, and happen they did." N. T. Wright, *The New Testament and the People of God, Christian Origins and the Question of God* (London: Society for Promoting Christian Knowledge, 1992), 462–463.

[6] **On John's exile to Patmos during the reign of Nero:** "Some notices are ambiguous (e.g., Clement of Alexandria and Origen) and make it possible to argue that the emperor who banished John was Nero rather than Domitian (Hort, xvii). According to the Syriac apocryphal "History of John the Son of

Zebedee" (W. Wright, *Apocryphal Acts of the Apostles* [London and Edinburgh: Williams and Norgate, 1871] 2:55):

> After these things, when the Gospel was increasing by the hands of the Apostles, Nero, the unclean and impure and wicked king, heard all that had happened at Ephesus. And he sent (and) took all that the procurator had, and imprisoned him; and laid hold of S. John and drove him into exile; and passed sentence on the city that it should be laid waste.

"The angel of the Lord then appeared to Nero and frightened him into releasing John, and Nero thereafter did not dare to interfere with the affairs of the province of Asia (Wright, Apocryphal Acts 2:56–57). In one place Eusebius mentions that "Peter was crucified head downwards at Rome, Paul beheaded, and John exiled to an island" (Demonstr. evang. 3.5 [116c]; W. J. Ferrar, tr., Eusebius), giving the impression that these events occurred in close temporal proximity and that they occurred in Rome." David E. Aune, *Revelation 1–5, vol. 52A, Word Biblical Commentary* (Dallas: Word, Incorporated, 1998), 78.

"John's presence on Patmos has been explained in several ways: (1) He had been exiled to Patmos by the Roman authorities. (2) He traveled to Patmos for the purpose of proclaiming the gospel. (3) He went to Patmos in order to receive a revelation. The first explanation, held by many church fathers (Clement Alex. Quis Dives 42; Origen Hom. in Mt.M 7.51; 16.6; Eusebius Hist. Eccl. 3.18; Jerome Devirillustr; 10), appears most probable, even though it requires certain qualifications (see below). Tertullian preserves the view that John was exiled from Rome (De praescr; 36), a view possibly confirmed by Eusebius (Demonstrevang; 3.5 [116c])…

John states that he was on Patmos διά, "because of," the word of God and the testimony of Jesus. Yet since διά with the accusative can express both cause ("because of, on account of") and purpose ("for"; cf. BDF §222), there is no grammatical basis for excluding any of the three explanations. On the other hand, the use of similar phrases in 6:9; 20:4 in explicit connection with martyrdom suggests that John's presence on Patmos was the result of a capital penalty inflicted on him by Roman authorities. In Roman law poena capitalis, "capital punishment," denoted not only the death penalty but also loss of caput, i.e., citizenship or liberty (A. Berger, Roman Law, 634)." David E. Aune, *Revelation 1–5, vol. 52A, Word Biblical Commentary* (Dallas: Word, Incorporated, 1998), 81–82.

CHAPTER 20

[1] **The Scripture Cassandra quotes** is a paraphrase of Isaiah 55:9.

[2] **Christian denigration of the Jewish signs of covenant inclusion as circumcision, Sabbath and dietary laws**: See endnotes of Chapter 10 for Scriptures.

[3] **Lex Talionis:** Exodus 21:24. Eye for an eye was not a law of vengeance, it was intended to stop personal vengeance, and to keep unjust judges from prescribing too harsh of penalties for crimes (for example, death for theft). It was essentially an ancient version of our modern, "The punishment shall fit the crime."

[4] **The first prisoners of Nero's persecution:** "The first arrests were of a number of persons suspected of belonging to the new sect, who were "packed together," says Clement, in a prison which was itself a torture. They confessed their faith, which may have been taken as a confession of the charge. These arrests were followed by many others. The greater part of the accused seem to have been proselytes, who kept the terms of the decision given at Jerusalem. It is not to be supposed that true Christians denounced their brethren; but papers may have been seized, or half-initiated neophytes may have been broken down by torture." (Clement of Rome Ad Cor. i. 6; "Shepherd" of Hermas, i. vis. 8: 2. Tacitus Ann. xv. 44)" Ernest Renan, trans. Joseph Henry Allen, *The Antichrist: The Period From the Arrival of Paul in Rome to the End of the Jewish Revolution* (Boston, Roberts Brothers 1897), 144.

[5] **On Paul's presence in Rome during the Neronian persecution:** "The vigorous tradition of St Paul's acquittal and further journeys, perhaps in Spain, more probably in Asia Minor again, before he returned to Rome to die, perhaps as one of the martyrs of A.D. 64, we hold to be probable." Bernard W. Henderson, *The Life and Principate of the Emperor Nero* (London, Methuen, 1903), 345.

"J. N. D. Kelly, attaching considerable weight to the evidence for seeing Paul's execution as an incident in the wider persecution of Christians which broke out as a sequel to the great fire of Rome (dated in July, A.D. 64), has concluded that the view that Paul was released and, after a few years of liberty, was rearrested, imprisoned, condemned, and executed, "seems firmly grounded." F. F. Bruce, *The Book of the Acts, The New International Commentary on the New Testament* (Grand Rapids, MI: Wm. B. Eerdmans Publishing Co., 1988), 511.

[6] **Paul wrote the Thessalonian letters around AD 52:** "The letters to Thessalonica were written from Corinth around A.D. 52, and within just a few weeks of each other and not long after his visit in Thessalonica (1 Thess. 2:17).[6] According to Acts 17 and 18, Paul left Thessalonica to go to Berea and Athens for brief visits, and then on to Corinth, where he wrote the Thessalonian epistles." Dr. Kenneth L. Gentry, Jr. "The Man of Lawlessness: A Preteristic Postmillennial Interpretation of 2 Thessalonians 2," (Covenant Media Foundation, Paper PT550).

[7] **Son of Perdition:** 2Thessalonians 2:3.

[8] **The passage Paul quotes** is 2Thessalonians 2:9.

[9] **The "restrainer" was a play on the name Claudius:** "While Paul wrote 2 Thessalonians 2 he was under the reign of Claudius Caesar, who had just banished Jews for persecuting Christians (Suetonius, Claudius 24:5; cp. Acts 18:2). It may be that he employs a word play on Claudius' name. The Latin word for "restraint" is claudere, which is similar to "Claudius."[26] It is interesting that Paul shifts between the neuter and masculine forms of the "the restrainer" (2 Thess. 2:6, 7). This may indicate he includes both the imperial law and the present emperor in his designation "restrainer." While Claudius lived, Nero, the Man of Lawlessnes, was without power to commit public lawlessness. Christianity was free from the imperial sword until the Neronic persecution began in November, A.D 64." Dr. Kenneth L. Gentry, Jr. "The Man of Lawlessness: A Preteristic Postmillennial Interpretation of 2 Thessalonians 2," (Covenant Media Foundation, Paper PT550).

[10] **Identifying the Man of Lawlessness:** "The Man of Lawlessness is Nero Caesar, who also is the Beast of Revelation, as a number of Church Fathers believed.[23] The difficulty of this passage lies in the fact that Paul "describes the Man of Sin with a certain reserve" (Origen, Celsus 6:45) for fear of incurring "the charge of calumny for having spoken evil of the Roman emperor" (Augustine, City of God 20:19). Thus, Paul becomes very obscure, apparently hiding his prophecy regarding the coming evil of and judgment on the Roman emperor.

"Even early in Nero's reign, his evil was hidden from the public eye by careful tutors -- until he broke free of their influence and was publicly "revealed" for what he was. Roman historians write of Nero: "Although at first his acts of wantonness, lust, extravagance, avarice and cruelty were gradual and secret... yet even then their nature was such that no one doubted that they were defects of his character and not due to his time of life" (Suetonius, Nero 26). "Gradually Nero's vices gained the upper hand: he no longer tried to laugh them off, or hide, or deny them, but openly broke into more serious crime" (Nero 27, cp. 6). "After this, no considerations of selection or moderation restrained Nero from murdering anyone he please, on whatever pretext" (Nero 37). "Other murders were meant to follow. But the emperor's tutors, Sextus Afranius Burrus and Lucius Annaeus Seneca, prevented them.... They collaborated in controlling the emperor's perilous adolescence; their policy was to direct his deviations from virtue into licensed channels of indulgence" (Tacitus, Annals 13).

"The evil "mystery of lawlessness" was "already working," though restrained in Claudius' day (2 Thess.2:7). This is perhaps a reference to the evil conniving and plotting of Nero's mother, Agrippina, who may have poisoned Claudius so that Nero could ascend to the purple (Tacitus, Annals 12:62ff; Suetonius, Claudius 44). This is another indication for the preterist approach. The true nature of lawlessness was already at work in the imperial cultus and its rage for worship, though it had not yet jealously broken out upon the Christian community. In addition, the cunning machinations to secure imperial authority for Nero were afoot.

"Showing That He is God.

"The Roman emperor, according to Paul, "exalts himself above all that is called God or that is worshipped" (2 Thess. 2:4a). A warning of the evil potential of emperor worship was publicly exhibited just a few years before, when the emperor Caligula (Gaius) attempted to put his image in the Temple in Jerusalem (Josephus, Ant. 18:8:2-3).

"The phrase "so that he sits as God in the temple of God, showing himself that he is God" is interesting. When hoste ("so that") is followed by an infinitive (kathisai, "to sit"), it indicates a purpose intended, not necessarily a purpose accomplished.

"This was for all intents and purposes accomplished by future emperor Titus, who concluded the devastation of Jerusalem set in motion by Nero. Titus actually invaded the Temple in A.D. 70: "And now the Romans . . . brought their ensigns[29] to the temple, and set them over against its eastern gate; and there did they offer sacrifices to them, and there did they make Titus imperator, with the greatest acclamations of joy" (Josephus, Wars 6:6:1). By September, A.D. 70, the very Temple of which Paul spoke in 2 Thessalonians 2:4 was forever gone.

"Not only so but in Nero the imperial line eventually openly "opposed" (2 Thess. 2:4) Christ by persecuting His followers. Nero even began the persecution of Christians when he presented himself in a chariot as the sun god Apollo, while burning Christians for illumination for his self-glorifying party.

"The mystery form of his character gave way to a revelation of his lawlessness in Nero's wicked acts. This occurred after the restrainer [Claudius, who maintained *religio licita*] was "taken out of the way," allowing Nero the public stage upon which he could act out his horrendous lawlessness." Dr. Kenneth L. Gentry, Jr. "The Man of Lawlessness: A Preteristic Postmillennial Interpretation of 2 Thessalonians 2," (Covenant Media Foundation, Paper PT550).

[11] **The Parousia "coming" of Christ in the Thessalonian letters**: Gary DeMar writes:

"Is "the coming of our Lord Jesus Christ" a reference to the Second Coming, that is, an event that is still in our future, or is it a coming in judgment upon first-century Jerusalem that would be the event to bring the "last days" to a close (2 Thess. 2:1)?[7] The word translated "coming" in verse 1 is the Greek word parousia, best translated as "presence" in other contexts (2 Cor. 10:10; Phil. 2:12). "The term itself does not mean 'return' or 'second' coming; it simply means 'arrival' or 'presence.'

"Translating parousia as "coming" is not at all improper, however, since the Bible's use of "coming" does not always mean bodily presence, as so many Old and New Testament passages make clear. In addition, we know that the Bible clearly states that "the coming [parousia] of the Lord" was said to be "at hand," that is, "near" to Christians living prior to the destruction of Jerusalem in A.D. 70 (James 5:8). How could James have told his readers to "be patient ... until the "coming of the Lord" if the Lord's coming was not "near" for them? James bases his call for patience upon the fact that the Lord's coming was near, near for those who first read his letter. "James clearly believed, as others of his time did, that the Coming of Christ was imminent. Since, then, there is not long to wait, his plea for patience is greatly reinforced."[10]

"God's presence was a sign of blessing because of Israel's special covenantal status (Isa. 55:3; Jer. 1:19). God's departure was a sign of judgment. For the nations, God's presence was a sign of judgment because of their wickedness. Because of Israel's abominations, God's presence left the temple (Ezek. 5–11). Israel was then treated like the nations and would hide from and lament His presence in the future. In similar fashion, because of Israel's rejection of the Messiah and the persecution of His church, Christ's bride, God would make His presence known to Israel in the form of judgment. God rejected His once-covenanted people and their temple of stone because of the nation's rejection of the promised Son of Man (Matt. 23:38; 24:1). Like Ezekiel (Ezek. 8), Jesus inspected the temple, found it filled with abominations (Matt. 21:12–13), and left it desolate (23:38). He returned in A.D. 70 to inspect the temple for a final time and found it full of abominations. His presence now abides with a new people of God constructed as a "spiritual house," the true temple of God (1 Peter 2:4–10; cf. 2 Cor. 6:14–18). In effect, Christ's parousia in 2 Thessalonians 2:1 is the fulfillment of the promise that the presence of Christ will reside with the true Israel forever (Rom. 2:28–29; 9:6; 10:12; Gal. 6:15–16; Phil. 3:3; Col. 3:11; Heb. 8:8, 10). Remember, during His earthly ministry Jesus "came out from the temple" (Matt. 24:1), foretold its destruction (24:15–34), and returned in A.D. 70 to destroy it (22:7).

"There is no doubt that Jesus' "coming" in 2 Thessalonians 2:1 should be attributed to the first century since the time indicators ("has come," "now," "already") leave no room in this passage for a coming in the distant future (e.g., Matt. 16:27–28; 24:29–31; 26:64; Heb. 10:37; James 5:7–8; Rev. 2:5, 16; 3:11).

Jesus' coming in A.D. 70 was a coming in judgment upon an apostate nation." Gary DeMar, *Last Days Madness: Obsession of the Modern Church* (Powder Springs, American Vision, 1999), 274-277.

[12] **"Unless the rebellion comes first"**: "For that [Day of the Lord] will not come, unless the rebellion comes first, and the man of lawlessness is revealed." 2 Thessalonians 2:3. Some translations use "apostasy" as opposed to "rebellion." The Greek word used is "apostasia."

"The word "falling away" is apostasia, which occurs only here and in Acts 21:21 in the New Testament. Historically, the word may apply either to a political or to a religious revolt.[20] But to which does it refer here? Does it refer to a future worldwide apostasy from the Christian faith, as per pessimistic eschatologies? Amillennialist William Hendriksen writes that this teaches that "by and large, the visible Church will forsake the true faith." Dispensationalist Constable comments: "This rebellion, which will take place within the professing church, will be a departure from the truth that God has revealed in His Word." Or does the apostasia refer to a political rebellion of some sort?

"A good case may be made in support of the view that it speaks of the Jewish apostasy/rebellion against Rome. Josephus certainly speaks of the Jewish War as an apostasia against the Romans (Josephus, Life 4). Probably Paul merges the two concepts of religious and political apostasy here, though emphasizing the outbreak of the Jewish War, which was the result of their apostasy against God.

"This may be inferred from 1 Thessalonians 2:16, where Paul states of the Jews that they "always fill up the measure of their sins [i.e., religious apostasia against God]; but wrath has come upon them to the uttermost [i.e., the result of political apostasia against Rome]." The apostasia [revolt] Paul mentions will lead to the military devastation of Israel (Luke 21:21-22; 23:28-31; Acts 2:16-20). The filling up of the measure of the sins of the fathers (Matt. 23:32) leads to Israel's judgment, thereby vindicating the righteous slain in Israel (Matt. 23:35; cf. Matt. 24:2-34). The apostasia of the Jews against God by rejecting their Messiah (Matt 21:37-39; 22:2-6), led to God's providentially turning them over to judgment via their apostasia against Rome (Matt. 21:40-42; 22:7). The emphasis must be on the revolt against Rome in that it is future and datable, whereas the revolt against God was ongoing and cumulative. Such is necessary to dispel the deception Paul was concerned with. In conjunction with this final apostasy and the consequent destruction of Jerusalem, Christianity and Judaism were forever separated and both are exposed to the wrath of Rome.

"For political apostasia see the Septuagint at Ezra 4:12, 15, 19; Neh. 2:19; 6:6. For religious apostasia see the Septuagint at Josh. 22:22; 2 Chr. 29:19; and 33:19, and in the New Testament Acts 21:21." Dr. Kenneth L. Gentry, Jr. "The Man of Lawlessness: A Preteristic Postmillennial Interpretation of 2 Thessalonians 2," (Covenant Media Foundation, Paper PT550).

[13] **Paul's multitude of sufferings for Christ spoken of here:** 2 Corinthians 11:23-27. The rest of his words are composited from 2Timothy 4:7-8; 1Thessalonians 2:16.

[14] **The apostles and Jesus accuse the Jews of killing the prophets and the Messiah**: 1 Thessalonians 2:14–16 [Paul] [14] For you, brothers, became imitators of the churches of God in Christ Jesus that are in Judea. For you suffered the same things from your own countrymen as they did from the Jews, [15] who killed both the Lord Jesus and the prophets, and drove us out, and displease God and oppose all mankind [16] by hindering us from speaking to the Gentiles that they might be saved—so as always to fill up the measure of their sins. But wrath has come upon them at last!

Matthew 23:32–36 [Jesus][32] Fill up, then, the measure of your fathers. [33] You serpents, you brood of vipers, how are you to escape being sentenced to hell? [34] Therefore I send you prophets and wise men and scribes, some of whom you will kill and crucify, and some you will flog in your synagogues and persecute from town to town, [35] so that on you may come all the righteous blood shed on earth, from the blood of righteous Abel to the blood of Zechariah the son of Barachiah, whom you murdered between the sanctuary and the altar. [36] Truly, I say to you, all these things will come upon this generation.

Matthew 21:33–45 [33] [Jesus]"Hear another parable. There was a master of a house who planted a vineyard and put a fence around it and dug a winepress in it and built a tower and leased it to tenants, and went into another country. [34] When the season for fruit drew near, he sent his servants to the tenants to get his fruit. [35] And the tenants took his servants and beat one, killed another, and stoned another. [36] Again he sent other servants, more than the first. And they did the same to them. [37] Finally he sent his son to them, saying, 'They will respect my son.' [38] But when the tenants saw the son, they said to themselves, 'This is the heir. Come, let us kill him and have his inheritance.' [39] And they took him and threw him out of the vineyard and killed him. [40] When therefore the owner of the vineyard comes, what will he do to those tenants?" [41] They said to him, "He will put those wretches to a miserable death and let out the vineyard to other tenants who will give him the fruits in their seasons." [42] Jesus said to them, "Have you never read in the Scriptures: " 'The stone that the builders rejected has become the cornerstone; this was the Lord's doing, and it is marvelous in our eyes'? [43] Therefore I tell you, the kingdom of God will be taken away from you and given to a people producing its fruits. [44] And the one who falls on this stone will be broken to pieces; and when it falls on anyone, it will crush him." [45] When the chief priests and the Pharisees heard his parables, they perceived that he was speaking about them.

Acts 2:22–23 [Peter][22] "Men of Israel, hear these words: Jesus of Nazareth, a man attested to you by God with mighty works and wonders and signs that God did through him in your midst, as you yourselves know— [23] this Jesus, delivered up according to the definite plan and foreknowledge of God, you crucified and killed by the hands of lawless men.

Acts 7:51–53 [Stephen] "You stiff-necked people, uncircumcised in heart and ears, you always resist the Holy Spirit. As your fathers did, so do you. [52] Which of the prophets did your fathers not persecute? And they killed those who announced beforehand the coming of the Righteous One, whom you have now betrayed and murdered, [53] you who received the law as delivered by angels and did not keep it."

[15] **The devil's time is short**: This statement that Paul makes actually comes from Revelation 12:12.

CHAPTER 21

[1] **Paul's martyrdom in Rome on the Ostian Way:** "[Paul] was convicted and beheaded with the sword at the third milestone on the Ostian Way, at a place called Aquae Salviae. These last proceedings against him may well have been an incident in Nero's proceedings against Christians about A.D. 65." Gerald F. Hawthorne, Ralph P. Martin, and Daniel G. Reid, eds., *Dictionary of Paul and His Letters* (Downers Grove, IL: InterVarsity Press, 1993), 687.

"All tradition says that St. Paul, as became his status as a Roman citizen, suffered martyrdom by decapitation, being led out of the city to the third milestone upon the Ostian Road, at the spot known as Aquae Salviae." George Edmunson, *The Church In Rome In The First Century An Examination Of Various Controverted Questions Relating To Its History, Chronology, Literature, And Traditions* (New York, Longmans Green, 1913), 163.

[2] **42 Months begins**: "Most commentators agree with Mounce that the period of forty-two months (13:5b) "is the traditional period for religious persecution" (249–50) as drawn from Daniel and rooted in "the period of Jewish suffering under the Syrian despot Antiochus Epiphanes in 157–164 B.C." I would agree that because of the forty-two months of Jewish suffering under Antiochus, this time frame became an image of persecution. And since the God of theology is also the God of history, he causes the original historical time frame to repeat itself in the Neronic persecution. Revelation's stated near term time frame (1:1, 3; 22:6, 10), the fact that John himself is already in "tribulation" (1:9), and that the seven-headed beast seems to be ancient Rome with Nero as its reigning head (13:2; 17:9–10). As Farrar (466) puts it: "The simplest explanation is that it refers to the time which elapsed between the beginning of Nero's persecution in Nov., 64, and his death in June, 68, which is almost exactly three and a half years". Noted church historian J. L. von Mosheim writes of Nero's persecution: "The dreadful persecution which took place by order of this tyrant, commenced at Rome about the middle of November, in the year of our Lord 64... This dreadful persecution ceased but with the death of Nero. The empire, it is well known, was not delivered from the tyranny of this monster until the year 68, when he put an end to his own life."24 This covers a period right at forty-two months. Ellis (1999: 246) differs only by a month or two: "The Neronian persecution probably began in early 65 and continued to be official policy until Nero's death on 9 June 68."Kenneth L. Gentry, Jr., *The Divorce of Israel: A Redemptive-Historical Interpretation of Revelation Vol. 2* (Dallas, GA: Tolle Lege Press, 2016), 216-217.

[3] **On Nero's circus used for the persecution of Christians**: "The tyrant scrupled not to charge them with the act of burning Rome; and he satiated his fury against them by such outrages as are unexampled in history. They were covered with the skins of wild beasts, and torn by dogs; were crucified, and set on fire, that they might serve for lights in the night-time. Nero offered his garden for this spectacle, and exhibited the games of the Circus by this dreadful illumination. Sometimes they were covered with wax and other combustible materials, after which a sharp stake was put under their chin, to make them stand upright, and they were burnt alive, to give light to the spectators." Tranquillus, Gaius Suetonius (2011-03-24). *The Lives of the Twelve Caesars, Volume 06: Nero* (Kindle Locations 661-665). Kindle Edition.

On the red grantie obelisk in Nero's Circus: See Ernest Renan, trans. Joseph Henry Allen, *The Antichrist: The Period From the Arrival of Paul in Rome to the End of the Jewish Revolution* (Boston, Roberts Brothers 1897), 146; Bernard W. Henderson, *The Life and Principate of the Emperor Nero* (London, Methuen, 1903), 127.

[4] **On Nero's projection of himself as Apollo on his chariot:** "At Rome he rode in the chariot which Augustus had used in his triumphs in days gone by, and wore a purple robe and a Greek cloak adorned with stars of gold, bearing on his head the Olympic crown and in his right hand the Pythian." Suetonius, *Lives of the Twelve Caesars, Nero* 25.

[5] **Tacitus calls the show of killing Christians a spectaculum:** Edward Champlin, *Nero* (Massachussetts, Harvard University Press, 2003), 122.

[6] **Nero's attack on the Christians was not focused exclusively on blame for the fire, but for their identity as Christians:** "First, then, the confessed members of the sect were arrested; next, on their disclosures, vast numbers were convicted, not so much on the count of arson as for hatred of the human race." Tacitus, *The Annals* 15.44.

[7] **Charges against the Christians of hatred of the human race, cannibalism, perversion, magic and superstition:** "The offences with which the Christians were charged under Nero appear to have been, according to Tacitus, of the same character as those of which Pliny the Younger speaks in his famous letter from Bithynia to the Emperor Trajan, as the 'crimes adhering to the name,' and which we find described in the writings of the second-century Christian Apologists, perhaps more succinctly than any other by Athenagoras (about 177 A.D.), who writes. 'Three things are alleged against us: Atheism, Thyestean feasts, Oedipodean intercourse.' The refusal to take part in the ceremonies or to recognise the gods of the national religion constituted the crime of Atheism. The secret assemblies, the bringing of children to them for the rite of baptism, the words of consecration in the Holy Eucharist, the salutation with 'a holy kiss,' were travestied by the enemies of Christianity into charges of murder, cannibalism, and promiscuous intercourse, which were accepted as true by public opinion already in the days of Nero, and which still remained a fixed article of popular belief and execration when Tertullian wrote his 'Apology' about a century and a half later. These were the flagitia to which Tacitus attaches the epithets atrocia and pudenda, abominations horrible and shameful.

"That the Christians were also condemned for the crime of 'magic' may be inferred from the fact that their religion is styled by Tacitus a most pernicious superstition - abilis superstitio - and by Suetonius a strange and maleficent superstition - superstitio nova ac malefica - (the word maleficus having juristically the special signification of a magician or sorcerer), and the punishment in the Vatican Gardens was that specially assigned to those convicted of practising magical arts.

"The crime of 'hatred of the human race,' however, was the charge which included all these other accusations, and henceforth during the succeeding centuries was to render the mere name of Christian a sufficient ground for summary." George Edmunson, *The Church In Rome In The First Century An Examination Of Various Controverted Questions Relating To Its History, Chronology, Literature, And Traditions* (New York, Longmans Green, 1913), 135-136.

[8] **The Neronian persecution:** It is becoming fashionable amongst scholars to deny or downplay the Neronian persecution of Christians in order to discredit the New Testament and the victimization of Christians in history. The two main secular Roman sources for the event are Tacitus, and Suetonius (below). One recent writer, Stephen Dando-Collins, in his book *The Great Fire of Rome*, constructs a conspiracy theory of later Christian scribes changing the original Roman texts, so that the Christians would replace the "real" victims of Nero's blame, Egyptian worshippers of Isis. He asserts that Nero was

fascinated with Isis worship and then for no explicable reason turns against those worshippers and blames them for the Great Fire. He then fantasizes later Christian scribes replacing the word "Egyptians" with "Christians." The theory is more revealing of the author's prejudice when it becomes apparent that he has absolutely no documentation for any element of his theory beyond speculation and fictional imposition. Not a single footnote in his otherwise "scholarly" examination, thus revealing agenda masquerading as scholarship.

The main ancient writings of the Nerionian persecution that are the sources for this chapter are as follows:

"Neither human help, nor imperial munificence, nor all the modes of placating Heaven, could stifle scandal or dispel the belief that the fire had taken place by order. Therefore, to scotch the rumour, Nero substituted as culprits, and punished with the utmost refinements of cruelty, a class of men, loathed for their vices, whom the crowd styled Christians. Christus, the founder of the name, had undergone the death penalty in the reign of Tiberius, by sentence of the procurator Pontius Pilatus, and the pernicious superstition was checked for a moment, only to break out once more, not merely in Judaea, the home of the disease, but in the capital itself, where all things horrible or shameful in the world collect and find a vogue. First, then, the confessed members of the sect were arrested; next, on their disclosures, vast numbers were convicted, not so much on the count of arson as for hatred of the human race. And derision accompanied their end: they were covered with wild beasts' skins and torn to death by dogs; or they were fastened on crosses, and, when daylight failed were burned to serve as lamps by night. Nero had offered his Gardens for the spectacle, and gave an exhibition in his Circus, mixing with the crowd in the habit of a charioteer, or mounted on his car. Hence, in spite of a guilt which had earned the most exemplary punishment, there arose a sentiment of pity, due to the impression that they were being sacrificed not for the welfare of the state but to the ferocity of a single man." Tacitus, *The Annals* 15.44

"Punishment was inflicted on the Christians, a class of men given to a new and mischievous superstition." Suetonius, *Lives of the Twelve Caesars, Nero 16.*

Tertullian writing in A.D. 200: "Consult your histories; you will there find that Nero was the first who assailed with the imperial sword the Christian sect, making progress then especially at Rome. But we glory in having our condemnation hallowed by the hostility of such a wretch. For any one who knows him, can understand that not except as being of singular excellence did anything bring on it Nero's condemnation." Tertullian, "The Apology, 5" in *Latin Christianity: Its Founder, Tertullian*, ed. Alexander Roberts, James Donaldson, and A. Cleveland Coxe, trans. S. Thelwall, vol. 3, *The Ante-Nicene Fathers* (Buffalo, NY: Christian Literature Company, 1885), 22.

Famous early church historian, Eusebius writes this about the Neronian persecution: "When the government of Nero was now firmly established, he began to plunge into unholy pursuits, and armed himself even against the religion of the God of the universe...

"But with all these things this particular in the catalogue of his crimes was still wanting, that he was the first of the emperors who showed himself an enemy of the divine religion.

"The Roman Tertullian is likewise a witness of this. He writes as follows: "Examine your records. There you will find that Nero was the first that persecuted this doctrine, particularly then when after subduing all the east, he exercised his cruelty against all at Rome. We glory in having such a man the leader in our punishment. For whoever knows him can understand that nothing was condemned by Nero unless it was something of great excellence."

"Thus publicly announcing himself as the first among God's chief enemies, he was led on to the slaughter of the apostles. It is, therefore, recorded that Paul was beheaded in Rome itself, and that Peter likewise was crucified under Nero." Eusebius of Caesaria, "The Church History of Eusebius," in *Eusebius: Church History, Life of Constantine the Great, and Oration in Praise of Constantine*, ed. Philip Schaff and Henry Wace, trans. Arthur Cushman McGiffert, *vol. 1, A Select Library of the Nicene and Post-Nicene Fathers of the Christian Church, Second Series* (New York: Christian Literature Company, 1890), 128-129.

[9] **On Peter's martyrdom in Rome:** "Peter's death can be dated with a high probability in A.D. 64 or 65." Richard J. Bauckham, *2 Peter, Jude, vol. 50, Word Biblical Commentary* (Dallas: Word, Incorporated, 1998), 159.

"Saint Peter was led across the river to Nero's circus on the Vatican field, and crucified as a common felon." Bernard W. Henderson, *The Life and Principate of the Emperor Nero* (London, Methuen, 1903), 446.

On Peter being crucified upside down: "First Clement is the first noncanonical document that refers to the martyrdoms of Peter and Paul…A significant number of scholars believe 1 Clement 5.1-4 provides early attestation for their martyrdoms…

"In the Martyrdom of Peter, when Peter approaches the place of execution, he gives a speech to the people and the cross (36.7-8). He concludes by saying, "But it is time for you, Peter, to surrender your body to those who are taking it. Take it, then, you whose duty it is. I request you therefore, executioners, to crucify me head-downwards in this way and no other." Peter gives a final speech while upside down on the cross and then dies (40.11).

"Is the upside-down crucifixion of Peter a reliable tradition? The earliest church father who mentions it is Origen in volume 3 of his Commentary on Genesis in the mid-third century (c. 230). And yet he makes no mention of Peter's prolonged speech. It is uncertain whether Origen derived this from an independent tradition or from the Acts of Peter. There is evidence Roman executioners varied their crucifixion practices for their sadistic pleasure, so it is not intrinsically implausible Peter was crucified upside. It is possible the tradition preserves an early memory of Peter's upside-down crucifixion, but the evidence is simply inconclusive." Sean Joslin McDowell, *A Historical Evaluation Of The Evidence For The Death Of The Apostles As Martyrs For Their Faith* (Southern Baptist Theological Seminary, Dissertation, 2014), 145-147.

[10] **Tunica Molesta, the shirt of torment:** Ernest Renan, trans. Joseph Henry Allen, *The Antichrist: The Period From the Arrival of Paul in Rome to the End of the Jewish Revolution* (Boston, Roberts Brothers 1897), 147.

"[The Christians] were fastened on crosses, and, when daylight failed were burned to serve as lamps by night. Nero had offered his Gardens for the spectacle." Tacitus, *The Annals* 15.44.

[11] **Nero rode his chariot among the burning Christians as torches for the Circus:** Nero would have "illuminations" for the evening during the combined festival days of Juno, Minerva, Jupiter and Feronia, goddess of fire, beginning November 13. This was when he used Christians as human torches. This was when he arrived on his chariot." Frederic w. Farar, *The Early Days of Christianity* (New York, Russell and Company, 1885), 39.

[12] **This attitude about Nero's disgraceful "acting" was shared by others in authority**: Tacitus, *The Annals* 15.65.

[13] **Damnatio ad bestias, condemnation by beasts:** "condemnation to the beasts," damnatio ad bestias, normally meant that the criminals, men and women, often naked, sometimes bound or sometimes with inadequate weapons, would be exposed to ferocious wild animals. But on this occasion they have themselves become the beasts, and are attacked by hunting dogs." Edward Champlin, *Nero* (Massachussetts, Harvard University Press, 2003), 121.

"And derision accompanied their end: they were covered with wild beasts' skins and torn to death by dogs; or they were fastened on crosses, and, when daylight failed were burned to serve as lamps by night. Nero had offered his Gardens for the spectacle, and gave an exhibition in his Circus, mixing with the crowd in the habit of a charioteer, or mounted on his car." Tacitus, The Annals 15.44

[14] **Nero's near-sightedness and use of a spyglass at the circus:** "Nero was, without doubt, present at these spectacles. As he was near-sighted, he used to put to his eye on such occasions a concave lens of "emerald," which served him as an eyeglass. He liked to exhibit his connoisseurship in matters of sculpture; it is said that he made brutal remarks on his mother's dead body, praising this point and criticising that. Living flesh quivering in a wild beast's jaw, or a poor shrinking girl, screening herself by a modest gesture, then tossed by a bull and cast in lifeless fragments on the gravel of the arena, must exhibit a play of form and colour worthy of an artist-sense like his. Here he was, in the front row, on a low balcony, in a group of vestals and curule magistrates." Ernest Renan, trans. Joseph Henry Allen, *The Antichrist: The Period From the Arrival of Paul in Rome to the End of the Jewish Revolution* (Boston, Roberts Brothers 1897), 151.

[15] **On Gabbaras the Egyptian giant in this chapter:** "There was at that time an Egyptian of a most voracious appetite, who would digest raw flesh, or any thing else that was given him. It was credibly reported, that the emperor was extremely desirous of furnishing him with living men to tear and devour." Tranquillus, Gaius Suetonius (2011-03-24). *The Lives of the Twelve Caesars, Volume 06: Nero 37* (Kindle Locations 406-407). Kindle Edition.

"It is even believed that it was his wish to throw living men to be torn to pieces and devoured by a monster of Egyptian birth, who would crunch raw flesh and anything else that was given him." Suetonius, *Lives of the Twelve Caesars, Nero 37*, Loeb Edition.

"The tallest man that has been seen in our times, was one Gabbaras by name, who was brought from Arabia by the Emperor Claudius; his height was nine feet and as many inches." Pliny the Elder, *The Natural History, Book 7:16 (74-76)*, ed. John Bostock (Medford, MA: Taylor and Francis, Red Lion Court, Fleet Street, 1855), 2157.

On the nakedness of the victims: "Thus "condemnation to the beasts," damnatio ad bestias, normally meant that the criminals, men and women, often naked, sometimes bound or sometimes with inadequate weapons, would be exposed to ferocious wild animals." Edward Champlin, *Nero* (Massachussetts, Harvard University Press, 2003), 122.

"[Christian victims] Bound naked and torn apart by starving dogs; set on fire as human torches in the night; or hammered onto wooden crosses to hang until they perished." Faulkner, Neil (2012-09-30). *Apocalypse: The Great Jewish Revolt Against Rome AD 66-73* (Kindle Locations 482-485). Amberley Publishing. Kindle Edition.

[16] **Violation of women:** "By reason of jealousy women being persecuted, after that they had suffered cruel and unholy insults as Danaids and Dircæ, safely reached the goal in the race of faith, and received a noble reward, feeble though they were in body." Joseph Barber Lightfoot and J. R. Harmer, *The Apostolic Fathers* (London: Macmillan and Co., 1891), 59.

[17] **Religio illicita and Christianity:** Some scholars claim that there was no general edict issued against the Christians so that the magistrate could pursue it as a police action instead. Bernard W. Henderson, *The Life and Principate of the Emperor Nero* (London, Methuen, 1903), 446; Leon Hardy Canfield, *The Early Persecutions of the Christians* (New York, Columbia, 1913), 33, 60; Gilbert, John (2015-02-27). *Parallel Lives, Parallel Nations Volume Two: A Narrative History Of Rome & The Jews, Their Relations And Their Worlds* (161 BC-135 AD) (p. 272), Kindle Edition.

CHAPTER 22

[1] **Gehenna**: Duane F. Watson, "Gehenna (Place)," ed. David Noel Freedman, *The Anchor Yale Bible Dictionary* (New York: Doubleday, 1992), 926.

The Greek word for "hell" used in New Testament translation is Gehenna. Some have believed that this was the name of a garbage dump outside Jerusalem that burned with perpetual flames, and Jesus used it as a metaphor for the fires of judgment. But recent scholarship tends to disregard this thesis as lacking both exegetical weight and hard archeological evidence. In fact, Gehenna is Greek for "Valley of Hinnom," the valley that bordered the south and western sides of Jerusalem. This valley had a dark history in Israel's past as the location of tophets, or burning places for sacrifice to Molech, the underworld god. Israelites would "pass their children through the fire" as human sacrifice. God became so angry with this abomination that the prophet Jeremiah pronounced a fiery curse on the area destroyed by King Josiah around 632 B.C. (Jer. 7:29–34; 19:1–15). It would become known as the "Valley of Slaughter," and a synonym for future judgment/destruction of people and nations in this life as well as the next. Both Second Temple literature and Jesus' teachings used Gehenna as a reference to the future final judgment (Matt. 13:42, 30; 25:41. See also 1 En. 10:13; 48:8–10; 100:7–9; 108:4–7; Jdt 16:17; 2 Bar. 85:13). So, yes it was a metaphor for fiery punishment, but a far richer meaning than a burning garbage dump. It provided incarnate location for the belief in the eschatological judgment of God upon evil.

For a fictional portrayal of the spiritual reality of Gehenna, see the novel by Brian Godawa, *Jesus Triumphant* (Embedded Pictures, 2015).

[2] **Michael, the archangel guardian of Israel**: Daniel 10:15, 21. Daniel 10 pictures the notion of the spiritual principalities behind the nations at war. More details about the seven archangels, including Michael can be found in 1Enoch 20:1-8 (see below) and others. Though 1Enoch is not considered Scripture, it is nevertheless quoted and drawn from by the New Testament authors in Jude 6, 14-16, 1Peter 3:19-20, and 2Peter 2:4-5.

1Enoch 20:1-8 And these are the names of the holy angels who watch. 2 Uriel, one of the holy angels, who is over the world and over Tartarus. 3 Raphael, 4 one of the holy angels, who is over the spirits of men. Raguel, one of the holy angels who †takes vengeance on† the world of the luminaries. 5 Michael, one of the holy angels, to wit, he that is set over the best part of mankind «and» over chaos. 6 Saraqâêl, one of the holy angels, who is set over the spirits, who sin in the spirit. 7 Gabriel, one of the holy angels, who is over Paradise and the serpents and the Cherubim. 8 Remiel, one of the holy angels, whom God set over those who rise. Robert Henry Charles, ed., *Pseudepigrapha of the Old Testament, vol. 2* (Oxford: Clarendon Press, 1913), 201.

[3] **Assyrian Exile**: "Following the death of Jeroboam II, anarchy reigned in the N kingdom. Zechariah (746–745)… Menahem became a vassal of the Assyrians who required that he pay a heavy tribute to keep his throne (2 Kgs 15:19–20).

"Unfortunately for Israel, Hoshea did not remain a compliant vassal to Assyria as did Ahaz. Upon hearing of Tiglath-Pileser's death in 724, Hoshea began negotiations with Egypt to secure its support for a revolt against Assyria. When Hoshea made his move, Shalmaneser V, the new Assyrian monarch, easily swept Israel's army aside. After a three year siege, the Assyrians destroyed Samaria, incorporated what remained of the N kingdom into the Assyrian provincial system, and exiled many of Israel's leading citizens (Oded 1970). By 721, the Kingdom of Israel ceased to exist as an independent nation." Leslie J. Hoppe, "Israel, History of: Monarchic Period," ed. David Noel Freedman, *The Anchor Yale Bible Dictionary* (New York: Doubleday, 1992), 565.

Babylonian Exile: "Judah's destiny passed into Babylonian hands when Nebuchadnezzar defeated Egypt at the battle of Carchemish in 605. Jehoiakim accepted his new master, but four years later he foolishly rebelled (2 Kgs 25:1–2). The Babylonians moved against Jerusalem in 598. Jehoiakim died at the outset of the siege (2 Kgs 25:6). Jeremiah implies that Jehoiakim was assassinated (Jer 22:18–19); but Jer 36:30 and 2 Chr 36:6 assert that he was exiled to Babylon. Jehoiachin (also known as Jeconiah and Coniah 598–597) succeeded his father and surrendered to Nebuchadnezzar after three months. The king, his family, and many leading citizens went to Babylon as prisoners following the surrender of Jerusalem in 597." Leslie J. Hoppe, "Israel, History of: Monarchic Period," ed. David Noel Freedman, *The Anchor Yale Bible Dictionary* (New York: Doubleday, 1992), 566.

Return from Exile: The books of Ezra and Nehemiah tell how the Jews return from exile in Babylonia and rebuild the city of Jerusalem and the temple.

[4] **Christ's fooling the spiritual powers, "the mystery of the Gospel"**: Ephesians 3:9–10 And to bring to light for everyone what is the plan of the mystery hidden for ages in God who created all things, 10 so that through the church the manifold wisdom of God might now be made known to the rulers and authorities in the heavenly places.

1 Corinthians 2:7–8 But we impart a secret and hidden wisdom of God, which God decreed before the ages for our glory. 8 None of the rulers of this age understood this, for if they had, they would not have crucified the Lord of glory.

Ephesians 3:4–6 The mystery of Christ, 5 which was not made known to the sons of men in other generations as it has now been revealed to his holy apostles and prophets by the Spirit. 6 This mystery is that the Gentiles are fellow heirs, members of the same body, and partakers of the promise in Christ Jesus through the gospel.

Christ's victory over the spiritual authorities: 1 Peter 3:18–22 For Christ also suffered once for sins, the righteous for the unrighteous, that he might bring us to God, being put to death in the flesh but made alive in the spirit, 19 in which he went and proclaimed to the spirits in prison, 20 because they formerly did not obey, when God's patience waited in the days of Noah, while the ark was being prepared, in which a few, that is, eight persons, were brought safely through water. 21 Baptism, which corresponds to this, now saves you, not as a removal of dirt from the body but as an appeal to God for a good conscience, through the resurrection of Jesus Christ, 22 who has gone into heaven and is at the right hand of God, with angels, authorities, and powers having been subjected to him.

Colossians 2:15 He disarmed the rulers and authorities and put them to open shame, by triumphing over them in him.

2 Corinthians 2:14 But thanks be to God, who in Christ always leads us in triumphal procession, and through us spreads the fragrance of the knowledge of him everywhere.

Ephesians 4:8 "Therefore it says, "When he ascended on high he led a host of captives, and he gave gifts to men."

John 12:31–32 "Now is the judgment of this world; now will the ruler of this world be cast out. 32 And I, when I am lifted up from the earth, will draw all people to myself."

John 16:11 "concerning judgment, because the ruler of this world is judged."

The Veil of Holy of Holies: Matthew 27:51 "And behold, the curtain of the temple was torn in two, from top to bottom. And the earth shook, and the rocks were split."

The separation of Jew and Gentile eliminated by the cross: Ephesians 2:13–16 But now in Christ Jesus you who once were far off have been brought near by the blood of Christ. 14 For he himself is our peace, who has made us both one and has broken down in his flesh the dividing wall of hostility 15 by abolishing the law of commandments expressed in ordinances, that he might create in himself one new man in place of the two, so making peace, 16 and might reconcile us both to God in one body through the cross, thereby killing the hostility.

Hebrews 9:8–13 By this the Holy Spirit indicates that the way into the holy places is not yet opened as long as the first section is still standing 9 (which is symbolic for the present age). According to this arrangement, gifts and sacrifices are offered that cannot perfect the conscience of the worshiper, 10 but deal only with food and drink and various washings, regulations for the body imposed until the time of reformation. 11 But when Christ appeared as a high priest of the good things that have come, then through the greater and more perfect tent (not made with hands, that is, not of this creation) 12 he entered once for all into the holy places, not by means of the blood of goats and calves but by means of his own blood, thus securing an eternal redemption.

From all tribes and nations: Daniel 7:13–14 "Behold, with the clouds of heaven there came one like a son of man, and he came to the Ancient of Days and was presented before him. 14 And to him was given dominion and glory and a kingdom, that all peoples, nations, and languages should serve him; his dominion is an everlasting dominion, which shall not pass away, and his kingdom one that shall not be destroyed.

Revelation 11:15 Then the seventh angel blew his trumpet, and there were loud voices in heaven, saying, "The kingdom of the world has become the kingdom of our Lord and of his Christ, and he shall reign forever and ever."

Isaiah 2:2–4 It shall come to pass in the latter days that the mountain of the house of the LORD shall be established as the highest of the mountains, and shall be lifted up above the hills; and all the nations shall flow to it, 3 and many peoples shall come, and say: "Come, let us go up to the mountain of the LORD, to the house of the God of Jacob, that he may teach us his ways and that we may walk in his paths." For out of Zion shall go the law, and the word of the LORD from Jerusalem. 4 He shall judge between the nations, and shall decide disputes for many peoples; and they shall beat their swords into plowshares, and their spears into pruning hooks; nation shall not lift up sword against nation, neither shall they learn war anymore.

Isaiah 56:7 these I will bring to my holy mountain, and make them joyful in my house of prayer; their burnt offerings and their sacrifices will be accepted on my altar; for my house shall be called a house of prayer for all peoples."

Acts 2:16–17 But this is what was uttered through the prophet Joel: 17 " 'And in the last days it shall be, God declares, that I will pour out my Spirit on all flesh, and your sons and your daughters shall prophesy, and your young men shall see visions, and your old men shall dream dreams.

The Israel of God as all believers: Galatians 6:16

Messiah inherits all the earth: Psalm 2:7–9 I will tell of the decree: The LORD said to me, "You are my Son; today I have begotten you. 8 Ask of me, and I will make the nations your heritage, and the ends of the earth your possession. 9 You shall break them with a rod of iron and dash them in pieces like a potter's vessel."

Psalm 72:8 May he have dominion from sea to sea, and from the River to the ends of the earth!

Daniel 7:13–14 "Behold, with the clouds of heaven there came one like a son of man, and he came to the Ancient of Days and was presented before him. 14 And to him was given dominion and glory and a kingdom, that all peoples, nations, and languages should serve him; his dominion is an everlasting dominion, which shall not pass away, and his kingdom one that shall not be destroyed.

[5] **The grafted and natural branches of the root**: Romans 11:13-24.

Christian Church as God's people, holy nation, priests: 1 Peter 2:8–9 [Jews] stumble because they disobey the word, as they were destined to do. 9 But you are a chosen race, a royal priesthood, a holy nation, a people for his own possession, that you may proclaim the excellencies of him who called you out of darkness into his marvelous light.

Jerusalem as a corpse: Matthew 24:28.

[6] **Gospel had been proclaimed in all creation under heaven at the time of Paul**: Colossians 1:23; Romans 10: 14-18.

[7] **Jerusalem size and population**: "Jerusalem doubled in size during the Roman period, expanding considerably to the N and NW: it comprised about 450 acres, with a population of 80,000 or more." Philip J. King, "Jerusalem (Place)," ed. David Noel Freedman, The Anchor Yale Bible Dictionary (New York: Doubleday, 1992), 753.

[8] **Capital punishment in Roman governed Judea**: "Footnote 92: A. N. Sherwin-White gives a convincing case that Roman law delegated capital decisions solely to their own governing officials. The only exceptions were "free cities," and Jerusalem did not have this status. The picture of John 18:31 is therefore correct. (Roman Society and Roman Law in the New Testament [Oxford: Clarendon, 1963], 1–23, 38.) For the contrary view (that the Sanhedrin could punish capital cases involving religious matters under the Roman procurators), see P. Winter, The Trial of Jesus (Berlin: Walter de Gruyter, 1961), 75–90. Winter's view is based primarily on late rabbinical sources; Sherwin-White's, on Roman law. A different solution is that of P. Gaechter, who argues that the Sanhedrin used an interim period between Roman procurators as opportunity to pass their own sentence on Stephen: "The Hatred of the House of Annas," TS 8 (1947): 16–23." John B. Polhill, Acts, vol. 26, The New American Commentary (Nashville: Broadman & Holman Publishers, 1992), 208–209.

[9] **The harlot that rides the beast**: Revelation 17:3-6; 13:11.

Israel as adulterous harlot with idols: Ezekiel 16:15-59; Ezekiel 23; 2Kings 17:7-17; Jeremiah 3:1-11; Hosea 1-2.

The harlot that rides the beast represents the corrupt Jewish leaders: "Since the harlot is dressed in the distinctive robe of the high priest which is worn only on holy occasions (Ex 28:2-4, 41, 43), and since she possesses a "gold cup" as used in libations (Ex 25:29; 1Ki 7:50; cp. m. Yoma 3:10), Rev is presenting the holy city (cp. 11:1) under the guise of the high-priest engaged in his sacerdotal duties…

"That the gold cup is "full of abominations and of the unclean things of her immorality further identifies the harlot as Jerusalem. The kai here is probably epexegetical, signifying that she is "full of abominations, which are, the uncleanness of her immorality." In the OT, the word *abominations* is often a religious term signifying that which the God of Israel detests and "uncleanness" is a cultic term related to Israel's separation to God. This religio-cultic concern is strongly Jewish, well fitting first-century Jerusalem…

"So in John's drama the priestly libations God ordains for holy worship are replaced in Jerusalem's high-priestly system: their golden libation bowls now are filled with uncleanness because of their spilling the innocent blood of Christ and Christians. Rather than offering humble sacrifices to God in true worship, the temple system destroys the followers of the Lamb…

"John portrays Jerusalem's situation as a sexual liaison (she is a "harlot" committing "immorality," 17:2, 4-5) with Rome. In the background of ch 17 is the "league of friendship and mutual alliance" with Rome, beginning with Julius Caesar (1 Macc 8:17–30; 14:24, 40; Jos. Ant. 12:10:6 §414–19; 13:5:8 §163–65; 14:10:1–8 §185–216; 16:6:2–3 §162–66; 19:9:2 §360–65).36 In 1 Macc 14:40 the Jews call themselves "friends, allies, and brothers of Rome," and were, according to Smallwood (2001: 7) "immensely proud of the alliance." Josephus (Ant. 14:10:1 §186) writes: "it seems to me to be necessary here to give an account of all the honors that the Romans and their emperors paid to our nation, and of the leagues of mutual assistance they have made with it." Philo also mentions that the Jews are "friends to Caesar"… John is painting Jerusalem in the same way Isaiah and Jeremiah did as they spoke of the first temple's destruction: "How the faithful city has become a harlot, / She who was full of justice! / Righteousness once lodged in her, / But now murderers" (Isa 1:21). "You have lain down as a harlot . . . . Also on your skirts is found / The lifeblood of the innocent poor" (Jer 2:20d; 34a; cp. 7:6; 19:3-4; 22:11, 17)." Kenneth L. Gentry, Jr., *The Divorce of Israel: A Redemptive-Historical Interpretation of Revelation Vol. 2* (Dallas, GA: Tolle Lege Press, 2016), 435, 429, 430, 416-417.

[10] **Antonia Fortress**: John F. Hall, "Antonia, Tower of (Place)," ed. David Noel Freedman, *The Anchor Yale Bible Dictionary* (New York: Doubleday, 1992), 274.

[11] **The martyrdom of James, son of Zebedee**: Acts 12:1–3 "About that time Herod the king laid violent hands on some who belonged to the church. He killed James the brother of John with the sword, 3 and when he saw that it pleased the Jews, he proceeded to arrest Peter also. This was during the days of Unleavened Bread."

"According to Jewish law, execution by sword was the punishment for murder or apostasy (m. Sanhedrin 9:1; Deut 13:6-18).19 Herod lived as a faithful Jew, so he would naturally have been concerned to stop the growth of any heretical sect. According to Deuteronomy 13:6-18, if an individual entices the Jews to "go and serve other gods," then that person is to be stoned to death. But if that person entices the entire city to follow other gods then that person is to be killed with the sword. Kistemaker concludes, "In the eyes of Herod Agrippa, James had led the city of Jerusalem astray." Agrippa seemingly had both political and religious reasons for having James killed with the sword." Sean Joslin McDowell, *A Historical Evaluation Of The Evidence For The Death Of The Apostles As Martyrs For Their Faith* (Southern Baptist Theological Seminary, Dissertation, 2014), 311.

[12] **Stephen's words of condemnation**: Acts 7:51–53 "You stiff-necked people, uncircumcised in heart and ears, you always resist the Holy Spirit. As your fathers did, so do you. [52] Which of the prophets did your fathers not persecute? And they killed those who announced beforehand the coming of the Righteous One, whom you have now betrayed and murdered, [53] you who received the law as delivered by angels and did not keep it." For the entire story of Stephen's martyrdom, see Acts 6:8-7:60.

[13] **Start of Christian persecution in Jerusalem**: Acts 8:1 "And Saul approved of [Stephen's] execution. And there arose on that day a great persecution against the church in Jerusalem, and they were all scattered throughout the regions of Judea and Samaria, except the apostles."

[14] **Pinnacle of the temple**: "Designates a part of the TEMPLE. It has traditionally been identified with the southeast corner of the outer court, which overlooked the Kidron valley and was so high that "if anyone looked down from the rooftop, combining the two elevations, he would become dizzy …" (Josephus Ant. xv.11.5 [412])." N. J. Opperwall, "Pinnacle," ed. Geoffrey W. Bromiley, *The International Standard Bible Encyclopedia, Revised* (Wm. B. Eerdmans, 1979–1988), 872.

[15] **The death of James the Just (Righteous):** "Ananus, who, as we have told you already, took the high priesthood, was a bold man in his temper, and very insolent; he was also of the sect of the Sadducees, who are very rigid in judging offenders, above all the rest of the Jews, as we have already observed; (200) when, therefore, Ananus was of this disposition, he thought he had now a proper opportunity [to exercise his authority]. Festus was now dead, and Albinus was but upon the road; so he assembled the sanhedrin of judges, and brought before them the brother of Jesus, who was called Christ, whose name was James, and

some others, [or, some of his companions]; and when he had formed an accusation against them as breakers of the law, he delivered them to be stoned." Flavius Josephus, *Antiquities* 20.199-200

"And, when many were fully convinced by these words, and offered praise for the testimony of James, and said, "Hosanna to the son of David," then again the said Pharisees and scribes said to one another, "We have not done well in procuring this testimony to Jesus. But let us go up and throw him down, that they may be afraid, and not believe him." And they cried aloud, and said: "Oh! oh! the just man himself is in error." Thus they fulfilled the Scripture written in Isaiah: "Let us away with the just man, because he is troublesome to us: therefore shall they eat the fruit of their doings." So they went up and threw down the just man, and said to one another: "Let us stone James the Just." And they began to stone him: for he was not killed by the fall; but he turned, and kneeled down, and said: "I beseech Thee, Lord God our Father, forgive them; for they know not what they do."Hegesippus, "Fragments from His Five Books of Commentaries on the Acts of the Church," in *Fathers of the Third and Fourth Centuries: The Twelve Patriarchs, Excerpts and Epistles, the Clementina, Apocrypha, Decretals, Memoirs of Edessa and Syriac Documents, Remains of the First Ages*, ed. Alexander Roberts, James Donaldson, and A. Cleveland Coxe, trans. B. P. Pratten, vol. 8, *The Ante-Nicene Fathers* (Buffalo, NY: Christian Literature Company, 1886), 763.

"These things are related at length by Hegesippus, who is in agreement with Clement. James was so admirable a man and so celebrated among all for his justice, that the more sensible even of the Jews were of the opinion that this was the cause of the siege of Jerusalem, which happened to them immediately after his martyrdom for no other reason than their daring act against him.

"Josephus, at least, has not hesitated to testify this in his writings, where he says, "These things happened to the Jews to avenge James the Just, who was a brother of Jesus, that is called the Christ. For the Jews slew him, although he was a most just man." Eusebius of Caesaria, "The Church History of Eusebius," in Eusebius: *Church History, Life of Constantine the Great, and Oration in Praise of Constantine*, ed. Philip Schaff and Henry Wace, trans. Arthur Cushman McGiffert, *vol. 1, A Select Library of the Nicene and Post-Nicene Fathers of the Christian Church, Second Series* (New York: Christian Literature Company, 1890), 127.

[16] **Jesus' claim of judgment on Jerusalem and the temple**: Matthew 24:1–2 "Jesus left the temple and was going away, when his disciples came to point out to him the buildings of the temple. 2 But he answered them, "You see all these, do you not? Truly, I say to you, there will not be left here one stone upon another that will not be thrown down."

Matthew 24:30 "Then will appear in heaven the sign of the Son of Man, and then all the tribes of the earth will mourn, and they will see the Son of Man coming on the clouds of heaven with power and great glory."

Paul's reiteration of Jerusalem judgment and cloud coming: 1 Thessalonians 2:14–16 "For you, brothers, became imitators of the churches of God in Christ Jesus that are in Judea. For you suffered the same things from your own countrymen as they did from the Jews, 15 who killed both the Lord Jesus and the prophets, and drove us out, and displease God and oppose all mankind 16 by hindering us from speaking to the Gentiles that they might be saved—so as always to fill up the measure of their sins. But wrath has come upon them at last!"

2 Thessalonians 1:7–9 "When the Lord Jesus is revealed from heaven with his mighty angels 8 in flaming fire, inflicting vengeance on those who do not know God and on those who do not obey the gospel of our Lord Jesus. 9 They will suffer the punishment of eternal destruction."

Peter's claim of cloud coming and judgment: 2 Peter 3:7, 10–13 The heavens and earth that now exist are stored up for fire, being kept until the day of judgment and destruction of the ungodly… But the day of the Lord will come like a thief, and then the heavens will pass away with a roar, and the heavenly bodies will be burned up and dissolved, and the earth and the works that are done on it will be exposed. 11 Since all these things are thus to be dissolved, what sort of people ought you to be in lives of holiness and godliness, 12 waiting for and hastening the coming of the day of God, because of which the heavens will be set on fire and dissolved, and the heavenly bodies will melt as they burn! 13 But according to his promise we are waiting for new heavens and a new earth in which righteousness dwells."

Stephen's affirmation of the destruction of the temple and Jesus' cloud coming: Acts 6:14 "for we have heard him say that this Jesus of Nazareth will destroy this place and will change the customs that Moses delivered to us."

Acts 7:56 And [Stephen] said, "Behold, I see the heavens opened, and the Son of Man standing at the right hand of God."

James the Just and the cloud coming of Jesus: "The aforesaid scribes and Pharisees accordingly set James on the summit of the temple, and cried aloud to him, and said: "O just one, whom we are all bound to obey, forasmuch as the people is in error, and follows Jesus the crucified, do thou tell us what is the door of Jesus, the crucified." And he answered with a loud voice: "Why ask ye me concerning Jesus the Son of man? He Himself sitteth in heaven, at the right hand of the Great Power, and shall come on the clouds of heaven."

[17] **The temple dimensions**: "As enlarged by Herod the Great, the Temple area occupied an elongated square of from 925 to 950 feet and upwards. — footnote: Many modern writers have computed the Temple area at only 606 feet, while Jewish authorities make it much larger than we have stated it. The computation in the text is based on the latest and most trustworthy investigations, and fully borne out by the excavations made on the spot by Capts. Wilson and Warren." Alfred Edersheim, *The Temple, Its Ministry and Services as They Were at the Time of Jesus Christ.* (London: James Clarke & Co., 1959), 38.

[18] **Warning of death to Gentiles**: "A marble screen 4 1/2 feet high, and beautifully ornamented, bore Greek and Latin inscriptions, warning Gentiles not to proceed, on pain of death. One of those very tablets, bearing almost the same words as those given by Josephus, has been discovered in late excavations." Alfred Edersheim, *The Temple, Its Ministry and Services as They Were at the Time of Jesus Christ.* (London: James Clarke & Co., 1959), 46.

Dimensions of the Inner Court: Alfred Edersheim, *The Temple, Its Ministry and Services as They Were at the Time of Jesus Christ.* (London: James Clarke & Co., 1959), 51.

[19] **Herod as Daniel's "willful king" of Daniel 11:36-45:** Philip Mauro presents a strong argument for the willful king of Daniel 11:36-45 as being Herod. Though this is not the only good possibility, as will be seen later in this series, Titus is another good fit. A free pdf of Philip Mauro's *The Seventy Weeks and the Great Tribulation* can be found online at:
http://www.preteristarchive.com/Books/pdf/1921_mauro_seventyweeks.pdf

Daniel 11:36–39 "And the king shall do as he wills. He shall exalt himself and magnify himself above every god, and shall speak astonishing things against the God of gods. He shall prosper till the indignation is accomplished; for what is decreed shall be done. [37] He shall pay no attention to the gods of his fathers, or to the one beloved by women. He shall not pay attention to any other god, for he shall magnify himself above all. [38] He shall honor the god of fortresses instead of these. A god whom his fathers did not know he shall honor with gold and silver, with precious stones and costly gifts. [39] He shall deal with the strongest fortresses with the help of a foreign god. Those who acknowledge him he shall load with honor. He shall make them rulers over many and shall divide the land for a price.

[20] **The Great Tribulation during the first century**: Matthew 24:15–21 "So when you see the abomination of desolation spoken of by the prophet Daniel, standing in the holy place (let the reader understand), 16 then let those who are in Judea flee to the mountains… 21 For then there will be great tribulation, such as has not been from the beginning of the world until now, no, and never will be.

Matthew 24:34 "Truly, I say to you, this generation will not pass away until all these things take place."

John writes that everything in his Revelation is about to take place in his time period, which places the Great Tribulation within the first century: Revelation 1:1 The revelation of Jesus Christ, which God gave him to show to his servants the things that must soon take place. He made it known by sending his angel to his servant John,

Revelation 1:3 Blessed is the one who reads aloud the words of this prophecy, and blessed are those who hear, and who keep what is written in it, for the time is near.

Revelation 22:10 And he said to me, "Do not seal up the words of the prophecy of this book, for the time is near.

Revelation 1:9 I, John, your brother and partner in the tribulation and the kingdom…

Revelation 7:14 And he said to me, "These are the ones coming out of the great tribulation. They have washed their robes and made them white in the blood of the Lamb."

The Last Days occurred in the first century during the time of Christ and immediately after:
Hebrews 1:1–2 Long ago, at many times and in many ways, God spoke to our fathers by the prophets, 2 but in these last days he has spoken to us by his Son, whom he appointed the heir of all things, through whom also he created the world.

Hebrews 9:26 But as it is, he has appeared once for all at the end of the ages to put away sin by the sacrifice of himself.

1 Peter 1:20 He was foreknown before the foundation of the world but was made manifest in the last times for the sake of you

Acts 2:16–17 But this is what was uttered through the prophet Joel: 17 " 'And in the last days it shall be, God declares, that I will pour out my Spirit on all flesh…

1 Corinthians 10:11 [11] Now these things happened to them as an example, but they were written down for our instruction, on whom the end of the ages has come.

Hebrews 10:24–25 [24] And let us consider how to stir up one another to love and good works, [25] not neglecting to meet together, as is the habit of some, but encouraging one another, and all the more as you see the Day drawing near.

[1] **The four factions described here**: Josephus explains each of these "four philosophies" that struggled for control within the Israel ruling class. He calls the last one, The Fourth Philosophy, but it pretty much embodies the Zealots and other revolutionary sects of similar perspective. His descriptions can be found in Flavius Josephus, *The Antiquities* 18.10-25.

The background histories of Simon bar Giora and John bar Levi: Though Simon bar Giora and John bar Levi of Gischala become significant warrior generals in Josephus' *Wars of the Jews*, little to nothing is known of their origins. I have used creative license here.

[2] **Hanukkah, the Festival of Dedication or Festival of Lights**: "The original eight day rededication was based on this event: 1 Maccabees 4:36-61. See also, Flavius Josephus, *Jewish Antiquities* 12.323-326 (12.7.7).

"Many Jews retained an instinctive reaction that all things Greek were dangerous to their ancestral religion. The attitude was reinforced by the festival of Hannukah, which celebrated the victory of the Maccabees against Hellenism; despite lack of biblical authority for its observance the festival probably remained popular in the first century A.D." Martin Goodman, *Ruling Class of Judaea: The Origins of the Jewish Revolt Against Rome, A. D. 66-70* (Cambridge University Press, 1993), 12.

[3] **Persecution of Christians in Jerusalem**: "Making offensive speeches against the temple (τόπος) and the law (νόμος) is the accusation which they level against Stephen (6:13). This certainly marks a change of direction. It is not any longer an interpretation of the past which is at stake but the precepts recommended by the Christians…

"References to persecution and even murder are made again and again. Paul accuses himself of having put Christians to death (22:4; *cf.* 9:1). The execution of James carried out by Herod Antipas (12:2) is only part of an attempt to please the Jews and to κακῶσαί τινας τῶν ἀπὸ τῆς ἐκκλησίας (functionaries of the church?). The Jews of the Diaspora are described as having incited (13:50) people against the Christians, instigated persecution by sinister means (17:5) and actually themselves carried out harassment (14:2). They are characterised as having been propelled by zeal (an indicative term!) in this activity (13:45; 17:5). Their machinations are a standing feature on the journeys of Paul. They are, however, only mentioned in order to convince the reader that the apostle was justified in rending his garment and in turning exclusively to the Gentiles (18:6)…

"A number of actions are indicated in Acts: searching of houses (8:3), ὑποβάλλειν of witnesses (6:11), flogging (22:19), taking into custody (8:3; 22:19), fettering (9:21; 22:4), forced renunciation of the faith (26:11), tormenting (26:11), stoning by witnesses (7:58f.), application of lynch justice (9:1 φόνος), and the public display of agreement with such measures (8:1 συνευδοκεῖν), which is equally or possibly even more abhorrent than the rash action of a persecutor." Ernst Bammel, "Jewish Activity against Christians in Palestine according to Acts," in *The Book of Acts in Its First Century Setting: The Book of Acts in Its Palestinian Setting*, ed. Richard Bauckham and Bruce W. Winter, vol. 4 (Grand Rapids, MI; Carlisle, Cumbria: William B. Eerdmans Publishing Company; The Paternoster Press, 1995), 358–360.

[4] **Liturgy of Hanukkah**: "The festival of dedication, which is named Hanukkah in Hebrew, is the Jewish holiday which celebrates the reconsecration of the Jerusalem temple and its altar to the traditional service of the Lord in 165 or 164 B.C.E. It begins on the 25th day of the month Kislev (the 9th month in the lunisolar calendar; it coincides with parts of November and December) and lasts for 8 days…

"Hanukkah came to include lamps and lights at each one's home. As part of the pre-festival renovations and repairs, 1 Macc 4:49–50 notes that the candelabrum was brought into the temple and that its lamps were lit so that they gave light in the temple; 2 Macc 1:8; 10:3 allude to the same events."

Hanukkah also involved carrying palm branches and reciting the Hallel in their liturgy (Psalm 113-118). James C. VanderKam, "Dedication, Feast of," ed. David Noel Freedman, *The Anchor Yale Bible Dictionary* (New York: Doubleday, 1992), 123-124.

"These three observances bear so striking a resemblance to what we know about the Feast of Tabernacles, that it is difficult to resist the impression of some intended connection between the two, in consequence of which the daily singing of the 'Hallel,' and the carrying of palm branches was adopted during the Feast of the Dedication, while the practice of Temple-illumination was similarly introduced into the Feast of Tabernacles." Alfred Edersheim, *The Temple, Its Ministry and Services as They Were at the Time of Jesus Christ.* (London: James Clarke & Co., 1959), 334.

[5] Psalm 116:17-19.

The Hallel Psalms are Psalm 113-118.

[6] Psalm 118:5-6.

[7] **Flogging/Scourging**: "Scourging was the only form of corporal punishment allowed in the OT. While the number of stripes varied with the offense, OT law set the upper limit at forty stripes to spare the culprit unnecessary humiliation (Dt. 25:1–3). In order to prevent any possibility of breaking this law, thirty-nine became the maximum possible number of lashes. Although many offenses could receive corporal punishment, the law specifically stated that a man who wrongly slandered his wife should be beaten (Dt. 22:18). According to later Jewish practice the minister (Heb. ḥazzān) of the synagogue meted out the punishment to the guilty individual; after the hands of the culprit were bound to a pillar, the minister used a calf-hide whip to inflict the stripes, one-third given upon the chest and two-thirds given upon the back (Mish Makkoth iii.12)." D. W. Wead, "Scourge," ed. Geoffrey W. Bromiley, *The International Standard Bible Encyclopedia*, Revised (Wm. B. Eerdmans, 1979–1988), 358.

[8] **Scorpion scourge**: "Particularly cruel was the use of a special whip, probably with bone or rock on the ends of the thongs, called the "scorpion" due to its potential to inflict a painful sting (1 K. 12:11, 14; 2 Ch. 12:11, 14)." D. W. Wead, "Scourge," ed. Geoffrey W. Bromiley, *The International Standard Bible Encyclopedia*, Revised (Wm. B. Eerdmans, 1979–1988), 358.

[9] Psalm 118:7.

[10] **The Feast of Dedication similar to the Feast of Tabernacles**: Though there is no description of the exact kind of sacrifices performed on Hanukkah, since the feast is considered so similar to Tabernacles, I decided to use the same sacrifices as well.

Tabernacles: "We have for the week 70 bullocks, 14 rams, and 98 lambs, or altogether 182 sacrifices (26 × 7)." Alfred Edersheim, *The Temple, Its Ministry and Services as They Were at the Time of Jesus Christ.* (London: James Clarke & Co., 1959), 276.

The fire on the altar: "A learned Jewish writer, Dr. Herzfeld, suggests, that to commemorate the descent of fire from heaven upon the altar in the Temple of Solomon,4 'the feast of lights' was instituted when the sacred fire was relit on the purified altar of the second Temple." Alfred Edersheim, *The Temple, Its Ministry and Services as They Were at the Time of Jesus Christ.* (London: James Clarke & Co., 1959), 335.

2 Maccabees 10:5–6. "Now it so happened that the cleansing of the sanctuary took place on the very day on which it had been profaned by aliens, on the twenty-fifth day of the same month, which is Chislev. 6 And they celebrated it for eight days with gladness like a feast of tabernacles, remembering how, not long before, during the feast of tabernacles they had been wandering like wild beasts in the mountains and the caves." Robert Henry Charles, ed., *Apocrypha of the Old Testament* (Oxford: Clarendon Press, 1913).

[11] **This description of the temple taken from**: Alfred Edersheim, *The Temple, Its Ministry and Services as They Were at the Time of Jesus Christ.* (London: James Clarke & Co., 1959), 54.

[12] Psalm 118:22-23.

[13] **Joshua bar Annas**: This guy really existed and did these things. Josephus uses the name Jesus bar Ananus, but Jesus is Greek for the Hebrew Joshua. In order to minimize confusion with Jesus the Christ, I have him use the Hebrew version in this text. This also stresses his connection with Moses later on in the story. Also, since his surname was the same as the high priest Ananus who is his adversary, I changed it to Annas, another form of Ananus, so there would be no confusion.

Josephus does not say Jesus (Joshua) bar Ananus is a Christian. But Josephus showed a decidedly anti-Christian bias by virtually ignoring their presence in Jerusalem in his books. It is entirely reasonable to conclude that Jesus (Joshua) bar Ananus may have been a Christian, since his main message was a repetition of a prophecy made infamous by Jesus of Nazareth. That prophecy was the destruction of the city of Jerusalem and its temple in Matthew 24. It would not be helpful to Josephus' agenda to admit such a thing, but reading between the lines may uncover the hidden truth.

Here is the first half of what Josephus wrote about Jesus (Joshua) bar Ananus: "Jesus, the son of Ananus, a plebeian and a husbandman, who, four years before the war began, and at a time when the city was in very great peace and prosperity, came to that feast whereon it is our custom for everyone to make tabernacles to God in the temple (301) began on a sudden cry aloud, "A voice from the east, a voice from the west, a voice from the four winds, a voice against Jerusalem and the holy house, a voice against the bridegrooms and the brides, and a voice against this whole people!" This was his cry, as he went about by day and by night, in all the lanes of the city. (302) However, certain of the most eminent among the populace had great indignation at this dire cry of his, and took up the man, and gave him a great number of severe stripes; yet did not he either say anything for himself, or anything peculiar to those that chastised him, but still he went on with the same words which he cried before. (303) Hereupon our rulers supposing, as the case proved to be, that this was a sort of divine fury in the man, brought him to the Roman procurator; (304) where he was whipped till his bones were laid bare; yet did he not make any supplication for himself, nor shed any tears, but turning his voice to the most lamentable tone possible, at every stroke of the whip his answer was, "Woe, woe to Jerusalem!" Flavius Josephus, *Wars of the Jews* 6.300-30304.

[14] Psalm 118:25-27.

[15] **The acts of sacrifice**: "The Rabbis mention the following five acts as belonging to the offerer of a sacrifice: the laying on of hands, slaying, skinning, cutting up, and washing the inwards. These other five were strictly priestly functions: Catching up the blood, sprinkling it, lighting the altar fire, laying on the wood, bringing up the pieces, and all else done at the altar itself." Alfred Edersheim, *The Temple, Its Ministry and Services as They Were at the Time of Jesus Christ.* (London: James Clarke & Co., 1959), 112–113.

"The burnt-offering was always to be a male animal, as the more noble, and as indicating strength and energy. The blood was thrown on the angles of the altar below the red line that ran round it. Then 'the sinew of the thigh,' the stomach and the entrails, etc., having been removed (in the case of birds also the feathers and the wings), and the sacrifice having been duly salted, it was wholly burned." Alfred

Edersheim, *The Temple, Its Ministry and Services as They Were at the Time of Jesus Christ*. (London: James Clarke & Co., 1959), 127.

[16] **This language is drawn from**: Revelation 6:9-10; 8:4.

[17] **Portents described here in Josephus**: Josephus writes of multiple omens that occur on several different festival occasions before the War began in AD 66. I have conflated them together here and placed them under the Feast of Dedication in AD 64 for the sake of the story. But the meaning of these alleged omens remains the same as in Josephus.

"Thus also, before the Jews' rebellion, and before those commotions which preceded the war, when the people were come in great crowds to the feast of unleavened bread, on the eighth day of the month Xanthicus [Nisan], and at the ninth hour of the night, so great a light shone round the altar and the holy house, that it appeared to be bright day time; which light lasted for half an hour. (291) This light seemed to be a good sign to the unskillful, but was so interpreted by the sacred scribes, as to portend those events that followed immediately upon it. (292) At the same festival also, a heifer, as she was led by the high priest to be sacrificed, brought forth a lamb in the midst of the temple. (293) Moreover, the eastern gate of the inner [court of the] temple, which was of brass, and vastly heavy, and had been with difficulty shut by twenty men, and rested upon a basis armed with iron, and had bolts fastened very deep into the firm floor, which was there made of one entire stone, was seen to be opened of its own accord about the sixth hour of the night. (295) This also appeared to the vulgar to be a very happy prodigy, as if God did thereby open them the gate of happiness. But the men of learning understood it, that the security of their holy house was dissolved of its own accord, and that the gate was opened for the advantage of their enemies. (296) So these publicly declared, that this signal foreshowed the desolation that was coming upon them." Flavius Josephus, *The Wars of the Jews*, 6.289-300.

[18] **Voice heard in the temple, "Let us remove ourselves"**: "Moreover at that feast which we call Pentecost, as the priests were going by night into the inner [court of the] temple, as their custom was, to perform their sacred ministrations, they said that, in the first place, they felt a quaking, and heard a great noise (300) and after that they heard a sound as of a great multitude, saying, "Let us remove hence." Flavius Josephus, *The Wars of the Jews*, 6.289-300.

Rushing wind as a symbol of the Holy Spirit: Acts 2:2.

[19] **Heifer**: "A young cow that has yet to produce a calf." B. S. Easton and R. K. Harrison, "Heifer," ed. Geoffrey W Bromiley, The International Standard Bible Encyclopedia, Revised (Wm. B. Eerdmans, 1979–1988), 672.

[20] **The strong man**: Mark 3:26–27 [Jesus:] "And if Satan has risen up against himself and is divided, he cannot stand, but is coming to an end. 27 But no one can enter a strong man's house and plunder his goods, unless he first binds the strong man. Then indeed he may plunder his house."

CHAPTER 24

[1] **The unclean spirit returns with sevenfold worse**: The passage Apollyon quotes from is Matthew 12:43-45.

[2] **The description of the holy temple here is taken from**: Alfred Edersheim, *The Temple, Its Ministry and Services as They Were at the Time of Jesus Christ*. (London: James Clarke & Co., 1959), 47-60; and Flavius Josephus, *The Wars of the Jews*, 5:199-237.

[3] **Apollyon here quotes from**: Isaiah 14:12-16, traditionally considered a reference to Satan.

[4] **Waters above the heavens before Yahweh's throne**: Genesis 1:6–7 6 And God said, "Let there be an expanse in the midst of the waters, and let it separate the waters from the waters." 7 And God made the expanse and separated the waters that were under the expanse from the waters that were above the expanse.

378

Psalm 148:1–4 [1] Praise the LORD! Praise the LORD from the heavens; praise him in the heights! [2] Praise him, all his angels; praise him, all his hosts! [3] Praise him, sun and moon, praise him, all you shining stars! [4] Praise him, you highest heavens, and you waters above the heavens!

Psalm 29:10 [10] The LORD sits enthroned over the flood; the LORD sits enthroned as king forever. The context of this Psalm is not the flood waters of Noah's deluge, but the celestial sea before God's throne.

[5] **The Location of the Garden of Eden**: For the story behind this reference to Eden being located in the mountains of Armenia and its destruction, see *Enoch Primordial*, Book 2 of the Biblical Fantasy series, *Chronicles of the Nephilim* by Brian Godawa (Embedded Pictures, 2012).

"The novel *Enoch Primordial* includes the Garden of Eden as a location important to the plot of the story. For those who believe it was an historical place, there are as many suggestions for its location as there are Bible commentators. We just don't know. The strongest hints are found in one passage, Genesis 2:10-14 that speaks of Eden at the headwaters of four rivers, The Pishon (in the land of Havilah), the Gihon (in the land of Cush), the Tigris, and the Euphrates.

"The Tigris and Euphrates we know, but the Pishon and Gihon we do not. And if the flood was historical, whether global or local, then the terrain affected by that cataclysm would be significantly altered to derail all speculation. However, it's still fun to try.

"Archaeologist David Rohl takes the Bible as basically truthful about the people and events it speaks of in history. He has looked at geographical, linguistic, and archaeological evidence of the ancient and modern Near East, and has made a persuasive argument that the land of Eden was in the mountainous valley area known to us as Armenia, where modern Turkey, Iran, Syria, and Iraq all meet.

"Bible readers often mistake the Garden of Eden for Eden itself. But Genesis speaks of "the Lord God planting a garden in Eden in the east" (Gen 2:8). So the Garden was in the eastern part of a land called "Eden."

"Rohl places the Garden in the Adji Chay valley adjacent to Lake Urmia and nestled in the volcanic mountainous ranges of the Savalan in the north and the Sahand in the south. He shows how that area is at the headwaters of the Tigris and Euphrates as well as two other rivers he suggests are the Pishon (Araxes) and Gihon (Kezel Uzun).

"The interesting variety of environments of volcanoes, mountains, lakes and forests were an inspiring setting to tell my story, so the map I've provided in the novel shows that I have followed Rohl's scholarship on the location of that most elusive Paradise." Brian Godawa, *Enoch Primordial* (Embedded Pictures, 2012, 2014), 340-341.

[6] **Temple as symbolic of the Garden of Eden**: "There are hints that the Garden of Eden was the archetypal Temple in which the first man worshipped God.

"First, Israel's Temple was the place where the priest experienced God's unique presence, and Eden was the place where Adam walked and talked with God. The same Hebrew verbal form (hithpael), hithallek, used for God's 'walking back and forth' in the Garden (Gen. 3:8), describes God's presence in the Tabernacle (Lev. 26:12; Deut. 23:14 [15]; 2 Sam. 7:6–7).

"Secondly, Genesis 2:15 says God placed Adam in the Garden 'to cultivate [work] it and to keep it'. The two Hebrew words for 'cultivate and keep' are usually translated 'serve and guard' elsewhere in the Old Testament. When these two words (verbal ['abad and shamar] and nominal forms) occur together in the Old Testament (within an approximately fifteen-word range), they sometimes have this meaning and refer either to Israelites 'serving' God and 'guarding [keeping]' God's word (approximately ten times) or to priests who 'keep' the 'service' (or 'charge') of the Tabernacle (see Num. 3:7–8; 8:25–26; 18:5–6; 1 Chr. 23:32; Ezek. 44:14).

"Thirdly, when Adam failed to guard the Temple by sinning and letting in an unclean serpent to defile the sanctuary, Adam lost his priestly role, and the two cherubim took over the responsibility of 'guarding' the Garden Temple: God 'stationed the cherubim … to guard the way to the tree of life' (so Gen. 3:24). Likely, their role became memorialized in Israel's later Temple when God commanded Moses to make two statues of cherubim and stationed them on either side of the 'ark of the covenant' in the 'holy of holies'.

"Fourthly, the 'tree of life' itself was probably the model for the lampstand placed directly outside the 'holy of holies'. The lampstand looked like a small, flowering tree with seven protruding branches from a central trunk, three on one side and three on the other, and one branch going straight up from the trunk in the middle. Exodus 25:31–36 pictures the lampstand having a flowering and fructifying appearance of a tree with 'bulbs and flowers', 'branches' and 'almond blossoms' (see Exod. 25:31–36; likewise, see Josephus, Ant. III:145).

"Fifthly, that the Garden of Eden was the first Temple is also suggested by observing that Israel's later Temple had wood carvings which gave it a garden-like atmosphere: 1 Kings 6:18, 29 says there was 'cedar ... carved in the shape of gourds and open flowers' (v. 18); 'on the walls of the temple round about' and on the wood doors of the inner sanctuary were 'carvings of cherubim, palm trees, and open flowers' (vv. 29, 32, 35); beneath the heads of the two pillars placed at the entrance of the holy place were 'carved pomegranates' (1 Kgs. 7:18–20).

"Sixthly, Eden was on a mountain (Ezek. 28:14, 16); Israel's Temple was on Mount Zion (e.g. Exod. 15:17); and the eschatological Temple was to be located on a mountain (Ezek. 40:2; 43:12; Rev. 21:10).

"Seventhly, just as a river flowed out from Eden (Gen. 2:10), so the eschatological Temple in both Ezekiel 47:1–12 and Revelation 21:1–2 has a river flowing out from its centre (and likewise Rev. 7:15–17 and probably Zech. 14:8–9). Later Judaism understood that from 'the tree of life' streams flowed (Midr. Rab. Gen. 15:6; 2 Enoch [J] 8:3, 5). Indeed, Ezekiel generally depicts eschatological Mount Zion (and its Temple) in the colours of Eden in an attempt to show that the promises originally inherent in Eden would be realized in the fulfilment of his vision.

"Eighthly, Genesis 2:12 says that 'good gold' and 'bdellium and onyx stone' were in 'the land of Havilah', apparently where Eden was. Of course, various items of Tabernacle furniture were made of gold, as were the walls, ceiling, and floor of the holy of holies in Solomon's Temple (1 Kgs. 6:20–22). Furthermore, the onyx stones decorated both the Tabernacle and Temple, as well as the high priestly garments (Exod. 25:7; 28:9–12, 20; 1 Chr. 29:2). Gold and onyx are also found together on the priest's clothing (Exod. 28:6–27) and are mentioned together as composing parts of the Temple (1 Chr. 29:2).

"Ninethly, the ark in the holy of holies, which contained the Law (that led to wisdom), echoes the tree of the knowledge of good and evil (that also led to wisdom). The touching of both the ark and this tree resulted in death.

"Tenthly, the entrance to Eden was from the east (Gen. 3:24), which was also the direction from which one entered the Tabernacle and later Temples of Israel and would be the same direction from which the latter-day Temple would be entered (Ezek. 40:6)." Gregory Beale, "The Final Vision of the Apocalypse and Its Implications for a Biblical Theology of the Temple," in *Heaven on Earth*, ed. T. Desmond Alexander and Simon Gathercole (Carlisle [England: Paternoster Press, 2004), 197–199.

[7] **The Cosmic Mountain in the Ancient Near East**: "It has been seen that mountains played an important role in the religious thought of the Ancient Near East of the first and second millennia. The term sometimes used to describe the holy mountain in English, cosmic mountain, has been based on a postulated Mesopotamian' Weltberg, or "world-mountain ." In this view, heaven and earth united were seen as a mountain. The base of the mountain was the earth and the peak was the top of the heavens. Thus the mountain was the central axis of the universe and was the connecting point between the different spheres." Richard J. Clifford, *The Cosmic Mountain in Canaan and the Old Testament* (Wipf & Stock Pub, 2010), 190.

The cosmic link between earthly and heavenly temples: "Temples had names in the ancient world (since naming was an expression of function and existence), and a name such as "Bond between Heaven and Earth" certainly captures the ideology beautifully.

"From the standpoint of deity, the temple is his/her estate and residence. The earthly temple was a symbol, an echo, a shadow of the heavenly residence. As such it served as a link, a bond, or even a portal to the heavenly residence. The heavenly archetypal temple can sometimes be identified as the cosmos itself. In Mesopotamia the ziggurat stood beside the temple as the place where the deity descended from the heavens to reside among the people and to receive their worship." John H. Walton, *Ancient Near*

Eastern Thought and the Old Testament: Introducing the Conceptual World of the Hebrew Bible (Grand Rapids, MI: Baker Academic, 2006), 113–114.

The temple as cosmic mountain: "The Temple of Yahweh in Israel was naturally associated with a cosmic mountain dwelling like Sinai because it was situated in Jerusalem on Mount Zion, the new Sinai. Psalm 48 makes this quite clear:

1 Great is the LORD and greatly to be praised
in the city of our God!
His holy mountain, 2 beautiful in elevation,
is the joy of all the earth,
Mount Zion, in the far north [Lit.: heights of the north],
the city of the great King (Psa 48:1–2 ESV).

"Zechariah 8:3 (ESV) echoes the same notion: "Thus says the LORD: I have returned to Zion and will dwell [literally, "will tabernacle"; shakan] in the midst of Jerusalem, and Jerusalem shall be called the faithful city, and the mountain of the LORD of hosts, the holy mountain."

"As anyone who has been to Jerusalem knows, Mount Zion isn't much of a mountain. It certainly isn't located in the geographical north—it's actually in the southern part of the country. So what's meant by "the heights of the north"?

"This description would be a familiar one to Israel's pagan neighbors, particularly at Ugarit. It's actually taken out of their literature. The "heights of the north" (Ugaritic: "the heights of tsaphon") is the place where Baal lived and, supposedly, ran the cosmos at the behest of the high god El and the divine council. The psalmist is stealing glory from Baal, restoring it to the One to whom it rightfully belongs—Yahweh. It's a theological and literary slap in the face, another polemic.

"This explains why the description sounds odd in terms of Jerusalem's actual geography. This is why Isaiah and Micah used phrases like "the mountain of the house of Yahweh" (Isa 2:2; Mic 4:1). The description is designed to make a theological point, not a geographical one. Zion is the center of the cosmos, and Yahweh and his council are its king and administrators, not Baal." Michael S. Heiser, *The Unseen Realm: Recovering the Supernatural Worldview of the Bible*, First Edition (Bellingham, WA: Lexham Press, 2015), 226–227.

Temple and Jerusalem as center of the earth: "These two passages from the Talmudic tractate Yoma present Mount Zion as the point from which creation proceeded, in other words, the one place of a genuinely primordial character in our world. The following midrash shows that the notion of increasing orders of centrality can be found even on the mountain itself:

> Just as the navel is positioned in the center of a man, thus is the Land of Israel positioned in the center of the world, as the Bible says, "dwelling at the very navel of the earth" (Ezek. 38:12), and from it the foundation of the world proceeds.... And the Temple is in the center of Jerusalem, and the Great Hall is in the center of the Temple, and the Ark is in the center of the Great Hall, and the Foundation Stone is in front of the Ark, and beginning with it the world was put on its foundation.

In short, the Temple is a visible, tangible token of the act of creation, the point of origin of the world, the "focus" of the universe." Jon D. Levenson, "The Temple and the World," *The Journal of Religion*, Vol. 64, No. 3 (Jul., 1984), 283.

[8] **The Harlot, the scarlet Beast and the dragon**: Revelation 13:1 [1] And I saw a beast rising out of the sea, with ten horns and seven heads, with ten diadems on its horns and blasphemous names on its heads.

The false prophet as the high priest of first century Israel: Revelation 19:20 And the beast was captured, and with it the false prophet who in its presence had done the signs by which he deceived those who had received the mark of the beast and those who worshiped its image.

"Corsini (333) perceptively observes that "the beast-prostitute pair… constitute a repetition of the two beasts of ch. 13, described here not only in their complementary aspect, but also in the complexity involved in the symbol." On the same page he continues: "The symbol of the prostitute, like the beast from the land / false prophet, also points to Judaism. The symbol signifies Judaism's perversion, through the metaphor of prostitution. Prostitution means idolatry and Judaism has become idolatrous because it adores the best and its statue, political authority. This is the case not because it accepts the political domination of the Romans.... Judaism adopts their mentality, their means and their goals."

"The angelomorphic Christ now declares that Babylon-Jerusalem has become a dwelling place of demons (18:2b). Here we see Babylon-Jerusalem associated with "demons" — and "every unclean spirit" (18:2c). This is not surprising in that the "false prophet" (the high-priestly aristocracy) issues death decrees against Christ and Christians (Ac 9:1-2, 21) when prompted by "unclean spirits," the "spirits of demons" (cf. 16:13-14). Kenneth L. Gentry, Jr., *The Divorce of Israel: A Redemptive-Historical Interpretation of Revelation Vol. 2* (Dallas, GA: Tolle Lege Press, 2016), 492.

On earth as it is in heaven or "as above, so below": "This concept as prayed by Jesus in the Lord's Prayer is rooted in the Deuteronomy 32 worldview. Deut 32:8-10 says that Yahweh divided the seventy nations according to the number of the fallen Sons of God and placed them under their authority. They became the "princes" (Dan. 10:13, 20-21) or "gods" of those pagan nations (Deut. 32:17; 4:19-21), rulers of those geographical territories.

"When earthly rulers battle on earth, the Bible describes the host of heaven battling with them in spiritual unity. In Daniel 10, hostilities between Greece and Persia is accompanied by the battle of heavenly Watchers over those nations (described as "princes").

"Daniel 10:13, 20-21 The prince of the kingdom of Persia withstood me twenty-one days, but Michael, one of the chief princes, came to help me, for I was left there with the kings of Persia." ...Then he said, "Do you know why I have come to you? But now I will return to fight against the prince of Persia; and when I go out, behold, the prince of Greece will come. [21] But I will tell you what is inscribed in the book of truth: there is none who contends by my side against these except Michael, your prince.

"When Sisera fought with Israel, the earthly kings and heavenly authorities (host of heaven) are described interchangeably in unity.

"Judges 5:19–20 "The kings came, they fought; then fought the kings of Canaan...From heaven the stars fought, from their courses they fought against Sisera.

"When God punishes earthly rulers, he punishes them along with the heavenly rulers ("host of heaven") above and behind them.

"Isaiah 24:21–22 On that day the LORD will punish the host of heaven, in heaven, and the kings of the earth, on the earth. They will be gathered together as prisoners in a pit; they will be shut up in a prison, and after many days they will be punished.

"Though this notion of territorial archons or spiritual rulers is Biblical and carries over into intertestamental literature such as the Book of Enoch (1 En. 89:59, 62-63; 67) and others, it seems to lessen at the time of the New Testament.

"Walter Wink points out that the picture of Watchers over nations is hinted at in 1 Cor. 4:9 where the apostle explains their persecution has "become a spectacle (theatre) to the world, to angels and to men." He explains that "the image of the Roman theater conjures up hostile and jeering crowds," and the angels are "heavenly representatives of the Gentile nations and people, who watch, not without malicious glee, the tribulations endured by the apostle to their peoples."

"The epistles speak of the spiritual principalities and powers that are behind the earthly rulers and powers to be sure (Eph. 6:12-13), but it appears to be more generic in reference. And after the death, resurrection, and ascension of Christ, these spiritual powers have been disarmed and overthrown (Col. 2:15, Luke 10:18), at least legally losing their hegemony (Eph. 1:20-23). The fallen angelic powers are still around, but have been defanged with the inauguration of the Messianic kingdom of God." Brian Godawa, *When Giants Were Upon the Earth: The Watchers, the Nephilim, and the Biblical Cosmic War of the Seed* (Embedded Pictures, 2014), 278-279.

Testament of Solomon 20.14–15 "I asked him, "Tell me, then, how you, being demons, are able to ascend into heaven." 15 He replied, "Whatever things are accomplished in heaven (are accomplished) in the same way also on earth." James H. Charlesworth, *The Old Testament Pseudepigrapha*, vol. 1 (New York; London: Yale University Press, 1983), 983.

[9] **The garments of the high priest in the Antonia from the reign of Claudius and procurator Fadus**: "He also at this time sent for the high priests and the principal citizens of Jerusalem, and this at the command of the emperor, and admonished them that they should lay up the long garment and the sacred vestment, which it is customary for nobody but the high priest to wear, in the tower of Antonia, that it might be under the power of the Romans, as it had been formerly." Flavius Josephus, *The Antiquities of the Jews*, 20.6.

For a description of the high priest's garments: Exodus 39.

[10] **The description of the Harlot reflects the priesthood of Israel**: Revelation 17:4–6 [4] The woman was arrayed in purple and scarlet, and adorned with gold and jewels and pearls, holding in her hand a golden cup full of abominations and the impurities of her sexual immorality. [5] And on her forehead was written a name of mystery: "Babylon the great, mother of prostitutes and of earth's abominations." [6] And I saw the woman, drunk with the blood of the saints, the blood of the martyrs of Jesus.

"Her dress reflects her covenantal status as a kingdom of priests, particularly reminding the first-century reader of Jerusalem's central Temple and its prominent High Priest (note his great authority in Acts 23:4). In Exodus 28 we read of the High Priest's ritual attire:

> And these are the garments which they shall make: a breast-piece and an ephod and a robe and a tunic of checkered work, a turban and a sash, and they shall make holy garments for Aaron your brother and his sons, that he may minister as priest to Me. And they shall take the gold and the blue and the purple and the scarlet material and the fine linen…. And the skillfully woven band, which is on it, shall be like its workmanship, of the same material: of gold, of blue and purple and scarlet material and fine twisted linen. And you shall take two onyx stones and engrave on them the names of the sons of Israel (Exo. 28:4–5, 8–9).

"His attire also matches the decor of the Tabernacle (the forerunner to the Temple): "Moreover you shall make the tabernacle with ten curtains of fine twisted linen and blue and purple and scarlet material; you shall make them with cherubim, the work of a skillful workman (Exo. 26:1). The Old Testament description of the Temple points out that the altar (which received the blood of sacrifices, Exo 24:6; 29:12; Lev 1:5) was gold —like the cup from which the Harlot drank the blood of the saints:

> The whole altar which was by the inner sanctuary he overlaid with gold (1 Kgs 6:22).

"Josephus provides us with a eyewitness description of the first century Temple, which also parallels the Harlot's dress: "The Temple's tapestry was Babylonian [!] tapestry in which blue, purple, scarlet, and linen were mingled" (War 5:5:4). He also mentions the prominence of gold in Temple vessels: "The greatest part of the vessels that were put in them was of silver and gold" (War 5:4:5).

"John's unusual focus on her forehead is significant not only in our present argument but later in another context, as well. In the description of the High Priest in the Old Testament we read:

> "You shall also make a plate of pure gold and shall engrave on it, like the engravings of a seal, 'Holy to the Lord'…. And it shall be on Aaron's forehead, and Aaron shall take away the iniquity of the holy things which the sons of Israel consecrate, with regard to all their holy gifts; and it shall always be on his forehead, that they may be accepted before the Lord (Exo. 28:36, 38).

"John dresses the Harlot in a way that draws our attention to her forehead. And when we look there, we see the opposite of what appears on the forehead of the High Priest, showing John's estimation of what the Holy City, Temple of God, and the priesthood have become. (Interestingly, Jeremiah also mentions the harlotrous forehead of Jerusalem in Jer. 3:3)." Kenneth L. Gentry Jr., *Perilous Times: A Study in Eschatological Evil* (Covenant Media Press, 1999), 77-79.

[11] **This description of the veil comes from**: Flavius Josephus, *The Wars of the Jews*, 5.213.

Veil torn: Matthew 27:50–51 [50] And Jesus cried out again with a loud voice and yielded up his spirit. [51] And behold, the curtain of the temple was torn in two, from top to bottom. And the earth shook, and the rocks were split.

Christ's sacrificial death allowed Gentiles into the holy place: Ephesians 2:14–16 [14] For he himself is our peace, who has made us both one and has broken down in his flesh the dividing wall of hostility [15] by abolishing the law of commandments expressed in ordinances, that he might create in himself one new man in place of the two, so making peace, [16] and might reconcile us both to God in one body through the cross, thereby killing the hostility.

Satan bound in the ministry of Jesus: (Matthew 12:27-29). In Rev 20:2-3, binding the satan if described as stopping his ability to "deceive the nations."

From every tribe and nation: Revelation 5:9–10 [9] [of Jesus] by your blood you ransomed people for God from every tribe and language and people and nation, [10] and you have made them a kingdom and priests to our God, and they shall reign on the earth."

Revelation 7:9 [9] After this I looked, and behold, a great multitude that no one could number, from every nation, from all tribes and peoples and languages, standing before the throne and before the Lamb, clothed in white robes, with palm branches in their hands,

Drawing all nations to Mount Zion: Isaiah 2:1-4.

[12] **Christ claiming the nations as his inheritance:** Psalm 2:8; Isaiah 2:1-5. For a fictional portrayal of this victory of Jesus Christ over the principalities and powers see Brian Godawa, *Jesus Triumphant* (Los Angeles, Embedded Pictures, 2015).

Spiritual rulers like Satan were tricked by the crucifixion: 1 Corinthians 2:7–8 [7] But we impart a secret and hidden wisdom of God, which God decreed before the ages for our glory. [8] None of the rulers of this age understood this, for if they had, they would not have crucified the Lord of glory.

[13] **Violation of God's details in the sanctuary resulted in death**: Leviticus 16:2 [2] and the LORD said to Moses, "Tell Aaron your brother not to come at any time into the Holy Place inside the veil, before the mercy seat that is on the ark, so that he may not die. For I will appear in the cloud over the mercy seat.

Exodus 28:35 And it shall be on Aaron when he ministers, and its sound shall be heard when he goes into the Holy Place before the LORD, and when he comes out, so that he does not die.

"That he may not die": "This conventional formula probably refers to the entire section and not just to the matter of the bells. Any deviation from the prescribed rules places the priest in the category of an unauthorized person and invalidates his service. He is thus an encroacher—Hebrew zar—in the sacred precincts. The formula expresses the severity with which such an offense is viewed." Nahum M. Sarna, Exodus, The JPS Torah Commentary (Philadelphia: Jewish Publication Society, 1991), 183.

More examples of death for violation of priestly duties in the holy place: Exod. 28:43; 30:21; Lev. 8:35; 10:7; 16:13.

[14] **Missing Cherubim from the Holy of Holies**: "The most holy place in Solomon's temple was a room of twenty cubits (approximately 9 m, 30 ft; see 1 K. 6:20) on a side. Flanking the ark were two cherubim made of olivewood and overlaid with gold (1 K. 6:23, 28); these faced the entrance of the most holy place (2 Ch. 3:13). In his temple plans Ezekiel retained the dimensions of the Solomonic inner sanctuary (Ezk. 41:4), and the same probably holds for the second temple founded by Zerubbabel (Ezr. 3). Since the ark was lost when the Babylonians destroyed Jerusalem in 587 B.C., the most holy place in the rebuilt temple had no furniture at all. There is no representation of the ark on the Arch of Titus, erected in Rome to commemorate the Romans' destruction of Jerusalem in A.D. 70; only furniture from the holy place is depicted." R. P. Gordon, "Most Holy Place," ed. Geoffrey W Bromiley, *The International Standard Bible Encyclopedia*, Revised (Wm. B. Eerdmans, 1979–1988), 426.

The most holy place of the temple was empty in the first century: "But the inmost part of the temple of all was of twenty cubits. This was also separated from the outer part by a veil. In this there was nothing at all. It was inaccessible and inviolable, and not to be seen by any; and was called the Holy of Holies."

Flavius Josephus and William Whiston, *The Works of Josephus: Complete and Unabridged* (Peabody: Hendrickson, 1987) *Wars of the Jews* 5.219.

Legend of the missing elements inside the ark of the covenant: 1 Esdras 1:54-55 "And they took all the holy vessels of the Lord, both great and small, with the vessels of the ark of the Lord, and the king's treasures, and carried them away unto Babylon. 55 And they burnt the house of the Lord, and brake down the walls of Jerusalem." Robert Henry Charles, ed., *Apocrypha of the Old Testament* (Oxford: Clarendon Press, 1913), 1 Esd 1:54–55.

"According to some Jewish traditions, the Babylonians removed the vessels of gold, silver, and bronze, but Jeremiah removed the ark and the sacred tablets and hid them from the Babylonians. This tradition may be traced at least to the historian Eupolemus (see Eusebius, Praep. Evang. 9.39). A similar account is related by Alexander Polyhistor of Miletus in the 1st century B.C.E., but he was probably dependent on Eupolemus for this story. In a variant of this account, Jeremiah hid the tent, the ark, and the altar of incense in a cave on the mountain from which Moses saw the Promised Land (2 Macc 2:4–8). Another source has it that Josiah hid the ark under a rock "in its place" (b. Yoma 53b–54a; m. Šeqal. 6:1–2). According to a legend, an angel descended from heaven during the destruction of Jerusalem and removed the sacred vessels from the temple (2 Bar. 6:7). These accounts are obviously ways of coping with the unthinkable destruction of the ark of divine presence at the hands of Gentile invaders. More credible is the lament over the desecration of the temple and plundering of the ark during the destruction of the First Temple (2 Esdr 10:20–23). In any case, all traditions point to the exilic period for the disappearance of the ark. It appears that the ark was not rebuilt for the Second Temple. Jeremiah declared that it was not to be made again (Jer 3:16)." C. L. Seow, "Ark of the Covenant," ed. David Noel Freedman, *The Anchor Yale Bible Dictionary* (New York: Doubleday, 1992), 390–391.

For a fictional story that uses the above legends about the whereabouts of the contents of the ark: see Brian Godawa and Charlie Wen, *The Dragon King: First Emperor of China* (Embedded Pictures Publishing, 2016).

[15] **The Foundation Stone of the temple, (Hebrew: *Eben Shetiya*):** Biblically, the cornerstone of the temple was a messianic metaphor. Jewish tradition then linked that cornerstone concept with the creation of the earth, Noah's flood, Abraham's sacrifice of Isaac, and David's rule.

> Isaiah 28:16 Therefore thus says the Lord GOD, "Behold, I am the one who has laid as a foundation in Zion, a stone, a tested stone, a precious cornerstone, of a sure foundation: 'Whoever believes will not be in haste.'

"Jews created a series of stories around that Rock, which, as we have seen, had been linked to the Foundation Stone (Even ha-Shetiyah) mentioned in Isaiah 28:16. Those legends found their way into the Mishnah, the Talmud, the Midrash and other Jewish texts. The Jewish legends sometimes revolved around figures in the Hebrew Bible, for instance that Abraham had nearly sacrificed his son Isaac on that Rock, and that Jacob had used the Rock for a pillow and then anointed it. Another story centered on Jonah who, when swallowed by the fish, saw the base of the Foundation Stone in an abyss beneath the Temple." Pamela C. Berger, *The Crescent on the Temple: the Dome of the Rock as Image of the Ancient Jewish Sanctuary* (Boston: Brill), 24-25.

"The construction of the earth was begun at the centre, with the foundation stone of the Temple, the Eben Shetiyah,[38] for the Holy Land is at the central point of the surface of the earth, Jerusalem is at the central point of Palestine, and the Temple is situated at the centre of the Holy City. In the sanctuary itself the Hekal is the centre, and the holy Ark occupies the centre of the Hekal, built on the foundation stone, which thus is at the centre of the earth.[39] Thence issued the first ray of light, piercing to the Holy Land, and from there illuminating the whole earth.[40]" Ginzberg, Louis. *The Legends of the Jews — Volume 1* (p. 5). K-Edition.

"From this wondrous dream Jacob awoke with a start of fright, on account of the vision he had had of the destruction of the Temple.[140] He cried out, "How dreadful is this place! this is none other but the house of God, wherein is the gate of heaven through which prayer ascends to Him." He took the stone made out of the twelve, and set it up for a pillar, and poured oil upon the top of it, which had flowed down from heaven for him, and God sank this anointed stone unto the abyss, to serve as the centre of the earth, the same stone, the Eben Shetiyah,[141] that forms the centre of the sanctuary, whereon the Ineffable Name is

graven, the knowledge of which makes a man master over nature, and over life and death.[142]"
Ginzberg, Louis. *The Legends of the Jews — Volume 1* (pp. 154-155). K-Edition.

Another Jewish legend about King David and the Foundation Stone (Eben Shetiyah): "Ahithophel's hostility toward David showed itself also on the following occasion. When David was digging the foundations of the Temple, a shard was found at a depth of fifteen hundred cubits. David was about to lift it, when the shard exclaimed: 'Thou canst not do it.' 'Why not?' asked David. 'Because I rest upon the abyss.' 'Since when?' 'Since the hour in which the voice of God was heard to utter the words from Sinai, 'I am the Lord thy God,' causing the earth to quake and sink into the abyss. I lie here to cover up the abyss.' Nevertheless David lifted the shard, and the waters of the abyss rose and threatened to flood the earth. Ahithophel was standing by, and he thought to himself: 'Now David will meet with his death, and I shall be king.' Just then David said: 'Whoever knows how to stem the tide of waters, and fails to do it, will one day throttle himself.' (69) Thereupon Ahithophel had the Name of God inscribed upon the shard, and the shard thrown into the abyss. The waters at once commenced to subside, but they sank to so great a depth that David feared the earth might lose her moisture, and he began to sing the fifteen 'Songs of Ascents,' to bring the waters up again. (70)" Ginzberg, Louis. *The Legends of the Jews — Volume 4* (K Locations 958-966). K-Edition.

The Foundation Stone in the Babylonian Talmud:

(b. Yoma 5:2, II.1.A)
II.1 A.   ... called Shetiyyah:
B. *A Tannaite statement:* From it the world was created [T. Kip. 2:14C].
C. *Our Mishnah-teaching accords with him who has said*, Out of Zion the world was created.
D. *For it has been taught on Tannaite authority*:
E. R. Eliezer says, "The world was created from its center: 'When the dust runs into a mass and the clods keep fast together' (Job 38:38)."

Jacob Neusner, *The Babylonian Talmud: A Translation and Commentary,* vol. 5a (Peabody, MA: Hendrickson Publishers, 2011), 200.

(b. Sukk. 4:9, V.3.A–4.B)
V.3 A.   *A Tannaite authority of the house of R. Ishmael:*
B. " 'In the beginning' (Gen. 1:1) is not to be read 'in the beginning,' but rather, 'he created the pit [of the altar].' "
V.4 A.   *It has been taught on Tannaite authority:*
B. R. Yosé says, "The cavity of the pits descended to the abyss...

Jacob Neusner, *The Babylonian Talmud: A Translation and Commentary,* vol. 5b (Peabody, MA: Hendrickson Publishers, 2011), 199.

The Foundation Stone in connected to Solomon in the Testament of Solomon: "Then I said to him, "What can you do for me?" He responded, "I am able to move mountains, to carry houses from one place to another, and to overthrow kings." I said to him, "If you have the power, lift this stone into the beginning of the corner of the Temple." ...When he had said these things, he went in underneath the stone, lifted it up, went up the flight of steps carrying the stone, and inserted it into the end of the entrance of the Temple. I, Solomon, being excited, exclaimed, "Truly the Scripture which says, *It was the stone rejected by the builders that became the keystone*, has now been fulfilled," and so forth." Testament of Solomon 23: James H. Charlesworth, *The Old Testament Pseudepigrapha*, vol. 1 (New York; London: Yale University Press, 1983), 985.

[16] **Tartarus and the imprisonment of the Watchers:** "1 Peter 3:18-20 speaks of Christ going down into Sheol to proclaim his triumph to the "spirits imprisoned" at the time of the flood. This act appears to be a typological replay of Enoch's own vision journey into Sheol to see the "prison house of the angels" who disobeyed at the flood (1 Enoch 21:9-10).

"But the story does not yet end there. You will notice that the location of punishment and binding of the fallen angels that we have already seen in 2 Peter is *Tartarus* in the Greek.

"2Pet. 2:4 For if God did not spare angels when they sinned, but cast them into hell [*tartarus*] and committed them to pits of darkness, reserved for judgment.

"What is important to realize is that the Greek word translated as "hell" in this English translation is not one of the usual New Testament Greek words for hell, *gehenna* or *hades*, but *tartarus*.

"The Greek poet Hesiod, writing around 700 B.C., described this commonly known underworld called Tartarus as the pit of darkness and gloom where the Olympian Titan giants were banished following their war with Zeus.

"Hesiod, *Theogony* lines 720-739 as far beneath the earth as heaven is above earth; for so far is it from earth to Tartarus…There by the counsel of Zeus who drives the clouds the Titan gods are hidden under misty gloom, in a dank place where are the ends of the huge earth. And they may not go out; for Poseidon fixed gates of bronze upon it, and a wall runs all round it on every side.

"Obviously, Peter does not affirm Greco-Roman polytheism by referring to Tartarus, but he is alluding to a Hellenistic myth that his readers, believer and unbeliever alike, would be very familiar with, subverting it with the Jewish traditional interpretation.

"Extra-Biblical Second Temple Jewish legends connected this legend of gods and bound Titans in Tartarus to the bound angelic Watchers and punished giants of Genesis 6.

"Sibylline Oracles 1:97-104, 119 enterprising Watchers, who received this appellation because they had a sleepless mind in their hearts and an insatiable personality. They were mighty, of great form, but nevertheless they went under the dread house of Tartarus guarded by unbreakable bonds, to make retribution, to Gehenna of terrible, raging, undying fire…draping them around with great Tartarus, under the base of the earth.

"Other well-known Second Temple literature reiterated this binding in the heart of the earth until judgment day:

"Jubilees 4:22; 5:10 And he wrote everything, and bore witness to the Watchers, the ones who sinned with the daughters of men because they began to mingle themselves with the daughters of men so that they might be polluted… And subsequently they [the Watchers] were bound in the depths of the earth forever, until the day of great judgment in order for judgment to be executed upon all of those who corrupted their ways and their deeds before the LORD.

"This "binding" or imprisoning of supernatural beings in the earth is expressed in 2 Peter's "cast into pits of darkness reserved for judgment" (3:19), 1 Peter's "disobedient spirits in prison" (v. 6), and Jude's "eternal bonds under darkness for the judgment of the great day" (2:4). But it is not altogether unheard of in the Old Testament.

I"sa. 24:21–23 On that day the LORD will punish
the host of heaven, in heaven,
and the kings of the earth, on the earth.
They will be gathered together
as prisoners in a pit;
they will be shut up in a prison,
and after many days they will be punished.

"Isaiah here is speaking of judgment upon Israel by the Babylonians around 600 B.C., but he evokes the same Enochian imagery of the angelic host of heaven (often linked to the astronomical heavenly bodies *and* earthly rulers) being overthrown and imprisoned in the earth until judgment day.

"Robert Newman notes that the Qumran Hebrew of the Isaiah scroll of this passage refers to a past event as its reference point: "They *were* gathered together as prisoners in a pit" (past tense). [16] This past event could very well be the antediluvian binding of the fallen host of heaven (*bene ha Elohim*) as an analogy for the future captivity of Israel."

"In the New Testament, the word *Hades* is used for the underworld, which was the Greek equivalent of Sheol. Jesus himself used the term Hades as the location of damned spirits in contrast with heaven as the location of redeemed spirits when he talked of Capernaum rejecting miracles, "And you, Capernaum, will you be <u>exalted to heaven</u>? You will be <u>brought down to Hades</u>" (Matt. 11:23). Hades was also the location of departed spirits in his parable of Lazarus and the rich man in Hades (Luke 16:19-31).

"In Greek mythology, Tartarus was another term for a location beneath the "roots of the earth" and beneath the waters where the warring giants called "Titans" were bound in chains because of their rebellion against the gods.[16] Peter uses a derivative of that very Greek word Tartarus to describe a similar location and scenario of angels being bound during the time of Noah and the warring Titans called "Nephilim."

"2Pet. 2:4-5 For if God did not spare <u>angels</u> when they sinned, but <u>cast them into hell</u> [*tartaroo*] <u>and committed them to chains</u> of gloomy darkness to be kept until the judgment; if he did not spare the ancient world, but preserved Noah.

"The Watery Abyss: In Mesopotamian cosmography, the Abyss (*Apsu* in Akkadian) was a cosmic subterranean lake or body of water that was between the earth and the underworld (Sheol), and was the source of the waters above such as oceans, rivers, and springs or fountains. In *The Epic of Gilgamesh*, Utnapishtim, the Babylonian Noah, tells his fellow citizens that he is building his boat and will abandon the earth of Enlil to join Ea in the waters of the Abyss that would soon fill the land.[16] Even bitumen pools used to make pitch were thought to rise up from the "underground waters," or the Abyss.

"Similarly, in the Bible the earth also rests on the seas or "the deep" (*tehom*) that produces the springs and waters from its subterranean waters below the earth.

Psa. 24:1-2The world, and those who dwell therein, for he has <u>founded it upon the seas</u>, and established it upon the rivers.

Psa. 136:6 To him who spread out the earth <u>above the waters</u>.

Gen. 49: 25 The Almighty who will bless you with blessings of heaven above, Blessings of <u>the deep that crouches beneath.</u>

Ex. 20:4 You shall not make for yourself a carved image, or any likeness of anything that is in heaven above, or that is in the earth beneath, or that is <u>in the water under the earth.</u>

"Leviathan is even said to dwell in the Abyss in Job 41:24 (LXX). When God brings the flood, part of the waters are from "the fountains of the great deep" bursting open (Gen. 7:11; 8:2)." Brian Godawa, *When Giants Were Upon the Earth: The Watchers, the Nephilim, and the Biblical Cosmic War of the Seed* (Embedded Pictures, 2014), 124-126; 102-103.

[17] **The Seal of Solomon:** The earliest documented source of the Seal of Solomon and his powers over the demonic realm are found in the Testament of Solomon, a Greek text written by Jews, dated as early as the first century with alterations, additions and recensions as late as the 1200s. During the rise of Islam, Muslims engaged in their own development of the legends of Solomon with power over the spiritual realm. D. C. Duling, "A New Translation and Introduction," in *The Old Testament Pseudepigrapha*, vol. 1 (New York; London: Yale University Press, 1983), 940. The Testament of Solomon contains the legends of Solomon forcing demons to help him build the temple without earthly instruments.

Isaiah 22:22–24 And I will place on his shoulder the key of the house of David. He shall open, and none shall shut; and he shall shut, and none shall open. [23] And I will fasten him like a peg in a secure place, and he will become a throne of honor to his father's house. [24] And they will hang on him the whole honor of his father's house, the offspring and issue, every small vessel, from the cups to all the flagons.

Solomon as magician and exorcist: "The view that Solomon was a magician goes back to ancient interpretations of 1 Kings 4:29–34 (5:9–14 in Heb.):

Yahweh gave Solomon immense wisdom and understanding, and a heart as vast as the sand on the seashore. The wisdom of Solomon surpassed the wisdom of all the sons of the East, and all the wisdom of Egypt. He was wiser than any other, wiser than Ethan the Ezrahite, wiser than Heman and Calcol and Darda, the cantors. He composed three thousand proverbs; and his songs numbered a thousand and five. He could talk about plants from the cedar in Lebanon to the hyssop growing on the wall; and he could talk of animals, and birds and reptiles and fish. Men from all nations came to hear Solomon's wisdom, and he received gifts from all the kings of the world, who heard of his wisdom.

This Old Testament tradition is expanded in the following way: Solomon's wisdom is increasingly seen to include magical knowledge, and his literary productivity grows to include magical incantations and magical books. The literary side to his productivity can already be observed in the Old Testament itself, for it is claimed that he authored Proverbs (Prov 1:1), Song of Songs (Song 1:1; cf. 1:5; 3:7, 9, 11; 8:11), Ecclesiastes (Eccl 1:1, 12, 16–18), and, if extended to the apocrypha, it is implied that he authored the Wisdom of Solomon (Wis Sol 8:10f.; 9:7f., 12). Other pseudepigraphic books include the Odes of Solomon, the Psalms of Solomon, and the work under consideration, the Testament of Solomon.

In the Wisdom of Solomon (Wis Sol 7:15–22), probably from second-century B.C. Egypt, it is claimed that Solomon knows astrology, "powers of roots," and "forces of spirits," in part an extension of his knowledge of plants in 1 Kings 5. Perhaps from about the same time and place came a Septuagint translator who changed 1,005 "songs" in 1 Kings 5:12 (4:32) to 5,000 "odes" (Gk. ōdai), and this may be the source of the later view that Solomon wrote "incantations" (Gk. epōdai; cf. Josephus, Ant 8.2.5(42-49)). In any case, it is clear that Solomon's fame grew in Egypt at a very early period.

Meanwhile, though sometimes difficult to trace, the popular tradition was also growing in Palestine. Josephus wrote that the Essenes, usually thought to have written the Dead Sea Scrolls, did "research into medicinal roots and properties of stones for the healing of diseases" (War 2.8.6(136)). It may be that Solomon was known among them as an exorcist of demons. Certainly, Abraham in the Genesis Apocryphon (1QapGen) and probably Daniel in the Prayer of Nabonidus (4QPrNab ar) are viewed as types of exorcists. Recently, there has turned up a curious recension of Psalm 91, which was known among the Rabbis as an exorcistic psalm (y.Shab 6:8b: "song for the stricken"; b.Shebuʿoth 15b: "song referring to evil demons"; y.ʿErub 10:26c: "song for the demons"), which contains Solomon's name just before the term "demons" in column 1. These Dead Sea Scrolls references are at least so early as the first century A.D."

"The interpretation of 1 Kings 5:13 (4:33) occurs again in the Targum Sheni to Esther.

Solomon *ruled over* the wild beasts, *over* the birds of the heaven, and *over* the creeping beasts of the earth, as well as *over the devils, the spirits of the night*; and he understood the language of all these according as it is written, "and he talked with the trees." [Italics mine.]

In this targum, Solomon's mastery over the demons includes the "demons of the night" (Heb. *lilîn*; cf. Isa 34:14, "night hag")." D. C. Duling, "A New Translation and Introduction," in *The Old Testament Pseudepigrapha*, vol. 1 (New York; London: Yale University Press, 1983), 945, 947.

"The earliest *Christian* tradition about the magical wisdom of Solomon, suggest some modern interpreters, is already implied in the New Testament. They refer primarily to the cryptic passage which states "something greater than Solomon is here" (Matt 12:42), which is followed by the story of the return of the unclean spirit (Matt 12:43–45). One is also led to raise the possibility with the Son of David pericope (Mark 12:35–37 and parallels) and the Markan theology as a whole, e.g. as a conception Mark opposed. But if such connections are rejected, the first clear reference in the Christian literary tradition is found in Origen's commentary on Matthew 26:63 in which Origen states, "It is customary to adjure demons with adjurations written by Solomon. But they themselves who use these adjurations sometimes use books not properly constituted; indeed they even adjure demons with some books taken from Hebrew." Possibly Origen was referring to the passage about Eleazar in Josephus, as do later Christian writers, but he might also have been thinking of the testament or the *Sepher Ha-Razim*." D. C. Duling, "A New Translation and Introduction," in *The Old Testament Pseudepigrapha*, vol. 1 (New York; London: Yale University Press, 1983), 949.

Josephus on Solomon's signet ring: "5. (42) Now the sagacity and wisdom which God had bestowed upon Solomon was so great, that he exceeded the ancients… He also composed books of odes and songs, a thousand and five; of parables and similitudes, three thousand… (45) God also enabled him to learn that skill which expels demons, which is a science useful and sanative to men. He composed such incantations also by which distempers are alleviated. And he left behind him the manner of using exorcisms, by which they drive away demons, so that they never return, (46) and this method of cure is of great force unto this day; for <u>I have seen a certain man of my own country whose name was Eleazar, releasing people that</u> <u>were demoniacal in the presence of Vespasian, and his sons, and his captains, and the whole multitude of</u> <u>his soldiers. The manner of the cure was this:—(47) He put a ring that had a root of one of those sorts</u> <u>mentioned by Solomon to the nostrils of the demoniac,</u> after which he drew out the demon through his nostrils; and when the man fell down immediately, he abjured him to return into him no more, making still mention of Solomon, and reciting the incantations which he composed. (48) And when Eleazar would persuade and demonstrate to the spectators that he had such a power, he set a little way off a cup or basin full of water, and commanded the demon, as he went out of the man, to overturn it, and thereby to let the spectators know that he had left the man; (49) and when this was done, the skill and wisdom of Solomon was shown very manifestly; for which reason it is, that all men may know the vastness of Solomon's abilities, and how he was beloved of God." FOOTNOTE: "<u>Some pretended fragments of these books of</u> <u>conjuration of Solomon are still extant in Fabricius's Cod. Pseudepigr. Vet. Test., p. 1054.</u>" Flavius Josephus and William Whiston, *The Works of Josephus: Complete and Unabridged* (Peabody: Hendrickson, 1987) Antiquities 8.42-47.

A legend of how Solomon got the signet ring from Michael: "Then it happened that while I was praying to the God of heaven and earth, there was granted me from the Lord Sabaoth through the archangel Michael a ring which had a seal engraved on precious stone. He said to me, "Solomon, Son of David, take the gift which the Lord God, the highest Sabaoth, has sent to you; (with it) you shall imprison all the demons, both female and male, and with their help you shall build Jerusalem when you bear this seal of God." Testament of Solomon 1:6-7. James H. Charlesworth, *The Old Testament Pseudepigrapha*, vol. 1 (New York; London: Yale University Press, 1983), 962.

[18] **High places**: "Apparently the Canaanite practices at the high places were proscribed for Israel rather than the use of such sites themselves. At least this is the inference derived from one of the sanctions at the end of the Holiness Code in which Yahweh says, "If you do not obey me, then I will destroy your high places, and knock down your incense altars, and throw your corpses on the memorial stelae of your idols, and my spirit will loathe you" (Lev. 26:30; cf. Ezk. 6:3–6). In any case, the high place seems to have survived as a legitimate site for sacrifice and worship in Israel until, ideally, the building of Solomon's temple (1 K. 3:2f); in practice, however, it continued till the reforms of Hezekiah (2 K. 18) and Josiah (2 K. 23)." L. T. Geraty, "High Place," ed. Geoffrey W Bromiley, *The International Standard Bible Encyclopedia*, Revised (Wm. B. Eerdmans, 1979–1988), 709.

[19] **Josephus' privileged background**: Flavius Josephus, *The Life of Flavius Josephus*, 1-2.

[20] **Sicarii first assassination of high priest under procurator Felix**: Flavius Josephus, *The Antiquities of the Jews*, 20.163-164; *Wars of the Jews*, 2.256.

CHAPTER 25

[1] Matthew 23:29-36.

This generation: "Each and every time "this generation" is used in the gospels, it refers to the generation to whom Jesus is speaking (Matt. 11:16; 12:41–42; 23:36; Mark 8:12; Luke 7:31; 11:30–32, 50–51; 17:25; cf. Gen. 7:1; Ps. 12:7; Heb. 3:10). "This generation" is never used as a reference to a future generation. Again, if Jesus had a future generation in mind, He would have said, "that generation will not pass away."

"Jesus is referring to world conditions in His day. The near demonstrative "this" is always used to describe what is near in terms of time and place. "The demonstrative[s] ... are of two kinds: near and distant. The near demonstratives, as the name denotes, points to someone or something 'near,' in close proximity. They appear as the singular word 'this' and its plural 'these.' The distant demonstratives, as their name suggests, appear as 'that' (singular), or 'those' (plural)." The near demonstrative always refers to something present-day as Greek lexicons and grammars demonstrate in their definitions.

•"This" refers "to something comparatively near at hand, just as ekeinos [that] refers to something comparatively farther away."

•"Sometimes it is desired to call attention with special emphasis to a designated object, whether in the physical vicinity or the speaker or the literary context of the writer. For this purpose the demonstrative construction is used.... For that which is relatively near in actuality or thought the immediate demonstrative [houtos] is used.... For that which is relatively distant in actuality or thought the remote demonstrative [ekeinos] is used."

Gary DeMar, *10 Popular Prophecy Myths Exposed: The Last Days Might Not Be as near as You Think* (Powder Springs, GA: American Vision, 2010), 153.

[2] Matthew 23:38.

[3] Matthew 24:4-5.

[4] **Descriptions of false messiahs during the time of the New Testament era**: Acts 5:36-37; 8:9-10; 13:6; 20:29-30; 2Timothy 3:1-13; 2Corinthians 11:12-15; Galatians 1:6-7; Revelation 2:2; 2:14-15; 2:20-24; 1John 2:18-26; 1John 4:1-3; 2John 7-9

False messiahs spoke of by Josephus: Josephus, *Jewish Wars*, 2.56; 2.118; 2.258-260; 2.261-265; 2.271-275; Josephus, *Antiquities of the Jews* 20.8; 20.97-98

Roman messianic prophecy: "There had spread over all the Orient an old and established belief, that it was fated at that time for men coming from Judaea to rule the world. This prediction, referring to the emperor of Rome, as afterwards appeared from the event, the people of Judaea took to themselves." Suetonius, *Lives of the Twelve Caesars, Vespasian* 4.5.

"But now, what did most elevate them in undertaking this war, was an ambiguous oracle that was also found in their sacred writings, how, "about that time, one from their country should become governor of the habitable earth." (313) The Jews took this prediction to belong to themselves in particular and many of the wise men were thereby deceived in their determination. Now, this oracle certainly denoted the government of Vespasian, who was appointed emperor in Judea." Josephus, *War of the Jews* 6.312-313, Flavius Josephus and William Whiston, *The Works of Josephus: Complete and Unabridged* (Peabody: Hendrickson, 1987).

[5] **Peace and security**: 1 Thessalonians 5:3 While people are saying, "There is peace and security," then sudden destruction will come upon them as labor pains come upon a pregnant woman, and they will not escape.

[6] **Pax Romana**: Pax Romana was Latin for "the peace of Rome" which ruled the known world at the time. So wars and rumors of wars would only be significant in this "time of peace." Since then, there has always been wars and rumors of wars all around the world, which would make this an irrelevant statement for any other time period in history, including the present.

"Under Tiberius things were quiet." (Tiberius' reign, AD 14- 37) Tacitus, *Histories* 5.9.

(January - March, A.D. 69) "The history on which I am entering is that of a period rich in disasters, terrible with battles, torn by civil struggles, horrible even in peace. Four emperors fell by the sword; there were three civil wars, more foreign wars, and often both at the same time. There was success in the East, misfortune in the West. Illyricum was disturbed, the Gallic provinces wavering, Britain subdued and immediately let go. The Sarmatae and Suebi rose against us; the Dacians won fame by defeats inflicted and suffered; even the Parthians were almost roused to arms through the trickery of a pretended Nero. Moreover, Italy was distressed by disasters unknown before or returning after the lapse of ages. Cities on the rich fertile shores of Campania were swallowed up or overwhelmed; Rome was devastated by conflagrations, in which her most ancient shrines were consumed and the very Capitol fired by citizens' hands. Sacred rites were defiled; there were adulteries in high places. The sea was filled with exiles, its cliffs made foul with the bodies of the dead." Tacitus, *Histories* 1.2.

[7] **Famines: A great famine in the days of Claudius**: Acts 11:27–29 Now in these days prophets came down from Jerusalem to Antioch. [28] And one of them named Agabus stood up and foretold by the Spirit that there would be a great famine over all the world (this took place in the days of Claudius). [29] So the disciples determined, every one according to his ability, to send relief to the brothers living in Judea.

Earthquakes and famines during the early first century: (During reign of Claudius) "This year witnessed many prodigies [signs and omens].... repeated earthquakes... further portents were seen in a shortage of corn, resulting in famine... it was established that there was no more than fifteen days supply of food in the city [Rome]. Only Heaven's special favour and a mild winter prevented catastrophe. Tacitus, *The Annals*, 12.43 Michael Grant (Penguin Books, 1989), page 271.

"How often have cities in Asia, how often in Achaia, been laid low by a single shock of earthquake! How many towns in Syria, how many in Macedonia, have been swallowed up! How often has this kind of devastation laid Cyprus in ruins! How often had Paphos collapsed! Not infrequently are tidings brought to us of the utter destruction of entire cities." Seneca in *Seneca Ad Lucilium Epistulae Morales*, Translated by Richard M Gummere, Vol 2, pg 437.

Earthquakes during the siege of Jerusalem: "Moreover at that feast which we call Pentecost, as the priests were going by night into the inner [court of the] temple, as their custom was, to perform their sacred ministrations, they said that, in the first place, they felt a quaking, and heard a great noise (300) and after that they heard a sound as of a great multitude, saying, "Let us remove hence." Flavius Josephus, *The Wars of the Jews*, 6.299-300.

"For there broke out a prodigious storm in the night, with the utmost violence, and very strong winds, with the largest showers of rain, with continual lightnings, terrible thunderings, and amazing concussions and bellowings of the earth, that was in an earthquake. (287) These things were a manifest indication that some destruction was coming upon men, when the system of the world was put into this disorder; and anyone would guess that these wonders foreshowed some grand calamities that were coming." Flavius Josephus, *The Wars of the Jews*, 4.286-287.

Signs from heaven (Luke 21:11): Luke 21:11 and there will be great earthquakes, and in various places plagues and famines; and there will be terrors and great signs from heaven.

"Signs that Preceded the Destruction [of Jerusalem AD 70]: Thus there was a star resembling a sword, which stood over the city, and a comet, that continued a whole year. (290) Thus also, before the Jews' rebellion, and before those commotions which preceded the war, when the people were come in great crowds to the feast of unleavened bread, on the eighth day of the month Xanthicus [Nisan], and at the ninth hour of the night, so great a light shone round the altar and the holy house, that it appeared to be bright day time; which light lasted for half an hour. (291) This light seemed to be a good sign to the unskillful, but was so interpreted by the sacred scribes, as to portend those events that followed immediately upon it. (292) At the same festival also, a heifer, as she was led by the high priest to be sacrificed, brought forth a lamb in the midst of the temple. (293) Moreover, the eastern gate of the inner [court of the] temple, which was of brass, and vastly heavy, and had been with difficulty shut by twenty men, and rested upon a basis armed with iron, and had bolts fastened very deep into the firm floor, which was there made of one entire stone, was seen to be opened of its own accord about the sixth hour of the night. (294) Now, those that kept watch in the temple came hereupon running to the captain of the temple, and told him of it: who then came up thither, and not without great difficulty, was able to shut the gate again. (295) This also appeared to the vulgar to be a very happy prodigy, as if God did thereby open them the gate of happiness. But the men of learning understood it, that the security of their holy house was dissolved of its own accord, and that the gate was opened for the advantage of their enemies. (296) So these publicly declared, that this signal foreshowed the desolation that was coming upon them. Besides these, a few days after that feast, on the twenty-first day of the month Artemisius [Jyar] (297) a certain prodigious and incredible phenomenon appeared; I suppose the account of it would seem to be a fable, were it not related by those that saw it (298) and were not the events that followed it of so considerable a nature as to deserve such signals; for, before sunsetting, chariots and troops of soldiers in their armor were seen (299) running about among the clouds, and surrounding of cities. Moreover at that feast which we call Pentecost, as the priests were going by night into the inner [court of the] temple, as their custom was, to perform their sacred ministrations, they said that, in the first place, they felt a quaking, and heard a great noise (300) and after that they heard a sound as of a great multitude, saying, "Let us remove hence." Flavius Josephus, *The Wars of the Jews*, 6.280-300.

"Secular historians of the time support the biblical record. "And as to earthquakes, many are mentioned by writers during a period just previous to 70 A.D. There were earthquakes in Crete, Smyrna, Miletus, Chios, Samos, Laodicea, Hierapolis, Colosse, Campania, Rome, and Judea. It is interesting to note that the city of Pompeii was much damaged by an earthquake occurring on February 5, 63 A.D." Henry Alford compiled the following list:

> The principal earthquakes occurring between this prophecy and the destruction of Jerusalem [in A.D. 70] were (1) a great earthquake in Crete, A.D. 46 or 47; (2) one at Rome on the day when Nero assumed the manly toga, A.D. 51; (3) one at Apamaea in Phrygia, mentioned by Tacitus, A.D. 53; (4) one at Laodicea in Phrygia, A.D. 60; (5) one in Campania.

"Notice the tight geographical area of these earthquakes within a period of just 12 years. Their severity and frequency have not been eclipsed in modern times.

"Flavius Josephus, an eyewitness to the events surrounding Jerusalem's destruction, describes an earthquake in Judea of such magnitude "that the constitution of the universe was confounded for the destruction of men." Gary DeMar, *10 Popular Prophecy Myths Exposed: The Last Days Might Not Be as near as You Think* (Powder Springs, GA: American Vision, 2010), 156–157.

[8] **Persecution of Christians**: Matthew 24:9-19.

Luke adds: Luke 21:12–18 [12] But before all this they will lay their hands on you and persecute you, delivering you up to the synagogues and prisons, and you will be brought before kings and governors for my name's sake. [13] This will be your opportunity to bear witness. [14] Settle it therefore in your minds not to meditate beforehand how to answer, [15] for I will give you a mouth and wisdom, which none of your adversaries will be able to withstand or contradict. [16] You will be delivered up even by parents and brothers and relatives and friends, and some of you they will put to death. [17] You will be hated by all for my name's sake. [18] But not a hair of your head will perish.

Persecution of Christians fulfilled: Matthew 10:22; Acts 8:1; 12:1-3; 18:12; 25:6-12; 2Corinthians 11:24. The book of Acts tells the story of how the apostles and first followers were brought before kings and governors, and delivered up to synagogues and prisons in persecution, just like Jesus prophesied they would be.

"Therefore, to scotch the rumour, Nero substituted as culprits, and punished with the utmost refinements of cruelty, a class of men, loathed for their vices, whom the crowd styled Christians. Christus, the founder of the name, had undergone the death penalty in the reign of Tiberius, by sentence of the procurator Pontius Pilatus, and the pernicious superstition was checked for a moment, only to break out once more, not merely in Judaea, the home of the disease, but in the capital itself, where all things horrible or shameful in the world collect and find a vogue. First, then, the confessed members of the sect were arrested; next, on their disclosures, vast numbers were convicted, not so much on the count of arson as for hatred of the human race. And derision accompanied their end: they were covered with wild beasts' skins and torn to death by dogs; or they were fastened on crosses, and, when daylight failed were burned to serve as lamps by night. Nero had offered his Gardens for the spectacle, and gave an exhibition in his Circus, mixing with the crowd in the habit of a charioteer, or mounted on his car. Hence, in spite of a guilt which had earned the most exemplary punishment, there arose a sentiment of pity, due to the impression that they were being sacrificed not for the welfare of the state but to the ferocity of a single man." Tacitus, *Annals* 15:44.

"He [Nero] first attempted to abolish the name of Christian." Sulpicius Severus, *Sacred History* 2:28.

"During his reign many abuses were severely punished and put down, and no fewer new laws were made… Punishment was inflicted on the Christians, a class of men given to a new and mischievous superstition." Suetonius, *Nero* 16.

"Consequently, to get rid of the report, Nero fastened the guilt and inflicted the most exquisite tortures on a class hated for their abominations, called Christians by the populace. Christus, from whom the name had its origin, suffered the extreme penalty during the reign of Tiberius at the hands of one of our procurators, Pontius Pilatus, and a most mischievous superstition, thus checked for the moment, again broke out not only in Judaea, the first source of the evil, but even in Rome, where all things hideous and shameful from every part of the world find their centre and become popular. Accordingly, an arrest was first made of all who pleaded guilty; then, upon their information, an immense multitude was convicted, not so much of the crime of firing the city, as of hatred against mankind. Mockery of every sort was added to their deaths. Covered with the skins of beasts, they were torn by dogs and perished, or were nailed to crosses, or were doomed to the flames and burnt, to serve as a nightly illumination, when daylight had expired. Nero offered his gardens for the spectacle, and was exhibiting a show in the circus, while he mingled with the people in the dress of a charioteer or stood aloft on a car. Hence, even for criminals who deserved extreme and exemplary punishment, there arose a feeling of compassion; for it was not, as it seemed, for the public good, but to glut one man's cruelty, that they were being destroyed." Suetonius, *Nero* 15.

"[Neronic Persecution] To these men who spent their lives in the practice of holiness, there is to be added a great multitude of the elect, who, having through envy endured many indignities and tortures, furnished. us with a most excellent example. ... being persecuted, after they had suffered terrible and unspeakable torments, finished the course of their faith with steadfastness." 1 Clement 6

[9] **Gospel proclaimed throughout the whole world**: Matthew 24:14.

Fulfillment: Colossians 1:23 the hope of the gospel that you have heard, which was proclaimed in all creation under heaven.

Colossians 1:6 the gospel, [6] which has come to you, as indeed in the whole world it is bearing fruit and increasing.

Romans 1:8 First, I thank my God through Jesus Christ for you all, because your faith is being proclaimed throughout the whole world.

Luke 2:1 Now it came about in those days that a decree went out from Caesar Augustus, that a census be taken of all the world. ["world" here is the same Greek word as in Matthew 24:14 and Romans 1:8, *Oikoumene*, so this means the Roman Empire in Scripture]

Romans 10:15–18 [15] And how are they to preach unless they are sent? As it is written, "How beautiful are the feet of those who preach the good news!" [16] But they have not all obeyed the gospel. For Isaiah says, "Lord, who has believed what he has heard from us?" [17] So faith comes from hearing, and hearing through the word of Christ. [18] But I ask, have they not heard? Indeed they have, for "Their voice has gone out to all the earth, and their words to the ends of the world."

Romans 16:25–26 [25] Now to him who is able to strengthen you according to my gospel and the preaching of Jesus Christ, according to the revelation of the mystery that was kept secret for long ages [26] but has now been disclosed and through the prophetic writings has been made known to all nations, according to the command of the eternal God, to bring about the obedience of faith

1 Timothy 3:16 [16] He was manifested in the flesh, vindicated by the Spirit, seen by angels, proclaimed among the nations, believed on in the world, taken up in glory.

1 Thessalonians 1:8 For not only has the word of the Lord sounded forth from you in Macedonia and Achaia, but your faith in God has gone forth everywhere, so that we need not say anything.

2 Corinthians 2:14 But thanks be to God, who in Christ always leads us in triumphal procession, and through us spreads the fragrance of the knowledge of him everywhere.

"The same historian [Josephus] records another fact still more wonderful than this. He says (9) that a certain oracle was found in their sacred writings which declared that at that time a certain person should go forth from their country to rule the world. He himself understood 11 that this was fulfilled in Vespasian. But Vespasian did not rule the whole world, but only that part of it which was subject to the Romans. With better right could it be applied to Christ; to whom it was said by the Father, "Ask of me, and I will give thee the heathen for thine inheritance, and the ends of the earth for thy possession." (10) At that very time, indeed, the voice of his holy apostles "went throughout all the earth, and their words to the end of the world." Eusebius, *Ecclesiastical Histories* 3.7.

"There may another very important, and very providential, reason be here assigned for this strange and foolish retreat of Cestius; which, if Josephus had been now a Christian, he might probably have taken notice of also; and that is, the affording the Jewish Christians in the city an opportunity of calling to mind the prediction and caution given them by Christ about thirty-three years and a half before, that "when they should see the abomination of desolation" [the idolatrous Roman armies, with the images of their idols in their ensigns, ready to lay Jerusalem desolate,] "stand where it ought not;" or, "in the holy place;" or, "when they should see Jerusalem encompassed with armies," they should then "flee to the mountains."

By complying with which those Jewish Christians fled to the mountains of Perea, and escaped this destruction. See Lit. Accompl. of Proph. pp. 69–70. Nor was there, perhaps, any one instance of a more unpolitic, but more providential conduct than this retreat of Cestius, visible during this whole siege of Jerusalem; which yet was providentially such a "great tribulation, as had not been from the beginning of the world to that time; no, nor ever should be."—Ibid., pp. 70–71." Josephus, *Wars of the Jews*, Note B, 2.539 (2:19:6)

[10] **Joseph's memory of Paul's concepts is drawn from**: 1 Thessalonians 1:10 and to wait for his Son from heaven, whom he raised from the dead, Jesus who delivers us from the wrath to come.

1 Corinthians 15:24–25 [24] Then comes the end, when he delivers the kingdom to God the Father after destroying every rule and every authority and power. [25] For he must reign until he has put all his enemies under his feet.

1 Corinthians 10:11 Now these things happened to them as an example, but they were written down for our instruction, on whom the end of the ages has come.

[11] **Abomination of Desolation**: Matthew 24:15-16.

Jacob's Trouble: A term used of the great suffering of the Jews in the Babylonian exile. After God frees the Jews and returns them to their land, he reminds them again of the future promise of the Messiah, referred to in the passage below as "David their king, whom I will raise up for them."

Jeremiah 30:7–9 [7] Alas! That day is so great there is none like it; it is a time of **distress for Jacob**; yet he shall be saved out of it. [8] "And it shall come to pass in that day, declares the LORD of hosts, that I will break his yoke from off your neck, and I will burst your bonds, and foreigners shall no more make a servant of him. [9] But they shall serve the LORD their God and David their king, whom I will raise up for them.

[12] **Daniel's Seventy Weeks**: Daniel 9:24–27 "Seventy weeks are decreed about your people and your holy city, to finish the transgression, to put an end to sin, and to atone for iniquity, to bring in everlasting righteousness, to seal both vision and prophet, and to anoint a most holy place. [25] Know therefore and understand that from the going out of the word to restore and build Jerusalem to the coming of an anointed one, a prince, there shall be seven weeks. Then for sixty-two weeks it shall be built again with squares and moat, but in a troubled time. [26] And after the sixty-two weeks, an anointed one shall be cut off and shall have nothing. And the people of the prince who is to come shall destroy the city and the sanctuary. Its end shall come with a flood, and to the end there shall be war. Desolations are decreed. [27] And he shall make a strong covenant with many for one week, and for half of the week he shall put an end to sacrifice and offering. And on the wing of abominations shall come one who makes desolate, until the decreed end is poured out on the desolator."

The following is excerpted from Kenneth L. Gentry, Jr., "Daniel's Seventy Weeks," paper PT551 (Covenant Media Foundation). http://www.cmfnow.com/articles/pt551.htm

The 7 weeks and 62 weeks to Messiah: "The first period of seven weeks must indicate something, for it is set off from the two other periods. Were it not significant, Daniel could have spoken of the sixty-nine weeks, rather than the "seven weeks and sixty-two weeks" (Dan. 9:25). This seven weeks (or forty-nine years) apparently witnesses the successful conclusion of the rebuilding of Jerusalem.[31] The city was rebuilt during this era, despite the opposition in "troublesome times" (cp. Neh. 4:18), which God ordained for them in this prophecy (Dan. 9:25). The second period of sixty-two weeks, extends from the conclusion of the rebuilding of Jerusalem to the introduction of the Messiah to Israel at His baptism at the beginning of His public ministry (Dan. 9:25), sometime around A.D. 26-30. This interpretation is quite widely agreed upon by conservative scholars, being virtually "universal among Christian exegetes"[32] excluding dispensationalists. The third period of one week is the subject of intense controversy between dispensationalism and other conservative scholarship.

The 6 messianic elements of Verse 24:

Finishing the transgression (v. 24): "Let us notice, first, that the Seventy Weeks will witness the finishing of the transgression. As just noted, Daniel's prayer of confession was regarding Israel's sins (Dan. 9:4ff) and the prophecy's focus is on Israel (Dan. 9:24a). Consequently, this finishing (Heb. kala) the transgression has to do with Israel's finishing, i.e., completing, her transgression against God. The finishing of that transgression occurs in the ministry of Christ, when Israel culminates her resistance to God by rejecting His Son and having Him crucified: "Last of all he sent his son to them, saying, 'They will respect my son.' But when the vinedressers saw the son, they said among themselves, 'This is the heir. Come, let us kill him and seize his inheritance'" (Matt. 21:37-38; cf. 21:33-45; Acts 7:51-52).

Put an end to sin (v. 24): "The second part of the couplet is directly related to the first: Having finished the transgression against God in the rejection of the Messiah, now the sins are sealed up (NASV marg.; Heb., chatham). The idea here is, as Payne observes, to seal or to "reserve sins for punishment."[41] Because of Israel's rejection of Messiah, God reserves punishment for her: the final, conclusive destruction of the Temple, which was reserved from the time of Jesus' ministry until A.D. 70 (Matt. 24:2, 34). The sealing or reserving of the sins indicates that within the "Seventy Weeks" Israel will complete her transgression and with the completing of her sin God will act to reserve (beyond the seventy weeks) their sins for judgment. This is a major point in the Lord's Olivet Discourse: Though just before His crucifixion Christ says, "Your house is left to you desolate" (Matt. 23:3[42]), He then reserves His judgment for one generation (Matt. 24:2, 34).

Atone for Iniquity (v.24): "The third result (beginning the second couplet) has to do with the provision of "reconciliation for iniquity."[43] The Hebrew word kaphar is the word for "atonement," i.e., a covering of sin. It clearly speaks of Christ's atoning death, which is the ultimate atonement to which all Temple rituals looked (Heb. 9:26[44]). This also occurred during His earthly ministry—at His death.

Everlasting righteousness (v. 24): "Because of this atonement to cover sin, the fourth result is that everlasting righteousness is effected. That is, the final, complete atonement establishes righteousness. This speaks of the objective accomplishment, not the subjective appropriation of righteousness. This was effected by Christ within the seventy week period, as well: "But now the righteousness of God apart from the law is revealed, being witnessed by the Law and the Prophets, even the righteousness of God" (Rom. 3:21-22a).

Seal up vision and prophecy (v. 24): "The fifth result (the first portion of the third couplet) has to do with the ministry of Christ on earth, which is introduced at His baptism: He comes "to seal up vision and prophecy." By this is meant that Christ fulfills (and thereby confirms) the prophecy. The careful dispensationalist resists the idea that this has to do with the sealing of prophecy in Christ's earthly ministry because He did not fulfill all prophecy at that time.[46] But neither does He within the seventy weeks (up through the Tribulation), nor in the "millennium"! For following these are the resurrection and the New Heavens and New Earth. Actually, the sealing of prophecy regards the subject of Daniel 9: the accomplishment of redemption from sin, i.e. atonement. This Christ accomplished: "Behold, we are going up to Jerusalem, and all [!] things that are written by the prophets concerning the Son of Man will be accomplished" (Luke 18:31; cp. Luke 24:44; Acts 3:18).

Anoint the Most Holy (v. 24): "Finally, the seventy years are for the following goal: "to anoint the Most Holy." This anointing [Heb. mashach] speaks of the introduction of "Christ" by means of His baptismal anointing. This seems clearly to be the case for the following reasons: (1) The overriding concern of Daniel 9:24-27 is Messianic. The Temple that is built after the Babylonian Captivity is to be destroyed after the seventy weeks (v. 27), with no further mention made of it. (2) In the following verses, the Messiah (Heb., mashiyach, "Christ," "Anointed One") is specifically named twice (vv. 25, 26). (3) Contrary to the dispensational interpretation, there is no evidence of an anointing of any Temple in Scripture—whether Solomon's original Temple, Zerubbabel's rebuilt Temple, Ezekiel's visionary Temple, or Herod's expanded Temple.

"(4) The "most holy" phraseology well speaks of the Messiah, who is "that Holy One who is to be born."[48] It is of Christ that the ultimate redemptive Jubilee is prophesied by Isaiah in these words: "The Spirit of the Lord GOD is upon Me, because the LORD has anointed Me to preach good tidings to the poor; He has sent Me to heal the brokenhearted, to proclaim liberty to the captives, and the opening of the prison to those who are bound; to proclaim the acceptable year of the LORD" (Isa. 61:1-2a; cp. Luke 4:17-21). It was at His baptismal anointing that the Spirit came upon Him (Mark 1:9-11). And this was introductory to His ministry, of which we read three verses later: "Jesus came to Galilee, preaching the gospel of the kingdom of God, and saying, 'The time is fulfilled [the Sixty-ninth week?[49]], and the kingdom of God is at hand. Repent, and believe in the gospel" (Mark 1:14-15). Christ is pre-eminently the Anointed One.

Messiah would confirm the covenant (v. 27): "The confirming of covenant (v. 27) refers to the prophesied covenantal actions of verse 24, which come about as the result of the Perfect Covenantal Jubilee (Seventy Weeks), and is mentioned as a result of Daniel's covenantal prayer (cf. v. 4). The covenant mentioned, then, is the divine covenant of God's redemptive grace.[53] Messiah came to confirm the covenantal promises: "to perform the mercy promised to our fathers and to remember His holy covenant" (Luke 1:72).[54] He confirmed the covenant by His death on the cross: "by so much more Jesus has become a surety of a better covenant" (Heb. 7:22b).[55] The word translated "confirm" (Heb: higbir) is related to the angel Gabriel's name, who brought Daniel the revelation of the Seventy Weeks (and who later brings the revelation of Christ's birth [Luke 1:19, 26]). "Gabriel" is based on the Hebrew gibbor, "strong one," a concept frequently associated with the covenant God.[56] The related word found in Daniel 9:27 means to "make strong, confirm."[57] This "firm covenant" brings about "everlasting righteousness" (Dan. 9:24) -- hence its firmness.

Messiah would put an end to sacrifice and offering (v. 27): "This confirmation of the covenant occurs "in the middle of the week" (v. 27). I have already shown that the seventieth week begins with the baptismal anointing of Christ. Then after three and one-half years of ministry—the middle of the seventieth week—Christ was crucified.[60] Thus, the prophecy states that by His conclusive confirmation of the covenant, Messiah will "bring an end to sacrifice and offering" (v. 27) by offering up Himself as a sacrifice for sin: "Now, once at the end of the ages, He has appeared to put away sin by the sacrifice of Himself" (Heb. 9:25-26; cp. Heb. 7:11-12, 18-22). Consequently, at His death the Temple veil was torn from top to bottom (Matt. 27:51) as evidence the sacrificial system was legally disestablished in the eyes of God (cf. Matt. 23:38), for Christ is the Lamb of God (John 1:29; 1 Pet. 1:19)."

[13] **When was the decree to rebuild made?:** "At first appearance it would seem to be Cyrus' decree in 538 B.C., which is mentioned in 2 Chronicles 36:22-23 and in Ezra 1:1-4; 5:13, 17, 6:3. Certainly Cyrus did give a command that the city be rebuilt (cf. Isa. 44:28), although the bulk of the references to his decree in the historical books have to do with the rebuilding of the Temple. Daniel, however, specifically speaks of the command to "restore and build Jerusalem," which is an important qualification.

"It is abundantly clear in the references to Jerusalem decades after Cyrus' decree that little was done towards rebuilding Jerusalem. Nehemiah speaks of Jerusalem's walls as fallen down (Neh. 1:3; 2:3-5, 17; 7:4). Zechariah speaks of Jerusalem as destroyed in his day (Zech. 14:11). He even speaks of its soon-coming rebuilding (Zech. 1:16).[29] The enemies of the Jews warn Artaxerxes that the Jews will become a problem if they rebuild the city (Ezra 4:12-23).

"The process of diligent rebuilding, which climaxed in a restored Jerusalem, seems to have begun either: (1) in seed in the spiritual revival under Ezra (Ezra 7); or (2) in actuality under the administration of Nehemiah (Neh. 2:1, 17-18; 6:15-16; 12:43).[30] There were several political commands preparing for the restoration of Jerusalem and one divine command: "So the elders of the Jews built, and they prospered through the prophesying of Haggai the prophet and Zechariah the son of Iddo. And they built and finished it, according to the commandment of the God of Israel, and according to the command of Cyrus, Darius, and Artaxerxes king of Persia" (Ezra 6:14)." Kenneth L. Gentry, Jr., "Daniel's Seventy Weeks," paper PT551 (Covenant Media Foundation). http://www.cmfnow.com/articles/pt551.htm

[14] **Cyrus the Persian as God's Anointed One:** Isaiah 44:28–45:1 Who says of Cyrus, 'He is my shepherd, and he shall fulfill all my purpose'; saying of Jerusalem, 'She shall be built,' and of the temple, 'Your foundation shall be laid.' " [1] Thus says the LORD to his anointed [Messiah], to Cyrus, whose right hand I have grasped, to subdue nations before him.

Josephus ultimately claimed that Vespasian, the emperor of Rome shortly after Nero, was the Messiah deliverer:

"The same historian [Josephus] records another fact still more wonderful than this. He says (9) that a certain oracle was found in their sacred writings which declared that at that time a certain person should go forth from their country to rule the world. He himself understood 11 that this was fulfilled in Vespasian. But Vespasian did not rule the whole world, but only that part of it which was subject to the Romans. With better right could it be applied to Christ; to whom it was said by the Father, "Ask of me, and I will give thee the heathen for thine inheritance, and the ends of the earth for thy possession." (10) At that very time, indeed, the voice of his holy apostles "went throughout all the earth, and their words to the end of the world." Eusebius, *Ecclesiastical Histories* 3.7.

"What did the most to induce the Jews to start this war, was an ambiguous oracle that was also found in their sacred writings, how, about that time, one from their country should become governor of the habitable earth. The Jews took this prediction to belong to themselves in particular, and many of the wise men were thereby deceived in their determination. Now this oracle certainly denoted the government of Vespasian, who was appointed emperor in Judea." Flavius Josephus, *Wars of the Jews* 6.312-313

"Josephus links his revelations with scriptural prophecy. Back in the cave at Jotapata, he was enabled to understand his dreams because he was "not ignorant of the prophecies in the sacred books" (War 3.352). What prophetic statements might have been associated with Vespasian? (a) Josephus himself says that they are "ambiguous utterances" (War3.352), which require special insight to be understood (b) We know that Josephus was especially fond of the book of Daniel. Although traditional Judaism did not ultimately include Daniel among the prophets, Josephus considered him "one of the greatest of the prophets" (Ant. 10.266). Josephus confirms the evidence of the NT that Daniel was widely read by first-century Jews, because that book was thought to have revealed events of their own time. That is, the four-kingdom scenario envisioned by Daniel (2:31-45), which seems to end with the reign of Antiochus Epiphanes (d. 164 BC), was understood by later Jews to present the Roman empire as the last world power (Ant. 10.276). This interpretation was doubtless enhanced by Dan 9:24-27, which counts seventy weeks of years (= 490) from the rebuilding of the temple to its final desecration and the appearance of an "anointed ruler." Since the temple had been rebuilt in about 500 BC (no one knew the exact dates), speculation was ripe throughout the first century that the end was near. Thus, although many biblical statements were interpreted by Jewish groups to refer to the awaited deliverer, we have good reason to suppose that Josephus was thinking of Daniel when he spoke of such prophecies." Steve Mason, *Josephus and the New Testament* (Hendrickson, 1993), 47.

The Roman view of a Messiah: "There had spread over all the Orient an old and established belief, that it was fated for men coming from Judaea to rule the world. This prediction, referring to the emperor of Rome -as afterwards appeared from the event- the people of Judaea took to themselves." Suetonius, *Life of Vespasian* 4.5.

"The majority [of the Jews] were convinced that the ancient scriptures of their priests alluded to the present as the very time when the Orient would triumph and from Judaea would go forth men destined to rule the world. This mysterious prophecy really referred to Vespasian and Titus, but the common people, true to the selfish ambitions of mankind, thought that this exalted destiny was reserved for them, and not even their calamities opened their eyes to the truth." Tacitus, *Histories* 5.13.

[15] Daniel 9:27.

[16] **Who was the Abomination of Desolation?:** Though the Maccabees considered Epiphanes as the "abomination of desolation," (1 Maccabees 1:54), DeMar points out that Jesus said this prophecy was yet to be fulfilled within Jesus' own generation (Matthew 24:15):

"An abomination in the Old Testament was "related to the desecrating of worship, either by outright false worship (Deut. 7:25; 27:15) or by a profanation of true worship (Lev. 7:18; Deut. 17:1)." This definition fits the situation leading up to the temple's desolation in A.D. 70 in a number of ways. While there is little agreement on what the abomination was that brought on the desolation, nearly all the older commentators are agreed that the desolation occurred in the temple's destruction in A.D. 70. We do know, however, that the abomination that brings on the desolation happens sometime between Jerusalem being "surrounded by armies" (Luke 21:20) and the destruction of the temple. Four events are put forth as possible "abominations." Gary DeMar, *Last Days Madness: Obsession of the Modern Church*, Fourth revised edition (Powder Springs, GA: American Vision, 1999), 103–104.

DeMar lists the four options for abomination as The Zealots, the Idumeans, the Romans and the Jews, and shows there is some validity to each of them.

Destruction of the temple in Daniel 9:26-27: "But now how are we to understand the latter portions of verses 26 and 27? What are we to make of the destruction of the city and sanctuary (v. 26) and the abomination that causes desolation (v. 27), which most evangelical commentators agree occurred in A.D. 70? In verse 26 we learn there are two events to occur after the sixty-ninth week: (1) The Messiah is to be "cut off," and (2) the city and sanctuary are to be destroyed. Verse 27a informs us that the Messiah's cutting off (v. 26a) is a confirmation of the covenant and is to occur at the half-way mark of the seventieth week. So the Messiah's death is clearly within the time-frame of the Seventy Weeks (as we expect because of His being the major figure of the fulfillment of the prophecy). The events involving the destruction of the city and the sanctuary with war and desolation (vv. 26b, 27b) are the consequences of the cutting off of the Messiah and do not necessarily occur in the seventy weeks time-frame. They are an addendum to the fulfillment of the focus of the prophecy, which is stated in verse 24.

"The destructive acts are anticipated, however, in the divine act of sealing up or reserving the sin of Israel for punishment. Israel's climactic sin—their completing of their transgression (v. 24) with the cutting off of Messiah (v. 26a) -- results in God's act of reserving their judgment until later. Israel's sin will not be reserved forever; it will be judged after the expiration of the seventy weeks. This explains the "very indefinite"[61] phrase "till the end of the war": the "end" will not occur in the seventy weeks. That end occurred in A.D. 70, as Christ makes abundantly clear in Matthew 24:15." Kenneth L. Gentry, Jr., "Daniel's Seventy Weeks," paper PT551 (Covenant Media Foundation). http://www.cmfnow.com/articles/pt551.htm

[17] **God's providential use of Assyria and his punishment of the same**: Isaiah 10:5–16 Ah, Assyria, the rod of my anger; the staff in their hands is my fury! [6] Against a godless nation I send him, and against the people of my wrath I command him, to take spoil and seize plunder, and to tread them down like the mire of the streets. [7] But he does not so intend, and his heart does not so think; but it is in his heart to destroy, and to cut off nations not a few; …When the Lord has finished all his work on Mount Zion and on Jerusalem, he will punish the speech of the arrogant heart of the king of Assyria and the boastful look in his eyes. [13] For he says: "By the strength of my hand I have done it, and by my wisdom, for I have understanding; I remove the boundaries of peoples, and plunder their treasures; like a bull I bring down those who sit on thrones. [14] My hand has found like a nest the wealth of the peoples; and as one gathers eggs that have been forsaken, so I have gathered all the earth; and there was none that moved a wing or opened the mouth or chirped." [15] Shall the axe boast over him who hews with it, or the saw magnify itself against him who wields it? As if a rod should wield him who lifts it, or as if a staff should lift him who is not wood! [16] Therefore the Lord GOD of hosts will send wasting sickness among his stout warriors, and under his glory a burning will be kindled, like the burning of fire.

God used Babylon to judge Israel, then he judged Babylon: Jeremiah 4:23-30; Isaiah 13:1-19.

[18] **Pharisees believed in providence, though not as strongly as the Essenes**: Now for the Pharisees, they say that some actions, but not all, are the work of fate, and some of them are in our own power, and that they are liable to fate, but are not caused by fate. But the sect of the Essenes affirm, that fate governs all things, and that nothing befalls men but what is according to its determination. Flavius Josephus, The *Antiquities of the Jews*, 13.171.

[19] **The Sign of the Son of Man**: Matthew 24:29-30.

Jesus said that the people of his generation would "see" him seated in heaven. This was not a literal seeing with eyes, but figurative of "understanding" that Jesus is at the right hand of God: Matthew 26:64 [64] Jesus said to him, "You have said so. But I tell you, from now on you will see the Son of Man seated at the right hand of Power and coming on the clouds of heaven."

Matthew 22:42–45 [42] "What do you think about the Christ? Whose son is he?" They said to him, "The son of David." [43] He said to them, "How is it then that David, in the Spirit, calls him Lord, saying, [44] " 'The Lord said to my Lord, "Sit at my right hand, until I put your enemies under your feet" '? [45] If then David calls him Lord, how is he his son?"

Luke 9:26-27 [26] For whoever is ashamed of me and of my words, of him will the Son of Man be ashamed when he comes in his glory and the glory of the Father and of the holy angels. [27] But I tell you truly, there are some standing here who will not taste death until they see the kingdom of God."

The Destruction of Jerusalem was the sign that Jesus is enthroned in heaven seated at God's right hand of power: Ephesians 1:20–23 [20] that he worked in Christ when he raised him from the dead and seated him at his right hand in the heavenly places, [21] far above all rule and authority and power and dominion, and above every name that is named, not only in this age but also in the one to come. [22] And he put all things under his feet and gave him as head over all things to the church, [23] which is his body, the fullness of him who fills all in all.

The right hand of God was a sign of omnipotent power: "The right hand of Yahweh was that which delivered Israel, shattering the enemy (Exod 15:6). Yahweh's right hand gains mighty victories for his people (Pss 20:7—Eng v 6; 44:4—Eng v 3; 98:1). To have Yahweh at one's right hand virtually assured victory, for it implied that Yahweh was supplying the might for the confrontation: "The Lord is at your right hand; he will shatter kings on the day of his wrath" (Ps 110:5). In a related usage, the position of honor is regularly at the host's right hand. To be at Yahweh's right hand is to be in the position of highest honor (Ps 110:1)." Joel F. Jr. Drinkard, "Right, Right Hand," ed. David Noel Freedman, *The Anchor Yale Bible Dictionary* (New York: Doubleday, 1992), 724.

[20] **Sun, moon and stars are symbols of rulers and in particular, Israel**: Judges 5:19 "The kings came and fought; Then fought the kings of Canaan At Taanach near the waters of Megiddo; They took no plunder in silver. 20 "The stars fought from heaven, From their courses they fought against Sisera.

Genesis 37:9 Now [Joseph] had still another dream, and related it to his brothers, and said, ... behold, the sun and the moon and eleven stars were bowing down to me." ... and his father rebuked him and said to him, ...Shall I and your mother and your brothers actually come to bow ourselves down before you to the ground?"

Revelation 12:1 And a great sign appeared in heaven: a woman clothed with the sun, and the moon under her feet, and on her head a crown of twelve stars; 2 and she was with child; and she cried out, being in labor and in pain to give birth.

Collapsing universe imagery in the Old Testament is a poetic reference to the fall and destruction of important rulers and cultures, not literal collapsing universes:

When God destroyed the first temple in 587 BC using the: Jeremiah 4:23–28 I looked on the earth, and behold, it was without form and void; and to the heavens, and they had no light. [24] I looked on the mountains, and behold, they were quaking, and all the hills moved to and fro...[27] For thus says the LORD, "The whole land shall be a desolation; yet I will not make a full end. [28] "For this the earth shall mourn, and the heavens above be dark."

When God judged Babylon in 539 BC using the Medes as his instrument: Isaiah 13:1–19 [1] The oracle concerning Babylon which Isaiah the son of Amoz saw... [4] The LORD of hosts is mustering a host for battle. [5] They come from a distant land, from the end of the heavens, the LORD and the weapons of his indignation, to destroy the whole land...[9] Behold, the day of the LORD comes, cruel, with wrath and fierce anger, to <u>make the land a desolation</u> and to destroy its sinners from it. [10] For <u>the stars of the heavens and their constellations will not give their light; the sun will be dark at its rising, and the moon will not shed its light...</u> [13] Therefore <u>I will make the heavens tremble, and the earth will be shaken out of its place</u>, at the wrath of the LORD of hosts in the day of his fierce anger... [17] Behold, I am stirring up the Medes against them.

When God judged Edom (Judah) using the Babylonians in 587 BC: Isaiah 34:2–5 [2] For the LORD is enraged against all the nations, and furious <u>against all their host</u>; he has <u>devoted them to destruction</u>, ... the <u>mountains shall flow with their blood</u>. [4] <u>All the host of heaven shall rot away, and the skies roll up like a scroll. All their host shall fall, as leaves fall from the vine</u>, like leaves falling from the fig tree. [5] For my sword has drunk its fill <u>in the heavens</u>; behold, it descends for judgment upon Edom, upon the people I have <u>devoted to destruction</u>.

When God judged Egypt in 580 BC, using Babylon: Ezekiel 32:7–8 [7] When I blot you out, I will cover the heavens and make their stars dark; I will cover the sun with a cloud, and the moon shall not give its light. [8] All the bright lights of heaven will I make dark over you, and put darkness on your land, declares the Lord GOD.

Ezekiel 30:12 [12] And I will dry up the Nile; I will bring desolation upon the land and everything in it, by the hand of foreigners; I am the LORD; I have spoken.

See also: Amos 8:9; Isaiah 30:25-31:4; Isaiah 24:1-23; 26:9; Zephaniah 3:8; Joel 1:1-5; Nahum 1:4-6.

The shaking of heavens and earth is NOT literal, but a metaphor for the overthrow of a covenant. Here is the New Covenant described in these terms of shaking heaven and earth: Haggai 2:6–7 [6] For thus says the LORD of hosts: Yet once more, in a little while, I will shake the heavens and the earth and the sea and the dry land. [7] And I will shake all nations, so that the treasures of all nations shall come in, and I will fill this house with glory, says the LORD of hosts.

Hebrews 12:26–28 [26] At that time his voice shook the earth, but now he has promised, "Yet once more I will shake not only the earth but also the heavens." [27] This phrase, "Yet once more," indicates the removal of things that are shaken—that is, things that have been made—in order that the things that cannot be shaken may remain. [28] Therefore let us be grateful for receiving a kingdom that cannot be shaken, and thus let us offer to God acceptable worship, with reverence and awe,

The first coming of Jesus and his ministry is described in the same symbolic terms of mountains being leveled, and valleys being upended: Isaiah 40:3–5 [3] A voice cries: "In the wilderness prepare the way of the LORD; make straight in the desert a highway for our God. [4] Every valley shall be lifted up, and every mountain and hill be made low; the uneven ground shall become level, and the rough places a plain. [5] And the glory of the LORD shall be revealed, and all flesh shall see it together, for the mouth of the LORD has spoken."

[21] Matthew 24:30.

[22] **Coming on the clouds**: I want to focus on the phrase, "coming on the clouds of heaven" to prove that it is not the physical return of Christ, but rather a metaphor for God's judgment upon Jerusalem for rejecting Messiah. I believe Jesus Christ will physically return to this earth, but I do not think that this passage teaches that doctrine. It teaches something else. And I am in good company with orthodox scholars through history who have posited this very interpretation of Matthew 24; Eusebius, John Calvin, John Lightfoot, John Gill, Phillip Schaff, Gary DeMar, Kenneth L. Gentry, R.C. Sproul and many others.

When considering the ancient Near Eastern context of this "cloud" image, I have previously written that the notion of deity coming on clouds or riding clouds like a chariot was already a powerful metaphor used of the god Baal in Canaan when Israel arrived there. Baal, the storm god, was called the great "Cloud-Rider"[22] who would dispense his judgments through thunder and lightning in his hand.[22] To ride the clouds was a sign of deity and judgment to the Canaanites. So it makes sense that the Biblical writers who were dispossessing Baal and his worshippers from the land would use the same epithets of Yahweh in a subversive way of saying Yahweh is God, not Baal.

In light of this connection of cloud-riding with deity and judgment, Jesus' statement becomes an implicit reference to His own deity and Messiahship rejected by the first century Jews which resulted in God's judgment upon Jerusalem (Matt. 21:33-45). Jesus is coming in judgment to vindicate His claims (Matt. 26:64), and He is going to do so by using the Roman armies of Titus to do His bidding.

Look at these Old Testament passages that use the concept of coming on the clouds as a metaphor for God coming in judgment upon cities or nations:

God's judgment on Egypt:

Isaiah 19:1 Behold, the LORD is riding on a swift cloud, and is about to come to Egypt.

Ezekiel 30:3 For the day is near, the day of the LORD is near; it will be a day of clouds, a time of doom for the nations.

God's judgment on Ninevah:

Nahum 1:3 In whirlwind and storm is His way, And clouds are the dust beneath His feet.

God's judgment on Israel:

Joel 2:2 Surely it is near, A day of darkness and gloom, A day of <u>clouds and thick darkness</u>.

Messiah as deity and kingly judge:

Daniel 7:13-14 "I kept looking in the night visions, And behold, <u>with the clouds of heaven</u> One like a Son of Man was coming, And He <u>came up</u> to the Ancient of Days And was presented before Him. And to Him was given dominion, Glory and a kingdom."

Did God literally or physically come riding on a cumulus nimbus in these passages? The answer is obvious: No. The notion of coming on the clouds with storm and lightning was an ancient Near Eastern motif of deity coming in judgment upon a city or nation. Egypt was plundered by the Assyrians (Isa. 9:23-25). Ninevah was destroyed by the hand of Nebuchadnezzar of Babylon (Ezek. 30:10). But God is described as the one who was using these pagan forces as His own means of judging those cities. This is how God "came on the clouds."

So Matthew 24 is God's description of judging Israel for rejecting Messiah by using the Roman armies to destroy the Temple and Jerusalem. Jesus didn't physically come riding on a cumulus nimbus, He "came on the clouds" in judgment by using the Roman armies to vindicate His claims of Messiahship. This was not a physical Second Coming, but a spiritual coming.

This was excerpted from Brian Godawa, *God Against the gods: Storytelling, Imagination and Apologetics in the Bible* (Embedded Pictures, 2016), 136-138.

The deified Son of Man in Daniel: Jesus used the term Son of Man of himself, which was a deliberate way of claiming deity. Notice in Daniel 7 below, the deification terms of coming on the clouds before the very throne of God. Many Jews considered this passage to illustrate two Yahwehs in heaven, the Father and the Son of Man.

Daniel 7:13–14 [13] "I saw in the night visions, and behold, with the clouds of heaven there came one like a son of man, and he came to the Ancient of Days and was presented before him. [14] And to him was given dominion and glory and a kingdom, that all peoples, nations, and languages should serve him; his dominion is an everlasting dominion, which shall not pass away, and his kingdom one that shall not be destroyed.

[23] **The high priest Ananus ben Ananus had James killed**: "when, therefore, Ananus was of this disposition, he thought he had now a proper opportunity [to exercise his authority]. Festus was now dead, and Albinus was but upon the road; so he assembled the sanhedrin of judges, and brought before them the brother of Jesus, who was called Christ, whose name was James, and some others, [or, some of his companions]; and when he had formed an accusation against them as breakers of the law, he delivered them to be stoned." Flavius Josephus, *The Antiquities of the Jews*, 20.200.

[24] **Joseph's accusation of demon possession foreshadows the demonic delusion of the priesthood**: Matthew 12:24-32, Jesus addresses those who called him demon possessed. He warns them that attributing the works of God to Satan is blasphemy that will not be forgiven. The premise of Revelation's condemnation of the priestly class of Israel as the blasphemous harlot is embodied in Joseph's accusation here.

[25] **Joshua (Jesus bar Ananus) as a Christian**: Josephus does not say Jesus (Joshua) bar Ananus is a Christian. But Josephus showed a decidedly anti-Christian bias by virtually ignoring their presence in Jerusalem in his books. It is entirely reasonable to conclude that Jesus (Joshua) bar Ananus may have been a Christian, since his main message was a repetition of a prophecy made infamous by Jesus of Nazareth. That prophecy was the destruction of the city of Jerusalem and its temple in Matthew 24. It would not be helpful to Josephus' agenda to admit such a thing, but reading between the lines may uncover the hidden truth. And it would also make sense for Josephus to truncate the actual details of Jesus bar Ananus preaching into an oversimplification. Josephus would not want to vindicate Jesus Christ by admitting his prophecy about the destruction of the temple and city.

Joshua (Jesus bar Ananus) would continue to preach this message throughout the siege of Jerusalem: "Hereupon our rulers supposing, as the case proved to be, that this was a sort of divine fury in the man, brought him to the Roman procurator; (304) where he was whipped till his bones were laid bare; yet did he not make any supplication for himself, nor shed any tears, but turning his voice to the most lamentable tone possible, at every stroke of the whip his answer was, "Woe, woe to Jerusalem!" (305) And when Albinus (for he was then our procurator) asked him who he was, and whence he came, and why he uttered such words; he made no manner of reply to what he said, but still did not leave off his melancholy ditty, till Albinus took him to be a madman, and dismissed him. (306) Now, during all the time that passed before the war began, this man did not go near any of the citizens, nor was seen by them while he said so; but he every day uttered these lamentable words, as if it were his premeditated vow, "Woe, woe, to Jerusalem!" (307) Nor did he give ill words to any of those that beat him every day, nor good words to those that gave him food; but this was his reply to all men, and indeed no other than a melancholy presage of what was to come. (308) This cry of his was the loudest at the festivals; and he continued this ditty for seven years and five months, without growing hoarse, or being tired therewith, until the very time that he saw his presage in earnest fulfilled in our siege, when it ceased." Josephus, *Wars of the Jews* 6.300-309.

[26] **This generation referred to the generation who was alive when Jesus spoke the words**: "Each and every time "this generation" is used in the gospels, it refers to the generation to whom Jesus is speaking (Matt. 11:16; 12:41–42; 23:36; Mark 8:12; Luke 7:31; 11:30–32, 50–51; 17:25; cf. Gen. 7:1; Ps. 12:7; Heb. 3:10). "This generation" is never used as a reference to a future generation. Again, if Jesus had a future generation in mind, He would have said, "that generation will not pass away."

"Jesus is referring to world conditions in His day. The near demonstrative "this" is always used to describe what is near in terms of time and place. "The demonstrative[s] ... are of two kinds: near and distant. The near demonstratives, as the name denotes, points to someone or something 'near,' in close proximity. They appear as the singular word 'this' and its plural 'these.' The distant demonstratives, as their name suggests, appear as 'that' (singular), or 'those' (plural)." The near demonstrative always refers to something present-day as Greek lexicons and grammars demonstrate in their definitions.

> •"This" refers "to something comparatively near at hand, just as ekeinos [that] refers to something comparatively farther away."

> •"Sometimes it is desired to call attention with special emphasis to a designated object, whether in the physical vicinity or the speaker or the literary context of the writer. For this purpose the demonstrative construction is used.... For that which is relatively near in actuality or thought the immediate demonstrative [houtos] is used.... For that which is relatively distant in actuality or thought the remote demonstrative [ekeinos] is used."

Gary DeMar, *10 Popular Prophecy Myths Exposed: The Last Days Might Not Be as near as You Think* (Powder Springs, GA: American Vision, 2010), 153.

CHAPTER 26

[1] **Hall of Hewn Stone**: "The place of meeting was most likely on the western boundary of the temple mount, E of the "Xystus" (i.e., "place of hewn stone") where a bridge (Wilson's Arch) connected the Upper City to the temple mount." W. J. Moulder, "Sanhedrin," ed. Geoffrey W. Bromiley, *The International Standard Bible Encyclopedia, Revised* (Wm. B. Eerdmans, 1979–1988), 332-333.

[2] **Sanhedrin deliberation**: The Sanhedrin: "Only the high priest could preside over the Sanhedrin (though later at Jamnia two scribes held the positions of president and assistant. Next in rank to the high priest were the chief priests, whose presence and power in the Sanhedrin were due to their office in the temple. They were uniformly members of the sadduccean aristocracy, which solidified them into a powerful party. Next came the elders, the term not being used in the original, broader sense of all members of the Sanhedrin, but in the later more narrow sense describing lay members of the Sanhedrin coming from the more influential families of Jerusalem, who like the chief priests were consistently Sadducees. The sadduccean monopoly of the Sanhedrin began to diminish under Queen Alexandra when the pharisaic scribes gained admission. Herod's hostility toward the nobility led to a substantial increase in the pharisaic influence in the Sanhedrin, to the point that in the Roman period the Pharisees' support was necessary for any decision to be made or carried out.

"Both in Palestine and in the Diaspora the Roman authorities tolerated "little" Sanhedrins, which were set up on the model of the Great Sanhedrin of Jerusalem. The Torah itself (Nu. 35:29) was considered to have authorized these lesser courts. They had twenty-three members in every town that had 120 adult male Jews." W. J. Moulder, "Sanhedrin," ed. Geoffrey W. Bromiley, *The International Standard Bible Encyclopedia, Revised* (Wm. B. Eerdmans, 1979–1988), 332-333.

"The center of the legal system was the Great Court of seventy-one members which met in the Chamber of Hewn Stone in Jerusalem. It tried tribes, false prophets, and high priests; sent the people forth to voluntary wars; approved additions to Jerusalem and the temple; set up tribal sanhedrins; and declared cities apostate (m. Sanh. 1.5–6). It also was the final court of appeals concerning the legitimacy of laws (11.2), and it executed rebellious elders (11.4)." Anthony J. Saldarini, "Sanhedrin," ed. David Noel Freedman, *The Anchor Yale Bible Dictionary* (New York: Doubleday, 1992), 978.

[3] **Josephus on Gessius Florus as described in this story**: "This Florus was so wicked, and so violent in the use of his authority, that the Jews took Albinus to have been [comparatively] their benefactor; so excessive were the mischiefs that he brought upon them. (254) For Albinus concealed his wickedness, and was careful that it might not be discovered to all men; but Gessius Florus, as though he had been sent on purpose to show his crimes to everybody, made a pompous ostentation of them to our nation, as never omitting any sort of violence, nor any unjust sort of punishment; (255) for he was not to be moved by pity, and never was satisfied with any degree of gain that came in his way; nor had he any more regard to great than to small acquisitions, but became a partner with the robbers themselves.

"Since it was this Florus who necessitated us to take up arms against the Romans, while we thought it better to be destroyed at once, than by little and little. Now this war began in the second year of the government of Florus, and the twelfth year of the reign of Nero." Flavius Josephus, *The Antiquities of the Jews*, 20.253-257.

[4] **Yeshua (Jesus) ben Gamaliel and the high priesthood**: I am using the Hebrew form of the same name of Jesus/Joshua/Yeshua in order to clearly separate him in name from Joshua (Jesus) the Christian preacher in this novel.

"Jesus, the son of Gamaliel, became the successor of Jesus, the son of Damneus, in the high priesthood, which the king had taken from the other; on which account a sedition arose between the high priests, with regard to one another; for they got together bodies of the boldest sort of the people, and frequently came, from reproaches, to throwing of stones at each other." Flavius Josephus, *The Antiquities of the Jews*, 20.213.

[5] **Ananus ben Ananus**: Ananus ben Ananus, though deposed in AD 62, remained an influential priest: "But, even if the details of their alignments are hazy, it is clear that the faction fighting that was to blossom in the sixties A.D. had already begun before the end of Cumanus' procuratorship in A.D. 52 (cf. A.J. 20.180) and it is highly likely that Ishmael was already opposed by the factions which came to the fore then, for the ambitious ex-High Priests who led them may well have been irked by the influence of a reigning High Priest as powerful as Ishmael. The first of those factions clustered around the sons of Ananus, who had been High Priest in A.D. 6 and was the father of five incumbents of the office (A.J. 18.26; 20.198). Three of those sons seem to have sunk into obscurity after their tenure, but two, Jonathan b. Ananus, High Priest in A.D. 36-7, and Ananus b. Ananus, High Priest in A.D. 62, did not.

"The prolific family of Ananus was thus in itself a powerful faction, but they also attracted allies from outside... The (slim) evidence for such a rapprochement lies in the friendship with Ananus b. Ananus of Jesus b. Gamalas, who was High Priest in c. A.D. 63.

"When Ananus was deposed as High Priest in A.D. 62 at the request of the new procurator Albinus and to the benefit of the new High Priest Jesus b. Damnaeus, Ananias took good care to be on friendly terms with both the procurator and Jesus, deploying his great wealth to good effect and reaching a peak of influence with Ananus b. Ananus' temporary decline (A.J. 20.205). In A.D. 66 Ananias' vehement opposition to revolt is in marked contrast to Ananus' eventual leadership of the rebels." Martin Goodman, *Ruling Class of Judaea: The Origins of the Jewish Revolt Against Rome, A. D. 66-70* (Cambridge University Press, 1993), 143-144 163.

[6] **Josephus on Gessius Florus as described in this story**: "Now Gessius Florus, who was sent as successor to Albinus by Nero, filled Judea with abundance of miseries. He was by birth of the city of Clazomenae, and brought along with him his wife Cleopatra (by whose friendship with Poppea, Nero's

wife, he obtained this government), who was no way different from him in wickedness." Flavius Josephus, *The Antiquities of the Jews*, 20.252.

[7] **Kidnap ransom of priest**: Though this incident occurred earlier, under the governor Albinus, I have included it here as an accurate example of the behavior of the Sicarii kidnappings. Flavius Josephus, *The Antiquities of the Jews*, 9.208-210.

[8] **The Sanhedrin and Rome regarding capital crimes**: "It was the task of the procurator to deal with violent political crime, but, for want of staff and time, he necessarily left less dangerous criminals to the disposition of local tribunals.8 Jerusalem therefore needed a court, just as the villages did (see above, p. 73), and that was the function of the Sanhedrin on most of the occasions when it was convened by the High Priest, as the narrative of the trials of, for instance, Paul and James makes clear (Acts 22.30-23.10; A.J. 20.200).

"There was nothing odd about a High Priest's advisory body having such a judicial function, for Josephus often speaks of the High Priest as the supreme judge (cf. c.Ap. 2.194). Much of the implementation of Roman law in this period was done by a magistrate with the help of friends. The 'council of judges' (cf. the phrase in A.J. 20.200) called by the High Priest could include whomever he thought fit (cf. c.Ap. 2.187,194), hence the silence of the sources about the methods and criteria for appointments to the Sanhedrin." Martin Goodman, *Ruling Class of Judaea: The Origins of the Jewish Revolt Against Rome, A. D. 66-70* (Cambridge University Press, 1993), 114-116.

[9] **High priesthood in Jerusalem as collaborators with Rome**: "The problem was not just that the High Priests appointed by Herod were his puppets (above, p. 41) but that they were blatantly his puppets, just as the incumbents after A.D. 6 were blatantly the political choices of Roman procurators (from A.D. 6 to 41), or Herodian princes (from A.D. 41 to 66)...

"At least six High Priests were deposed by Agrippa II in the turbulent ten years before the revolt." Martin Goodman, *Ruling Class of Judaea: The Origins of the Jewish Revolt Against Rome, A. D. 66-70* (Cambridge University Press, 1993),

"I suggest that one possible explanation may be that the Sanhedrin was not a regular political council at all, that it met only at the request of the High Priest as his advisory body, and that its influence was only as great as that of the sum total of its members...

"If the Sanhedrin was thus only an extension of the High Priest, why was such a council needed at all after A.D. 6? Two reasons can be suggested. Rome like the Seleucids needed a defined institutional body to which the responsibility for collecting taxes in Judea could be delegated." Martin Goodman, *Ruling Class of Judaea: The Origins of the Jewish Revolt Against Rome, A. D. 66-70* (Cambridge University Press, 1993), 114-116.

[10] The name *Israel* means "to struggle with God."

[11] **The Egyptian messiah prophet**: Acts 21:37–38 As Paul was about to be brought into the barracks, he said to the tribune, "May I say something to you?" And he said, "Do you know Greek? 38 Are you not the Egyptian, then, who recently stirred up a revolt and led the four thousand men of the Assassins out into the wilderness?"

Josephus:"But there was an Egyptian false prophet that did the Jews more mischief than the former; for he was a cheat, and pretended to be a prophet also, and got together thirty thousand men that were deluded by him." Flavius Josephus, *The Wars of the Jews*, 2.260-261.

"Moreover, there came out of Egypt about this time to Jerusalem, one that said he was a prophet, and advised the multitude of the common people to go along with him to the Mount of Olives, as it was called, which lay over against the city, and at the distance of five furlongs. (170) He said farther, that he would show them from hence, how, at his command, the walls of Jerusalem would fall down; and he promised that he would procure them an entrance into the city through those walls, when they were fallen down. (171) Now when Felix was informed of these things, he ordered his soldiers to take their weapons, and came against them with a great number of horsemen and footmen, from Jerusalem, and attacked the Egyptian and the people that were with him. He also slew four hundred of them, and took two hundred alive. (172) But the Egyptian himself escaped out of the fight, but did not appear any more." Flavius Josephus, *The Antiquities of the Jews*, 20.169-172.

On the discrepancy of numbers between Luke and Josephus: "In view of Josephus' track record with numbers, it is easier to believe he exaggerated, turning four thousand into many more, than that Luke, who had no obvious reason to change the figures, did the opposite." Ben Witherington III, *The Acts of the Apostles: A Socio-Rhetorical Commentary* (Grand Rapids, MI: Wm. B. Eerdmans Publishing Co., 1998).

CHAPTER 27

[1] **Mount Hermon and the Watchers**: 1 Enoch 6:1-8 In those days, when the children of man had multiplied, it happened that there were born unto them handsome and beautiful daughters. And the angels, the children of heaven, saw them and desired them; and they said to one another, "Come, let us choose wives for ourselves from among the daughters of man and beget us children." And Semyaz, being their leader, said unto them, "I fear that perhaps you will not consent that this deed should be done, and I alone will become (responsible) for this great sin." But they all responded to him, "Let us all swear an oath and bind everyone among us by a curse not to abandon this suggestion but to do the deed." Then they all swore together and bound one another by (the curse). And they were altogether two hundred; and they descended into 'Ardos, which is the summit of Hermon. And they called the mount Armon, for they swore and bound one another by a curse. And their names are as follows: Semyaz, the leader of Arakeb, Rame'el, Tam'el, Ram'el, Dan'el, Ezeqel, Baraqyal, As'el, Armaros, Batar'el, Anan'el, Zaqe'el, Sasomaspewe'el, Kestar'el, Tur'el, Yamayol, and Arazyal. 8 These are their chiefs of tens and of all the others with them."

Mount Bashan as location of the fall of the Watchers and place of the serpent: "Bashan was a deeply significant spiritual location to the Canaanites and the Hebrews. And as the Dictionary of Deities and Demons in the Bible puts it, Biblical geographical tradition agrees with the mythological and cultic data of the Canaanites of Ugarit that "the Bashan region, or a part of it, clearly represented 'Hell', the celestial and infernal abode of their deified dead kings," the Rephaim.

"Mount Hermon was in Bashan, and Mount Hermon was a location in the Bible that was linked to the Rephaim (Josh. 12:1-5), but was also the legendary location where the sons of God were considered to have come to earth and have sexual union with the daughters of men to produce the giant Nephilim. The non-canonical book of Enoch supports this same interpretation: "Enoch 6:6 And they were in all two hundred [sons of God]; who descended in the days of Jared on the summit of Mount Hermon, and they called it Mount Hermon, because they had sworn and bound themselves by mutual imprecations upon it." Brian Godawa, *When Giants Were Upon the Earth: The Watchers, the Nephilim, and the Biblical Cosmic War of the Seed* (Embedded Pictures, 2014), 75.

"Bashan/Bathan both also mean "serpent," so that the region of Bashan was "the place of the serpent." As we saw earlier, the divine serpent (nachash, another word so translated) became lord of the dead after his rebellion in Eden. In effect, Bashan was considered the location of (to borrow a New Testament phrase) "the gates of hell." Later Jewish writers understood these conceptual connections. Their intersection is at the heart of why books like 1 Enoch teach that demons are actually the spirits of dead Nephilim.

"Lastly, aside from Bashan being the gateway to the underworld, the region has another sinister feature identified in the Deuteronomy 3 passage: Mount Hermon. According to 1 Enoch 6:1–6, Mount Hermon was the place where the sons of God of Genesis 6 descended when they came to earth to cohabit with human women—the episode that produced the Nephilim. Joshua 12:4–5 unites all the threads: "Og king of Bashan, one of the remnant of the Rephaim, who lived at Ashtaroth and at Edrei and ruled over Mount Hermon."

"Just the name "Hermon" would have caught the attention of Israelite and Jewish readers. In Hebrew it's pronounced khermon. The noun has the same root as a verb that is of central importance in Deuteronomy 3 and the conquest narratives: kharam, "to devote to destruction." This is the distinct verb of holy war, the verb of extermination. It has deep theological meaning, a meaning explicitly connected to the giant clans God commanded Joshua and his armies to eradicate." Michael S. Heiser, *The Unseen Realm: Recovering the Supernatural Worldview of the Bible*, First Edition (Bellingham, WA: Lexham Press, 2015), 200–201.

[2] **Mount Sinai replacing Mount Hermon**: Psalm 68:15-22

[3] **Installing Messiah on Mount Zion as God's cosmic mountain**: Psalm 2:6.

[4] **For a detailed narrative of these actions by Jesus** in his death, descent into Hades, resurrection and ascension, see the eighth book in the *Chronicles of the Nephilim* series, Brian Godawa *Jesus Triumphant* (CA: Embedded Pictures Publishing).

Jesus builds his church upon the rock of Hermon: Matthew 16:13-20. "We've seen already that the Jewish tradition about the descent of the Watchers, the sons of God of Genesis 6:1–4, informed the writings of Peter and Jude. Now we see that the transfiguration of Jesus takes place on the same location identified by that tradition. Jesus picks Mount Hermon to reveal to Peter, James, and John exactly who he is—the embodied glory-essence of God, the divine Name made visible by incarnation. The meaning is just as transparent: I'm putting the hostile powers of the unseen world on notice. I've come to earth to take back what is mine. The kingdom of God is at hand." Michael S. Heiser, *The Unseen Realm: Recovering the Supernatural Worldview of the Bible, First Edition* (Bellingham, WA: Lexham Press, 2015), 286.

In the NT, Mount Zion is the new covenant in Christ that replaces Mount Sinai: Hebrews 12:18–24
[18] For you have not come to what may be touched, a blazing fire and darkness and gloom and a tempest [19] and the sound of a trumpet and a voice whose words made the hearers beg that no further messages be spoken to them. [20] For they could not endure the order that was given, "If even a beast touches the mountain, it shall be stoned." [21] Indeed, so terrifying was the sight that Moses said, "I tremble with fear." [22] But you have come to Mount Zion and to the city of the living God, the heavenly Jerusalem, and to innumerable angels in festal gathering, [23] and to the assembly of the firstborn who are enrolled in heaven, and to God, the judge of all, and to the spirits of the righteous made perfect, [24] and to Jesus, the mediator of a new covenant, and to the sprinkled blood that speaks a better word than the blood of Abel.

Panias as the Gates of Hades: "Scholar Judd Burton points out that Banias or Panias at the base of Mount Hermon in Bashan was a key worship site for the Greek goat-god Pan as early as the third century B.C. and earlier connections to the goat-idol Azazel (Judd H. Burton, Interview With the Giant: Ethnohistorical Notes on the Nephilim (Burton Beyond Press, 2009) 19-21.)." Brian Godawa, *When Giants Were Upon the Earth: The Watchers, the Nephilim, and the Biblical Cosmic War of the Seed* (Embedded Pictures, 2014), 210.

"In Matthew 16:13-20 is the famous story of Peter's confession of Jesus as the Christ, who then responds, "I tell you, you are Peter, and on this rock I will build my church, and the gates of hell [Hades] shall not prevail against it" (v. 18). Shortly after, Jesus leads them up to a high mountain where he is transfigured.

"In order to understand the spiritual reality of what is going on in this polemical sequence and its relevance to the cosmic War of the Seed, we must first understand where it is going on.

"Verse 13 says that Peter's confession takes place in the district of Caesarea Philippi. This city was in the heart of Bashan on a rocky terrace in the foothills of Mount Hermon. This was the celebrated location of the grotto of Banias or Panias, where the satyr goat god Pan was worshipped and from where the mouth of the Jordan river flowed. This very location was what was known as the "gates of Hades," the underworld abode of dead souls.

"The Jewish historian Josephus wrote of this sacred grotto during his time, "a dark cave opens itself; within which there is a horrible precipice, that descends abruptly to a vast depth; it contains a mighty quantity of water, which is immovable; and when anybody lets down anything to measure the depth of the earth beneath the water, no length of cord is sufficient to reach it."

"As scholar Judd Burton points out, this is a kind of ground zero for the gods against whom Jesus was fighting his cosmic spiritual war. Mount Hermon was the location where the Watchers came to earth, led their rebellion and miscegenation, which birthed the Nephilim (1 Enoch 13:7-10). It was their headquarters, in Bashan, the place of the Serpent, where Azazel may have been worshipped before Pan as a desert goat idol.

"When Jesus speaks of building his church upon a rock, it is as much a polemical contrast with the pagan city upon the rock, as it may have been a word play off of Peter's name, meaning "stone." In the ancient world, mountains were not only a gateway between heaven, earth, and the underworld, but also the habitations of the gods that represented their heavenly power and authority. The mountain before them, Hermon, was considered the heavenly habitation of Canaanite gods as well as the very Watchers before whose gates of Hades Jesus now stood. The polemics become clearer when one realizes that gates are not offensive weapons, but defensive means. Christ's kingship is storming the very gates of Hades/Sheol in the heart of darkness and he will build his cosmic holy mountain upon its ruins." Brian Godawa, *When Giants Were Upon the Earth: The Watchers, the Nephilim, and the Biblical Cosmic War of the Seed* (Embedded Pictures, 2014), 286-287.

[5] **On Ba'al's two weapons**: "One as a hammer like mace and the other "Ginsberg (1935:328) identified ṣmdm with the two-pieced maces excavated at Ugarit. The weapon consists of two pieces, a head latched onto a handle, specifically in Ginsberg's words (1935:328) "a mace with a stone head drilled through to adjust the wooden shaft, to which it is lashed tightly with thongs; and hence the name from the root ṣmd, 'to bind.' Such mace heads are found frequently in excavations.".

"A famous stele from Ugarit, sometimes called the "Baal au foudre" stele and housed in the Louvre, depicts Baal wielding two weapons. The weapon in his right hand is sometimes characterized as a mace (Amiet 1980:201).204 In his left hand Baal holds "tree-lightning" (Vanel 1965:84; Williams-Forte 1983:28, 30). Other examples of second millennium iconography of the storm-god depict him with a weapon (Vanel 1965:esp. 108; Seeden 1980:esp. 102), which appears at times as "branch-like lightning" (Williams-Forte 1983:26).".

The actual text of the Baal cycle where Kothar-wa-Hasis crafts the two weapons, Yagarrish/Yagrush ("Driver") and Ayyamarri/Ayamur ("Expeller") for Baal to defeat Yamm (Sea) and River (Nahar) is KTU 1.2.11-25:

Kothar fashions the weapons,
And he proclaims their names:
"Your name, yours, is Yagarrish:
Yagarrish, drive Yamm,
Drive Yamm from his throne,
[Na]har from the seat of his dominion.
"Your name, yours, is Ayyamarri:
Ayyamarri, expel Yamm,
Expel Yamm from his throne,
Nahar from the seat of his dominion.
Leap from Baal's hand,
Like a raptor from his fingers.
Strike the head of Prince Yamm,
Between the eyes of Judge River.
May Yamm sink and fall to the earth."
The weapon leaps from Baal's hand,
[Like] a raptor from his fingers,
It strikes the head of Prince [Yamm,]
Between the eyes of Judge River.

Mark S. Smith and Simon B. Parker, *Ugaritic Narrative Poetry, vol. 9, Writings from the Ancient World* (Atlanta, GA: Scholars Press, 1997), 103–104.

CHAPTER 28

[1] **Solemn Assembly**: "In the Pentateuch and the historical sections of the OT, including the religious calendars, this word generally refers to the final, or closing, day of an extended feast (Lev 23:36: Num 29:35; Deut 16:8; cf. also 2 Chron 7:9; Neh 8:18), though elsewhere it may simply designate a religious assembly, whether approved by Yahweh or not (cf. 2 Kings 10:20; Amos 5:21). Semantically the word ranges from simply a pious assembly of any sort to something approximating the miqrā' qōdeš that

brought a period of feasting to an end." C. E. Armerding, "Festivals and Feasts," *Dictionary of the Old Testament: Pentateuch* (Downers Grove, IL: InterVarsity Press, 2003), 302.

"Solemn assembly" is the AV and RSV translation of Heb. ʾaṣeret̲/ʾaṣārâ. The Hebrew term's derivaton from ʾāṣar ("restrain" or "close up"), as well as the contexts in which it occurs, suggests an occasion of fasting and abstention from work and other profane activities. The NEB renders it "closing ceremony" (Lev. 23:36; Nu. 29:35; Dt. 16:8; 2 Ch. 7:9; Neh. 8:18), "sacred ceremony" (2 K. 10:20; Am. 5:21), "day of abstinence" (Joel 1:14; 2:15), or simply "ceremony" (Isa. 1:13)." G. Chamberlain and N. J. Opperwall, "Solemn; Solemnly," ed. Geoffrey W. Bromiley, *The International Standard Bible Encyclopedia, Revised* (Wm. B. Eerdmans, 1979–1988), 566.

The prophet Joel calls for a solemn assembly in Joel 1:14: "The priests (who are still being addressed) are instructed to schedule (קַדְּשׁ, literally, "set aside") a fast day so that everyone, including the nation's leadership, can cry out (זְעַק) together to Yahweh for help (cf. Judg 6:7; Jer 11:11; 1 Sam 7:8). A typical one-day fast is probably envisioned (Judg 20:26; 1 Sam 14:24; Isa 58:3–5; Jer 36:6–9), involving cessation of routine activity, no eating, and special prayer. Fasting is a form of self-denial which, like wearing sackcloth, is intended to heighten the seriousness of one's appeal to God." Douglas Stuart, *Hosea–Jonah, vol. 31, Word Biblical Commentary* (Dallas: Word, Incorporated, 2002), 244.

"It has often been translated "solemn assembly." Kutsch, VT 2 (1952) 65–67, has shown, however, that this is too limited a translation, and that at its basis lies the idea of cessation, from work in particular. Thus it is not only the specific gathering, but the whole day which is referred to." H. G. M. Williamson, *Ezra, Nehemiah, vol. 16, Word Biblical Commentary* (Dallas: Word, Incorporated, 1998), 297.

Feast of Dedication: "There are similarities between the accounts of the Feast of Dedication, called "the festival of booths in the month of Chislev" (2 Macc. 1:9 [c. 124 B.C.]; cf. 10:6), and the Feast of Tabernacles (Lev. 23:42–43). Its association with the biblical Feast of Tabernacles lent Dedication a certain amount of scriptural legitimacy. Both festivals celebrated God's protection of Israel during her wanderings in the desert. Beyond this, the Feast of Dedication also commemorated God's intervention in the restoration of the temple, the apostasy among the Jews that had led to the temple's desecration, and the Jews' regaining of their religious (and national) freedom. As Josephus writes, "And from that time to the present we observe this festival, which we call the festival of Lights, giving this name to it, I think, from the fact that the right to worship appeared to us at a time when we hardly dared hope for it" (Ant. 12.7.7 §325; cf. 12.7.6–7 §§316–24)." Clinton E. Arnold, *Zondervan Illustrated Bible Backgrounds Commentary: John, Acts., vol. 2* (Grand Rapids, MI: Zondervan, 2002), 103.

[2] **Sword over the city:** "Thus there was a star resembling a sword, which stood over the city, and a comet, that continued a whole year." Flavius Josephus, *The Wars of the Jews*, 6.289-300.

[3] **Incident of the Roman soldier mooning and farting in the Temple**: "Now after the death of Herod, king of Chalcis, Claudius set Agrippa, the son of Agrippa, over his uncle's kingdom, while Cumanus took upon him the office of procurator of the rest, which was a Roman province, and therein he succeeded Alexander; under which Cumanus began the troubles, and the Jews ruin came on; (224) for when the multitude were come together to Jerusalem, to the feast of unleavened bread, and a Roman cohort stood over the cloisters of the temple (for they always were armed and kept guard at the festivals, to prevent any innovation which the multitude thus gathered together might take), one of the soldiers pulled back his garment, and cowering down after an indecent manner, turned his breech to the Jews, and made a noise as you might expect upon such a posture. (225) At this the whole multitude had indignation, and made a clamor to Cumanus, that he would punish the soldier; while the rasher part of the youth, and such as were naturally the most tumultuous, fell to fighting, and caught up stones, and threw them at the soldiers. (226) Upon which Cumanus was afraid lest all the people should make an assault upon him, and sent to call for more armed men, who, when they came in great numbers into the cloisters, the Jews were in a very great consternation; and being beaten out of the temple, they ran into the city; (227) and the violence with which they crowded to get out was so great, that they trod upon each other, and squeezed one another, till ten thousand of them were killed." Flavius Josephus, *The Wars of the Jews*, 2.223-227.

[4] **Messiah returning from the East through the Shoshan Gate or Golden Gate**: Nehemiah 3:29 "...the gate that looketh toward the east: And the glory of the Lord came into the house by the way of the gate whose prospect is toward the east."

Ezekiel 44:1-3 Then he brought me back to the outer gate of the sanctuary, which faces east; and it was shut. And he said to me, "This gate shall remain shut; it shall not be opened, and no one shall enter by it; for the LORD, the God of Israel, has entered by it; therefore it shall remain shut. Only the prince may sit in it to eat bread before the LORD; he shall enter by way of the vestibule of the gate, and shall go out by the same way."

[5] Genesis 3:24 says that the cherubim guard the Tree of Life with "the flame of the whirling sword." Scholar Ronald Hendel has argued that "the 'flame' is an animate divine being, a member of Yahweh's divine host, similar in status to the cherubim; the 'whirling sword' is its appropriate weapon, ever-moving, like the flame itself." Ronald S. Hendel, "'The Flame of the Whirling Sword': A Note on Genesis 3:24," *Journal of Biblical Literature*, Vol. 104, No. 4 (Dec., 1985), pp. 671-674.

Scholar P.D. Miller appeals to passages such as Psalm 104:4 where "fire and flame" are described as "Yahweh's ministers" to conclude a convergence of imagery with ancient Ugaritic texts that describe "fire and flame" as armed deities with flashing swords. He writes that "the cherubim and the flaming sword are probably to be recognized as a reflection of the Canaanite fiery messengers." Thus the Biblically strange, yet strangely Biblical presence in Enoch Primordial of the Cherubim and their divine fiery beings beside them brandishing whirling swords of flashing lightning. Patrick D. Miller, "Fire in the Mythology of Canaan and Israel," *Catholic Biblical Quarterly*, 27 no 3 Jl 1965, p 256-261.

[6] **Read the fictional narrative of this event in:** Brian Godawa, *Enoch Primordial* (CA: Embedded Pictures Publishing, 2012, 2014), 70-76.

[7] **The vision of heavenly armies**: This vision was claimed to have been seen by many witnesses according to Josephus around the Feast of Passover in AD 66. I have put it in AD 64 a couple years earlier, for the sake of tightening the story, but the meaning is the same: witnesses of the heavenly war that was coming. Even the pagan Roman Tacitus referred to it.

"Besides these, a few days after that feast, on the twenty-first day of the month Artemisius [Jyar], (297) a certain prodigious and incredible phenomenon appeared; I suppose the account of it would seem to be a fable, were it not related by those that saw it, (298) and were not the events that followed it of so considerable a nature as to deserve such signals; for, before sunsetting, chariots and troops of soldiers in their armor were seen (299) running about among the clouds, and surrounding of cities." Flavius Josephus and William Whiston, *The Works of Josephus: Complete and Unabridged* (Peabody: Hendrickson, 1987), *Wars*, 6.296-299, 742.

"Prodigies had indeed occurred, but to avert them either by victims or by vows is held unlawful by a people which, though prone to superstition, is opposed to all propitiatory rites. Contending hosts were seen meeting in the skies, arms flashed, and suddenly the temple was illumined with fire from the clouds. Of a sudden the doors of the shrine opened and a superhuman voice cried: "The gods are departing": at the same moment the mighty stir of their going was heard. Few interpreted these omens as fearful; the majority firmly believed that their ancient priestly writings contained the prophecy that this was the very time when the East should grow strong and that men starting from Judea should possess the world." Tacitus, *Histories* 5:13 http://penelope.uchicago.edu/Thayer/E/Roman/Texts/Tacitus/Histories/5A*.html

CHAPTER 29

[1] **Zealots and other revolutionary leaders**:

A.D. 6 – Judas of Galilee. Originator of the "Fourth Philosophy" of Josephus.
A.D. 35-60 - Eleazar ben Dinai, leader of Zealots. Josephus, *Antiquities* 20.5; *Wars of the Jews* 2.234.
A.D. 45 - Amram, Eleazar ben Dinai, banished. Tholomy executed Josephus, *Antiquities* 20.5.
After Christ - a Jewish leader brings armed Jews to Tirathaba near Mount Gerrazim, Samaria. Pilate captures them and slaughters them. Josephus, *Antiquities* 18:85.
A.D. 44-46 - Theudas; Josephus, *Wars of the Jews* 2.261; *Antiquities* 20.169f Under Cuspius Fadus (the Egyptian Paul referred to in Acts 21:38).
A.D. 46 - James and Simon, sons of Judas of Galilee crucified under Tiberius Alexander. Josephus, *Antiquities* 20.102.
A.D. 48-52 - Dortus; a leading Jew was condemned to death in Caesarea together with four other rebels,

because 'they had persuaded the people to break with Rome. Cumanus procurator. Josephus, *Antiquities* 20.130.

A.D. 54 - The Egyptian - Acts 21:38 (4000 men, not 30k per Josephus) Josephus, *Wars of the Jews* 2.261–63; *Antiquities* 20.168–72.

A.D. 54 - Sicarii kill Jonathan the High Priest. First one to be killed by them.

A.D. 60 - Eleazar ben Dinai — Leader of Zealots. Josephus, *Antiquities* 20.5; *Wars of the Jews* 2.234. Executed in Rome by Felix.

A.D. 60s - Jesus, son of Sapphias. In Galilee. Josephus, *Life* 66.

A.D. 66 - Manahem leader of Sicarii Wars, caught and killed Josephus, *Wars of the Jews* 2.433.

A.D. 66 - Eleazar ben Ananias (the high priest) took temple, went to Masada (Zealot).

A.D. 67-68 - Eleazar bar Simon took control of temple Zealot.

[2] **"No king but God":** But of the fourth sect of Jewish philosophy, Judas the Galilean was the author. These men agree in all other things with the Pharisaic notions; but they have an inviolable attachment to liberty; and say that God is to be their only Ruler and Lord." Flavius Josephus, *The Antiquities of the Jews*, 18.23.

[3] **This speech was drawn from**: Flavius Josephus, *The Antiquities of the Jews*, 18;1-25.

The Egyptian in this story also quotes a passage that Jesus quoted about his messiahship in Luke 4:17-19. Isaiah 61:1–2 The Spirit of the Lord GOD is upon me, because the LORD has anointed me to bring good news to the poor; he has sent me to bind up the brokenhearted, to proclaim liberty to the captives, and the opening of the prison to those who are bound; 2 to proclaim the year of the LORD's favor, and the day of vengeance of our God; to comfort all who mourn.

Old Testament passages about Yahweh returning to Zion: Isaiah 24:23 Then the moon will be confounded and the sun ashamed, for the LORD of hosts reigns on Mount Zion and in Jerusalem, and his glory will be before his elders.

Daniel 9:24 "Seventy weeks are decreed about your people and your holy city, to finish the transgression, to put an end to sin, and to atone for iniquity, to bring in everlasting righteousness, to seal both vision and prophet, and to anoint a most holy place.

Isaiah 35:4–6 Behold, your God will come with vengeance, with the recompense of God. He will come and save you." [5] Then the eyes of the blind shall be opened, and the ears of the deaf unstopped; [6] then shall the lame man leap like a deer, and the tongue of the mute sing for joy. For waters break forth in the wilderness, and streams in the desert.

Isaiah 52:7–10 How beautiful upon the mountains are the feet of him who brings good news, who publishes peace, who brings good news of happiness, who publishes salvation, who says to Zion, "Your God reigns." [8] The voice of your watchmen—they lift up their voice; together they sing for joy; for eye to eye they see the return of the LORD to Zion. [9] Break forth together into singing, you waste places of Jerusalem, for the LORD has comforted his people; he has redeemed Jerusalem. [10] The LORD has bared his holy arm before the eyes of all the nations, and all the ends of the earth shall see the salvation of our God.

Zechariah 8:2–3 "Thus says the LORD of hosts: I am jealous for Zion with great jealousy, and I am jealous for her with great wrath. [3] Thus says the LORD: I have returned to Zion and will dwell in the midst of Jerusalem, and Jerusalem shall be called the faithful city, and the mountain of the LORD of hosts, the holy mountain.

Psalm 96:12–13 [12] let the field exult, and everything in it! Then shall all the trees of the forest sing for joy [13] before the LORD, for he comes, for he comes to judge the earth. He will judge the world in righteousness, and the peoples in his faithfulness.

Psalm 98:8–9 Let the rivers clap their hands; let the hills sing for joy together [9] before the LORD, for he comes to judge the earth. He will judge the world with righteousness, and the peoples with equity.

See also: Isaiah 4:2-6; 40:3–5, 9–11; 59:15–17, 19–21; 62:10–11; 63:1, 3, 5, 9; 64:1; 66:12, 14–16, 18–19.

N.T. Wright quotes these passages above, among others, and explains: "But the geographical return from exile, when it came about under Cyrus and his successors, was not accompanied by any manifestations such as those in Exodus 40, Leviticus 9, 1 Kings 8, or even (a revelation to an individual) Isaiah 6. Never do we hear that the pillar of cloud and fire which accompanied the Israelites in the wilderness has led the people back from their exile. At no point do we hear that YHWH has now gloriously returned to Zion. At no point is the house again filled with the cloud which veils his glory. At no point is the rebuilt Temple universally hailed as the true restored shrine spoken of by Ezekiel. Significantly, at no point, either, is there a final decisive victory over Israel's enemies, or the establishment of a universally welcomed royal dynasty." N. T. Wright, *Jesus and the Victory of God, Christian Origins and the Question of God* (London: Society for Promoting Christian Knowledge, 1996), 621.

[4] **Jerusalem prisons**: "In addition to Herod's prison on the west side of the city and a prison in the fortress of Antonia, the Sanhedrin had a place of incarceration either in the temple or below the building where it met (i.e., the Xystus or "the Gazith")" Clinton E. Arnold, *Zondervan Illustrated Bible Backgrounds Commentary: John, Acts.,* vol. 2 (Grand Rapids, MI: Zondervan, 2002), 255.

[5] **Jews still in exile in the first century**: "Most Jews of this period, it seems, would have answered the question 'where are we?' in language which, reduced to its simplest form, meant: we are still in exile. They believed that, in all the senses which mattered, Israel's exile was still in progress. Although she had come back from Babylon, the glorious message of the prophets remained unfulfilled. Israel still remained in thrall to foreigners; worse, Israel's god had not returned to Zion. Nowhere in the so-called post-exilic literature is there any passage corresponding to 1 Kings 8:10f., according to which, when Solomon's temple had been finished, 'a cloud filled the house of YHWH, so that the priests could not stand to minister because of the cloud; for the glory of YHWH filled the house of YHWH'. Instead, Israel clung to the promises that one day the Shekinah, the glorious presence of her god, would return at last." N. T. Wright, *The New Testament and the People of God, Christian Origins and the Question of God* (London: Society for Promoting Christian Knowledge, 1992), 268–269.

CHAPTER 30

[1] **Berenice and her marriages**: "In A.D. 41 she married Marcus Julius Alexander, son of Alexander the alabarch. Ostraca from Egypt give some insight into Marcus' commercial activities (Fuks 1951). Upon Marcus' death shortly after the marriage, Bernice married her uncle, Herod of Chalcis before the end of A.D. 44; by him she had two sons, Berenicianus and Hyrcanus (Jos. JW 2.221; cf. Ant 19.276ff.; 20.104). After the death of Herod of Chalcis in A.D. 48, Bernice lived as a widow for a long time with her brother Agrippa II, who received her husband's kingdom from the emperor Claudius (Ant 20.104). Rumors of incest with her brother are said to have led her to marry Polemo of Cilicia." David C. Braund, "Bernice (Person)," ed. David Noel Freedman, *The Anchor Yale Bible Dictionary* (New York: Doubleday, 1992), 677.

[2] **Agrippa and Bernice incestuous relationship**: "Agrippa II's private life was not exemplary. His sister Bernice came to live with him after their uncle, who was also her second husband, Herod king of Chalcis, died in A.D. 48. Because of the rumors of incest, she resolved to marry Polemo of Cilicia, but shortly after this she returned to her relationship with her brother. This incestuous relationship became the common chatter in Rome (Ant. xx.7.3 [145–47]; Juvenal Satires vi.156–160)." H. W. Hoehner, "Herod," ed. Geoffrey W Bromiley, *The International Standard Bible Encyclopedia, Revised* (Wm. B. Eerdmans, 1979–1988), 697.

[3] **Power of a tyrant, temper of a slave**: This phrase (with a slight difference) was actually used by Tacitus of the procurator Felix (Tacitus *Annals* 12.54; *Histories* 5.9), but it was such a relevant and poignant line, I had to use it here of Agrippa.

CHAPTER 31

[1] **Catacombs**: "Subterranean burial was common in the ancient world, and catacombs, with their long ramifying passages, or closely related structures, can be found near Rome and in other Italian localities, on Sicily, Malta, and Milos, in Syria, in the region of Jerusalem, in NW Africa, and at Alexandria. They were used by Jews, pagans, and Christians. The most famous and extensive are near Rome. Like all Roman tombs, they enjoyed legal protection, and had to be dug outside the walls. Forty-one Christian catacombs survive there; they are of great interest for the social and religious history of the early Church."

F. L. Cross and Elizabeth A. Livingstone, eds., *The Oxford Dictionary of the Christian Church* (Oxford; New York: Oxford University Press, 2005), 300.

[2] **The catacombs as a safe place of worship during persecution of the church**: Herbert B. Workman, *Persecution in the Early Church: A Chapter in the History of Renunciation* (Jennings and Graham, 1906), 261; During the time of Tertullian (264).

"The catacombs under the city of Rome, unmentioned in the Bible, became famous for providing refuge for early Christians. Over 300 miles of underground passages extend 25 to 65 feet below the ground, outside the city gates." "Catacombs," ed. John D. Barry et al., *The Lexham Bible Dictionary* (Bellingham, WA: Lexham Press, 2012, 2013, 2014, 2015).

[3] **The catacombs were considered sacred by the Romans**: Herbert B. Workman, *Persecution in the Early Church: A Chapter in the History of Renunciation* (Jennings and Graham, 1906), 264.

[4] Psalm 110.

[5] **On the Baptism of infants in the catacombs**: "About this time it is certain that the distinction between Jew and Christian began to be generally recognised, and rumours to spread abroad, which probably had their origin in Jewish malice, by which the Christians were accused of holding impious orgies and horrible Thyestean feasts and of being a secret society of anarchists and criminals. It is not difficult to see that such slanders might be based upon distorted versions of Christian teaching, **of the baptism of infants in the Catacombs**, and of the nocturnal meetings of the brethren for the holding of the Agape meal and the partaking of the Eucharist." Footnote 3: The well-known Roman archaeologist, Orazio Marucchi, has discovered in the 1st-century cemetery of Cassandra on the lower floor an ancient baptistery that he has identified with 'according to their Acts the Martyrs Papias and Maurus were interred.' In any case this baptistery dates from the first century and the local traditions in the Acta are generally correct." George Edmunson, *The Church In Rome In The First Century An Examination Of Various Controverted Questions Relating To Its History, Chronology, Literature, And Traditions* (New York, Longmans Green, 1913), 117.

Infant Baptism: This scene is not an argument for infant baptism. It is merely an acknowledgment that some Christians did engage in the practice. The earliest example of a church father writing about infant baptism is Tertullian, who argues against it around A.D. 200. But this only proves that some Christians did in fact perform the ritual on infants or it would not be an issue to debate. Most Christians are agreed that baptism does not save one from their sins, it is only a covenant sign, and faith is the means through which it is applied (For by grace you have been saved through faith. And this is not your own doing; it is the gift of God, not a result of works, so that no one may boast." Ephesians 2:8–9).

"And so, according to the circumstances and disposition, and even age, of each individual, the delay of baptism is preferable; principally, however, in the case of little children. For why is it necessary—if (baptism itself) is not so necessary—that the sponsors likewise should be thrust into danger? Who both themselves, by reason of mortality, may fail to fulfil their promises, and may be disappointed by the development of an evil disposition, in those for whom they stood? The Lord does indeed say, "Forbid them not to come unto me." Let them "come," then, while they are growing up; let them "come" while they are learning, while they are learning whither to come; let them become Christians when they have become able to know Christ. Why does the innocent period of life hasten to the "remission of sins?" More caution will be exercised in worldly matters: so that one who is not trusted with earthly substance is trusted with divine! Let them know how to "ask" for salvation, that you may seem (at least) to have given "to him that asketh." For no less cause must the unwedded also be deferred—in whom the ground of temptation is prepared, alike in such as never were wedded by means of their maturity, and in the widowed by means of their freedom—until they either marry, or else be more fully strengthened for continence. If any understand the weighty import of baptism, they will fear its reception more than its delay: sound faith is secure of salvation." Tertullian, "On Baptism," in *Latin Christianity: Its Founder, Tertullian*, ed. Alexander Roberts, James Donaldson, and A. Cleveland Coxe, trans. S. Thelwall, vol. 3, *The Ante-Nicene Fathers* (Buffalo, NY: Christian Literature Company, 1885), 678.

[6] **Maranatha**: "'Our Lord, come!' or māran 'atā'—'Our Lord has come']. An ancient Palestinian Aramaic expression recorded in transliterated Aramaic in 1 Cor. 16:22 and in Greek translation (érchou, kýrie Iēsou) in Rev. 22:20. Scholars differ on (1) whether to divide the transliterated Aramaic as māran 'atā' or mārana' tā' (2) whether "Our Lord" could have been either māran or mārana' (in Aramaic), and

(3) whether "come" could have been ʾaṯa ʾ or ṯā ʾ. The problem is complex…As Fitzmyer and others have shown, the underlying Aramaic was probably an imperatival māranā ʾ ṯā ʾ, "Our Lord, come!" This interpretation is supported by the unambiguous translation of maranathá in Rev. 22:20 as a Greek imperative. Furthermore, Conzelmann argued that 1 Cor. 11:26 ("until he comes") is probably an allusion to the (maranathá) formula and so confirms an imperatival-eschatological interpretation of 1 Cor. 16:22." J. J. Hughes, "Maranatha," ed. Geoffrey W Bromiley, *The International Standard Bible Encyclopedia*, Revised (Wm. B. Eerdmans, 1979–1988), 243.

[7] **Imagery of Christ as Imperial**: Though such imagery as written in this chapter has been discovered only from the fourth century and afterward, it is entirely reasonable that discovered remains represent a tradition that began in the early years of the church. Earliest finds do not mean earliest origins. Thomas F. Mathews, *The Clash of Gods: A Reinterpretation of Early Christian Art* (Princeton University Press; Revised and Expanded edition, 1999), 8-15. Author Thomas F. Mathews acknowledges that ancient Christian art and icons are most commonly understood by the consensus of art historians to be subversive appropriation of the "Emperor Mystique" applied toward Jesus Christ. But he suggests a new theory that they are artistic representations of Christ's divinity, not anti-imperial propaganda. In either case, the polemical thrust is clearly one of subversion, and Roman Imperium was also considered divine status as well.

"Christ's entry into Jerusalem is another common image in ancient Christian art (Mathews, 23-53). It has long been considered an anti-imperial parade mocking the earthly glory of the emperor's ritual entry into a city, with the humility of God himself on a donkey. "Ironically, the entry into the city gates by the Roman Emperor is deliberately subverted in Christ's entry into Jerusalem on a donkey (Mt 21:1-5). The imperial visit, also referred to as Caesar's "adventus," included a parade of armed forces, followed by a golden chariot or throne carrying the emperor, crowned and carrying a palm branch. The citizens would shout salutations in awe of his godlike stature and salvific powers. In the Gospel version, Jesus arrives amid Hosannas ("Save, we pray") and palm branches. But his humble status, "gentle, and mounted on a donkey, even a colt, the foal of a beast of burden," subversively undermines worldly military or political power and glory. In fact, God's contempt for this ironic contrast is best described as mockery." (Ps 2:1-9, esp. v. 4)." Brian Godawa, *Word Pictures: Knowing God Through Story and Imagination* (Downers Grove, InterVarsity Press, 20019), 149.

"The absence of distinctly Christian imagery or iconography prior to the early third century has led to the assumption that Christianity avoided or had no icons/images, being opposed to both the theory and usage of imagery and favoring a spiritual understanding of faith. This hypothesis, now considered outdated, assumed that the developments of the late second or early third century represent the abandonment of these beliefs under the paganizing influences of converts… "through "conscientious eclecticism" Christians adopted/adapted pre-existing Roman material culture, imbuing Christian meanings upon pagan art forms and rejecting aspects of pagan material culture that were irreconcilable to Christianity. The iconography of an individual work might represent significantly different meanings to a Christian viewer and a pagan viewer." Benjamin Ioset, "Christian Monuments at Rome," ed. John D. Barry et al., *The Lexham Bible Dictionary* (Bellingham, WA: Lexham Press, 2012, 2013, 2014, 2015).

On the polemical contrast of Jesus with the emperor: Ethelbert Stauffer, *Christ and the Caesars: Historical Sketches* (Westminster Press, 1955).

"The phrase "son of God," though pregnant with other overtones that Paul will later cash out, has Davidic messiahship as its primary meaning, with echoes of Ps. 2 : 7 and 2 Sam. 7:14 in the background. The resurrection has installed Jesus of Nazareth as the Messiah of Israel, Paul insists, and therefore also the Lord to whose allegiance the world is now summoned.That is the burden of his song, the thrust of his euangelion. However unexpected, however shocking, however scandalous to Jews and foolish to Gentiles, this is the royal announcement that, from Paul's point of view, fulfills the prophecies of scripture and subverts the imperial gospel of Caesar…

"If Jesus is Messiah, he is also Lord, *kyrios*. It should now be apparent that the proper contexts for this term, too, are its Jewish roots on the one hand and its pagan challenge on the other. Taking them the other way around for the moment: the main challenge of the term, I suggest, was not to the world of private cults or mystery religions, where one might be initiated into membership of a group giving allegiance to some religion's "Lord." The main challenge was to the lordship of Caesar, which, though "political" from our point of view as well as in the first century, was also profoundly "religious." Caesar demanded worship as well as "secular" obedience: not just taxes, but sacrifices. He was well on his way to becoming the supreme divinity in the Greco-Roman world, maintaining his vast empire not simply by force — though there was of course plenty of that — but by the development of a flourishing religion that seemed to be trumping most others either by absorption or by greater attraction. Caesar, by being a servant of the state, had provided justice and peace to the whole world. He was therefore to be hailed as Lord and trusted as Savior. This is the world in which Paul announced that Jesus, the Jewish Messiah, was Savior and Lord...

"What was the immediate significance of this Jesus-and-Caesar contrast?... It was a challenge to an alternative loyalty. Jesus was the reality, Caesar the parody. It was the legitimation of the Christian church as the true empire of the true Lord." N.T. Wright, "Paul's Gospel and Caesar's Empire," in Ed. Richard A. Horsley, *Paul and Politics: Ekklesia, Israel, Imperium* (Penn., Trinity Press, 2000), 167-168, 174.

[8] **Apocalyptic literature**: "Apocalypse" in Greek simply means "revelation" or "disclosure." John Collins, an expert in apocalyptic literature defines it as a genre "with a narrative framework, in which a revelation is mediated by an otherworldly being to a human recipient, disclosing a transcendent reality which is both temporal, insofar as it envisages eschatological salvation, and spatial, insofar as it involves another, supernatural world." Yarbro Collins adds a point of clarification to the definition that apocalyptic is "intended to interpret present, earthly circumstances in light of the supernatural world and of the future, and to influence both the understanding and the behavior of the audience by means of divine authority."

Apocalyptic literature has the common elements of 1) being written as comfort to people who are suffering contemporary oppression 2) by referring to God's victory in history over oppressive forces 3) using fantastic imagery to express spiritual reality 4) in esoteric or symbolic terms in order to avoid outright suppression by the reigning powers in authority.

The well known books in the Bible of Daniel and Revelation are considered apocalyptic in their genre as Daniel and John are ushered into heaven and receive revelation about coming earthly historical events cloaked in poetic language to communicate the spiritual and theological meaning behind those events. They too are written as comfort to believers suffering persecution. They both contain symbolic fantastic imagery and are esoteric significations of governing authorities.

George W. E. Nickelsburg, *1 Enoch: a Commentary on the Book of 1 Enoch*, ed. Klaus Baltzer, *Hermeneia—a Critical and Historical Commentary on the Bible* (Minneapolis, MN: Fortress, 2001), 1, 9.

John J. Collins, "The Jewish Apocalypses," ed. John Joseph Collins, *Semeia 14* (1979): 22.

John J. Collins, "Apocalypses and Apocalypticism: Early Jewish Apocalypticism," ed. David Noel Freedman, *The Anchor Yale Bible Dictionary* (New York: Doubleday, 1992), 283.

CHAPTER 32

---

[1] **Ekklesia as "gathering" or "assembly." Also translated as "church":** ekklēsía—
'gathering'...Although Gk. ekklēsía became a distinctively Christian word, it has both a Greek and an OT history. In the Greek world it was used of a public assembly summoned by a herald (< ek, "out," and kaleín, "to call"; cf. Acts 19:32, 39f). In the LXX it was used for the Heb. qāhāl, which denotes the congregation or people of Israel, especially as gathered before the Lord (cf. Acts 7:38)." G. W. Bromiley, "Church," ed. Geoffrey W. Bromiley, *The International Standard Bible Encyclopedia, Revised* (Wm. B. Eerdmans, 1979–1988), 693.

[2] False messiahs in the desert: Matthew 24:23-28.

Fighting against spiritual principalities and powers: Ephesians 6:12.

[3] Revelation 13.

[4] A side-by-side comparison of some Ugaritic religious texts about the Canaanite god Baal with Old Testament passages reveals a common narrative: Yahweh, the charioteer of the clouds, metaphorically battles with Sea (Hebrew: yam) and River (Hebrew: nahar), just as Baal, the charioteer of the clouds, struggled with Yam (sea) and Nahar (river), which is also linked to victory over a sea dragon/serpent.

UGARTIC TEXTS	OLD TESTAMENT
'Dry him up. O Valiant Baal! Dry him up, O Charioteer of the Clouds! For our captive is Prince Yam [Sea], for our captive is Ruler Nahar [River]!' (KTU 1.2:4.8-9) What manner of enemy has arisen against Baal, of foe against the Charioteer of the Clouds? Surely I smote the Beloved of El, Yam [Sea]? Surely I exterminated Nahar [River], the mighty god? Surely I lifted up the dragon, I overpowered him? I smote the writhing serpent, Encircler-with-seven-heads! (KTU 1.3:3.38-41)	Did Yahweh rage against the rivers, Or was Your anger against the rivers (nahar), Or was Your wrath against the sea (yam), That You rode on Your horses, On Your chariots of salvation? (Hab. 3:8) In that day Yahweh will punish Leviathan the fleeing serpent, With His fierce and great and mighty sword, Even Leviathan the twisted serpent; And He will kill the dragon who lives in the sea. (Isa 27:1) "You divided the sea by your might; you broke the heads of the sea monsters on the waters. You crushed the heads of Leviathan. (Psa 74:13-14)

Baal fights Sea and River to establish his sovereignty. He wins by drinking up Sea and River, draining them dry, which results in Baal's supremacy over the pantheon and the Canaanite world order. In the second passage, Baal's battle with Sea and River is retold in other words as a battle with a "dragon," the "writhing serpent" with seven heads. Another Baal text calls this same dragon, "Lotan, the wriggling serpent." The Hebrew equivalents of the Ugaritic words tannin (dragon) and lotan are tannin (dragon) and liwyatan (Leviathan) respectively. The words are etymologically equivalent. Not only that, but so are the Ugaritic words describing the serpent as "wriggling" and "writhing" in the Ugaritic text (brh and 'qltn) with the words Isaiah 27 uses of Leviathan as "fleeing" and "twisting" (bariah and 'aqalaton). Notice the last Scripture in the chart that refers to Leviathan as having multiple heads just like the Canaanite Leviathan. Bible scholar Mitchell Dahood argued that in that passage of Psalm 74:12-17 the author implied the seven heads by using seven "you" references to God's powerful activities surrounding this mythopoeic defeat of Leviathan.

The Apostle John adapted this seven-headed dragon into his Revelation as a symbol of Satan as well as a chaotic demonic empire (Rev 12:3; 13:1; 17:3). Jewish Christians in the first century carried on this motif in texts such as the Odes of Solomon that explain Christ as overthrowing "the dragon with seven heads… that I might destroy his seed."

Thus, the Canaanite narrative of Lotan (Leviathan) the sea dragon or serpent is undeniably employed in Old Testament Scriptures and carried over into the New Testament as well.

See Brian Godawa, "Leviathan," *When Giants Were Upon the Earth: The Watchers, the Nephilim, and the Biblical Cosmic War of the Seed* (Embedded Pictures, 2014), 86-87.

[5] **The number of his name is 666**: Revelation 13:18.

Numerology in the ancient world: "Due to this ancient phenomenon of the two-fold use of alphabets, riddles employing numbers which concealed names were common. This phenomenon is called a "crypto~am" by modern scholars. Among the Greeks it was called isopsephia ('numerical equality'); among the Jews it was called gimatnya ('mathematical'). Any given name could be reduced to its numerical equivalent by adding up the mathematical value of all of the letters of the name.

"Archaeologists have discovered many illustrations of cryptograms as graffiti on ancient city walls that have been excavated. One example has been found in the excavations at Pompeii. There the Greek inscription reads: "philo es anthmos phi mu epsilon" ("I love her whose number is 545"). Zahn notes of this example that "The name of the lover is concealed; the beloved will know it when she recognises her name in the sum of the numerical value of the 3 letters phi mu epsilon, i.e., 545 ph = 500 + m = 40 + e = 5)." Ken Gentry, *The Beast of Revelation* (Tyler, TX: Instituted for Christian Economics, 1989, 1994), 31.

[6] **Severus reads from**: Revelation 17:9.

The seven hills: Rome was known throughout the ancient world as the city of seven hills, whose names are: Capitoline, Aventine, Caelian, Esquiline, Quirinal, Viminal, and Palantine. Numerous Roman writers used the phrase "seven hills" as a locution for Rome." Clinton E. Arnold, *Zondervan Illustrated Bible Backgrounds Commentary: Hebrews to Revelation., vol. 4* (Grand Rapids, MI: Zondervan, 2002), 346.

[7] **Women as joint heirs in God's kingdom**: 1 Peter 3:7.

[8] **Women, Jew, Gentile, freedman, slave, all equal in Christ**: Colossians 3:11; 1 Corinthians 12:13; Galatians 3:28.

[9] **The Great City**: Revelation 17:18; Revelation 18.

[10] **The fourth beast**: Daniel 7:15-22.

[11] **The fourth beast**: "The fourth beast has teeth of iron and claws of bronze, taken from the bottom half of the great image of Daniel 2. The historical fulfillment bears out this double sequence. First gold and silver, Babylon and Persia, both from the east, both existing at the same time, with Persia taking over Babylon. Then bronze and iron, Greece and Rome, both from the west, both existing at the same time, with Rome taking over Greece." James B. Jordan, *The Handwriting on the Wall: A Commentary on the Book of Daniel* (Powder Springs, GA: American Vision, 2007), 373–374.

Daniel 2 and the metal statue: "The traditional understanding of this sequence is as follows: The silver empire is that of the Persians and Medes. The bronze empire is that of the Greeks. The iron empire is that of the Romans. The arrival of the stone is the coming of Jesus, whose work and teaching struck Rome shortly after His ascension, most prominently when Paul arrived there in Acts 28. Rome was definitely shattered at that time, though it took a while (a few centuries) for the wind of the Spirit operating through the Church to blow away all the chaff-like pieces.

"Most traditional commentators are vague about the terra cotta, opining that perhaps it means that the Roman empire included lots of different people in it, and therefore was unstable. I have argued above that it refers to the apostate Jews and Herods."James B. Jordan, *The Handwriting on the Wall: A Commentary on the Book of Daniel* (Powder Springs, GA: American Vision, 2007), 185.

[12] **Messiah stone cut without hands**: Daniel 2: 40-45.

[13] **"Sections" of the letter in this story correspond to the same number chapters in the book of Revelation.**

The Revelation verses Alexander quotes: "And the woman that you saw is the great city that has dominion over the kings of the earth." Revelation 17:18.

"Then I heard another voice from heaven saying, "Come out of her, my people, lest you take part in her sins, lest you share in her plagues; 5 for her sins are heaped high as heaven, and God has remembered her iniquities." Revelation 18:4–5.

"And the merchants of the earth weep and mourn for her, since no one buys their cargo anymore, 12 cargo of gold, silver, jewels, pearls, fine linen, purple cloth, silk, scarlet cloth, all kinds of scented wood, all kinds of articles of ivory, all kinds of articles of costly wood, bronze, iron and marble, 13 cinnamon, spice, incense, myrrh, frankincense, wine, oil, fine flour, wheat, cattle and sheep, horses and chariots, and slaves, that is, human souls." Revelation 18:11–13

"And in her was found the blood of prophets and of saints, and of all who have been slain on earth." Revelation 18:24.

[14] Revelation 18:2.

[15] **The seven kings**: Revelation 17:10.

"A number of commentators see these "seven kings" as representing the first seven Caesars of Rome (cf. Stuart 2:325; Terry 431; Ratton 206; Renan, 215; Clark 109; Chilton 436; Mulholland 1996, 101; Prignet 481). We may find a list of the first twelve Caesars in Suetonius' famous work, *The Lives of the Twelve Caesars*. He lists them as follows:

1. Julius Caesar (59–44 B.C.)
2. Augustus Caesar (31 B.C.–A.D. 14)
3. Tiberius Caesar (A.D. 14-37)
4. Gaius Caesar (a.k.a Caligula) (37–41)
5. Claudius Caesar (41–54)
6. Nero Caesar (45–68)
7. Galba Caesar (June 68 to January 69)

"We find this order of emperors also in Josephus (Ant. 19:1:11 §75; cp. 18:2:2 §32–33; 18:6:10 §224); Sib. Or. 5:12-51; 4 Ezra 11-12 [2 Es 12:15]82; Theophilus (Ad Auto. 3:2783); Dio Chysostom (Or. 34:7); Clement of Alexandria (Strom. 1:21); and maybe, Barnabas 4:3-6. On this reckoning, the five that have "fallen" would be Julius through Claudius. That they are "fallen [epesen]" alludes "to the eminent rank of those whose death is declared" as in 2Sa 3:38. TDNT (6:161) notes that this word is commonly used of dying, particularly in the LXX (cf. Prignet 493). The sixth one who "is" (Gk.: estin, 17:10b) would be Nero. Regarding the seventh who will come and "must remain a little while [oligon auton dei meinai]" we should note that following Nero's thirteen year rule Galba takes the reins of government. But he rules for only seven months (June, AD 68 —January, AD 69), the shortest reigning emperor to that time." Kenneth L. Gentry, Jr., *The Divorce of Israel: A Redemptive-Historical Interpretation of Revelation Vol. 2* (Dallas, GA: Tolle Lege Press, 2016), 453-454.

The Beast as a collective kingdom and an individual king: Revelation 17:9–12 [9] This calls for a mind with wisdom: the seven heads are seven mountains on which the woman is seated; [10] they are also seven kings **[collective kingdom]**, five of whom have fallen, one is, the other has not yet come, and when he does come he must remain only a little while. [11] As for the beast that was and is not, it is an eighth **[individual king]** but it belongs to the seven, and it goes to destruction. [12] And the ten horns that you saw are ten kings who have not yet received royal power, but they are to receive authority as kings for one hour, together with the beast.

[16] **The number of Nero's name**: "An ancient Hebrew spelling of Nero Caesar's name is רסק וורנ (Nrwn Qsr). Archaeological finds from Murabba'at document this spelling in an Aramaic manuscript dating to the second year of Nero's reign. This spelling provides us with precisely the numerical value of 666, which is as follows: Nrwn: N =50; R =200; W =6; N =50 Qsr: Q =100; S =60; R =200.

"Today "the majority of modern scholars find a reference to Nero in Revelation 13:18" (Bauckham 1993a:384); it is by "far the most widely accepted solution" (Robinson 1976: 235)." Kenneth L. Gentry, Jr., *The Divorce of Israel: A Redemptive-Historical Interpretation of Revelation Vol. 2* (Dallas, GA: Tolle Lege Press, 2016), 285-286.

"In the midst of his Latin history, Suetonius records a sample of a Greek lampoon that was circulated after the burning of Rome, which occurred in A.D. 64 'Neopsephon Neron idian rrwtera apektine.' The translation of' this lampoon is: "A calculation new. Nero his mother slew."G J. C. Rolfe notes in the Loeb Classical Library edition of Suetonius' works that "the numerical value of the Greek letters in Nero's name (1005) is the same as that of the rest of the sentence; hence we have an equation, Nero = the slayer of his own mother." It is quite interesting to note that there were already anti-Nero cryptograms circulating when John wrote Revelation." Ken Gentry, *The Beast of Revelation* (Tyler, TX: Instituted for Christian Economics, 1989, 1994), 32.

[17] **"Sections" of the letter in this story correspond to the same number chapters in the book of Revelation.**

The Beast's war on the saints or "holy ones": Revelation 13:7–10 Also it was allowed to make war on the saints and to conquer them. And authority was given it over every tribe and people and language and nation, [8] and all who dwell on earth will worship it, everyone whose name has not been written before the foundation of the world in the book of life of the Lamb who was slain. [9] If anyone has an ear, let him

418

hear: [10] If anyone is to be taken captive, to captivity he goes; if anyone is to be slain with the sword, with the sword must he be slain. Here is a call for the endurance and faith of the saints.

[18] **The Mark of the Beast as symbolic of systemic and institutional identity with the Imperial Cult of Caesar:** "A number of scholars emphasize the Roman practice of marking slaves and soldiers to demonstrate ownership or loyalty, in that charagma (engraved, etched, or imprinted mark, BAGD 1077) is used in that way in the first century (Beale 715; Beasley-Murray 218; Stuart 2:289). Even in Scripture slaves literally receive a mark to demonstrate their loyalty to a master (e.g., Ex 21:6; Dt 15:17). The practice of physical marking is commonplace in ancient times, and is still practiced today in Hindu countries, especially among Vishnu and Siva devotees. The term is also used "often" as "an official stamp on writings . . , esp. the imperial stamp to attest the validity of decrees etc." (TDNT 9:416)...

We must note that the mark is on the "forehead" and/or "hand" (cp. 13:16 with 20:4). John's imagery source, which the beast parodies and reverses, appears ultimately to derive from Dt 6, a very important, well-known, and influential section of the Law containing the "Shema Israel" (Dt 6:4-9). This In Dt 6 the devout Jew is to keep "these words which I am commanding you today" (6:6) and to "bind them as a sign [sēmeion] on your hand and they shall be as frontals on your forehead" (6:8). The design of this Mosaic command is spiritual: the faithful must believe in one God and let his law govern their every thought (forehead) and deed (hand), for "you shall love the Lord your God with all your heart and with all your soul and with all your might" (Dt 6:5). "The 'forehead' represents ideological commitment and the 'hand' the practical outworking of that commitment" (Beale 717). The temple leadership (erroneously) see themselves as promoting the worship of the one true God and encouraging men to true faith and holy practice." Kenneth L. Gentry, Jr., *The Divorce of Israel: A Redemptive-Historical Interpretation of Revelation Vol. 2* (Dallas, GA: Tolle Lege Press, 2016), 277-278.

"By the end of the century, in the middle of which Paul came through the eastern empire preaching the message of Jesus, these developments had produced a new civic and religious reality. The highest honour a city could now hope for was to become neōkoros, temple-guardian for the Sebastoi, the Augustus-family. Worshipping the emperors was well on the way to becoming a central and vital aspect not only of life in general but of civic and municipal identity. Whatever we say about either the intentions or the effects of Roman rulers from Julius Caesar to Vespasian, the richly diverse phenomena we loosely call 'imperial cult' were a vital part of a complex system of power, communication and control, in other words, of all the things empires find they need to do. The (highly variegated) imperial cult was an 'institutional metaphor' which supplied 'a brief formula for the fundamental structure of the social system, which otherwise could not be put into words', and which worked actively 'to transmit this system to future generations'" N. T. Wright, *Paul and the Faithfulness of God, vol. 4, Christian Origins and the Question of God* (Minneapolis: Fortress Press, 2013), 341.

"The evidence now available, including that from epigraphy and archaeology, appears to show that the cult of Caesar, so far from being one new religion among many in the Roman world, had already by the time of Paul's missionary activity become not only the dominant cult in a large part of the empire, certainly in the parts where Paul was active, but was actually the means (as opposed to overt large-scale military presence) whereby the Romans managed to control and govern such huge areas as came under their sway. The emperor's far-off presence was made ubiquitous by the standard means of statues and coins (the latter being the principal mass medium of the ancient world), reflecting his image throughout his domains; he was the great benefactor, through whom the great blessings of justice and peace, and a host of lesser ones besides, were showered outwards upon the grateful populace — who in turn worshipped him, honored him, and paid him taxes." N.T. Wright, "Paul's Gospel and Caesar's Empire," in Ed. Richard A. Horsley, *Paul and Politics: Ekklesia, Israel, Imperium* (Penn., Trinity Press, 2000), 161.

CHAPTER 33

[1] **Nero's Golden House and Colossus**: "He made a palace extending all the way from the Palatine to the Esquiline, which at first he called the House of Passage, but when it was burned shortly after its completion and rebuilt, the Golden House. Its size and splendour will be sufficiently indicated by the following details. Its vestibule was large enough to contain a colossal statue of the emperor a hundred and

twenty feet high; and it was so extensive that it had a triple colonnade." Suetonius, *Lives of the Twelve Caesars, Nero* 31.1.

[2] **On Caligula's attempt to place a statue of himself in the temple**: Philo of Alexandria, *On the Embassy to Gaius* 30.203

Antiochus Epiphanes abominable acts referred to here: 2 Maccabees 6:1–13.

Though the Maccabees considered Epiphanes as the "abomination of desolation," (1 Maccabees 1:54), DeMar points out that Jesus said this prophecy was yet to be fulfilled within Jesus' own generation (Matthew 24:15):

"An abomination in the Old Testament was "related to the desecrating of worship, either by outright false worship (Deut. 7:25; 27:15) or by a profanation of true worship (Lev. 7:18; Deut. 17:1)." This definition fits the situation leading up to the temple's desolation in A.D. 70 in a number of ways. While there is little agreement on what the abomination was that brought on the desolation, nearly all the older commentators are agreed that the desolation occurred in the temple's destruction in A.D. 70. We do know, however, that the abomination that brings on the desolation happens sometime between Jerusalem being "surrounded by armies" (Luke 21:20) and the destruction of the temple. Four events are put forth as possible "abominations." Gary DeMar, *Last Days Madness: Obsession of the Modern Church*, Fourth revised edition (Powder Springs, GA: American Vision, 1999), 103–104.

DeMar lists the four options for abomination as The Zealots, the Idumeans, the Romans and the Jews, and shows there is some validity to each of them.

[3] **The description of the Domus Aurea used here** comes from Suetonius, *Lives of the Twelve Caesars, Nero* 31.

[4] **Tigellinus' debauchery**: "Ofonius Tigellinus. Born of obscure parentage, he had grown from an immoral youth into a vicious old man. He rose to the command first of the Police, and then of the Praetorian Guards, finding that vice was a shortcut to such rewards of virtue. In these and other high offices he developed the vices of maturity, first cruelty, then greed. He corrupted Nero and introduced him to every kind of depravity; then ventured on some villainies behind his back, and finally deserted and betrayed him." Tacitus, *The Histories* 1.72.

"Tigellinus constructed a raft on Agrippa's lake and on it set a feast that could then be moved about, towed along by other vessels. The vessels were trimmed with gold and ivory, and the oarsmen were male prostitutes who were grouped according to age and sexual expertise. Tigellinus had sought out birds and wild animals from distant lands, and sea creatures all the way from the ocean. On the lake's banks stood brothels filled with women of distinction, and on the other side common prostitutes were to be seen in the nude." Tacitus, *The Annals* 15.37.

"Sofonius Tigellinus, in whose case the attractions were the licentiousness of his past and his infamy. Neither belied his known habits: Tigellinus took the firmer hold over the mind of the prince and was made free of his most intimate debauches; Rufus enjoyed an excellent character with the people and the troops, and laboured under that disadvantage in his relations with Nero." *The Annals* 14.51

"The Emperor's new favourite was Tigellinus, a man of the most profligate morals, who omitted nothing that could gratify the inordinate appetites of his prince, at the expense of all decency and virtue. During this period, Petronius gave vent to his indignation, in the satire entitled Satyricon." C. Suetonius Tranquillus, *Suetonius: The Lives of the Twelve Caesars; An English Translation, Augmented with the Biographies of Contemporary Statesmen, Orators, Poets, and Other Associates*, ed. Alexander Thomson (Medford, MA: Gebbie & Co., 1889). C. *Petronius*, Chapter 1.

[5] **For the description of Nero's debaucheries described in this paragraph**: Suetonius, *Lives of the Twelve Caesars, Nero* 26-29.

[6] Craig Williams, *Roman Homosexuality: Ideologies of Masculinity in Classical Antiquity* (New York, Oxford Press 199), Appendix 2: Marriage Between Males, 245-252.

[7] **Homosexual marriage in ancient Rome**: "It seems clear that some Romans did participate in formal wedding ceremonies in which one male was married to another (hostile outsiders imagined the full

ceremony, complete with dowry, bridal veil, and ritual acclamations) and that these men considered themselves joined as spouses. But it is equally clear that such marriages were, by traditional Roman standards, anomalous in view of the fundamental nature of *matrimonium*, a hierarchical institution that was aimed at creating legitimate offspring as well as a route for the transmission of property (patrimonium) and that required the participation of a woman as subordinate partner. In traditional Roman terms, a marriage between two fully gendered "men" was inconceivable; if two males were joined together, one of them had to be "the woman."

> (Juvenal, *Satires* 2.122-31)
> 'Surely you would shudder and think it a greater monstrosity if a woman gave birth to a calf or a cow to a lamb? Flounces, a long dress, and a veil: this is what is worn by one who [as a Salian priest] carried the sacred objects that swayed from the mystic strap, sweating under the figure-of-eight shields. O father of the city, where did so great a crime, now among your Latin shepherds, come from? Gradivus [Mars], where did this stinging nettle come from that has now struck your grandsons? Look! A man renowned for his family background and his wealth is handed over [in marriage] to a man, and you do not shake your helmet, or strike the ground with your spear-point, or complain to your father?'

"The 'great crime' (nefas tantum) so loudly decried is not homosexual marriage but the fact that a man, and a noble one at that, is playing the woman's role, wearing the veil and being given to a husband, and a man of lower status at that, as his bride." Craig Williams, *Roman Homosexuality: Ideologies of Masculinity in Classical Antiquity* (New York, Oxford Press 199), 249, 251.

[8] **The marriage of Pythagoras to Nero**: Cassius Dio, *Roman History*, 62.28.2

"Nero took to himself two bedfellows, Pythagoras to treat as a man and Sporus as a woman." Cassius Dio, Roman History, 63.13.1-2.

"Nero himself, defiled by every natural and unnatural lust had left no abomination in reserve with which to crown his vicious existence; except that, a few days later, he became, with the full rites of legitimate marriage, the wife of one of that herd of degenerates,9 who bore the name of Pythagoras. The veil was drawn over the imperial head, witnesses were despatched to the scene; the dowry, the couch of wedded love, the nuptial torches, were there: everything, in fine, which night enshrouds even if a woman is the bride, was left open to the view." Tacitus, *The Annals* 15.37.

[9] **The Piso Conspiracy**: Tacitus writes in much detail of this plot in Tacitus, *The Annals* 15.48-74.

[10] **Tribune Subrius Flavus' confession**: Suetonius, *Lives of the Twelve Caesars, Nero* 67.

[11] **Lucan and Rufus in the conspiracy**: Tacitus, *The Annals* 15.49.

[12] **Nymphidius was later appointed co-prefect with Tigellinus**: Tacitus, *The Annals* 15.72.

[13] **Nero starting Neronia earlier than summer in AD 65**: "Considering it of great importance to appear in Rome as well, he repeated the contest of the Neronia before the appointed time." Suetonius, *Lives of the Twelve Caesars, Nero* 21.1-2

[14] **Titus went with Nero on his Greece tour**: Stephen Dando-Collins, *The Great Fire of Rome: The Fall of the Emperor Nero and His City* (Da Capo Press, 2010), 313.

[15] Cited in F.F. Bruce, *Paul: Apostle of the Heart Set Free* (1977; reprint, Cumbria, U.K.: Paternoster, 2000), p. 247.

CHAPTER 34

[1] **Theater of Pompey**: Edward Champlin, *Nero* (Massachussetts, Harvard University Press, 2003), 62.

[2] **Titus' divorce**: Gavin Townend, "Some Flavian Connections," *The Journal of Roman Studies* (1961), 57. Suetonius, *Lives of Twelve Caesars, Titus* 4.

[3] **Description of Vespasian as presented in this chapter**: Suetonius, *Lives of the Twelve Caesars, Vespasian* 4.4-5; 13; 20.

[4] Vespasian saw Nero perform at the Neronia competition and fell asleep: Tacitus, *The Annals* 16.5.

Vespasian's habit of falling asleep and annoying Nero: Suetonius, *Lives of the Twelve Caesars, Vespasian* 4.4.

[5] **Antonia Caenis was Vespasian's long time adulteress lover**: Suetonius, *Lives of the Twelve Caesars, Vespasian* 3.1; Cassius Dio, *Roman History*, 66.14.

[6] **Vespasian had traded mules at one point**: Suetonius, *Lives of the Twelve Caesars, Vespasian* 4.2.

[7] **The temple completed and unemployment**: Flavius Josephus, *The Antiquities of the Jews*, 20.9.19.

[8] **About Gessius Florus and the trouble he caused as described here**: Flavius Josephus, *The Antiquities of the Jews* 20.252; The Wars of the Jews 2.277-292

[9] **Gessius Florus' wife and Poppaea**: "Now Gessius Florus, who was sent as successor to Albinus by Nero, filled Judea with abundance of miseries. He was by birth of the city of Clazomenae, and brought along with him his wife Cleopatra (by whose friendship with Poppea, Nero's wife, he obtained this government), who was no way different from him in wickedness." Flavius Josephus, *The Antiquities of the Jews*, 20.252.

[10] **About Florus' deception of Cestius**: Flavius Josephus, *The Antiquities of the Jews* 2.280-283.

[11] **Vespasian the Muleteer**: Suetonius, *Lives of the Twelve Caesars, Vespasian* 4.2.

[12] **The Neronian Quinquennial as described here**: Tacitus, *The Annals* 16.4-5; Suetonius, *Lives of the Twelve Caesars, Nero* 12.3-4; Cassius Dio, *Roman History*, 62.19-21.

CHAPTER 35

[1] **Fatal Charades**: Tertullian writes of these fatal charades as violent plays in A.D. 197. Though this is a full century after Nero, many scholars like Coleman below find evidence of this going back to Nero himself.

"Then, again, when the likeness of a god is put on the head of an ignominious and infamous wretch, when one impure and trained up for the art in all effeminacy, represents a Minerva or a Hercules, is not the majesty of your gods insulted, and their deity dishonored? Yet you not merely look on, but applaud. You are, I suppose, more devout in the arena, where after the same fashion your deities dance on human blood, on the pollutions caused by inflicted punishments, as they act their themes and stories, doing their turn for the wretched criminals, except that these, too, often put on divinity and actually play the very gods. We have seen in our day a representation of the mutilation of Attis, that famous god of Pessinus, and a man burnt alive as Hercules. We have made merry amid the ludicrous cruelties of the noonday exhibition, at Mercury examining the bodies of the dead with his hot iron; we have witnessed Jove's brother, mallet in hand, dragging out the corpses of the gladiators." Tertullian, "The Apology, 15," in Latin Christianity: Its Founder, Tertullian, ed. Alexander Roberts, James Donaldson, and A. Cleveland Coxe, trans. S. Thelwall, vol. 3, *The Ante-Nicene Fathers* (Buffalo, NY: Christian Literature Company, 1885), 30.

"An epigram of Lucillius dating from the reign of Nero records the crematio of a miscreant, known as Meniscus, before a large number of spectators (Anth. Pal. II. l84):

"'Out of Zeus' Hesperidean garden Meniscus-like Heracles before him-lifted three golden apples. Why so? When he was caught, he-like Heracles before him-furnished a great spectacle to everyone: burnt alive...

"We need not envisage an elaborate, lengthy enactment: a club and a lionskin would be enough to identify Meniscus as Heracles, and to add a dimension of theatricality to his fate." K. M. Coleman, "Fatal Charades: Roman Executions Staged as Mythological Enactments," *The Journal of Roman Studies*, Vol. 80 (1990), 60.

"Why do these fatal charades cluster in the first two centuries of the empire? Our earliest evidence comes from the reign of Nero, our latest from the Severan age; most of it clusters under Nero and Titus...

"Since the participants in these occasional spectacles were usually prisoners-of-war and damnati, aumachiae were effectively an extension en masse of the gladiatorial duel, and thus a form of 'indirect' death penalty. These battles were staged in a quasi-historical setting: under Julius Caesar in 46 B.C. 4,000 oarsmen and 2,000 soldiers fought as 'Tyrians' and 'Egyptians', clearly a fictitious engagement designed to accommodate an exotic scenario...

"The most spectacular *naumachia* recorded was fought under Claudius in A.D. 52 in the fictitious context of Sicilians against Rhodians; 19,000, destined to die, participated on the Fucine Lake...

"Nero, like Augustus, pitted 'Athenians' against 'Persians' (Dio 61.9.5)." K. M. Coleman, "Fatal Charades: Roman Executions Staged as Mythological Enactments," *The Journal of Roman Studies*, Vol. 80 (1990), 70-71.

"The unhappy wretch was dragged into the arena, richly attired as a god or hero devoted to death; and then, in his torment, he exhibited some tragic scene of a story consecrated by sculptors and poets. At one time, it might be Hercules, raving in torment on Mt. (Eta, tearing off the poisoned shirt of Nessus, a tunic of flaming pitch; at another, Orpheus, rent in pieces by a bear; or Daedalus, hurled from the sky and devoured by beasts; or Pasiphae, assaulted by the bull; or Attys, son of Croesus, slain with a javelin - possibly an error for Adonis, torn by a boar; or at times there would be horrible masquerades, in which men were clad in red mantles as priests of Saturn, and women as priestesses of Ceres with frontlets on their brows; or, again, there were dramatic scenes, in which the actor was really put to death, like Laureolus; or, perhaps, tragic deeds like that of Mucius Scaevola. At the close of the entertainment Mercury, with a wand of red-hot iron, would touch each body to see if it should stir; while lackeys in masks, personating Pluto or Orcus, dragged out the corpses by the feet, knocking in the head any that might still show signs of life...

"Regarding the torment of Dirce, there can be no doubt at all. A well-known colossal group in the museum at Naples is that of the Farnese Bull, in which Amphion and Zethus are fastening Dirce to the horns of a wild bull, which will drag her through the rocks and briers of Cithmron. This poor piece of Rhodian sculpture, taken to Rome in the time of Augustus, was an object of universal admiration. What finer subject for that brutal style of art brought into vogue by the cruelty of the time, which consisted in turning famous sculptures into living pictures? An inscription and a fresco at Pompeii seem to prove that this dreadful scene was often exhibited in the arena, when a woman was to suffer death. Fastened by the hair, naked, to the horns of a wild bull, these poor creatures were exposed to the wanton gaze of a ferocious mob." Ernest Renan, trans. Joseph Henry Allen, *The Antichrist: The Period From the Arrival of Paul in Rome to the End of the Jewish Revolution* (Boston, Roberts Brothers 1897), 148-150.

[2] **The accusations against the Christians enumerated in this paragraph**: Leon Hardy Canfield, *The Early Persecutions of the Christians* (New York, Columbia, 1913), 23.

[3] **Cassius Dio on Pythagoras**: "Nero married the freedman Pythagoras after Poppea was dead. Later, "Nero took to himself two bedfellows, Pythagoras to treat as a man and Sporus as a woman." Cassius Dio, *Roman History* 63.13.1-2.

[4] **Sympathy for the Christian martyrs**: "Hence, in spite of a guilt which had earned the most exemplary punishment, there arose a sentiment of pity, due to the impression that they were being sacrificed not for the welfare of the state but to the ferocity of a single man." Tacitus, *The Annals* 15.44.

[5] **The myth of Actaeon**: "By the same token, presenting the Christians as beasts to be torn by the dogs must have reminded spectators of Actaeon transformed into a stag and torn to pieces by hunting dogs. His sacrilegious crime had been to gaze upon the goddess Diana while she bathed. Diana was not only goddess of the hunt, she was also goddess of the moon, and it would be appropriate to propitiate her with the lives of the criminals who had supposedly attacked her temple." Edward Champlin, *Nero* (Massachussetts, Harvard University Press, 2003), 123.

[6] **Tertullian on Roman misunderstanding of Christian beliefs**: "Others, again, certainly with more information and greater verisimilitude, believe that the sun is our god. We shall be counted Persians perhaps, though we do not worship the orb of day painted on a piece of linen cloth, having himself

everywhere in his own disk. The idea no doubt has originated from our being known to turn to the east in prayer. But you, many of you, also under pretence sometimes of worshipping the heavenly bodies, move your lips in the direction of the sunrise. In the same way, if we devote Sun-day to rejoicing, from a far different reason than Sun-worship, we have some resemblance to those of you who devote the day of Saturn to ease and luxury, though they too go far away from Jewish ways, of which indeed they are ignorant. But lately a new edition of our god has been given to the world in that great city: it originated with a certain vile man who was wont to hire himself out to cheat the wild beasts, and who exhibited a picture with this inscription: The God of the Christians, born of an ass. He had the ears of an ass, was hoofed in one foot, carried a book, and wore a toga. Both the name and the figure gave us amusement." Tertullian, "The Apology 16," in Latin Christianity: Its Founder, Tertullian, ed. Alexander Roberts, James Donaldson, and A. Cleveland Coxe, trans. S. Thelwall, vol. 3, *The Ante-Nicene Fathers* (Buffalo, NY: Christian Literature Company, 1885), 31.

For Roman misunderstanding of Jews and their religion during the time of Nero, see Tacitus, *The Histories* 5.2-5.

[7] **On the bestial rape of female victims in the arena**: "Although instances of bestiality are known in which women have performed intercourse with various animals,172 and in certain cultures such enactments are allegedly performed as public entertainment, and although the fine lady in Apuleius' novel, infatuated with Lucius in the shape of an ass, successfully consummates her passion, how are we to envisage intercourse between a woman and a bull in the arena?…The most effective method of rousing taurine lust, however, would be to smear upon the woman's genitalia the vaginal secretions of a cow in season. Were she a condemned prisoner, it would obviously not matter if her internal organs were damaged in such an enactment; indeed, the expectation is that she would be killed, if not in the encounter with the bull then dispatched afterwards by the sword." K. M. Coleman, "Fatal Charades: Roman Executions Staged as Mythological Enactments," *The Journal of Roman Studies*, Vol. 80 (1990), 63-64.

[8] **Mercury and Pluto at the fatal charades**: We have made merry amid the ludicrous cruelties of the noonday exhibition, at Mercury examining the bodies of the dead with his hot iron; we have witnessed Jove's brother, mallet in hand, dragging out the corpses of the gladiators." Tertullian, "The Apology, 15," in Latin Christianity: Its Founder, Tertullian, ed. Alexander Roberts, James Donaldson, and A. Cleveland Coxe, trans. S. Thelwall, vol. 3, *The Ante-Nicene Fathers* (Buffalo, NY: Christian Literature Company, 1885), 30.

[9] **The myth of Dirce**: "Dirce too can be fitted into Nero's spectaculum, and she was much closer to what the audience normally enjoyed. Dirce, wife of the King of Thebes, was an ingeniously wicked stepmother who (in one version of the story) tried to trick her stepsons into attacking their long-suffering mother. The angry youths turned instead on Dirce the violence intended for their mother: they tied their stepmother by her hair to the horns of a bull, which then trampled and gored her to death. The death of Dirce was a common enough theme in art, and death by tying to bulls is a well-attested hazard of the Roman arena, but again it was a particularly pointed punishment for the condemned arsonists of 64." Edward Champlin, *Nero* (Massachussetts, Harvard University Press, 2003), 123-125.

The Danaids and Dircae as fatal charades: Clement of Rome writes of these fatal charades in Nero's persecution, though without detail. "To these men who spent their lives in the practice of holiness, there is to be added a great multitude of the elect, who, having through envy endured many indignities and tortures, furnished us with a most excellent example. Through envy, those women, the Danaids and Dircae, being persecuted, after they had suffered terrible and unspeakable torments, finished the course of their faith with steadfastness, and though weak in body, received a noble reward." Clement of Rome, *The First Epistle of Clement to the Corinthians, 6.*

[10] **The myth of Danaus**: "The fifty daughters of Danaus were the subject of one of the most familiar of myths. Danaus, having fallen out with his brother Aegyptus, fled from Egypt to Greece where, with Apollo's help, he seized the city of Argos. The fifty sons of Aegyptus, who had been betrothed to his daughters, the Danaides, pursued them to Argos and demanded them in marriage. On the wedding night all but one of the fifty daughters, following the command of their father, slew their bridegrooms. In Hades the forty nine murderesses were punished terribly for their crime, condemned to carry water in leaking jars throughout eternity. How could this be translated into the setting of a Roman amphitheater? It might

be a tedious spectacle for a crowd looking for rivers of blood, but Roman audiences were satisfied with the sketchiest of symbols: give each woman a jar, then let loose the beasts. The point of the entertainment lies not in the manner of punishment but in the persons of the criminals or victims." Edward Champlin, *Nero* (Massachussetts, Harvard University Press, 2003), 123-125.

Coleman gives more details: "Since the mythological Dirce was bound to the horns of a bull by her two stepsons in revenge for having plotted against their mother, it is easy to imagine how realistically her fate could be re-enacted in the arena. More difficult is Clement's claim that some of the martyrs were presented as the daughters of Danaus, since the Danaids' traditional punishment for having murdered their bridegrooms was the endless task of pouring water into bottomless containers, a scenario plainly lacking in spectacular appeal. In the instances of 'Orpheus' and 'Daedalus', however, we have already seen that the mode of execution by which the protagonists in the charades were dispatched need not match their traditional fate in myth. Thus, a group of female prisoners furnished with jugs would immediately remind the audience of the Danaids, and they might then be executed in a manner not necessarily corresponding to any known variant of the story.' It seems legitimate to adduce here a piece of evidence which, though it does not involve enacting a mythological scene, nevertheless demonstrates that prisoners could be forced to appear in the arena in an assumed guise as part of their penalty."

"If Clement of Rome was writing under Nero, then the charades displaying the Danaids and Dirce presumably belong with Nero's persecution of the Christians after the fire and at a time of increasingly overt dissatisfaction with his reign. Titus' inauguration of the Flavian Amphitheatre was perhaps rather a dedication of his extensions to it; Vespasian may well have inaugurated the first three storeys." K. M. Coleman, "Fatal Charades: Roman Executions Staged as Mythological Enactments," *The Journal of Roman Studies*, Vol. 80 (1990), 66, 73.

The Danaids: "Christian ladies of the highest rank must have their share in these horrors. Some played the part of the Danaids... it may be that these wretched maidens exhibited in succession the whole series of the punishments of Tartarus, and died after hours of torment. Representations of the world below were then in fashion. A few years before A.D. 41, some Egyptians and Nubians came to Rome, and had great success in exhibitions by night, displaying by order the horrors of Tartarus, in conformity with pictures existing at Thebes, particularly those on the tomb of Sethi I." Ernest Renan, trans. Joseph Henry Allen, *The Antichrist: The Period From the Arrival of Paul in Rome to the End of the Jewish Revolution* (Boston, Roberts Brothers 1897), 148.

[11] **Nero's interest in Egypt**: Nero was going through a period in which he was obsessed with all things Egyptian, and it has been suggested that his interest in Isis came about through the influence of Chaeremon, former librarian at the Sarapium, the temple of Sarapis, at Alexandria. This Egyptian Stoic was said to be briefly Nero's tutor when he was a boy. It has also been suggested that once Nero became emperor, Apollonius of Tyrana, a client of Nero's who, guided by Egyptian priests, professed himself to be a teacher from heaven and was a follower of Isis, influenced Nero's beliefs. Many scholars believe that Nero, wracked by guilt after he brought about the murder of his mother in AD 59, began a search for spirituality that saw him, for a time at least, personally embrace the cult of Isis, the mother goddess. While his interest in Egypt and Egyptian customs had not waned by AD 64, Nero seems to have moved on from Isis in his restless quest for spiritual relief." Stephen Dando-Collins, *The Great Fire of Rome: The Fall of the Emperor Nero and His City* (Da Capo Press, 2010), 24.

[12] **Tortures of Tartarus in the Egyptian Books of the Netherworld, The Coffin Texts, The Book of the Dead, The Book of Caverns**: "However, when the damned died, their flesh was torn away by demons and their mummy wrappings were removed so that their bodies were left to decompose. In the underworld that the blessed successfully navigate, their order of things is reversed, even to the extent that the damned have to walk upside down, eat their own excrement and drink their own urine. Their hands are tied behind their backs, often around stakes. Their heads and limbs are severed from their bodies and their flesh is cut off their bones. Their hearts are removed and their ba-souls are separated from their bodies, forever unable to return to them...

"They are continuously punished by demons, who are the representatives of chaos. Indeed, the demons are often recruited from the ranks of the damned themselves, so that they torture and kill one another. They are subjected to knives and swords and to the fire of hell, often kindled by fire spitting snakes.

"These horrible punishments were carried out in the "slaughtering place" or "place of destruction", and presided over by the fierce goddess Sekhmet, whose butchers hack their victims to pieces and burn them with inextinguishable fire, sometimes in deep pits or in cauldrons in which they are scorched, cooked and reduced to ashes. Demons feed on their entrails and drink their blood.

"Another location was the Lake of Fire, which was first mentioned in the Book of Two Ways in the Coffin Text (Spell 1054/1166) and illustrated in the *Book of the Dead* (Chapter 126). Like the "outer darkness." John Watson, "Tour Egypt: The Hell of Ancient Egypt.
http://www.touregypt.net/featurestories/hell.htm

CHAPTER 36

[1] **Poppaea's luxurious excess**: "The extremes of luxury indulged in by this Sabina I will indicate in the briefest terms. She caused gilded shoes to be put on the mules that drew her and caused five hundred asses that had recently foaled to be milked daily that she might bathe in their milk. For she bestowed the greatest pains on the beauty and brilliancy of her person, and this is why, when she noticed in a mirror one day that her appearance was not comely, she prayed that she might die before she passed her prime." Cassius Dio, *Roman History* 62.27.4 - 62.28.1.

[2] **Backlash of sympathy for the Christians**: "Hence, in spite of a guilt which had earned the most exemplary punishment, there arose a sentiment of pity, due to the impression that they were being sacrificed not for the welfare of the state but to the ferocity of a single man." Tacitus, *The Annals* 15.44.

[3] **On Poppaea's death as depicted in this chapter**: "Sabina also perished at this time through an act of Nero's; either accidentally or intentionally he had leaped upon her with his feet while she was pregnant." Cassius Dio, *Roman History* 62.27.4 - 62.28.1.

"He dearly loved Poppaea, whom he married twelve days after his divorce from Octavia, yet he caused her death too by kicking her when she was pregnant and ill, because she had scolded him for coming home late from the races." Suetonius, *The Twelve Caesars Nero* 35.3.

"After the close of the festival, Poppaea met her end through a chance outburst of anger on the part of her husband, who felled her with a kick during pregnancy." Tacitus, *The Annals* 16.6.1.

CHAPTER 37

[1] **Cassandra is thinking of Paul's warning about Satan as an angel of light**: 2 Corinthians 11:14 And no wonder, for even Satan disguises himself as an angel of light.

[2] **Gabriel quotes from 1 John to Cassandra**: 1 John 4:1–3 [1] Beloved, do not believe every spirit, but test the spirits to see whether they are from God, for many false prophets have gone out into the world. [2] By this you know the Spirit of God: every spirit that confesses that Jesus Christ has come in the flesh is from God, [3] and every spirit that does not confess Jesus is not from God. This is the spirit of the antichrist.

1 John 2:22 Who is the liar but he who denies that Jesus is the Christ? This is the antichrist, he who denies the Father and the Son.

1 John 2:2 He is the propitiation for our sins, and not for ours only but also for the sins of the whole world.

[3] **Cassandra's doctrinal test of her spiritual experience is based on**: 1 Corinthians 12:3 Therefore I want you to understand that no one speaking in the Spirit of God ever says "Jesus is accursed!" and no one can say "Jesus is Lord" except in the Holy Spirit.

James 2:19 You believe that God is one; you do well. Even the demons believe—and shudder!

CHAPTER 38

[1] **The examples of God's sovereign providence and foreordination referenced in Alexander's thoughts**:

Pharaoh: Romans 9:17–18 [17] For the Scripture says to Pharaoh, "For this very purpose I have raised you up, that I might show my power in you, and that my name might be proclaimed in all the earth." [18] So then he has mercy on whomever he wills, and he hardens whomever he wills.

Exodus 11:9 Then the LORD said to Moses, "Pharaoh will not listen to you, that my wonders may be multiplied in the land of Egypt."

Nebuchadnezzar: Jeremiah 25:9 [9] behold, I will send for all the tribes of the north, declares the LORD, and for Nebuchadnezzar the king of Babylon, my servant, and I will bring them against this land and its inhabitants, and against all these surrounding nations. I will devote them to destruction, and make them a horror, a hissing, and an everlasting desolation.

Cyrus: Isaiah 45:1–4 [1] Thus says the LORD to his anointed, to Cyrus, whose right hand I have grasped, to subdue nations before him and to loose the belts of kings, to open doors before him that gates may not be closed: [2] "… it is I, the LORD, the God of Israel, who call you by your name. [4] For the sake of my servant Jacob, and Israel my chosen, I call you by your name, I name you, though you do not know me.

Joseph's brothers is another powerful example: Genesis 50:17–21 [17] 'Say to Joseph, "Please forgive the transgression of your brothers and their sin, because they did evil to you." ' And now, please forgive the transgression of the servants of the God of your father." Joseph wept when they spoke to him. [18] His brothers also came and fell down before him and said, "Behold, we are your servants." [19] But Joseph said to them, "Do not fear, for am I in the place of God? [20] As for you, you meant evil against me, but God meant it for good, to bring it about that many people should be kept alive, as they are today. [21] So do not fear; I will provide for you and your little ones." Thus he comforted them and spoke kindly to them.

[2] **Examples of how God judging the instruments of his choosing for their own sins**:

Pharaoh: Exodus 7:14–16 [14] Then the LORD said to Moses, "Pharaoh's heart is hardened; he refuses to let the people go. [15] Go to Pharaoh in the morning, as he is going out to the water. Stand on the bank of the Nile to meet him, and take in your hand the staff that turned into a serpent. [16] And you shall say to him, 'The LORD, the God of the Hebrews, sent me to you, saying, "Let my people go, that they may serve me in the wilderness." But so far, you have not obeyed.

Nebuchadnezzar: Jeremiah 25:11–14 [11] This whole land shall become a ruin and a waste, and these nations shall serve the king of Babylon seventy years. [12] Then after seventy years are completed, I will punish the king of Babylon and that nation, the land of the Chaldeans, for their iniquity, declares the LORD, making the land an everlasting waste. [13] I will bring upon that land all the words that I have uttered against it, everything written in this book, which Jeremiah prophesied against all the nations. [14] For many nations and great kings shall make slaves even of them, and I will recompense them according to their deeds and the work of their hands."

Jews and Romans killing Christ: Acts 2:23 [23] this Jesus, delivered up according to the definite plan and foreknowledge of God, you crucified and killed by the hands of lawless men.

Acts 4:27–28 [27] for truly in this city there were gathered together against your holy servant Jesus, whom you anointed, both Herod and Pontius Pilate, along with the Gentiles and the peoples of Israel, [28] to do whatever your hand and your plan had predestined to take place.

God judging the Jews for killing Christ: Matthew 21:40–43 [40] When therefore the owner of the vineyard comes, what will he do to those tenants?" [41] They said to him, "He will put those wretches to a miserable death and let out the vineyard to other tenants who will give him the fruits in their seasons." [42] Jesus said to them, "Have you never read in the Scriptures: " 'The stone that the builders rejected has become the cornerstone; this was the Lord's doing, and it is marvelous in our eyes'? [43] Therefore I tell you, the kingdom of God will be taken away from you and given to a people producing its fruits.

[3] **Cassandra's analogy of the potter and clay is quoted from Paul**: Romans 9:19–24 [19] You will say to me then, "Why does he still find fault? For who can resist his will?" [20] But who are you, O man, to answer back to God? Will what is molded say to its molder, "Why have you made me like this?" [21] Has the potter no right over the clay, to make out of the same lump one vessel for honorable use and another for

427

dishonorable use? [22] What if God, desiring to show his wrath and to make known his power, has endured with much patience vessels of wrath prepared for destruction, [23] in order to make known the riches of his glory for vessels of mercy, which he has prepared beforehand for glory— [24] even us whom he has called, not from the Jews only but also from the Gentiles?

[4] **Paul's potter and clay analogy was drawn from the prophetic tradition in Israel**: Jeremiah 18:1–11 [5] Then the word of the LORD came to me: [6] "O house of Israel, can I not do with you as this potter has done? declares the LORD. Behold, like the clay in the potter's hand, so are you in my hand, O house of Israel... [11] Now, therefore, say to the men of Judah and the inhabitants of Jerusalem: 'Thus says the LORD, Behold, I am shaping disaster against you and devising a plan against you. Return, every one from his evil way, and amend your ways and your deeds.'

Isaiah 64:8 But now, O LORD, you are our Father; we are the clay, and you are our potter; we are all the work of your hand.

[5] **The Poisoning of Serenus and his tribunes and centurions**: Pliny the Elder, *Natural Histories* 22.47.

[6] **The rejection of the Jews by Yahweh**: Jesus' parable of the tenants and the vineyard, concludes, Matthew 21:38–45 But when the tenants saw the son, they said to themselves, 'This is the heir. Come, let us kill him and have his inheritance.' 39 And they took him and threw him out of the vineyard and killed him. 40 When therefore the owner of the vineyard comes, what will he do to those tenants?" 41 They said to him, "He will put those wretches to a miserable death and let out the vineyard to other tenants who will give him the fruits in their seasons." 42 Jesus said to them, "Have you never read in the Scriptures: " 'The stone that the builders rejected has become the cornerstone; this was the Lord's doing, and it is marvelous in our eyes'? 43 Therefore I tell you, the kingdom of God will be taken away from you and given to a people producing its fruits. 44 And the one who falls on this stone will be broken to pieces; and when it falls on anyone, it will crush him." 45 When the chief priests and the Pharisees heard his parables, they perceived that he was speaking about them.

Jesus' parable of the Great Banquet: Luke 14:23–24 And the master said to the servant, 'Go out to the highways and hedges and compel people to come in, that my house may be filled. [24] For I tell you, none of those men who were invited shall taste my banquet.' "

Acts 13:46 And Paul and Barnabas spoke out boldly, saying, "It was necessary that the word of God be spoken first to you. Since you thrust it aside and judge yourselves unworthy of eternal life, behold, we are turning to the Gentiles.

1 Thessalonians 2:14–16 For you suffered the same things from your own countrymen as they did from the Jews, [15] who killed both the Lord Jesus and the prophets, and drove us out, and displease God and oppose all mankind [16] by hindering us from speaking to the Gentiles that they might be saved—so as always to fill up the measure of their sins. But wrath has come upon them at last!

[7] **God's promise to Abraham of everlasting covenant, seed and land**: Genesis 17:4-10.

[8] **My Servant, a light to the nations**: Isaiah 49:6.

[9] **Cassandra quotes from** Isaiah 61:1–2.

[10] **Cassandra quotes from** Isaiah 53.

[11] **The earthly temple and order as a shadow of the real**: "They serve a copy and shadow of the heavenly things. For when Moses was about to erect the tent, he was instructed by God, saying, "See that you make everything according to the pattern that was shown you on the mountain." But as it is, Christ has obtained a ministry that is as much more excellent than the old as the covenant he mediates is better, since it is enacted on better promises." Hebrews 8:5–6.

"Thus it was necessary for the copies of the heavenly things to be purified with these rites, but the heavenly things themselves with better sacrifices than these. For Christ has entered, not into holy places made with hands, which are copies of the true things, but into heaven itself, now to appear in the presence of God on our behalf. Nor was it to offer himself repeatedly, as the high priest enters the holy places every year with blood not his own, for then he would have had to suffer repeatedly since the foundation of the world. But as it is, he has appeared once for all at the end of the ages to put away sin by the sacrifice of himself." Hebrews 9:23–26.

[12] **Cassandra quotes** Ephesians 2:8.

[13] **The Suffering Servant of Isaiah interpreted as the nation Israel**: Though this kind of argument was not a popular one in ancient days, there is some evidence of its early existence in the second century. As Michael Brown argues,

"The only ancient reference of any kind to the national interpretation of Isaiah 53 is actually found in a non-Jewish source, namely, a polemical work entitled Contra Celsum, written by the second-century Christian scholar Origen. In this work Origen refutes the arguments of an opponent of both Judaism and Christianity named Celsus, and while discussing Messianic prophecies, Origen makes reference to a disputation he once had with some learned Jews, stating that the Jews interpreted Isaiah 53 in terms of Israel's national suffering:

"Now I remember that, on one occasion, at a disputation held with certain Jews, who were reckoned wise men, I quoted these prophecies; to which my Jewish opponent replied, that these predictions bore reference to the whole people, regarded as one individual, and as being in a state of dispersion and suffering, in order that many proselytes might be gained, on account of the dispersion of the Jews among numerous heathen nations. And in this way he explained the words, "Thy form shall be of no reputation among men;" and then, "They to whom no message was sent respecting him shall see;" and the expression, "A man under suffering."

"Origen had an immediate reply to this line of interpretation:

"Many arguments were employed on that occasion during the discussion to prove that these predictions regarding one particular person were not rightly applied by them to the whole nation. And I asked to what character the expression would be appropriate, "This man bears our sins, and suffers pain on our behalf;" and this, "But He was wounded for our sins, and bruised for our iniquities;" and to whom the expression properly belonged, "By His stripes were we healed." For it is manifest that it is they who had been sinners, and had been healed by the Savior's sufferings (whether belonging to the Jewish nation or converts from the Gentiles), who use such language in the writings of the prophet who foresaw these events, and who, under the influence of the Holy Spirit, applied these words to a person. But we seemed to press them hardest with the expression, "Because of the iniquities of My people was He led away unto death." For if the people, according to them, are the subject of the prophecy, how is the man said to be led away to death because of the iniquities of the people of God, unless he be a different person from that people of God? And who is this person save Jesus Christ, by whose stripes they who believe on Him are healed, when "He had spoiled the principalities and powers (that were over us), and had made a show of them openly on His cross?" Michael L. Brown, *Answering Jewish Objections to Jesus: Messianic Prophecy Objections, vol. 3* (Grand Rapids, MI: Baker Books, 2003), 60–61.

[14] **Cassandra quotes from** Isaiah 53:8, 12.

[15] **See his offspring and prolong his days**: Isaiah 53:10.

[16] **Cassandra quotes from** Isaiah 7:14.

[17] **Rebekah as *almah***: Genesis 24:43.

Almah translated as "virgin": "At the outset we may confidently assert that the word 'almah is never employed of a married woman. At least one of these occurrences makes it clear that the word may designate one who is truly a virgin (Gen. 24:43). Rebekah is called an 'almah, but she is furthermore designated a bethulah, and it is said of her that a man had not known her. In one passage, namely, Proverbs 30:19, the word 'almah may possibly signify an immoral girl, but it does not indicate a married girl. Perhaps the closest equivalent in English is the word damsel or maiden. Neither of these is generally employed of a married woman. Yet even these words may not be precise equivalents, for whereas they could possibly refer to married women, 'almah does not do so. For these reasons it may be wisest, after all, to render 'almah in English by "virgin."

"In the light of these considerations it appears that Isaiah's choice of 'almah was deliberate. It seems to be the only word in the language which unequivocally signifies an unmarried woman. No other available

Hebrew word would clearly indicate that the one whom it designates was unmarried. Consequently, no other word would have been suitable for fulfilling the requirements of the sign such as the context demanded. None of these other words would have pointed to an unusual birth. Only ʾalmah makes clear that the mother was unmarried.

"If, however, the mother is an unmarried woman, a question arises. Was the child illegitimate or not? If the child were illegitimate, would such a birth be a sign? The whole context, indeed the whole Biblical context, rules this out. On the other hand, if the mother were a good woman, then the birth was out of the ordinary, an unusual birth. The mother is both unmarried and a good woman. When this fact is understood, it becomes apparent that in all history there is only one of whom this can be predicated, namely, Mary, the mother of the Lord." Edward Young, *The Book of Isaiah, Chapters 1–18, vol. 1* (Grand Rapids, MI: Wm. B. Eerdmans Publishing Co., 1965), 287–289.

[18] *Parthenos* in the Septuagint: "a maiden shall conceive. It is not possible to be dogmatic as to why Isaiah used the ambiguous ʾalmâ here instead of the unambiguous beṯûlâ. Nor is it clear what meaning should be assigned to ʾalmâ. Typically, the meaning given is "a young woman of marriageable age," with the clear implication that the conception is a natural one. However, conservative scholars have frequently pointed out that the word is never used of a married woman in the OT.21 So they have argued that the word denotes a sexually mature, but unmarried, young woman. It would be axiomatic in Hebrew society that such a woman would be a virgin. While the viginity would not be the main focus, as with beṯûlâ, nonetheless it would still follow. The English "maiden" comes very close to having the same denotations and connotations. Such an understanding has the significant virtue of explaining the origin of the LXX parthénos, "virgin," something those commentators opting for "a young woman of marriageable age" do not mention. Unless ʾalmâ had overtones of virginity about it, the LXX translation is inexplicable." John N. Oswalt, *The Book of Isaiah, Chapters 1–39, The New International Commentary on the Old Testament* (Grand Rapids, MI: Wm. B. Eerdmans Publishing Co., 1986), 210.

[19] The divine names of Isaiah 9: "Medieval Jewish commentators, combatting the prevailing messianic claims of Christians, argued that all this was simply in recognition of the birth of the crown prince, Hezekiah, and was only a simple royal birth hymn. However, this view flies in the face of the chronology of Hezekiah's birth, and even more seriously, it is evident from the language that no merely human king is being spoken of.15 This is clearly an eschatological figure, the Messiah…

"The titles underscore the ultimate deity of this child-deliverer. Although some commentators have expended a great deal of energy attempting to make these titles appear normal, they are not. Perhaps the primary way in which this is attempted is by reference to the Egyptian throne-names (cf. Wildberger). It was customary to give five throne-names to an Egyptian king upon his coronation. These were related to the various gods and were understood to have magical effect. Such names as "Mighty Bull appearing in Thebes" and "Enduring in Kingship, like Re in Heaven" were typical. On this basis some suggest that the same practice was followed for the equally human kings of Israel. However, several factors tell against this equation. First, there are not five names here but four, and only emendation can produce a fifth.19 Second, this is not a coronation hymn but a birth announcement. Third, the Egyptians believed their kings were gods and the names express that belief. But the Hebrews did not believe this. They denied that the king was anything more than the representative of God. To be sure, throne-names were probably used in Israel (cf. 2 K. 23:34; 24:17), but there is no evidence that they were of the Egyptian sort. R. A. Carlson has argued that the titles are part of a polemic against the Assyrians, attacking the extravagant claims made by the Assyrian monarchs about their wisdom and power. On this view, Isaiah's use of the titles means that wisdom and power really belonged to that king whom God would send to them. This view has much higher likelihood than the Egyptian one, but the point remains that such extravagant titling was not normal for Israelite kings. It is an expression of a belief that the one who would be born to rule over Israel in justice and righteousness would be possessed of divine attributes.22 All of this points to a remarkable congruence with the Immanuel prophecy." John N. Oswalt, *The Book of Isaiah, Chapters 1–39, The New International Commentary on the Old Testament* (Grand Rapids, MI: Wm. B. Eerdmans Publishing Co., 1986), 245–247.

[20] **Cassandra quotes from** Isaiah 9:6-7.

Jesus as the new temple, the promised land and the Seed of Abraham: See explanations in later chapters.

[21] **The scandal of the Gospel to the Roman and Jewish mind**: "Where is the one who is wise? Where is the scribe? Where is the debater of this age? Has not God made foolish the wisdom of the world? For since,

in the wisdom of God, the world did not know God through wisdom, it pleased God through the folly of what we preach to save those who believe. For Jews demand signs and Greeks seek wisdom, but we preach Christ crucified, a stumbling block to Jews and folly to Gentiles, but to those who are called, both Jews and Greeks, Christ the power of God and the wisdom of God. For the foolishness of God is wiser than men, and the weakness of God is stronger than men. For consider your calling, brothers: not many of you were wise according to worldly standards, not many were powerful, not many were of noble birth. But God chose what is foolish in the world to shame the wise; God chose what is weak in the world to shame the strong; God chose what is low and despised in the world, even things that are not, to bring to nothing things that are, so that no human being might boast in the presence of God." 1 Corinthians 1:20–29.

CHAPTER 39

[1] **Amulets**: "A small object worn on the body and generally hanging from the neck, supposed to afford protection against evil spirits. Amulets were common in all periods of Near Eastern antiquity, and many fine specimens have survived. Near Eastern amulets assumed many shapes, with animal and human figurines especially popular." R. K. Harrison, "Amulet," ed. Geoffrey W. Bromiley, *The International Standard Bible Encyclopedia*, Revised (Wm. B. Eerdmans, 1979–1988), 119.

[2] **Magic in Ephesus**: "Magical practices were prevalent throughout the entire Hellenistic world in the first century A.D. The city of Ephesus, however, bore the reputation for being something of a center for magical practices. B.M. Metzger states, "Of all ancient Graeco-Roman cities, Ephesus, the third largest city in the Empire, was by far the most hospitable to magicians, sorcerers, and charlatans of all sorts." O. Meinardus concurs: "Perhaps even more than Pisidian Antioch, Corinth, and Antioch-on-the-Orontes, this city of traders and sailors, of courtesans and rakes, swarmed with soothsayers and purveyors of charms." The magical practices at Ephesus continued well into the Christian era since it was the subject of Christian prophecy (Clem. of Alex., Exhort. 2.19): "Against whom does Heracleitus of Ephesus utter this prophecy? Against 'night roamers, magicians (μαγοt}, Bacchants, Lenaean revellers and devotees of the mysteries.'" "There is no doubt that magical practices were flourishing in the first century A. D. 70 Suetonius records that Augustus ordered 2,000 magical scrolls to be burned in the year 13 B.C. 71 The personalities of the Olympian gods had begun to wane as early as the fourth century B.C. and were soon replaced in popularity by magic and the mystery cults. 72 This time also marked a rapid increase in astrological beliefs. The syncretism and strong belief in the influence of supernatural forces common to these three related traditions are reflected in the numerous Greek magical papyri extant today." Clinton E. Arnold, Ephesians: *Power and Magic: The Concept of Power in Ephesians in Light of Its Historical Setting* (Baker, 1992), 16-17.

"Magic presupposed the existence of thousands of spirits—good and evil—involved in the affairs of day-to-day life. These spirits were thought of as gods and goddesses (e.g., Apollo and Artemis), divine mediators (e.g., Hermes, angeloi, paredroi), spirits of the untimely dead (biaiothanatoi), astral spirits, underworld spirits or various kinds of chthonic, or terrestrial spirits (see Religions). The practice of magic also assumed a system of inner connections between physical objects in the universe. An action performed on one object was thought to have a corresponding impact on another(the principle of sympathy and antipathy).

"Those who engaged in the ancient art of magic sought to solicit the help of various gods and spirits or to utilize the system of correspondences throughout the universe. This was achieved through various acts of ritual power. Through many literary texts and especially now through the numerous recently discovered papyrus texts (see Betz), lead curse tablets (see Gager), amulets and various other magical paraphernalia, we have a good idea of how much of this procedure was carried out.

"Magical conjurations typically consisted of three parts: an incantation, a ritual and a command. The naming of various spirits and gods was the key part of the incantation (e.g., "I entrust this binding-charm to you gods of the underworld: Pluto and Kore-Persephone, Ereschigal, Adonis also called Barbaritha, Hermes Katachthonios-Thoth . . . I conjure all daimones in this place to assist this daimon Antinoos" [New Documents, no. 8, lines 1–3])." Ralph P. Martin and Peter H. Davids, eds., *Dictionary of the Later New Testament and Its Developments* (Downers Grove, IL: InterVarsity Press, 1997), 701.

[3] **Paul in Ephesus**: For the story of Paul in Ephesus and the incidents of the Seven Sons of Sceva, and the riot caused by the idolmakers, see Acts 19.

"In his account of Paul's two-to three year ministry at Ephesus (Acts 19), Luke implies that there were a substantial number who practiced magic at Ephesus. Quite a number of these magicians were converted and as an expression of their new allegiance to the Lord Jesus, gathered all of their magical books together and burned them. Luke places an incredibly high monetary value on the burned books (Haenchen: 50,000 days' wages) which may indicate the vast number of books burned and/or that the books were extremely valuable, reflecting a high demand for them." Clinton E. Arnold, Ephesians: *Power and Magic: The Concept of Power in Ephesians in Light of Its Historical Setting* (Baker, 1992), 16-17

[4] **Ephesus had a strong magic and spiritual demonic reality**: "One of the dramatic incidents that Luke narrates about Paul's ministry in the city involves a failed exorcism attempt by an itinerant Jewish exorcist and priest named Sceva (Acts 19:13–20). When Sceva and his sons attempted to add the name of Jesus to their exorcistic formulae, the demonized man responded violently and the group was injured. According to Luke, this prompted a great fear and conviction within the believing community (Luke uses the perfect tense of πιστε ω to indicate that they were already Christians), and they brought out the magical texts they still possessed and burned them. In Luke's estimation, the value of the texts that went up in flames that day was the equivalent of 50,000 days' wages." Clinton E. Arnold, *Ephesians* (*Zondervan Exegetical Commentary on the New Testament*) (Zondervan, 20102), 45.

"Later Christian writers certainly had no problem in linking Artemis with the evil demonic realm. The Acts of Andrew speaks of a large crowd of demons which lived on a rock next to an image of Artemis and made the nearby road impassable. A Christian inscription specifically refers to Artemis as a "demon" and records the valiant action of a certain Demeas. who tore down the image of the Ephesian Artemis. The Christian interpretation of Artemis as a demon as well as her connection with magic and sorcery is further attested by the apocryphal Acts of John: 'Where is the power of the demon (Artemis of Ephesus)? Where are her sacrifices? Where are her dedication-festivals?- her feasts? - her garlands? Where is all that sorcery and poisoner's art that is sister to it?'" Clinton E. Arnold, *Ephesians: Power and Magic: The Concept of Power in Ephesians in Light of Its Historical Setting* (Baker, 1992), 27.

[5] **The Temple of Artemis recognized as asylum for criminals**: "For throughout the Greek cities there was a growing laxity, and impunity, in the creation of rights of asylum. The temples were filled with the dregs of the slave population; the same shelter was extended to the debtor against his creditor and to the man suspected of a capital offence; nor was any authority powerful enough to quell the factions of a race which protected human felony equally with divine worship. It was resolved, therefore, that the communities in question should send their charters and deputies to Rome." Tacitus, *The Annals* 3.60.

"Tacitus gives an account of the Ephesian embassy to Tiberius when the emperor was seeking to abolish the proliferation of asylums, which had become a dangerous abuse. He exempted this temple, which was one of the few which could prove their ancient right to the privilege (cf. Suet. Tib. 37). The fact of this asylum continued into the last days of the Artemisium, perhaps becoming seen increasingly as in conscious opposition to the growing power of the rival faith." Colin J. Hemer, *The Letters to the Seven Churches of Asia in Their Local Setting* (Grand Rapids, MI; Cambridge, U.K.; Livonia, MI: William B. Eerdmans Publishing Company; Dove Booksellers, 2001), 48.

CHAPTER 40

[1] **Description of Artemis**: "People living in Ephesus and western Asia Minor lived in constant dread of astral powers that controlled fate… The beautiful cult statue of the Ephesian Artemis depicts the goddess as wearing the signs of the zodiac as a necklace, expressing that as Queen of Heaven she had the power to break the bonds of fate." Clinton E. Arnold, Zondervan *Illustrated Bible Backgrounds Commentary: Romans to Philemon., vol. 3* (Grand Rapids, MI: Zondervan, 2002), 306.

The bulbous objects on Artemis: "The meaning of the rows of bulbous objects on the chest of Artemis has proved a mystery to interpreters. Some early Christian interpreters identified them as female breasts and saw this as an expression of a fertility motif. This interpretation has not been generally accepted because of the differences in shape. Numerous other ideas have been suggested such as eggs, grapes, nuts, and even steer testicles. The latter view has a number of prominent adherents because in some of the ancient religions, mutilated body parts were attached to the cultic image of a deity. The most convincing explanation yet has recently been offered by Sarah P. Morris, Steinmetz professor of classical archaeology and material culture at UCLA, who concludes that the bulbous objects are comparable to leather goatskin pouches, called kurša, known from Hittite practices. These little bags were filled with magical material and used as fetishes. She observes that the Hittite tutelary deities associated with the kurša were often associated with protecting people and places and were frequently invoked in oaths and called upon in magical rites. She suggests that an ancient Anatolian cult image at Ephesus, to which rows of such bags were attached, was the predecessor to the image of the Ephesian Artemis. As such, the bags functioned as symbols for fecundity, spiritual power, and protection." Clinton E. Arnold, *Ephesians (Zondervan Exegetical Commentary on the New Testament)* (Zondervan, 20102), 45.

The sacred stone that fell from the sky: Acts 19:35 "And when the town clerk had quieted the crowd, he said, "Men of Ephesus, who is there who does not know that the city of the Ephesians is temple keeper of the great Artemis, and of the sacred stone that fell from the sky?"

[2] **Obey your slave masters**: Paul's argument to Philemon regarding the acceptance of the returning slave, Onesimus was clearly the subversion of slavery. He told the runaway slave to return and follow the law, even though it was not just. But he told the slave owner to accept the Christian slave as his equal brother in Christ. That was the affirmation of obeying an unjust law, while undermining it. This is not an affirmation of slavery by Paul, it is the subversion of slavery through non-violent non-revolutionary means. Letter to Philemon.

CHAPTER 41

[1] **Horns of the altar**: "Projections at each of the four corners of the altar of burnt offering (Ex. 27:2; 38:2; Ezk. 43:15) and of the altar of incense (Ex. 30:2f.; 37:25f.). In both cases they were to be of one piece with the altar. Blood was smeared on the horns of the altar of burnt offering at the consecration of Aaron and his sons (Ex. 29:12), in the sin offering for a ruler (Heb. nāśî') or for one of the people (Lev. 4:25, 30, 34), and on the Day of Atonement (Lev. 16:18). The horns of the altar of incense were smeared with blood in the case of sin offerings for the high priest and the congregation of Israel (Lev. 4:7, 18). The cutting off of the horns in Am. 3:14 signifies the removal of Israel's last refuge from God's judgment." Geoffrey W. Bromiley, ed., "Horns of the Altar," *The International Standard Bible Encyclopedia, Revised* (Wm. B. Eerdmans, 1979–1988), 758.

[2] **Horns of the altar as refuge:** Fugitives seeking asylum could cling to the horns, thus putting themselves under the divine protection (cf. 1 K. 1:50–53; 2:28; an addition in the LXX [2:29] reads, "I fled to the Lord"), though not in the case of wilful murder (1 K. 2:31–34; cf. Ex. 21:14); the horns appear to epitomize the holiness of the altar. Geoffrey W. Bromiley, ed., "Horns of the Altar," *The International Standard Bible Encyclopedia, Revised* (Wm. B. Eerdmans, 1979–1988), 758.

[3] **Human sacrifice to Artemis**: "At Patrae, in archaic times, the human sacrifices made to her wore on their heads garlands of corn ears (Pausanias 7, 20, 1)." G. Mussies, "Artemis," ed. Karel van der Toorn, Bob Becking, and Pieter W. van der Horst, *Dictionary of Deities and Demons in the Bible* (Leiden; Boston; Köln; Grand Rapids, MI; Cambridge: Brill; Eerdmans, 1999), 92.

"The surname of the god inside the chest is Aesymnetes (Dictator), and his chief attendants are nine men, elected by the people from all the citizens for their reputation, and women equal in number to the men. On one night of the festival the priest carries the chest outside. Now this is a privilege that this night has received, and there go down to the river Meilichus a certain number of the native children, wearing on their heads garlands of corn-ears. It was in this way that they used to array of old those whom they led to be sacrificed to Artemis.[2] But at the present day they lay aside the garlands of corn-ears by the goddess, and after bathing in the river and putting on fresh garlands, this time made of ivy, they go to the sanctuary of the Dictator." Pausanias, 7.20.1, *Pausanias Description of Greece with an English Translation* by W.H.S. Jones, Litt.D., and H.A. Ormerod, M.A., in 4 Volumes. (Medford, MA: Cambridge, MA, Harvard University Press; London, William Heinemann Ltd., 1918).

"Persons who had insulted and violated the filial cult of the goddess in Sardis had even been sentenced to death (I. Eph. Ia,2; IVBCE)."G. Mussies, "Artemis," ed. Karel van der Toorn, Bob Becking, and Pieter W. van der Horst, *Dictionary of Deities and Demons in the Bible* (Leiden; Boston; Köln; Grand Rapids, MI; Cambridge: Brill; Eerdmans, 1999), 96.

[4] **Paul's theme in Ephesus dealt with spiritual principalities and powers over the nations:** Ephesians 6:12 "For we do not wrestle against flesh and blood, but against the rulers, against the authorities, against the cosmic powers over this present darkness, against the spiritual forces of evil in the heavenly places."

Ephesians 3:10 "so that through the church the manifold wisdom of God might now be made known to the rulers and authorities in the heavenly places."

Ephesians 1:19–21 "according to the working of his great might 20 that he worked in Christ when he raised him from the dead and seated him at his right hand in the heavenly places, 21 far above all rule and authority and power and dominion, and above every name that is named, not only in this age but also in the one to come."

Ephesians 3:10–11 "so that through the church the manifold wisdom of God might now be made known to the rulers and authorities in the heavenly places."

For a thorough examination of the notion that the principalities and powers are divine authorities over the nations, see Ronn A. Johnson, *The Old Testament Background for Paul's Use of Principalities and Powers* (Dallas Theological Seminary, dissertation, 2004).

"Although Paul used many terms for the angelic powers known to Judaism, this does not mean that what he had to say about the powers of darkness would have been incomprehensible to the non Jew. While "principalities" (archai) and "authorities" (exousiai) seem to be uniquely Jewish expressions for the unseen realm, many of the other words he used were also used by Gentiles to refer to the world of spirits and invisible powers. Words like "powers" (dynameis), "dominions" ions" (kyriotetes), "thrones" (thronoi), "angels" (angeloi), "world rulers" (kosmokratores), "demons" (daimonia), "elemental spirits" (stoicheia) and "rulers" (archontes) were known and used by pagans, as evidenced in their magical and astrological texts." Clinton E. Arnold. *Powers of Darkness: Principalities & Powers in Paul's Letters* (Kindle Locations 1005-1009). Kindle Edition.

[5] **Christians fled to Kirkindje:** The interpretation of Grotius comes near the truth: "I will cause thy population to flee away to another place". We do not know whether the form in which he expresses his interpretation is due to the belief current in the country that the Christian people of Ephesus fled to the mountains and settled in a village four hours distant, called Kirkindje, which their descendants still consider to be the representative of the ancient Ephesus." William Ramsay, *The Letters to the Seven Churches of Asia and Their Place in the Plan of the Apocalypse* (London, Hodder and Stoughton, 1904), 244.

[6] **Tradition of Mary, the mother of Jesus, living near Ephesus**: "It was only during the fourth century that the leaders or the great writers of the Christian Church seem to have begun to interest themselves in the story of the life of the Virgin Mary for her own sake. Epiphanius about A.D. 375 remarks that the Scriptures say nothing about the death of the Virgin, whether she died or not, whether she was buried or not, and that in the Scriptures there is no authority for the opinion that when John went away into (the Province) Asia, he took her with him. But from the words of Epiphanius it seems clear and certain that popular tradition had already before his time been busy with her later life. Starting from the one recorded fact that she remained until her death under the care and keeping of St. John, it had woven into this something in the way of an account of her death, and the circumstances connected with it and with the burial. Doubtless it had interwoven some marvelous incidents in the story; and it would be possible to guess how these originated and were gradually elaborated. But the one thing that concerns our purpose is that Epiphanius must have known of the story that the Virgin had gone with St. John to Ephesus; otherwise he would not have taken the trouble to deny that it rested on any Scriptural foundation." Sir William Mitchell Ramsay, *Pauline and other studies in early Christian history* (London, Hodder and Stoughton, 1908), 144.

John cared for Mary after Jesus' death: John 19:25-27 "Now there stood by the cross of Jesus his mother, and his mother's sister, Mary the wife of Cleophas, and Mary Magdalene. When Jesus therefore saw his mother, and the disciple standing by, whom he loved, he saith unto his mother, Woman, behold thy son! Then saith he to the disciple, Behold thy mother! And from that hour that disciple took her unto his own home."

[7] **The Kharabu warriors**: This term is a fictional construct of an elite group of fighters that originated in my novel *Enoch Primordial*, and carried on into the rest of the *Chronicles of the Nephilim* series with poetic license. But it was based on the scholarly suggestion of archaeologist David Rohl, who argues that the cherubim may have been a mythological spiritualization of a very human tribe of sentinels called the Kheruba who guarded the Edenic paradise. David Rohl, *From Eden to Exile: The 5000-Year History of the People of the Bible* (Lebanon, TN: Greenleaf Press, 2002), 31-32.

Did the Biblical writers draw from their ancient Near Eastern neighbors for their concepts of the cherubim or were they distorted pagan memories of the "myth that was true"?

But that's not all. Genesis 3:24 says that the cherubim guard the Tree of Life with "the flame of the whirling sword." Scholar Ronald Hendel has argued that "the 'flame' is an animate divine being, a member of Yahweh's divine host, similar in status to the cherubim; the 'whirling sword' is its appropriate weapon, ever-moving, like the flame itself." Ronald S. Hendel, "'The Flame of the Whirling Sword': A Note on Genesis 3:24," *Journal of Biblical Literature*, Vol. 104, No. 4 (Dec., 1985), pp. 671-674.

Scholar P.D. Miller appeals to passages such as Psalm 104:4 where "fire and flame" are described as "Yahweh's ministers" to conclude a convergence of imagery with ancient Ugaritic texts that describe "fire and flame" as armed deities with flashing swords. He writes that "the cherubim and the flaming sword are probably to be recognized as a reflection of the Canaanite fiery messengers." Thus the Biblically strange, yet strangely Biblical presence in Enoch Primordial of the Cherubim and their divine fiery beings beside them brandishing whirling swords of flashing lightning. Patrick D. Miller, "Fire in the Mythology of Canaan and Israel," *Catholic Biblical Quarterly*, 27 no 3 Jl 1965, p 256-261.

[8] **These statements of Marcellus come from Jesus**: Matthew 24:36-50.

CHAPTER 42

[1] **Recapitulation or cyclical spiral structure of Revelation**: "Mounce puts it well when he notes: "While there is a rather clearly discernible literary development [between the seals, trumpets, and bowls], it is not to represent a corresponding chronological development. The three series cover the same period of travail" (though he sees this occurring toward the end of history). I will argue in my exposition of the trumpets that they actually flow out of and expand on the sixth seal. Though the images move in a cyclical fashion, however, they are not purely circular. John's predicament is not that of comedian Steven Wright who complains that once he owned a home with a circular driveway, which he greatly disliked because he could not go anywhere. After all, Rev's drama certainly heads somewhere. Actually Rev's movement is characteristically Johannine in involving a spiraling motion (as do John and 1 John) which re-cast earlier prophecies, even though "each series is not simply a repetition of the previous one, but is a development of it". This is "like the Gospel of John, the same theology is repeated over and over again, each time going a little deeper, and carrying the message further, like waves on a seashore". "The Gospel and epistles of St John stand out from the rest of the New Testament writings for their concentric or circular structure".

"Fiorenza and Paulien call Rev's movement a conical spiral. Metzger agrees, adding that "the book involves a series of parallel yet ever-progressing sections. These bring [matters] before the reader, over and over again, but in climacteric form." This style is called climacteric, based on a Greek word speaking of climbing stairs: the Greek word *klimax* means "ladder, flight of stairs" (BAGD 549). John's spiral structure allows parallel treatment of the events simultaneously with an upward progress within each cycle. Between the parallel cycles the visions make rhetorical progress in terms of the judgments' growing intensity. Witherington argues that "the threefold '7' judgments are basically describing one reality (though perhaps in progressively more intense or complete ways) for they all conclude with the same final judgment." Kenneth L. Gentry, Jr., *The Divorce of Israel: A Redemptive-Historical Interpretation of Revelation Vol. 2* (Dallas, GA: Tolle Lege Press, 2016), 157-158.

[2] **Second bowl and trumpet**: Revelation 8:8–9 [8] The second angel blew his trumpet, and something like a great mountain, burning with fire, was thrown into the sea, and a third of the sea became blood. [9] A third of the living creatures in the sea died, and a third of the ships were destroyed.

Revelation 16:3 The second angel poured out his bowl into the sea, and it became like the blood of a corpse, and every living thing died that was in the sea.

Third bowl and trumpet: Revelation 8:10–11 [10] The third angel blew his trumpet, and a great star fell from heaven, blazing like a torch, and it fell on a third of the rivers and on the springs of water. [11] The name of the star is Wormwood. A third of the waters became wormwood, and many people died from the water, because it had been made bitter.

Revelation 16:4–7 [4] The third angel poured out his bowl into the rivers and the springs of water, and they became blood. [5] And I heard the angel in charge of the waters say, "Just are you, O Holy One, who is and who was, for you brought these judgments. [6] For they have shed the blood of saints and prophets, and you have given them blood to drink. It is what they deserve!" [7] And I heard the altar saying, "Yes, Lord God the Almighty, true and just are your judgments!"

Fourth bowl and trumpet: Revelation 8:12–13 The fourth angel blew his trumpet, and a third of the sun was struck, and a third of the moon, and a third of the stars, so that a third of their light might be darkened, and a third of the day might be kept from shining, and likewise a third of the night. [13] Then I looked, and I heard an eagle crying with a loud voice as it flew directly overhead, "Woe, woe, woe to those who dwell on the earth, at the blasts of the other trumpets that the three angels are about to blow!"

Revelation 16:8–9 The fourth angel poured out his bowl on the sun, and it was allowed to scorch people with fire. [9] They were scorched by the fierce heat, and they cursed the name of God who had power over these plagues. They did not repent and give him glory.

Sixth bowl and trumpet: Revelation 9:13–14 [13] Then the sixth angel blew his trumpet, and I heard a voice from the four horns of the golden altar before God, [14] saying to the sixth angel who had the trumpet, "Release the four angels who are bound at the great river Euphrates."

Revelation 16:12 The sixth angel poured out his bowl on the great river Euphrates, and its water was dried up, to prepare the way for the kings from the east.

Babylon (the Harlot) falls three times: Revelation 14:8 [8] Another angel, a second, followed, saying, "Fallen, fallen is Babylon the great, she who made all nations drink the wine of the passion of her sexual immorality."

Revelation 16:19 [19] The great city was split into three parts, and the cities of the nations fell, and God remembered Babylon the great, to make her drain the cup of the wine of the fury of his wrath.

Revelation 17:16 [16] And the ten horns that you saw, they and the beast will hate the prostitute. They will make her desolate and naked, and devour her flesh and burn her up with fire.

Seven Trumpets	Seven Bowls
1. Hail, fire, destruction of earth, trees, grass (8:7)	1. Loathsome sores (16:2)
2. Sea life dies from blood (8:9)	2. Sea becomes blood; sea life dies (16:3)
3. Rivers and springs poisoned (8:10)	3. Rivers and springs turn to blood (16:4)
4. Stellar bodies afflicted (8:12)	4. Sun scorches men (16:8)
5. Bottomless pit opened; smoke darkens the air (9:1–11)	5. Beast's kingdom darkened (16:10–11)
6. Angels at Euphrates unleash large army upon men (9:13-19)	6. Euphrates dries up allowing kings to assemble for Armageddon (16:12-16)
7. Kingdom of this world becomes Christ's (11:15–18)	7. Cities of the nations fall as God remembers their evil (16:17–21)

A chart from Kenneth L. Gentry, Jr., *The Divorce of Israel: A Redemptive-Historical Interpretation of Revelation Vol. 1* (Dallas, GA: Tolle Lege Press, 2016), 706.

[3] **Nebuchadnezzar's dream of a metallic statue** destroyed by a cornerstone cut without hands. That stone was Messiah, whose kingdom would grow to fill the earth like a mountain: Daniel 2:31-45.

Daniel's dream of the beasts representing Medo-Persia and Greece: Daniel 8.

[4] **Daniel's vision under Darius of the Greek kingdom**: Daniel 11.

[5] **Ezekiel's influence on Revelation**: "A sampling of the OT influence from Ezekiel is quite remarkable. The following few, clear samples illustrate how Ezekiel impacts Rev at significant points: (1) The all-important throne-room vision of God in Rev 4:1–11 draws from Eze 1. (2) In 5:10 the double-sided scroll in God's hand on the throne that initiates the divine judgments strongly reflects Eze 3:3. In addition, note: (3) the marking of the foreheads (Eze 9:4; Rev 7:3); (4) the coals thrown to the earth from heaven (Eze 10:2; Rev 8:5); (5) the four judgments related to the fourth seal (Eze 14:21; Rev 6:8); (6) Gog and Magog (Eze 38–39; Rev 20:7–10); (7) the birds flocking to their prey as symbols of divine judgment (Eze 39:17ff; Rev 19:17ff); (8) the glorified Jerusalem (Eze. 40–47; Rev 21); and more. According to Beale and Carson (2007:1086) "Goulder (1981: 343–49) has argued that broad portions of Ezekiel have been the dominant influence on at least twelve major sections of Revelation (Rev. 4; 5; 6:1–8; 6:12—7:1; 7:2–8; 8:1–5; 10:1–7; 14:6–12; 17:1–6; 18:9–24; 20:7–10; 21:22).

"Carrington goes so far as to declare that "the Revelation is a Christian rewriting of Ezekiel. Its fundamental structure is the same. Its interpretation depends upon Ezekiel." Goulder observes even further that "these uses of Ezekiel are a dominant influence on the structure of Revelation, since they are placed to a marked extent in the same order as they occur in Ezekiel itself." Vogelgesang agrees that "the order of Ezekelian passages used in Revelation approximate the order of Ezekiel itself."

"Boxall provides us with a helpful table demonstrating Ezekiel's influence on Revelation:
Rev 1 = Eze 1
Rev 4 = Eze 1
Rev 5 = Eze 2
Rev 6 = Eze 5–7
Rev 7:1–2 = Eze 7:2–3
Rev 7–8 = Eze 9–10
Rev 10 = Eze 2–3 (cp. Rev 5)
Rev 10–13 = Eze 11–14 (echoes)
Rev 11:1–2 = Eze 40
Rev 13:11–18 = Eze 14
Rev 17 = Eze 16, 23
Rev 18 = Eze 26–28
Rev 19:11–21 = Eze 29, 32 (39)
Rev 20:1–3 = Eze 29, 32
Rev 20:4–6 = Eze 37
Rev 20:7–10 = Eze 38:1–39:20
Rev 10:11–15 = Eze 39:21–29
Rev 21–22 = Eze 40–48"
Kenneth L. Gentry, Jr., *The Divorce of Israel: A Redemptive-Historical Interpretation of Revelation Vol. 1* (Dallas, GA: Tolle Lege Press, 2016), 121.

CHAPTER 43

[1] **Bashan and the land of Dan**: "Genesis 49:17 as "a serpent in the way, a viper by the path, that bites the horse's heels so that the rider falls backward." This serpentine connection rings ominously familiar with the Genesis 3:15 prophetic curse on the Serpent's Seed biting the heels of Eve's Seed. And is it mere coincidence that the tribe of Dan lost their apportioned land in Canaan (Josh. 19:47), leading them to take the territory of the city Laish (Judg. 18) in the far north of Bashan, "place of the serpent," in the foothills of Mount Hermon, the location of the Watchers' fall and the pagan community of Banias that worshipped Azazel?" Brian Godawa, Appendix, *Joshua Valiant*, (Los Angeles, CA: Embedded Pictures Publishing,

2013), 322. See also, Judd H. Burton, *Interview With the Giant: Ethnohistorical Notes on the Nephilim* (Burton Beyond Press, 2009) 20.

Og of Bashan: Deuteronomy 3:1–11 [Moses speaking:]"Then we turned and went up the way to Bashan. And Og the king of Bashan came out against us, he and all his people, to battle at Edrei. [2] But the LORD said to me, 'Do not fear him, for I have given him and all his people and his land into your hand. And you shall do to him as you did to Sihon the king of the Amorites, who lived at Heshbon.' [3] So the LORD our God gave into our hand Og also, the king of Bashan, and all his people, and we struck him down until he had no survivor left. [4] And we took all his cities at that time—there was not a city that we did not take from them—sixty cities, the whole region of Argob, the kingdom of Og in Bashan. [5] All these were cities fortified with high walls, gates, and bars, besides very many unwalled villages. [6] And we devoted them to destruction, as we did to Sihon the king of Heshbon, devoting to destruction every city, men, women, and children. [7] But all the livestock and the spoil of the cities we took as our plunder. [8] So we took the land at that time out of the hand of the two kings of the Amorites who were beyond the Jordan, from the Valley of the Arnon to Mount Hermon [9] (the Sidonians call Hermon Sirion, while the Amorites call it Senir), [10] all the cities of the tableland and all Gilead and all Bashan, as far as Salecah and Edrei, cities of the kingdom of Og in Bashan. [11] (For only Og the king of Bashan was left of the remnant of the Rephaim. Behold, his bed was a bed of iron. Is it not in Rabbah of the Ammonites? Nine cubits was its length, and four cubits its breadth, according to the common cubit.)

War of the Seed: Brian Godawa's *Chronicles of the Nephilim* series tells this storyline that extends through the entire Bible.

Genesis 3:15 "I will put enmity between you and the woman, and between your offspring and her offspring; he shall bruise your head, and you shall bruise his heel."

"The seminal promise is, of course, that God would send a seed of the woman who would crush the head of the seed of the serpent and in the process would have his heel bruised (Gen. 3:15). There is a predictive element in this, certainly, but there is no single one-time fulfillment of this. Instead, we see variations on this theme repeated all through Scripture:

1) The prophesied star of Jacob would "crush the forehead of Moab" (Num. 24:17).

2) Jael kills Sisera (and by proxy King Jabin, an oppressor of Israel) by driving a tent spike through his head (Judges 4).

3) After he learns his wicked sons were killed in battle and the ark was lost, wicked priest Eli falls over backwards and breaks his neck (1 Sam. 4).

4) David kills Goliath with a stone to the head, then cuts off his head (the stone, by the way, is a "smooth stone" from a brook—a stone cut out without hands) (1 Sam. 17).

5) The usurper-king Abimelech attacked and murdered his own brethren, but was killed when a woman threw a millstone from a tower window and "crushed his skull" (Judges 9).

6) Absalom, son of David, guilty of murdering his older brother and leading a conspiracy for the control of the government, is eventually routed in battle and flees into the woods, only to be caught by his head in a tree. He is killed while hanging there. (2 Sam. 18).

7) David enshrined the language of this promise in Ps. 68:21–22 (cf. 74:12–14).

8) Psalm 110:1 refers to making Christ's enemies His footstool. (This becomes by far the most referenced Old Testament passage in the New Testament.)

9) The seminal promise is repeated in a later context, Habakkuk 3:13.

10) Jesus alludes to it as something accomplished already (Luke 10:18–19).

"Now, the image is again mentioned by Paul in Romans 16:20 as something that was about to occur for his audience "soon." This is a highly probable reference to AD 70." Joel McDurmon, *We Shall All Be Changed: A Critique Of Full Preterism And A Defense Of A Future Bodily Resurrection Of The Saints* (Atlanta GA: American Vision, 2012), 15-16.

Romans 16:20 The God of peace will soon crush Satan under your feet. (written before AD 70).

[2] **The Gates of Hades and the Abyss**: In Matthew 16:13-20 is the famous story of Peter's confession of Jesus as the Christ, who then responds, "I tell you, you are Peter, and on this rock I will build my church, and the gates of hell [Hades] shall not prevail against it" (v. 18). Shortly after, Jesus leads them up to a high mountain where he is transfigured.

"In order to understand the spiritual reality of what is going on in this polemical sequence and its relevance to the cosmic War of the Seed, we must first understand where it is going on.

"Verse 13 says that Peter's confession takes place in the district of Caesarea Philippi. This city was in the heart of Bashan on a rocky terrace in the foothills of Mount Hermon. This was the celebrated location of the grotto of Banias or Panias, where the satyr goat god Pan was worshipped and from where the mouth of the Jordan river flowed. This very location was what was known as the "gates of Hades," the underworld abode of dead souls.

"The Jewish historian Josephus wrote of this sacred grotto during his time, "a dark cave opens itself; within which there is a horrible precipice, that descends abruptly to a vast depth; it contains a mighty quantity of water, which is immovable; and when anybody lets down anything to measure the depth of the earth beneath the water, no length of cord is sufficient to reach it."(Wars of the Jews 1:405, Flavius Josephus and William Whiston, The Works of Josephus: Complete and Unabridged (Peabody: Hendrickson, 1987)." Brian Godawa, *When Giants Were Upon the Earth: The Watchers, the Nephilim, and the Biblical Cosmic War of the Seed* (Embedded Pictures, 2014), 287.

Pan and Panias: Scholar Judd Burton points out that Banias or Panias at the base of Mount Hermon in Bashan was a key worship site for the Greek goat-god Pan as early as the third century B.C.. He argues that Panias is a kind of ground zero for the gods against whom Jesus was fighting his cosmic spiritual war. Mount Hermon was the location where the Watchers came to earth, led their rebellion and miscegenation, which birthed the Nephilim (1 Enoch 13:7-10). It was their headquarters, in Bashan, the place of the Serpent, where Azazel may have been worshipped before Pan as a desert goat idol. Judd H. Burton, *Interview With the Giant: Ethnohistorical Notes on the Nephilim* (Burton Beyond Press, 2009) 15-23.

The Abyss: "In Mesopotamian cosmography, the Abyss (Apsu in Akkadian) was a cosmic subterranean lake or body of water that was between the earth and the underworld (Sheol), and was the source of the waters above such as oceans, rivers, and springs or fountains. In The Epic of Gilgamesh, Utnapishtim, the Babylonian Noah, tells his fellow citizens that he is building his boat and will abandon the earth of Enlil to join Ea in the waters of the Abyss that would soon fill the land. Even bitumen pools used to make pitch were thought to rise up from the "underground waters," or the Abyss.

"Similarly, in the Bible the earth also rests on the seas or "the deep" (tehom) that produces the springs and waters from its subterranean waters below the earth.

"Psa. 24:1-2 The world, and those who dwell therein, for he has founded it upon the seas, and established it upon the rivers.

"Psa. 136:6 To him who spread out the earth above the waters.

"Gen. 49: 25 The Almighty who will bless you with blessings of heaven above, Blessings of the deep that crouches beneath.

"Ex. 20:4 You shall not make for yourself a carved image, or any likeness of anything that is in heaven above, or that is in the earth beneath, or that is in the water under the earth.

"Leviathan is even said to dwell in the Abyss in Job 41:24 (LXX) . When God brings the flood, part of the waters are from "the fountains of the great deep" bursting open (Gen. 7:11; 8:2)." Brian Godawa, *When Giants Were Upon the Earth: The Watchers, the Nephilim, and the Biblical Cosmic War of the Seed* (Embedded Pictures, 2014), 102-103.

[3] **Azazel and Panias**: In Leviticus 16, we read of the sacrificial offering on the Day of Atonement. Among other sacrifices, the high priest would take two goats for atonement of the people. One, he would kill as blood sacrifice on the altar, and the other, he would transfer the sins of the people onto the goat by

confession and the laying on of his hands. This action of transferring the bloodguilt onto the "other" is where we got the concept of "scapegoat."

But that is not the most fascinating piece of this puzzle. For in verses 8–10 and 26, the priest is told to send the goat "away into the wilderness to Azazel" (v. 10)! You read that right: *Azazel*.

> Leviticus 16:7-10 Then he shall take the two goats and set them before the Lord at the entrance of the Tent of Meeting. And Aaron shall cast lots over the two goats, one lot for the Lord and the other lot <u>for Azazel</u>. And Aaron shall present the goat on which the lot fell for the Lord and use it as a sin offering, but the goat on which the lot fell <u>for Azazel</u> shall be presented alive before the Lord to make atonement over it, that it may be sent away into the wilderness <u>to Azazel</u>.

The name Azazel is not explained anywhere in the Old Testament, but we've heard that name before in the book of 1Enoch (1 Enoch 8:1; 9:6; 10:4–8; 13:1–2; 54:5; 55:4; 69:2). Azazel was one of the lead Watchers who led the rebellion of 200 Watchers to mate with the daughters of men. And that Watcher was considered bound in the desert of Dudael.

The natural question arises whether this is the same sacrifice to goat demons that Yahweh condemns in the Leviticus and Isaiah. But a closer look dispels such concerns.

The first goat was "for Yahweh" and the second "for Azazel" (v. 8). But whereas the first goat was a sacrifice, the second was not. As commentator Jacob Milgrom claims, "In pre-Israelite practice [Azazel] was surely a true demon, perhaps a satyr, who ruled in the wilderness—in the Priestly ritual he is no longer a personality but just a name, designating the place to which impurities and sins are banished."

Milgrom then explains that in the ancient world, purgation and elimination rites went together. The sending out of the scapegoat to Azazel in the wilderness was a way of banishing evil to its place of origin which was described as the netherworld of chaos, where its malevolent powers could no longer do harm to the sender. This wilderness of "tohu and wabohu" or emptiness and wasteland was precisely the chaos that Yahweh pushed back to establish his covenantal order of the heavens and earth, so it was where all demonic entities were considered to reside. [Jacob Milgrom, A Continental Commentary: Leviticus: A Book of Ritual and Ethics, 169 (Minneapolis, MN: Fortress Press, 2004)]

So Azazel could very well have been considered the father or leader of the goat demons. In the book of 1Enoch, Azazel is imprisoned in an opening in the desert of Dudael (1Enoch 13:4–8). But scholar Judd Burton argues that this unknown location might very well be connected to Mount Hermon, the original home of the Watchers when they came down to the earth (1Enoch 6:6). He points out that a very important "opening" existed near Hermon in the Grotto of Pan at the site called Banias. In the Hellenistic period (200 B.C.) the Greeks established a shrine to Pan, the satyr god of nature and shepherding, that became quite influential in the worship of Pan in the Greco-Roman period.

Judd then speculates that the shrine was originally to Azazel in antediluvian days because of the close similarities between Azazel and Pan. Firstly, both deities were associated with the goat. Secondly, Pan was driven by primal sexual lusts, just as Azazel lusted after human women and led the Watchers to mate with them. Thirdly, both Pan and Azazel were adept at war craft. The victory at Marathon in 490 BC was attributed to Pan, just as the art of making weapons and waging war was attributed to Azazel. And lastly, "with regard to the mystical, Pan and Azazel are also kindred spirits. The Greeks associated Pan with divination and prophecy, and Azazel himself took an active role in revealing the mystical knowledge of heaven to humanity." (Judd H. Burton, *Interview With the Giant: Ethnohistorical Notes on the Nephilim* (Burton Beyond Press, 2009) 20.)

It was this cave grotto at Banias near Hermon that may be the mysterious Dudael location or the memorial to Azazel's imprisonment. The Seirim clan of Banias in my novels *Joshua Valiant* and *Caleb Vigilant* embodies this spiritual and theological reality. And this is how I appropriated Azazel's original binding at the Flood in *Noah Primeval*, by having him bound in a desert called Dudael, but his final binding occurred at Mount Hermon in *Joshua Valiant*. It was a both/and theological unity.

Semyaza as co-leader of the fallen angels: 1 Enoch 10:11-12 And to Michael God said, "Make known to Semyaza and the others who are with him, who fornicated with the women, that they will die together with them in all their defilement. And when they and all their children have battled with each other, and

440

when they have seen the destruction of their beloved ones, bind them for seventy generations underneath the rocks of the ground until the day of their judgment and of their consummation, until the eternal judgment is concluded." James H. Charlesworth, *The Old Testament Pseudepigrapha, vol. 1* (New York; London: Yale University Press, 1983), 18.

1 Enoch 9:6-9 You see what Azaz'el has done; how he has taught all (forms of) oppression upon the earth. And they revealed eternal secrets which are performed in heaven (and which) man learned. (Moreover) Semyaza, to whom you have given power to rule over his companions, co-operating, they went in unto the daughters of the people on earth; and they lay together with them—with those women— and defiled themselves, and revealed to them every (kind of) sin. As for the women, they gave birth to giants to the degree that the whole earth was filled with blood and oppression. James H. Charlesworth, *The Old Testament Pseudepigrapha, vol. 1* (New York; London: Yale University Press, 1983), 17.

Fall of the 200 Watchers at Hermon: 1 Enoch 6:1-6 In those days, when the children of man had multiplied, it happened that there were born unto them handsome and beautiful daughters. And the angels, the children of heaven, saw them and desired them; and they said to one another, "Come, let us choose wives for ourselves from among the daughters of man and beget us children." And Semyaz, being their leader, said unto them, "I fear that perhaps you will not consent that this deed should be done, and I alone will become (responsible)d for this great sin." But they all responded to him, "Let us all swear an oath and bind everyone among us by a curse not to abandon this suggestion but to do the deed." Then they all swore together and bound one another by (the curse). And <u>they were altogether two hundred; and they descended into 'Ardos, which is the summit of Hermon</u>. And they called the mount Armon, for they swore and bound one another by a curse. James H. Charlesworth, *The Old Testament Pseudepigrapha, vol. 1* (New York; London: Yale University Press, 1983), 15.

The fall of the Sons of God in Genesis: Genesis 6:1–6 When man began to multiply on the face of the land and daughters were born to them, [2] the sons of God saw that the daughters of man were attractive. And they took as their wives any they chose. [3] Then the LORD said, "My Spirit shall not abide in man forever, for he is flesh: his days shall be 120 years." [4] The Nephilim were on the earth in those days, and also afterward, when the sons of God came in to the daughters of man and they bore children to them. These were the mighty men who were of old, the men of renown. [5] The LORD saw that the wickedness of man was great in the earth, and that every intention of the thoughts of his heart was only evil continually. [6] And the LORD regretted that he had made man on the earth, and it grieved him to his heart.

Gods of the seventy nations: Biblically, the Gentile nations are reduced to the seventy as listed in Genesis 10 after the flood. Those nations are then put under the authority of the fallen sons of God that they worshipped (Deut 32:8-10). Yahweh kept Israel ("Jacob") for himself. At Pentecost (Acts 2), the tongues of those represented seventy nations expresses the victory Jesus had to overcome the authority of the principalities and powers to draw the nations back into the kingdom of God (Isa 2)

[4] **For a fictional narrative of Jesus at the Gates of Hades and his descension into the underworld as described here see**: Brian Godawa, *Jesus Triumphant* (Los Angeles, Embedded Pictures, 2015).

1 Peter 3:18–22 For Christ also suffered once for sins, the righteous for the unrighteous, that he might bring us to God, being put to death in the flesh but made alive in the spirit, [19] in which he went and proclaimed to the spirits in prison, [20] because they formerly did not obey, when God's patience waited in the days of Noah…through the resurrection of Jesus Christ, [22] who has gone into heaven and is at the right hand of God, with angels, authorities, and powers having been subjected to him

[5] **Armageddon**: "The correct (Hebrew) term John uses to describe the climactic end-times battle is *harmagedon*. This spelling becomes significant when we try to discern what this Hebrew term means. The first part of the term (har) is easy. In Hebrew har means "mountain." Our term is therefore divisible into har-magedon, "Mount (of) magedon…the Hebrew phrase behind John's Greek transliteration of our mystery Hebrew term is actually h-r-m-'-d. But what does that mean? If the first part (h-r) is the Hebrew word har ("mountain"), is there a har m-'-d in the Hebrew Old Testament? There is—and it's stunning when considered in light of the battle of "Armageddon" and what we discussed in the previous chapter about the supernatural north and antichrist.The phrase in question exists in the Hebrew Bible as har mo'ed. Incredibly, it is found in Isaiah 14:13…the phrase har mo'ed was one of the terms used to describe the dwelling place of Yahweh and his divine council—the cosmic mountain…When John draws on this ancient Hebrew phrase, he is indeed pointing to a climactic battle at Jerusalem. Why? Because Jerusalem

is a mountain—Mount Zion. And if Baal and the gods of other nations don't like Yahweh claiming to be Most High and claiming to run the cosmos from the heights of Zaphon/Mount Zion, they can try to do something about it." Michael S. Heiser, *The Unseen Realm: Recovering the Supernatural Worldview of the Bible, First Edition* (Bellingham, WA: Lexham Press, 2015), 369-373.

Spiritual war of cosmic mountains: Isaiah 14:13-15. For the fictional depiction of this spiritual war of cosmic mountains see Brian Godawa *Jesus Triumphant: Chronicles of the Nephilim Book 8* (Embedded Pictures, 2015). For an explanation of the theology behind that fiction see the appendix of that same book, pages 308-311. For the academic defense of the interpretation, see Michael S. Heiser, *The Unseen Realm: Recovering the Supernatural Worldview of the Bible, First Edition* (Bellingham, WA: Lexham Press, 2015), 288-295.

Armageddon as battle of cosmic mountains: Richard J. Clifford, *The Cosmic Mountain in Canaan and the Old Testament* (Wipf & Stock Pub, 2010).

Armageddon and the Coming of the Lord: Revelation 16:16; 19:11-21; 1Thessalonians 4:13-17.

Made in the USA
Monee, IL
30 November 2024

71757398R00252